Hormones in Blood

Hormones in Blood

THIRD EDITION

Volume 2

Edited by

C. H. GRAY
Division of Clinical Chemistry,
Clinical Research Centre, Harrow,
Middlesex, UK

V. H. T. JAMES
Department of Chemical Pathology,
St. Mary's Hospital Medical School,
London, UK

1979

ACADEMIC PRESS

LONDON · NEW YORK · SAN FRANCISCO

A Subsidiary of Harcourt Brace Jovanovich, Publishers

ACADEMIC PRESS INC. (LONDON) LTD.
24/28 Oval Road
London NW1

United States Edition published by
ACADEMIC PRESS INC.
111 Fifth Avenue
New York, New York 10003

British Library Cataloguing in Publication Data
Hormones in blood.
Vol. 2 – 3rd ed.
1. Hormones
2. Blood
I. Gray, Charles Horace
II. James, Vivian Hector Thomas
612'.405   QP571   78–73882
ISBN 0-12-296202-8

Printed in Great Britain by
Page Bros. (Norwich) Ltd.
Mile Cross Lane, Norwich.

Contributors to Volume 2

D. R. BANGHAM, *National Institute for Biological Standards and Control, Holly Hill, Hampstead, London NW3 6RB, UK.*

MARGERY A. BARRAND, *Department of Pharmacology, University of Cambridge, Hills Road, Cambridge CB2 2QS, UK.*

S. R. BLOOM, *Department of Medicine, Royal Postgraduate Medical School, Hammersmith Hospital, Du Cane Road, London W12 0HS, UK.*

B. A. CALLINGHAM, *Department of Pharmacology, University of Cambridge, Hills Road, Cambridge CB2 2QS, UK.*

T. L. CLEMENS, *Department of Medicine, The Middlesex Hospital, Mortimer Street, London W1N 8AA, UK.*

L. J. DEFTOS, *Endocrine Section, Veterans Administration Hospital, 3350 La Jolla Village Drive, La Jolla, California 92161, USA.*

G. J. DOCKRAY, *Physiology Laboratory, University of Liverpool, Liverpool L69 3BX, UK.*

C. R. W. EDWARDS, *Department of Endocrinology, St. Bartholomews Hospital Medical School, West Smithfield, London EC1A 7BE, UK.*

R. J. FLOWER, *Department of Prostaglandin Research, The Wellcome Research Laboratories, Langley Court, Beckenham, Kent BR3 3BS, UK.*

G. N. HENDY, *Department of Medicine, The Middlesex Hospital, Mortimer Street, London W1N 8AA, UK.*

I. G. LEWIN, *Department of Medicine, The Middlesex Hospital, Mortimer Street, London W1N 8AA, UK.*

J. L. H. O'RIORDAN, *Department of Medicine, The Middlesex Hospital, Mortimer Street, London W1N 8AA, UK.*

S. E. PAPAPOULOS, *Department of Medicine, The Middlesex Hospital, Mortimer Street, London W1N 8AA, UK.*

J. A. SALMON, *Department of Prostaglandin Research, The Wellcome Research Laboratories, Langley Court, Beckenham, Kent BR3 3BS, UK.*

G. A. SMYTHE, *St. Vincent's Hospital, Garvan Institute of Medical Research, Darlinghurst, NSW 2010, Australia.*

Preface

When the second edition of "Hormones in Blood" was published in 1967, endocrinology had reached a stage when new methodology had opened up our knowledge of the normal levels in blood of those hormones and metabolites known at that time. During the 11 years which have elapsed since then not only have methods of hormone analysis advanced mainly towards greater precision and accuracy but well established hormones have been shown to be heterogeneous, prohormones and new hormones have been identified, and much has been learned of control mechanisms, interaction and synergism between hormones, metabolic pathways as well as of the details of the molecular basis of action. During this period the rate of the development of the subject of endocrinology has accelerated so much that at no time did it seem opportune to attempt to bring out a new and up-dated edition, even allowing for the publisher's agreement to publish if possible within six months of receipt of manuscripts.

At present, endocrinology has reached a stage for taking stock of its position. The value and limitations of radioimmunoassay (RIA) have been recognised, competitive protein binding and receptor assays have been developed, the latter especially has combined the sensitivity of RIA with a specificity which approximates with rather less discrepancy to biological activity; there is ever increasing development of sensitive biological assays using isolated or culture cells and even intracellular membranes. These new methods have been so rigidly characterised for the hormones being analysed, there is no special chapter devoted to them as there was in 1967 for gas-liquid chromatography (GLC) gel filtration, thin-layer chromatography, immuno-assay, and spectrophotometry. However, three general techniques, high pressure liquid chromatography, non-isotopic immunoassay and gas-liquid chromatography-mass spectrometry have warranted separate chapters, the first because despite its great resolving power it has not yet been widely used with hormones, even with the polypeptides for which it is specially suited; with the development of more sensitive detectors it will inevitably be found to have many applications. The second will ultimately replace RIA by a method less demanding of expensive equipment, although the disagreement between international bodies concerned with standardisation in enzyme assays suggest that the widespread application of enzyme-immunoassay may have to be delayed. The combination of GLC with mass spectrometry has mostly been of value in the detailed analyses of urinary steriods, but Dr Smythe in his new chapter on serotonin has no doubt that it is only the expense of the equipment which prevents its wide use.

The third edition of "Hormones in Blood" has other new chapters, two on gastro-intestinal peptides; one on vitamin D because it is the precursor of the true hormone 1,25-dihydroxycholecalciferol, which, with parathyroid hormone play so important a role in calcium metabolism, a chapter on somatomedin and one on erythropoietin. Dr Schally and his colleague have reviewed the enormous changes brought about by the identification, synthesis, mode of action and practical application of what in 1967 were only known as hypothalamic releasing and inhibiting factors.

We have given much thought as to whether the prostaglandins should be regarded as hormones and have decided that they are, because they function as chemical messengers and are carried in the blood to remote target organs as well as targets within the cells or structures in which they are synthesised. The field has expanded enormously since their discovery, and the recognition of the various prostaglandins and their precursors and metabolites has been more than usually dependent on the development of more sensitive and specific forms of analysis, especially with the now widely appreciated heterogeneity of the peptide hormones. The editors hope that there will be some cross-fertilisation of ideas and that some of the experimental techniques may prove to be of value in endocrinology.

The acceptance of SI units by some countries and not others has presented a problem. Where possible we have provided all concentrations in SI units along with traditional units. To avoid enlarging tables undesirably we have provided conversion factors. When early work is described in which methods had not been properly established (e.g. with the steroids and smaller poly-peptides) traditional units alone have been given; more recent results obtained when methods and standard preparations were available have been presented in both systems of units.

The symbols and abbreviations which have been used are those which are generally accepted in current scientific publications. We have in addition used u for international units and, unless otherwise stated, $\pm$ refers to the s.e.m. All temperatures are in °C (Celcius).

We are grateful to those authors who complied so splendidly with the request for prompt delivery of their manuscripts, as well as to those who relieved our anxiety by producing their manuscripts better late than never. As some contributors were unable to meet our deadline and did not conform to our stated requirements, rather than delay publication we decided not to return these chapters for revision, which accounts for a few of the chapters being less comprehensive than we would have liked. Our thanks are also due to Miss Nancy Blamey for all the help she gave us during preparation of this publication, and to Miss Helen Wortham of Academic Press who has been so patient with us, especially in respect of some late changes we required.

C. H. GRAY and V. H. T. JAMES   *June, 1979*

Standards for Hormones

D. R. BANGHAM

Almost all assays to estimate the concentration of a hormone are comparative assays, in which the test sample is compared with a measured quantity of a reference preparation of the hormone. For hormones such as steroids and peptides of a few residues, any preparation of the pure chemical may be suitable for this purpose providing it complies with precise specifications of identity and purity. But for hormones of more complex structure (such as glycoproteins or peptides of more than say 20 residues) that cannot be completely characterised by chemical and physical means alone, it is necessary to use suitably prepared reference materials. Moreover, in order to be able to correlate results obtained using them, it is necessary to relate such reference materials ultimately in terms of a single preparation, which has recognised international status. It is for this purpose that a service of international biological standards and reference materials has been provided since 1925. This service is administered under the aegis of the Expert Committee on Biological Standardisation of the World Health Organization; and the following list includes those International Standards and International Reference Preparations of hormones as well as other reference preparations currently distributed from the National Institute for Biological Standards and Control.

Certain hormones, such as thyrotrophin (TSH), follicle stimulating hormone (FSH), luteinising hormone (LH) and human chorionic gonadotrophin (HCG), are particularly complex, e.g. they appear to consist of heterogeneous mixtures of slightly dissimilar glycoproteins. In these instances, and until there is general and sustained agreement on its exact chemical structure, a hormone is identified by the biological response that it elicits; since it is the standard that is used as the yardstick with which to measure that activity, it is thus the material used in the standard that helps to "define" that hormone. It is essential that such a standard is thoroughly characterised by chemical, physical and biological procedures to obtain information on its identity, purity, activity, stability and suitability to serve as a standard for use with various assay methods. Such evidence is a prerequisite for the establishment of each WHO International Reference Material and is summarised in the report on each standard, which is usually published (see list of standards). Guidance on how to prepare, ampoule and characterise international, national and laboratory standards has been published (Annex 4, 29th Report of WHO ECBS, 1978).

The introduction of radioimmunoassays, hormone receptor assays and other protein binding assays highlighted many fundamental problems of standardisation in hormone assays. While a hormone is identified as that (form of a) molecule that directly elicits the characteristic biological response that defines it, many problems arise from the lack of—or inappropriate—specificity of many protein-binding assay systems for a single "form" of a hormone. Thus a sample of biological fluid or a tissue extract may contain precursor forms and metabolised fragments of the hormone, or artefactually altered forms caused by *in vitro* handling. Other hormones such as TSH, LH, FSH and HCG are naturally heterogeneous, that is they exist as populations of slightly dissimilar molecules.

The problems for standards arising from such diversity of molecular forms has been discussed in detail (Bangham and Cotes, 1974; 26th Report of WHO ECBS, 1975). The subject is currently under active consideration by special committees of WHO, the International Federation of Clinical Chemistry, the International Society of Endocrinology and the International Atomic Energy Agency.

Meanwhile new international preparations consisting where possible of the most highly purified preparations of hormones are established each year and are listed in successive reports of the ECBS of WHO.

BIOLOGICAL STANDARDS AND REFERENCE MATERIALS

The following reference materials are available to scientists in limited quantities for use as standards to define units of biological activity or as reference materials for binding assays. Some of these preparations have been provided and characterised as a result of international collaboration; some of them have been designated British or International Standards or Reference Preparations. They are not for administration to man.

Ampoules of these preparations, together with relevant information, are issued in response to written application from the scientist concerned, stating the purpose for which the material is required, addressed to:

National Institute for Biological Standards and Control,
Holly Hill, Hampstead, London NW3 6RB, UK.

REFERENCES

Bangham, D. R. and Cotes, P. M. (1974). Standardization and standards. *Br. med. Bull.* **30**, 12.

26th Report of WHO Expert Committee on Biological Standardization (1975). WHO Tech. Rep. Ser. No. 565.

29th Report of WHO Expert Committee on Biological Standardization (1978). WHO Tech. Rep. Ser. No. 626.

30th Report of WHO Expert Committee on Biological Standardization (1979). WHO Tech. Rep. Ser. (in press).

Standard	Ampoule code No.	Defined activity	Approximate composition of ampoule contents	Other information
1st IS for glucagon, porcine, for bioassay	69/194	1·49 u/amp	1·5 mg glucagon, 5 mg lactose, 0·24 mg sodium chloride	*Acta endocr., Copenh.* **77**, 705, 1974; *J. biol. Stand.* **3**, 263, 1975
1st IRP of glucagon, porcine, for immunoassay	69/194	1·49 u/amp	1·5 mg glucagon, 5 mg lactose, 0·24 mg sodium chloride	*J. biol. Stand.* **3**, 263, 1975; *Acta endocr., Copenh.* **77**, 705, 1974.
4th IS for insulin, bovine and porcine, for bioassay	58/6	24·0 u/mg	100 mg crystals, 42% porcine insulin, 58% bovine insulin	*Bull. Wld Hlth Org* **20**, 1209, 1959; *Diabetologia* **11**, 581, 1975
1st IRP of insulin, human, for immunoassay	66/304	3·0 u/amp	130 μg insulin, 5 mg sucrose	WHO/BS/74.1084
Insulin C-peptide for immunoassay	76/561	2·5 nm/amp	10 μg synthetic human insulin C-peptide analogue, 50 μg human albumin	synthetic (64-formyllysine) human proinsulin 31-65 WHO/BS/78. 1223
2nd IS for chorionic gonado-trophin, human, for biossay	61/6	5,300 u/amp	2 mg chorionic gonadotrophin, 5 mg lactose	*Bull. Wld Hlth Org.* **31**, 111, 1964
1st IRP of chorionic gonado-trophin, human, for immunoassay	75/537	650 u/amp	70 μg chorionic gonadotrophin, 5 mg human albumin	*Bull. Wld Hlth Org.* **54**, 463, 1976
1st IRP of α-subunit of chorionic gonadotrophin, human, for immunoassay	75/569	70 u/amp	70 μg chorionic gonadotrophin α-subunit, 5 mg human albumin	*Bull. Wld Hlth Org.* **54**, 463, 1976
1st IRP of β-subunit of chorionic gonadotrophin, human, for immunoassay	75/551	70 u/amp	70 μg chorionic gonadotrophin β-subunit, 5 mg human albumin	*Bull. Wld Hlth Org.* **54**, 463, 1976

Standard	Ampoule code No.	Defined activity	Approximate composition of ampoule contents	Other information
1st IRP for FSH/LH, human, pituitary, for bioassay	69/104	FSH 10 u/amp LH 25 u/amp	0·5 mg FSH/LH, lactose 1·25 mg	*J. clin. Endocr. Metab.* **36**, 647, 1973
1st IRP of LH, human pituitary, for immunoassay	68/40	77 u/amp	11·6 µg LH, 5 mg lactose, 1 mg human albumin, 1 mg sodium chloride	*Acta endocr., Copenh.* **88**, 250, 1978
IS FSH/LH, human, urinary, for bioassay	70/45	FSH-54 u/amp LH-46 u/amp	1 mg human post-menopausal urine extract, 5 mg lactose	*Acta endocr., Copenh.* **83**, 700, 1976
Gonadorelin	77/596	38 nm/amp	36 nmoles synthetic gonadorelin, 2·5 mg lactose, 0·5 mg human albumin	ovine sequence WHO/BS/78. 1219
Angiotensin I (Asp Isoleu[5])	71/328	9 µg/amp nominal	9 µg synthetic angiotensin I, 2 mg mannitol	*Clin. Sci. mol. Med.* **48**, 135.S, 1978
Angiotensin II (Asp Ileu[5])	70/302	24 µg/amp nominal	24 µg synthetic angiotensin II, 2 mg mannitol	*Clin. Sci. mol. Med.* **48**, 135.S, 1978
1st IRP of renin, human, for bioassay	68/356	0·1 u/amp	0·27 mg renal extract, 5 mg lactose, phosphate buffer	*Clin. Sci. mol. Med.* **48**, 135.S, 1978
IRP calcitonin, human, for bioassay	70/234	1·0 u/amp	10 µg synthetic calcitonin of sequence found in tumours, 5 mg mannitol	WHO/BS/78. 1229
1st IRP of calcitonin, porcine, for bioassay	70/306	1·0 u/amp	10 µg purified extract, 5 mg mannitol	WHO/BS/74. 1077
1st IRP of calcitonin, salmon, for bioassay	72/158	80 u/amp	20 µg synthetic salmon calcitonin I, 2 mg mannitol	WHO/BS/74. 1077

Preparation	Code No.	Defined unitage	Contents	Reference
1st **IRP** of parathyroid hormone, bovine, for bioassay	67/342	200 u/amp	0·6 mg gland extract, 5 mg lactose	WHO/BS/74. 1078
1st **IRP** of parathyroid hormone, bovine, for immunoassay	71/324	2·0 u/amp	1 µg purified extract, 200 µg human albumin, 1 mg lactose	WHO/BS/74. 1078
Parathyroid hormone, human, for immunoassay	75/549	0·25 u/amp	250 ng extract of human adenomata, 250 µg human albumin, 1·25 mg lactose	
3rd **IS** for corticotrophin (ACTH), porcine, for bioassay. International Working Standard	59/16	5·0 u/amp	50 µg pituitary extract, 5 mg lactose	*Bull. Wld Hlth Org.* **27**, 395, 1962
	various	5·0 u/amp		
Corticotrophin, human	74/555		11·6 µg corticotrophin, 5 mg human albumin, 2·5 mg mannitol	WHO/BS/78. 1233
2nd **IRP** of erythropoietin, human, urinary, for bioassay	67/343	10 u/amp	2 mg urinary extract containing erythropoietin, 3 mg sodium chloride	*Bull. Wld Hlth Org.* **47**, 99, 1972
Gastrin I, human (G-17)	68/439	12 u/amp	12·6 µg synthetic gastrin as hexamonium salt, 5 mg lactose, phosphate buffer	
Gastrin II, porcine (G-17)	66/138	10 u/amp	10 µg gastrin II, 5 mg sucrose, phosphate buffer	
2nd **IS** for serum gonadotrophin, equine, for bioassay	62/1	1600 u/amp	0·8 mg extract, 5 mg lactose	*Bull. Wld Hlth Org.* **35**, 761, 1966
2nd **IS** for prolactin, ovine, for bioassay	57/8	22 u/mg	10 mg extract	*Bull. Wld Hlth Org.* **29**, 721, 1963

Standard	Ampoule code No.	Defined activity	Approximate composition of ampoule contents	Other information
IRP prolactin, human, for immunoassay	75/504	0·650 u/amp	20 µg extract, 1 mg human albumin, 5 mg lactose	*J. Endocr. Copenh.* **80**, 157, 1979
IRP of placental lactogen, human, for immunoassay	73/545	0·850 mu/amp	850 µg placental lactogen, 5 mg mannitol	*Br. J. Obstet. Gynaec.* **85**, 451, 1978
1st IS for growth hormone, bovine, for bioassay	55/1	1·0 u/mg	30 mg purified growth hormone	WHO/BS/77.1156
1st IRP of growth hormone, human. for immunoassay	66/217	0·35 u/amp	175 µg growth hormone, 5 mg sucrose, phosphate buffer	
1st IS for thyrotrophin, bovine, for bioassay	53/11	13·5 u/mg	1 part pituitary extract, 19 parts lactose	*Bull. Wld Hlth Org.* **13**, 917, 1955
1st IRP of TSH, human, for immunoassay	68/38	147 u/amp	46·2 µg TSH extract, 5 mg lactose, 1 mg human albumin	
4th IS oxytocin for bioassay	76/575	12·5 u/amp	24 µg synthetic oxytocin acetate, 5 mg human albumin, citric acid	WHO/BS/78.1227
1st IS arginine vasopressin for bioassay	77/501	8·2 u/amp	20 µg synthetic arginine vasopressin, 5 mg human citric acid	WHO/BS/78.1231
1st IS lysine vasopressin	77/512	7·7 u/amp	30 µg synthectic lysine vasopressin acetate, 5 mg human albumin, citric acid	WHO/BS/78.1230

Contents of Volume 2

I. Parathyroid Hormone
G. N. HENDY, S. E. PAPAPOULOS, I. G. LEWIN and J. L. H. O'RIORDAN

II. Vitamin D
S. E. PAPAPOULOS, I. G. LEWIN, T. L. CLEMENS, G. N. HENDY and J. L. H. O'RIORDAN

III. Calcitonin
L. J. DEFTOS

Contents of Volume 1

Contents of Volume 3

I. Parathyroid Hormone

G. N. HENDY, S. E. PAPAPOULOS, I. G. LEWIN and
J. L. H. O'RIORDAN

INTRODUCTION

At the present time we have reached a particularly exciting point in the study of parathyroid hormone (PTH) and reference to the previous edition of this book will show how the position has advanced in the past ten years. After the relatively crude bioassays for PTH the era of immunoassay has brought great insight into the role of PTH in health and disease. However, immunoassays have also brought with them many problems of interpretation, particularly concerning the heterogeneity of the hormone in the circulation and the relationship between immunoassay and biologically active PTH. The introduction of region specific immunoassays and, more recently, highly sensitive cytochemical bioassays may help to clarify these issues.

Owing to the scarcity of highly purified human PTH many studies have depended upon PTH extracted from the bovine and porcine species. Recently the complete amino acid sequence of human PTH has been determined and synthesis of considerable parts of the molecule is now possible. This allows more detailed study of the chemical and biological properties of different regions of the human hormone molecule. The intracellular events preceding hormonal secretion and the roles of hormonal precursors to PTH are now better understood.

Previously regarded as a hormone in isolation, PTH is now seen to play a complex part in the integrated control of calcium metabolism. In this chapter we present a view of PTH as it appears to us today. However, we anticipate further changes with interest.

A. CHEMICAL CONSTITUTION AND MAIN PHYSICAL PROPERTIES

In recent years much progress has been made in advancing our knowledge of the chemistry of PTH. This has been due to refinements in the techniques of protein chemistry, both in the rapid development of sensitive, efficient techniques for structural analysis of polypeptide hormones and the methods available for peptide synthesis.

Biologically active PTH was first extracted from bovine parathyroid glands by Collip (1925) and others using hot hydrochloric acid. Subsequently, it was realised that considerable hydrolysis of the hormone occurred during this extraction procedure. The introduction of phenol as an extracting agent (Aurbach, 1959) which provided high yields of relatively stable hormone, represented a great advance. Later the use of urea and cold hydrochloric acid was shown to be an efficient extraction method for PTH (Rasmussen, Sze and Young, 1964). The extracted hormone was further purified, either by counter current distribution (Aurbach, 1959) or gel filtration (Rasmussen and Craig, 1962; Aurbach and Potts, 1964). However, a quantity of non-hormonal contaminants remained in these preparations which made sequence analysis difficult (Potts, Aurbach and Sherwood, 1966). It was not until 1970 that further improvements in the purification technique permitted the isolation of homogeneous preparations of the hormone (Brewer and Ronan, 1970; Keutmann, Aurbach, Dawson, Niall, Deftos and Potts, 1971).

In the following section the extraction and chemistry of PTH of animal origin will be described first and the isolation and chemistry of human PTH will then be considered in relation to bovine and porcine PTH.

1. Bovine and Porcine Parathyroid Hormone

(a) Isolation

It is advisable to extract and purify the bovine or porcine hormones from parathyroid glands collected from slaughterhouses. The glands should be immediately deep-frozen ($-70°$) at the time of excision.

The glands are first homogenised in acetone, defatted in hexane and dried under a vacuum. The resulting powder is extracted with 88% phenol (Aurbach, 1959) and fractionated successively with 20% acetic acid in acetone, ether and 6% sodium chloride in 20% acetic acid, and then precipitated with 4% trichloroacetic acid (TCA). This TCA-PTH material is generally 10% pure although under favourable conditions the potency can be as high as 25%.

For further purification, the TCA-PTH is subjected to gel filtration on Sephadex G-100 (Aurbach and Potts, 1964) and then ion-exchange chromatography on carboxymethyl cellulose (Potts et al., 1966). Keutmann et al. (1971) described the isolation of three forms of bovine PTH which eluted at different positions from a column of carboxymethyl cellulose run in buffers containing 8M urea. These variants of the hormone differed slightly from one another in amino acid composition and were considered to be isohormones. The structure of the major isohormone (bovine PTH-I) will be considered in the next section. It has a calculated mw of 9563. The amino acid composition of bovine PTH-II was also determined and shown to differ from bovine PTH-I in containing a single threonine residue and one less valine residue. The amino acid composition of bovine PTH-III closely resembles that of bovine PTH-II in that it contains threonine.

Porcine PTH has also been isolated by Woodhead, O'Riordan, Keutmann, Stoltz, Dawson, Niall, Robinson and Potts (1971) using similar techniques to those used in the isolation of the bovine hormone, although use of urea in the buffers at the ion-exchange chromatography stage was not required in order to obtain the polypeptide in homogeneous form. It has a calculated mw of 9423.

A biologically active fragment comprising residues 1–65 of PTH has been isolated from bovine parathyroid glands (Murray, Muzaffar, Parsons and Keutmann, 1975). This was observed as an extra optical density peak eluting from a column of Sephadex G-100. The physiological significance, if any, of this fragment is unclear.

(b) *Primary structure*

The major portion of the sequence of bovine PTH was obtained through automated Edman degradation by the phenylisothiocyanate procedure carried out on the intact molecule. Degradations of up to 66 residues were carried out (Brewer and Ronan, 1970; Niall, Keutmann, Sauer, Hogan, Dawson, Aurbach and Potts, 1970). Sequence analysis of the remainder of the molecule was achieved by Edman degradation of peptide fragments obtained by limited tryptic digestion at arginine residues. Peptides obtained after cyanogen bromide treatment and chymotryptic digestion also provided confirmation of the sequence.

Bovine PTH is a single chain 84 amino acid polypeptide (Fig. 1), devoid of cystine residues and containing only four aromatic residues, namely, a single tryptophan (residue 23), tyrosine (residue 43) and two phenylalanines (residues 7 and 34). It has two proline residues (at positions 51 and 83); the location of these residues is probably important in the conformation of the hormone since proline residues disrupt helical structure in polypeptide molecules. Two methionine residues are located in the amino-terminal portion of the molecule at positions 8 and 18; oxidation of these residues results in loss of biological activity. A group of three basic residues (Arg–Arg–Lys) is repeated twice in the sequence at positions 25, 26 and 27, and 52, 53 and 54.

The sequence of the porcine hormone (Sauer, Niall, Hogan, Keutmann, O'Riordan and Potts, 1974) differs at seven positions from that of the bovine molecule (Fig. 1). It lacks tyrosine and it contains a single methionine residue at position 8.

(c) *Secondary and tertiary structure*

Brewer (1972) studied the secondary structure of bovine PTH by circular dichroism (CD) and infra red spectroscopy. It appeared that PTH exists predominantly as a random coil in aqueous solution with at most only three turns of helix (10–15 % of sequence). Brewer (1972) also assessed the tertiary structure of bovine PTH by analysis of the fluorescence and circular dichroic behaviour of the aromatic residues. These studies indicated that the tryptophan and tyrosine residues (at positions 23 and 43) were in close proximity in the molecule. This conformational association could be broken with denaturing agents. In a hydrophobic environment (simulating a membrane receptor site) there was a marked increase (to 50 %) in the helical content of PTH.

Cohn, MacGregor, Sinha, Huang, Edelhoch and Hamilton (1974) measured the hydrodynamic (Stoke's) radii of the bovine hormone by comparing its rate of migration during gel filtration with those of standard peptides of

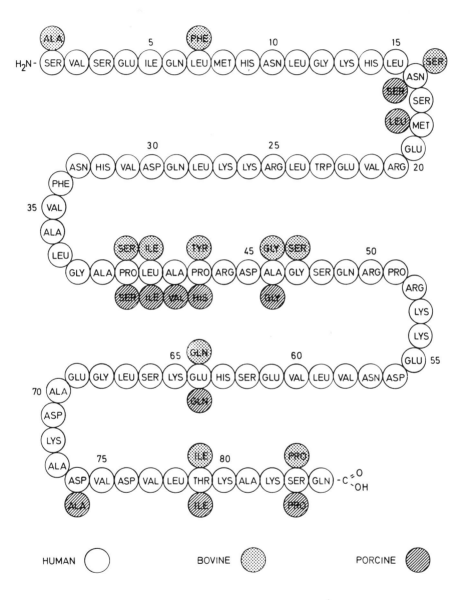

Fig. 1. Comparison of the amino acid sequence of human, bovine and porcine PTH. The backbone sequence represents the human hormone; the residues standing away from the main chain indicate sequence changes found in the bovine and porcine hormones.

known hydrodynamic radii. They concluded that PTH was a highly asymmetrical molecule which became more compact at physiological pH.

Fiskin, Cohn and Peterson (1977) used dark-field electron microscopy to visualise the three-dimensional structure of the hormone. A number of individual images were then integrated to give a composite structure. There appeared to be two predominant regions to the structure—presumably amino- and carboxyl-terminal—connected through a short stalk. The extent and location within the PTH molecule of secondary structure was calculated by means of the predictive model of Chou and Fasman (1974). In this model the amino-terminal region (residues 1–37) appears to consist primarily of two helices folded together by a β-turn and the carboxyl-terminal region (residues 38–84) a mixture of random coils and two helices. Additional β-turns may exist within the coil region spanning residues 38–54. The dimensions of this combination can be fitted into the composite structure visualised by electron microscopy. This model has yet to be confirmed by X-ray crystallography.

2. Human Parathyroid Hormone

(a) *Isolation*

Study of the human hormone has been especially difficult because of the scarcity of starting material and also because reports of the primary structure of the amino-terminal part of the molecule have not agreed. The isolation and chemistry of human PTH will be dealt with in this separate section.

The extraction procedure used was essentially the same as that used for the bovine or porcine hormones, but with modifications designed to improve the yield (Keutmann, Barling, Hendy, Segre, Niall, Aurbach, Potts and O'Riordan, 1974). In this way, sufficient human PTH has been isolated to elucidate the primary structure, to use as an immunoassay standard and to use as an immunogen to produce specific antibodies.

The only practical source of human PTH for these studies has been parathyroid adenomas and hyperplastic glands which have been collected from patients with hyperparathyroidism at the time of surgery. The amount of PTH isolated from human tissue is only 15–20% of that which can be isolated from an equivalent weight of bovine or porcine glands. During the isolation of human PTH there is an extensive loss of immunoassayable hormone over the successive extraction steps (Keutmann, Hendy, Boehnert, O'Riordan and Potts, 1978a). Less than 30% of the immunoreactive PTH present at the beginning of the extraction is recovered as TCA precipitates. This loss is due in part to the presence of fragments that are soluble in 4% TCA. These fragments may be recovered for immunological study (Dibella,

Gilkinson, Flueck and Arnaud, 1978; Keutman *et al.*, 1978a). Figure 2 shows the elution pattern after gel filtration of a desalted supernatant fraction from 4% TCA treatment of a human parathyroid tissue extract. The elution profile was defined by radioimmunoassays specific for the amino- and carboxyl-terminal regions. Although a small amount of intact hormone was present, most of the immunoassayable hormone eluted as fragments derived from both ends of the molecule. These fragments may be the products of

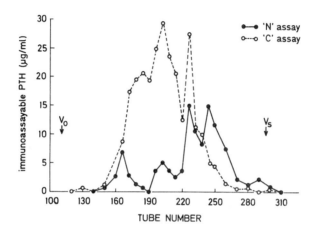

Fig. 2. During the isolation of human parathyroid hormone a large amount of immunoassayable hormone is lost. Some of this material can be recovered from the supernatant fraction after precipitation of the hormone with TCA. Gel filtration of such supernatant fractions and region-specific immunoassay of the eluate shows that the material consists mainly of fragments, smaller than the intact hormone (eluting at tube 165 above). These fragments are derived from both the amino- and carboxyl-terminal regions. (Reproduced with permission from Keutmann *et al.*, 1978a.)

cleavage occurring within the glands *in vivo* and/or of autolysis after collection of the pooled tissue.

The human PTH fractions precipitated with TCA were further purified by gel filtration and ion-exchange chromatography as for the bovine and porcine hormones. A feature of the isolation of human PTH has been that at the final ion-exchange purification step, some preparations of the hormone eluted in multiple fractions (Keutmann *et al.*, 1978a). From chemical analysis it appears unlikely that these fractions represent separated isohormones. Possibly alteration of the more labile side-chain functions of certain amino acids takes place during storage and/or extraction of the tissue, thus accounting for the different elution positions of structurally similar material.

(*b*) *Primary structure of human PTH*

The amino acid sequence of the 84 residues of the human PTH molecule has been determined (Keutmann, Sauer, Hendy, O'Riordan and Potts, 1978b), although two alternative structures have been proposed for the amino-terminal region differing at residues 22, 28 and 30 (Brewer, Fairwell, Ronan, Sizemore and Arnaud, 1972; Niall, Sauer, Jacobs, Keutmann, Segre, O'Riordan, Aurbach and Potts, 1974).

Brewer *et al.* (1972) studied the sequence of the first 34 amino acids by automated Edman degradation in the sequencer. This 1–34 sequence differed from this region in the bovine hormone by six residues and in the porcine hormone by five residues. Subsequent investigations have cast some doubt on the assignment of certain residues in the human PTH 1–34 sequence as reported by Brewer *et al.* (1972), although Brewer, Ronan, Fairwell, Rittel and Arnaud (1975) have reported confirmation of their original findings.

Niall *et al.* (1974) reported a sequence for the amino-terminal 37 residues of human PTH which contained less sequence changes from the bovine and porcine molecules. They used a high sensitivity sequencing procedure employing ^{35}S-labelled phenylisothiocyanate of high specific activity as the coupling agent. Niall and his colleagues found that within this region human PTH differed from bovine PTH at three positions (residues 1, 7 and 16 as shown in Fig. 1) and porcine PTH at two positions (residues 16 and 18). Brewer *et al.* (1972) had also proposed differences at positions 22 (glutamine rather than glutamic acid), position 28 (lysine rather than leucine) and at position 30 (leucine rather than aspartic acid).

Synthetic 1–34 peptides have been prepared according to both proposed sequences (Andreatta, Hartmann, Johl, Kamber, Maier, Riniker, Rittel and Sieber, 1973; Tregear, van Reitschoten, Greene, Niall, Keutmann, Parsons, O'Riordan and Potts, 1974) and their properties in immunoassays and biological assays have been tested in a number of laboratories. The most relevant studies have been those using native human PTH and comparing its behaviour with that of synthetic peptides. For example, it has been shown that the immunochemical properties of the 1–34 peptide (sequence of Niall *et al.*, 1974) and native hormone are identical, whereas the 1–34 peptide (sequence of Brewer *et al.*, 1972) is less reactive in a number of immunoassay systems using a variety of antisera (Hendy, Barling and O'Riordan, 1974; Segre and Potts, 1976). For most of the bioassay work insufficient human PTH has been available for comparison. However in adenyl cyclase systems using membranes from a number of different animal species, the 1–34 (Niall) peptide is of far greater potency than the 1–34 (Brewer) peptide. For example, using human renal adenyl cyclase, Hunt, MacNeil and Martin (1978) found the 1–34 (Niall) peptide to be 140 times more potent than 1–34 (Brewer).

While these studies strongly support the sequence of Niall *et al.* (1974) as being correct, indirect evidence such as this is not definitive and the amino-terminal region of human PTH has been reinvestigated by a number of techniques.

Keutmann, Niall, O'Riordan and Potts (1975) re-examined the structure of the amino-terminal portion of human PTH by Edman degradation on a new preparation of the hormone, and also by a biosynthetic technique. In this approach ^{14}C or tritiated amino acids were incorporated during bio-synthesis of the human hormone in slices of parathyroid glands *in vitro*. The appropriate amino acid residues were then determined as the ^{14}C or tritiated phenylthiohydantoin derivatives of the amino acid after Edman degradation or by peptide isolation after appropriate cleavage with endopeptidase, or both. The results from both examination of a new preparation of the hormone and the biosynthetic studies confirmed the previous findings of Niall *et al.* (1974) at residues 22, 28 and 30.

The remainder of the human PTH molecule was sequenced using overlapping peptides prepared by digestion of the native molecule with trypsin, chymotrypsin, staphylococcal protease and thermolysin. The biosynthetic labelling technique was also extremely valuable in confirming the assignment of certain residues, and demonstrating the absence of certain residues; for example, in showing that tyrosine was not present in human PTH, but indicating that the low levels of tyrosine seen on amino acid analysis were due to a non-hormonal contaminant (Keutmann *et al.*, 1978a).

The completion of the primary structure of the human hormone allows comparison with the structure of the bovine and porcine hormones (Fig. 1). The human and the bovine molecules differ by 11 residues as do the human and porcine molecules. The human hormone contains eight unique assignments. In each case, except one, the sequence differences within the three species could arise from a single step mutation in the triplet base codon. The exception is the Tyr–Pro substitution at residue 43 in the bovine and human molecules which would require a two base shift (Dayhoff, 1972).

A large part of the sequence is conserved in the three species studies so far. Conservation of the sequence within the biologically active amino-terminal third of the molecule is to be expected as the requirements of PTH receptors will apply constraints in the sequence changes allowed. The Arg–Lys–Lys sequence is repeated in all three sequences at residues 26, 27, 28 and 52, 53, 54. These sites would be susceptible to cleavage by an enzyme of trypsin-like specificity, although whether this is of any physiological significance has yet to be shown. The carboxyl-terminal region contains relatively few changes which might suggest a role for this sequence which has so far been assigned no biological function.

3. Structure–Function Studies with Synthetic Peptides

The amino-terminal third of the PTH molecule contains all the structural requirements for biological activity: both calcium-mobilising, and phosphaturic, activities. Structure–function studies have been carried out using synthetic PTH peptides in both *in vivo* and *in vitro* bioassays. Receptors on different target organs may have different requirements for binding of the hormone and also for activation of the biological response, therefore studies with one particular bioassay system may not necessarily apply to a different bioassay system. Most of the studies with synthetic PTH peptides have been carried out using kidney adenyl cyclase preparations. The initial studies used rat kidney, although later work has been done with chick, bovine, porcine, canine and human membranes. These species are more suitable as, unlike the rat preparations, they do not contain enzymes which degrade PTH.

The synthetic bovine PTH 1–34 peptide, prepared by Potts, Tregear, Keutmann, Niall, Sauer, Deftos, Dawson, Hogan and Aurbach (1971), appears to be equipotent, on a molar basis, with the intact bovine molecule in a number of bioassay systems. Amino acid deletions from either the amino- or carboxyl-terminus of the active fragment resulted in a decline in biological activity and demonstrated that the minimum continuous sequence required for biological activity is that spanning 2–27 (Tregear, van Reitschoten, Greene, Keutmann, Niall, Reit, Parsons and Potts, 1973). The renal adenyl cyclase appears to be especially sensitive to loss or alteration of the amino-terminal residue 1. Extension of the peptide chain at the amino-terminus also leads to loss of activity.

It has been known for some time that the biological activity of bovine PTH is reversibly destroyed by oxidation of at least one of the methionine residues (Rasmussen and Craig, 1962). Bovine and human PTH have two methionines at positions 8 and 18, whereas porcine PTH has only one, at position 8. Oxidation of this single methionine in porcine PTH likewise destroys biological activity and the position may be the more important one in those species in which there are two methionine residues (O'Riordan, Woodhead, Hendy, Parsons, Robinson, Keutmann, Dawson and Potts, 1974). A fragment comprising the active 1–34 region of bovine PTH with insertion of norleucine instead of methionine residues at positions 8 and 18 has been found to retain significant biological activity (Rosenblatt, Goltzman, Keutmann, Tregear and Potts, 1976). Thus, whereas alteration of the side-chain of methionine itself by oxidation to the more negatively charged sulphoxide form will destroy biological activity, the methionines can be replaced completely with retention of biological activity.

The structural requirements for binding to receptors are different from those for activation. Bovine PTH-(3–34) lacks agonist activity *in vitro* and *in vivo*, but appears able to bind hormone receptor sites, because it can inhibit the activity of native bovine PTH-(1–84) and synthetic bovine PTH-(1–34) in stimulating canine renal adenyl cyclase. However, bovine PTH-(3–34) does not inhibit bovine PTH-(1–84) on a molar basis, but a several hundred fold excess of inhibitor to agonist is required to effect 50 % inhibition. Therefore, the two amino-terminal amino acids are not only essential for stimulation of adenylate cyclase but must also have an effect of avidity of receptor binding. Modification of the bovine PTH-(1–34) sequence can enhance activity. For example, substitution of tyrosine for the phenylalanine at the carboxyl-terminus (residue 34) and conversion of the carboxyl-terminal group to a carboxamide (CO_2H to $CONH_2$) enhances activity. An unmodified trypto-phan at position 23 appears not to be essential for hormone binding (Nosen-blatt, Callahan, Mahaffey, Pont and Potts, 1977).

B. BIOSYNTHESIS

The cells of the parathyroid glands contain few secretory granules and the store of PTH is small compared with the quantity of stored hormone in some other endocrine glands. It is probable therefore that secretion must be associated with continual synthesis. Studies of the biosynthesis of PTH have led to the discovery of two larger precursor forms of PTH, Proparathyroid hormone (ProPTH) and Preproparathyroid hormone (PreProPTH).

1. Proparathyroid Hormone

Hamilton, MacGregor, Chu and Cohn (1971) first demonstrated that besides PTH another polypeptide having hypercalcaemic activity was synthesised by the parathyroid glands. This peptide was more basic than PTH as judged by its behaviour on carboxymethylcellulose. Pulse-labelling and pulse-chase experiments using radioactively-labelled amino acids incubated with bovine parathyroid gland slices demonstrated a precursor–product relation-ship between the newly discovered peptide and PTH (Kemper, Habener, Potts and Rich, 1972; Cohn, MacGregor, Chu, Kimmel and Hamilton, 1972). After 10 min of incubation of parathyroid gland slices with radioactive amino acids the principal labelled polypeptide was the "prohormone" (Fig. 3). It was more basic than PTH and of greater molecular weight as judged by its behaviour on polyacrylamide gels.

   Extraction and purification of several thousand bovine parathyroid glands yielded sufficient prohormone for the structural analysis of the amino-terminal region. A hexapeptide sequence, Lys–Ser–Val–Lys–Lys, was detected followed by the known sequence of bovine PTH (Hamilton, Niall, Jacobs, Keutmann, Potts and Cohn, 1974). The finding of only six extra amino acids at the amino-terminus was somewhat surprising because amino acid analysis of the material had indicated as many as 19 extra residues. However, Habener, Kemper, Potts and Rich (1973) concluded that the carboxyl-terminus of the prohormone was identical with that of PTH, by analysis of cleavage products of samples of radioactive ProPTH after treatment with either cyanogen

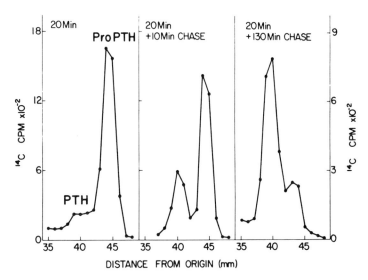

Fig. 3. Polyacrylamide gel electrophoresis of extracts of parathyroid gland slices to show conversion of radioactively-labelled ProPTH to PTH. After a 20 min incubation with radioactive amino acids, the medium was removed and fresh medium containing unlabelled amino acids was added. Analyses were made at 20 min, 20 min + 10 min "chase" and 20 min + 130 min "chase". (Reproduced with permission from Habener *et al.*, 1977b.)

bromide or trypsin. Cohn and Hamilton (1976) have presented data based on limited degradation with carboxyl-terminal specific endopeptidases which suggested that there may be extra amino acids at the carboxyl terminus. In order to resolve this problem it has been suggested (Habener, Kemper, Rich and Potts, 1977b) that the ProPTH used for the compositional and sequence analysis was contaminated by a small amount of another protein that has a blocked amino terminus. Current evidence strongly suggests that there is no additional amino acid sequence at the carboxyl terminus of Pro-PTH (also see later section on PreProPTH).

Besides that of bovine ProPTH, the amino acid sequence of the prohormone specific hexapeptide has been determined for human (Jacobs, Kemper, Niall, Habener and Potts, 1974; Huang, Chu, Hamilton, MacGregor, and Cohn, 1975), porcine (Chu, Huang, Littledike, Hamilton and Cohn, 1975), canine and chicken (Cohn and Hamilton, 1976) proparathyroid hormones (Table 1). A high degree of homology exists between the hexapeptide sequences of each molecule. The human and bovine sequences are identical while that of the chicken contains the most changes, but these are commonly occurring substitutions (Dayhoff, 1972). In each case the basic lysyl–arginyl sequence precedes residue 1 in the PTH 1–84 sequence.

Table 1

Amino acid sequences of the proparathyroid hormone hexapeptides of human, bovine, porcine, canine and chicken origin. Residue 1 is the amino-terminal amino acid of the 84-residue parathyroid hormone molecule.

	-6 -1 1
Human	H_2N-Lys-Ser-Val-Lys-Lys-Arg-Ser
Bovine	H_2N-Lys-Ser-Val-Lys-Lys-Arg-Ala-
Porcine	H_2N-Lys-Pro-Ile-Lys-Lys-Arg-Ser-
Canine	H_2H-Lys-Pro-Val-Lys-Lys-Arg-Ser-
Chicken	H_2N-Arg-Pro-Met-Met-Lys-Arg-Ser-

2. Preproparathyroid Hormone

The development of a highly sensitive cell free system derived from wheat germ (Roberts and Paterson, 1973) made it possible to translate relatively crude preparations of mRNA under conditions in which virtually no proteolytic activity was present to modify the products of translation. Thus Kemper, Habener, Mulligan, Potts and Rich (1974a) were able to analyse the protein products synthesised in response to bovine parathyroid RNA in the wheat germ system without the interference of post-translational cleavages. Fractions of mRNA sedimenting between 8S and 15S on a sucrose gradient were incubated in a cell free system containing radioactive amino acids that labelled the newly synthesised protein.

The acid-soluble radioactive proteins that were synthesised in response to the parathyroid mRNA were analysed by electrophoresis on polyacrylamide gels. A single band of radioactivity predominated; this protein was of higher molecular weight than ProPTH. Analyses of the radioactive peptide fragments found after tryptic cleavage of the protein indicated that it contained peptides indistinguishable from those of ProPTH and PTH and also that it contained additional peptides not found in ProPTH or PTH. Analyses of the peptide fragments of the PreProPTH produced by cleavage with cyanogen bromide

B

suggested that the additional sequence of amino acids was at the amino-terminal but not at the carboxyl-terminal end of the molecule. Therefore it was feasible to determine the amino acid sequence of the cell free product by Edman degradation. This was achieved using the biosynthetic micro-sequencing technique already described for analysis of the prohormones and human parathyroid hormone. This involved isolation of preparations of PreProPTH synthesised in separate incubations in the cell free system in the presence of different combinations of radioactively-labelled amino acids. These studies showed that the 'Pre' peptide consists of a sequence of 25 amino acids covalently attached by a glycyl–lysyl-bond to the sequence of ProPTH (Fig. 4). The sequence is hydrophobic containing five methionine, three valine, two leucine and two isoleucine residues. An unusual feature is

BOVINE PREPROPARATHYROID HORMONE

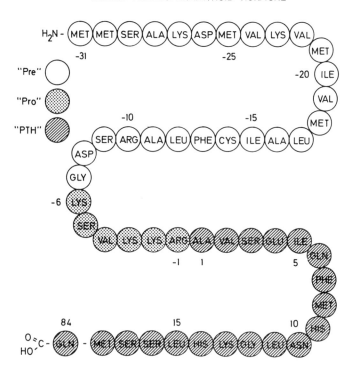

Fig. 4. Amino acid sequence of bovine preproparathyroid hormone. Radiolabelled prehormone was synthesised in a wheat-germ cell free system by addition of bovine RNA and radioactive amino acids. Little, if any, intact PreProPTH is normally formed *in vivo*.

the presence of methionyl–methionyl at the amino terminus (Kemper, Habener, Ernst, Potts and Rich, 1976).

3. Purification and Characterisation of mRNA for PreProPTH

The molecular weight of parathyroid mRNA is approximately 190,000 as determined by sedimentation analysis on sucrose gradients containing formamide (Stolarsky and Kemper, 1978). This corresponds to 550 nucleotides, approximately 200 more than the 345 that are required to code for the 115 amino acids of PreProPTH. Some of these additional nucleotides can be accounted for by the presence of a sequence of polyadenylate at the 3′ end of the mRNA. Excess polynucleotide sequence in mRNAs in relation to the size of the proteins for which they code has been a common finding. The presence of a polyadenylate sequence in the mRNA for PreProPTH has facilitated its purification by selective adsorption to and elution from oligo (2′-deoxythymidylic acid)-cellulose columns. At the other end of the mRNA, the 5′ end, there is also a unique structure which consists of 7-methyl-guanosine which is attached with its 5′ hydroxyl to the 5′ hydroxyl of the penultimate base, thereby leaving a free 3′ hydroxyl. This so-called capped structure is apparently required for the activity of eukaryotic rRNAs, and it can be removed chemically by treatment with periodate and aniline (Kemper, 1976).

4. PreProPTH cDNA

DNA complimentary in sequence to the RNA for bovine PreProPTH has been synthesised using reverse transcriptase from avian myeblastosis virus. In a linked transcription–translation system using RNA polymerase and cell free extract from wheat germ, the DNA directed the synthesis of a protein identified as PreProPTH by amino acid sequencing, electrophoresis and immunoprecipitation (Kronenberg, Roberts, Habener, Potts and Rich, 1977). This parathyroid cDNA may be a suitable starting material for nucleotide sequence analysis (Maxam and Gilbert, 1977) and also for construction of hybridisation assays for the detection of mRNA in parathyroid tissues under various physiological conditions.

5. Biosynthesis of Parathyroid Hormone and Intracellular Translocation

Studies of PTH biosynthesis *in vitro* indicate that PTH, the predominant cellular hormonal product, arises from PreProPTH via two successive cleavages: PreProPTH to ProPTH and ProPTH to PTH. Kinetic pulse and pulse-chase labelling studies using intact slices of bovine parathyroid glands show that small amounts of radioactive PreProPTH are detectable and reach a maximum at 2 min, ProPTH is detectable by 1 min and PTH is not detectable until 15 min (Habener, Potts and Rich, 1976). A role is suggested for the PTH precursors in the segregation and translocation of the hormonal polypeptides within the subcellular organelles.

PreProPTH is the major protein synthesised by translation of parathyroid mRNA in the wheat germ cell free system and it appears to be the initial protein coded for by the gene for PTH. The amino-terminal methionine is incorporated into the PreProPTH selectively by initiator methionyl tRNA (Kemper, Habener, Potts and Rich, 1976). Recently prehormone forms of secreted polypeptides and proteins other than PTH have been identified. For example, larger forms of immunoglobulins, pancreatic secretory proteins, albumin, human placental lactogen, human growth hormone, prolactin and proinsulin were demonstrated in the products of translation of the respective mRNAs in wheat germ cell free systems. All these larger initial precursor forms have a hydrophobic amino-terminal extension of approximately 20–25 amino acid residues.

(a) *Signal hypothesis*

Evidence has accumulated which suggests that the synthesis of all secreted peptides follow similar pathways. The so-called signal hypothesis (Milstein, Brownlee, Harrison and Matthews, 1972; Blobel and Dobberstein, 1975) suggests a mechanism for the translation of mRNAs for secretory proteins on membrane bound ribosomes and the transfer of the peptide chain across the microsomal membrane by the ribosome membrane junction. This results in the segregation of secretory proteins from other intracellular proteins within the transport pathway. This theory proposes that all mRNAs for exportable proteins code for a "signal peptide". This is the amino-terminal extension to the peptide sequence; it is metabolically short-lived, only being present in nascent, incomplete chains. When the growing polypeptide chain is approximately 20–30 amino acids long it emerges from the large ribosomal subunit and, after enzymatic removal of the initiator methionyl residue, penetrates the microsomal membrane, thereby causing several receptor proteins of the endoplasmic reticulum to aggregate to form a tunnel in the membrane (Fig. 5). The tunnel in the large ribosomal subunit links with the newly formed tunnel in the membrane. The signal peptide leads the nascent chain through the endoplasmic reticulum membrane and into the intracisternal space. Before or just as the protein chain is completed the signal peptide is removed by a membrane-bound enzyme called a "signalase" or "clipase" enzyme. When the peptide chain is complete it is released from the ribosome and the membrane tunnel is eliminated. The ribosome is then ready to translate any other mRNAs independently of whether they do or do not contain "signal codons".

The synthesis of PreProPTH appears to follow the above scheme and confirms certain proposals of the hypothesis. Evidence that the enzyme(s) converting PreProPTH to ProPTH reside in the endoplasmic reticulum membranes has come from a comparison of the products resulting from the translation of parathyroid mRNA in the wheat germ cell free system (which

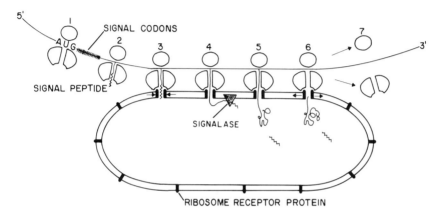

Fig. 5. Schematic representation of the "signal hypothesis" for the synthesis of secretory proteins on ribosomes, starting with the initiator formyl methionine coded for by the base sequence AUG. See text for details. (Reproduced with permission from Campbell and Blobel, 1976.)

is devoid of reticular membranes) and those in the Krebs ascites cell free system (which contains reticular membranes). PreProPTH is the sole hormonal product synthesised in the wheat germ cell free system (Kemper *et al*, 1974), whereas both PreProPTH and ProPTH appear as products of synthesis in the Krebs ascites cell free system; ProPTH predominates (Habener, Kemper, Potts and Rich, 1975).

(b) Transport of ProPTH to the Golgi complex

The delay of about 15 min before proteolytic cleavage of ProPTH to PTH corresponds to the time required for the transport of newly synthesised protein to the Golgi complex and it is suggested that the prohormone specific hexapeptide may be involved in the transport of the prohormone within the cisternal space from the rough endoplasmic reticulum to the Golgi. The process of translocation of ProPTH requires energy and is likely to be mediated by the action of microtubules (Chu, MacGregor, Hamilton and Cohn, 1974).

(c) *Proteolytic cleavage of ProPTH to PTH in the Golgi complex*

The particulate fractions of parathyroid glands contain trypsin-like activity that preferentially cleaves the Arg–Ala bond joining the ProPTH specific hexapeptide sequence to PTH without additional cleavages in the sequence of PTH itself (MacGregor, Chu and Cohn, 1976). The hexapeptide sequence once removed is further modified by carboxypeptidase B-like activity (Habener, Chang and Potts, 1977). This dual enzyme activity may be universally involved in the processing of prohormonal precursors.

Some PTH is stored in secretory granules until released into the circulation. However, mature secretory granules are extremely scarce in the parathyroid gland, immature vesicles are more abundant suggesting that a proportion of the PTH may be transported directly to the periphery of the cell without being packaged in granules (MacGregor, Hamilton and Cohn, 1975).

(d) *Regulation of PTH biosynthesis*

Calcium is the major regulator of the activity of the parathyroid glands. In studies with parathyroid slices *in vitro* a change in medium calcium concentration changed the biosynthesis of ProPTH only slightly and the conversion of ProPTH to PTH was independent of the extracellular calcium concentration. Calcium does not appear to directly affect the activity of the cleavage enzymes converting ProPTH to PTH because no alteration in rates of efficiency of conversion of the prohormone to the hormone was seen throughout a 4-hr period in the studies *in vitro* (Habener, Kemper and Potts, 1975). However regulation of intracellular stores of PTH may occur through a pathway of intracellular turnover of PTH and/or ProPTH. High concentrations of extracellular calcium stimulate, and low concentrations inhibit, intracellular degradation of the hormone (Chu, MacGregor, Anast, Hamilton and Cohn, 1973). Thus inhibition of stimulation of this degradative pathway may provide a way of rapidly increasing or decreasing the amounts of hormone available for secretion before the rates of hormone biosynthesis have time to adjust to the required extent. The existence of this type of calcium-controlled pathway has yet to be verified as no evidence is currently available on specific degradation peptides formed in the gland. It has been suggested that the degradation occurs by rapid general proteolysis rather than by limited specific endopeptidase activity (Habener *et al.*, 1975). A calcium-regulated peptidase has been demonstrated in the parathyroid glands (Fischer, Oldham, Sizemore and Arnaud, 1972). Magnesium does not appear to affect the biosynthesis or intracellular degradation of PTH (Habener *et al.*, 1975).

6. Parathyroid Secretory Protein

Products other than PTH may be secreted from the parathyroid gland. At least one protein distinct from PTH is secreted from parathyroid tissues during studies *in vitro*. This protein was termed parathyroid secretory protein (PSP) (Kemper, Habener, Rich and Potts, 1974). PSP is a protein of high mw (150,000) that is released from the parathyroid gland in response to changes in calcium concentration in the medium; the fractional stimulation or inhibition of release, respectively, of PSP due to lowering or raising of ambient calcium concentrations shows precisely the same pattern as that of PTH itself. At present the biological function of PSP is unknown.

7. Ectopic Tumours

Hypercalcaemia associated with malignancy not involving bone or parathyroid glands has been recognised for years. It was originally suggested that it might result from the tumour producing a parathyroid hormone-like substance. Other studies indicate that the hypercalcaemia may be due to secretion by the tumour of prostaglandins (Tashjian, 1975) or osteoclastic activation factor (Horton, Raisz, Simmons, Oppenheim and Mergenhagen, 1972). It seems that some ectopic tumours do synthesise and secrete a parathyroid hormone-like substance although the incidence of this is disputed. Sherwood, O'Riordan, Aurbach and Potts (1968b) obtained evidence that parathyroid hormone is present in some tumour extracts but not in others. Benson, Riggs, Pickard and Arnaud (1974) reported the detection of more than one form of immunoreactive parathyroid hormone in the serum of cancer patients with hypercalcaemia. It was suggested that one of the immunoreactive forms resembled PreProPTH. Greenberg Martin and Sutcliffe (1973) found that a monolayer cell culture of a hypernephroma secreted substances resembling ProPTH and Hamilton, Hartman, MacGregor and Cohn (1977) demonstrated that a tissue culture of slices of a human squamous cell carcinoma synthesised parathyroid hormone-like peptides.

C. SECRETION, ACTION AND METABOLISM

1. Control of PTH Secretion

The principal factor modulating PTH secretion is the concentration of ionised calcium in the blood, although many other factors can affect the release of the hormone, including magnesium, adrenergic agonists and antagonists, polar vitamin D metabolites and cAMP. The physiological

significance and exact role of some of these factors is still only partially understood. The development of parathyroid cell culture systems in which the
effects of a variety of agents on hormone release into the medium can be
tested (e.g. Brown, Hurwitz and Aurbach, 1976) is an important technical
advance. Use of this and similar techniques should expand our knowledge
of the parathyroid secretory process.

(a) Calcium

Patt and Luckhardt (1942) showed that the rate of release of PTH from the
parathyroid glands *in vivo* was inversely related to the calcium concentration in the blood perfusing the gland. Since then these observations have been
confirmed and greatly extended by radioimmunoassay studies using gland
perfusion techniques in the cow (Sherwood, Potts, Care, Mayer and Aurbach,
1966). This inverse relationship has also been demonstrated *in vitro* by many
workers (e.g. Habener and Potts, 1976).

However, the change in PTH secretion does not bear a simple relationship to the change in plasma calcium. There is evidence based on perfusion
of calf parathyroid glands *in vivo* (Mayer, Habener and Potts, 1976) that the
glands constantly secrete some PTH, even in the presence of hypercalcaemia,
and that they are best adapted to correct hypocalcaemia of even the slightest
degree as soon as it occurs. The rapidity with which the parathyroid glands
respond to acute changes in calcium concentration suggests that the major
regulation of secretory activity occurs at the level of stored preformed hormone
rather than *de novo* synthesis.

(b) Magnesium

As with calcium there is an inverse relationship between plasma magnesium
concentrations and the rate of PTH secretion; high magnesium concentrations suppress and low magnesium concentrations stimulate PTH secretion
both *in vivo* (Buckle, Care, Cooper and Gitelman, 1968) and *in vitro* (Targovnik, Rodman and Sherwood, 1971). However in comparison with calcium
the effect of physiological concentrations of magnesium on PTH secretion
may only be slight. On a molar basis two to three times the concentration of
magnesium as calcium is required to produce the same effect upon PTH
secretion (Blum, Mayer and Potts, 1974; Habener and Potts, 1976).

Very low magnesium concentrations may be associated with reversible
failure of PTH secretion in man (Anast, Mohs, Kaplan and Burns, 1972)
and PTH secretion *in vitro* is markedly reduced if magnesium concentrations are very low (Targovnik *et al.*, 1971). In order to explain this it has been
suggested that magnesium is an essential co-factor for the adenylate cyclase
of the parathyroid gland which may be involved in the secretory process.

(c) *Cyclic 3',5'-adenosine monophosphate (cAMP)*

Activation of adenyl cyclase with production of cAMP is an intermediate step in the secretion of a number of polypeptide hormones (Robison, Butcher and Sutherland, 1971). Dibutyryl cAMP, which is resistant to degradation by phosphodiesterase, and also theophylline, which by inhibiting phosphodiesterase activity elevates local concentrations of cAMP, have been found to stimulate PTH secretion *in vitro* (Abe and Sherwood, 1972). An adenylate cyclase has been identified in canine parathyroids which is inhibited by calcium (Dufresne and Gitelman, 1972). It is probable therefore that parathyroid adenylate cylase is important in the control of PTH secretion.

(d) *Phosphate*

It has been suggested that plasma phosphate concentrations directly influence PTH secretion; however, at least in acute experiments, its action is only indirect (Sherwood, Mayer, Ramberg, Kronfield, Aurbach and Potts, 1968), probably mediated through its effect on plasma calcium.

(e) *Polar vitamin D metabolites*

1,25-dihydroxycholecalciferol(1,25-$(OH)_2D_3$) labelled with tritium becomes localised in the chick parathyroid glands as well as in the gut and the kidney (Henry and Norman, 1975) suggesting that parathyroid glands might be directly influenced by 1,25-$(OH)_2D_3$. Support for this comes from studies which demonstrated specific 1,25-$(OH)_2D_3$ cytosolic receptors in chick parathyroid glands (Brumbaugh, Hughes and Haussler, 1975). However discrepant results have been obtained from studies designed to show whether the active vitamin D metabolite stimulated or inhibited, PTH secretion. Care, Bates, Swaminathan, Scanes, Peacock, Mawer, Taylor, DeLuca, Tomlinson and O'Riordan (1975) studied the acute effect of 1,25-$(OH)_2D_3$ on PTH secretion in the goat and reported variable results, sometimes a stimulation of secretion and sometimes no effect. Chertow, Baylink, Wergedal and Norman (1975) reported a decrease in PTH secretion *in vivo* and by bovine gland slices *in vitro* after addition of 1,25-$(OH)_2D_3$. However, most recently it has been reported that a bolus injection of 1,25-$(OH)_2D_3$ given to the parathyroid glands of dogs *in vivo* caused an immediate release of PTH (Henry, Wecksler and Norman, 1978).

In contrast to the uncertainty as to the effect of 1,25-$(OH)_2D_3$ on PTH secretion, it seems that both 24,25-dihydroxycholecalciferol (Care *et al.*, 1975; Henry *et al.*, 1978) and 25,26-dihydroxycholecalciferol (Care, Pickard, Papapoulos, O'Riordan and Redel, 1978) suppress PTH secretion.

(*f*) *Other possible regulators of PTH secretion*

(*1*) *Catecholamines.* Beta-adrenergic agonists stimulate PTH release in several species (Williams, Hargis, Bowser, Henderson and Martinez, 1973; Fischer, Blum and Binswanger, 1973; Kukreja, Johnson, Ayala, Banerjee, Bowser, Hargis and Williams, 1976) and also parathyroid cAMP production (Brown, Hurwitz and Aurbach, 1977). These effects appear to be specific as beta adrenergic receptors have been detected on isolated bovine parathyroid cells by means of a radioiodine labelled beta-blocking agent, iodohydroxy-benzylpindolol (Brown *et al.*, 1977). The receptors appear to be of the beta-2 type as the production of cAMP and release of PTH were both greater for isoprenaline than for noradrenaline. The beta-blocking agent propranolol inhibited PTH release when this was stimulated by beta-adrenergic agonists, but not when stimulated by low calcium concentrations, suggesting that these two regulators of secretion act independently of one another (Brown *et al.*, 1977). Recently dopamine has been shown to stimulate PTH release (Brown, Caroll and Aurbach, 1977), but the physiological significance of this and also of the other catecholamine effects on PTH secretion, has yet to be established.

(*2*) *Calcitonin.* Calcitonin at very high concentrations of over 100 ng/ml causes PTH release from parathyroid tissue *in vitro* (Fischer, Oldham, Sizemore and Arnaud, 1971; Sherwood and Abe, 1972) but there is currently no evidence to suggest that physiological concentrations play an important role in the regulation of PTH secretion.

2. Action

PTH acts primarily on the kidney and on bone. In addition to causing phosphaturia, PTH increases the renal tubular reabsorption of calcium which with the mobilisation of calcium from bone results in the elevation of the plasma calcium level. There is continuing controversy as to which organ is the most important in controlling acutely the plasma calcium concentration (Talmage, 1956; Nordin and Peacock, 1969). In addition PTH has a variety of other actions, only some of which will be discussed here.

(*a*) *PTH action on the kidney*

(*1*) *Phosphaturia.* The phosphaturic effect of PTH was first observed by Greenwald and Gross (1925). There was controversy over whether PTH had a direct tubular action on phosphate transport or whether it produced phosphaturia by altering renal haemodynamics, but this has been resolved with the availability of highly purified PTH. Parathyroid extracts contaminated with non-hormonal proteins can produce renal vasodilation, increasing glomerular filtration rate (GFR) and renal plasma flow by up to 40%. Purified preparations cause phosphaturia within minutes without any rise in GFR. PTH inhibits proximal tubular reabsorption of phosphate thus increasing the phosphate load to the distal nephron. Studies in dogs have shown that PTH also inhibits distal tubular phosphate reabsorption (Agus, Puschett, Senesky and Goldberg, 1971).

(2) *Adenyl cyclase.* The phosphaturic action of PTH is probably mediated in both the proximal and distal tubule by renal cortical adenyl cyclase, stimulating the formation of cAMP from ATP. Administration of PTH to both man and animals causes a rapid increase in urinary cAMP which precedes the phosphaturic response (Chase and Aurbach, 1967). This increase in cAMP is almost entirely of renal origin (Kaminsky, Broadus, Hardman, Jones, Ball, Sutherland and Liddle, 1970; Tomlinson, Barling, Albano, Brown and O'Riordan, 1974) (Fig. 6). By microdissection of the rabbit nephron, PTH dependent adenyl cyclase activity has been found in proximal and

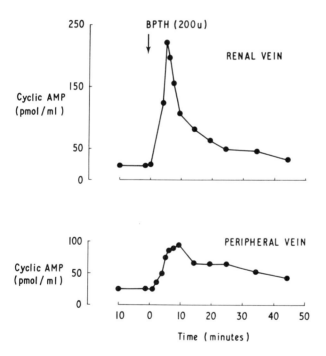

Fig. 6. The increase in plasma cAMP observed after intravenous administration of PTH to man is mainly of renal origin. After an injection of 200 u of bovine PTH the concentration of plasma cAMP rose more quickly and reached a greater level, in a renal vein than in a peripheral vein. (Reproduced with permission from O'Riordan *et al.*, 1976.)

distal segments which are sites of action of PTH on phosphate transport (Chabardes, Imbert, Clique, Montegut and Morel, 1975).

Further support for a mediating role of adenylate cyclase in the phosphaturic effect of PTH comes from the study of patients with pseudohypoparathyroidism, a condition characterised by end-organ resistance to the action of PTH (Lewin, Papapoulos, Tomlinson, Hendy and O'Riordan, 1978). In normal subjects and patients with primary or surgical hypoparathyroidism an intravenous injection of PTH causes a rapid rise in plasma and urinary cAMP; in contrast in patients with pseudohypoparathyroidism the cAMP and phosphaturic responses are impaired (Chase, Melson and Aurbach, 1969; Tomlinson, Hendy and O'Riordan, 1976a). This suggests that a primary defect at the PTH receptor-adenyl cyclase complex results in failure of cAMP production and absent phosphaturia.

Although the effects of PTH on phosphate transport in the kidney appear to be mediated by cAMP which in turn modulates cellular processes by activation of protein kinases, the precise intracellular mechanisms involved are unknown.

As with a number of polypeptide hormones prolonged stimulation of the adenyl cyclase with high levels of PTH leads to an impairment in the production of cAMP (Tomlinson, Hendy and O'Riordan, 1976b). Patients with primary hyperparathyroidism show an impaired plasma and urinary cAMP response to an intravenous injection of PTH compared to normal subjects (Tomlinson, Hendy, Pemberton and O'Riordan, 1976). This "down-regulation" or impairment in response was most marked in patients with the highest levels of endogenous hormone, although there was improvement in the response after parathyroidectomy when endogenous PTH levels had fallen to the normal range (Lewin, Hendy, Papapoulos and O'Riordan, 1978).

(3) *Calcium transport.* PTH causes a reduction in calcium clearance by stimulating net tubular reabsorption of calcium. Administration of PTH is usually associated with a fall in urinary calcium excretion (Agus, Gardner, Beck and Goldberg, 1973) and parathyroidectomy is followed by a rise in calcium excretion, despite a fall in plasma calcium (Biddulph, Hirsch, Cooper and Munson, 1970). However, in primary hyperparathyroidism urinary calcium excretion may be increased but this is due to the high filtered load of calcium.

PTH appears to have a dual action on renal calcium transport. It inhibits fractional and absolute calcium reabsorption in the proximal tubule but there is enhanced absorption distally. The precise distal site remains to be determined but some evidence points to the collecting ducts. The proximal action of PTH on calcium transport, as with phosphate and sodium, appears to be mediated by cAMP as infusion of dibutyryl cAMP produces identical effects. However, the mechanism of the distal hypocalciuric action of PTH is not clear as infusion of dibutyryl cAMP does not always produce a fall in calcium excretion (see Goldberg, Agus and Goldfarb, 1976).

(4) *Other effects of PTH on the kidney.* PTH reduces sodium reabsorption in the proximal tubule but minimum natriuresis may occur after PTH administration suggesting that sodium rejected proximally is reabsorbed distally (Goldberg *et al.*, 1976).

PTH affects magnesium transport, but this has not been clearly defined. After PTH administration to both animals and man contrary observations have been made of an increase or decrease in magnesium excretion. In primary hyperparathyroidism the plasma magnesium tends to be normal or low (King and Stanbury, 1970) and urinary magnesium tends to be normal or high, falling after parathyroidectomy (Heaton and Pyrah, 1963). The interpretation of these studies is difficult as there is competition for tubular reabsorption between calcium and magnesium in the absence of PTH and this may obscure any direct effect of PTH upon magnesium transport.

Aminoaciduria occurs in both primary (Hockaday, Wade and Keynes, 1968) and secondary hyperparathyroidism (Muldowney, Freaney and McGeeney, 1968), the excreted amino acids being those commonly found in disorders of proximal tubular reabsorption. This abnormality is frequently corrected by treatment of the hyperparathyroidism. The mechanism by which PTH increases amino acid excretion is not understood.

PTH stimulates the conversion of 25-hydroxycholecalciferol to 1,25-dihydroxycholecalciferol, the most active form of vitamin D by its action on the renal 1α-hydroxylase enzyme, both in the intact animal (Garabedian, Holick, DeLuca and Boyle, 1972) and *in vitro* (Rasmussen, Wong, Bikle and Goodman, 1972). Moreover, patients with primary hyperparathyroidism have higher mean levels of 1,25-dihydroxycholecalciferol than normal (Haussler, Baylink, Hughes, Brumbaugh, Wergedal, Shen, Nielsen, Counts, Bursac and McCain, 1976). The apparent effect of PTH on intestinal absorption of calcium might be mediated via its effect on the renal 1α-hydroxylase.

(b) Action of PTH on bone

PTH appears to have a dual action on bone. The initial effect, rapid in onset, is to promote an increased rate of release of calcium from bone mineral into blood. This transient action may be mediated through an effect of the hormone on osteocytes and a stimulation of the process of osteocytic osteolysis. The second effect of PTH on bone, resulting from a long continued increased concentration of PTH, is to promote extensive bone remodelling. This action, which persists for a long time after PTH in the blood has declined, may be mediated through stimulation of osteoclast replication and cellular activity.

In order to study bone free of modulating influences from other tissues, several groups have used organ culture procedures with calvaria or foetal limbs. The organ culture technique has been particularly useful for investigation of resorption since the bones readily demineralise and resorb in culture under the influence of various hormones. The biochemical alterations which have been detected during PTH-induced bone resorption in culture include; release of mineral, resorption of collagenous matrix, increase in cAMP, increase in hyaluronate synthesis, decrease in citrate decarboxylation, increase in lysosomal enzymes, decrease in collagen synthesis and decrease in alkaline phosphatase.

Thus PTH has a complex action on bone and also the net effect may be dependent upon the concentration of hormone. At high hormone concentrations there is a net increase in the rate of bone resorption both *in vivo* and *in vitro*, whereas at normal concentrations there is bone remodelling with no change of bone mass. Small amounts of PTH have also been reported to increase bone mass, both in the parathyroidectomised rat (Kalu, Pennock, Doyle and Foster, 1970) and in the dog (Parsons and Reit, 1974) suggesting that PTH may be a regulator of bone synthesis as well as degradation.

After stimulation of bone cells by PTH the earliest change is an activation of the membrane-bound adenylate cyclase (Chase and Aurbach, 1970). An early effect of PTH also on skeletal tissue is a change in membrane permeability and an ingress of calcium into bone cells (Parsons and Robinson, 1971). Both cAMP and intracellular calcium ions have been proposed to act as second messengers for the effect of PTH.

The mechanism by which a net transfer of calcium occurs from bone across bone cells to blood is not understood, although speculative models involving a "bone fluid compartment" comprising a fluid bathing bone mineral crystals and containing rapidly exchangeable calcium ions, have been proposed (Rasmussen, 1972; Robertson, 1976; Newman and Ramp, 1972). The reservoir of rapidly exchangeable calcium ions would therefore allow bone cells to take part in the minute to minute regulation of plasma calcium.

There is evidence that adequate concentrations of vitamin D are an absolute requirement for PTH to exert its effect on bone resorption (Rasmussen, DeLuca, Arnaud, Hawker and Von Stedingk, 1963).

3. Secretion and Metabolism

PTH in the circulation of man is heterogeneous, differing immunologically from hormone extracted from human parathyroid tissue (Berson and Yalow, 1968a) and this is caused by the presence of fragments of the native 84 amino acid molecule (mw 9500). The origin of this hormonal heterogeneity has been debated for some years. There is good evidence, from studies *in vivo*, in both man and cattle (Habener, Powell, Murray, Mayer and Potts, 1971) and *in vitro* experiments using monolayer cell cultures of human parathyroid tissue (Martin, Greenberg and Melick, 1972) that the main secretory product of the parathyroid glands is the intact 84 amino acid molecule. In contrast to pancreatic islet cells which may secrete up to 10% of proinsulin with respect to insulin, the parathyroids apparently do not secrete significant amounts of ProPTH relative to PTH (Habener, Stevens, Tregear and Potts, 1976).

In patients with primary hyperparathyroidism, circulating immuno-reactive PTH appears to consist predominantly of a large carboxyl-terminal fragment (estimated mw 6000) and thus is devoid of biological activity (Habener, Segre, Powell, Murray and Potts, 1972; Segre, Habener, Powell, Tregear and Potts, 1972). These investigators favour the hypothesis that the 9500 mw species is secreted into the circulation, metabolism of the hormone occurs in peripheral tissues, the biologically active amino-terminal region is rapidly degraded and the inactive carboxyl-terminal region is less rapidly metabolised and persists in the circulation. However, other workers have reported that, in addition to the carboxyl-terminal fragment(s), a similar, biologically active amino-terminal fragment is present in the circulation in significant amounts (Canterbury and Reiss, 1972; Canterbury, Levey and Reiss, 1973). Studies in man after infusion of bovine PTH have shown that the amino-terminal region of PTH is cleared extremely rapidly ($T_{\frac{1}{2}} = 5$ min) whereas the carboxyl-terminal region of the hormone persists for some hours in the circulation (Papapoulos, Hendy, Tomlinson, Lewin and O'Riordan, 1977) (Fig. 7). After either intravenous administration of synthetic human PTH 1–34 to normal subjects or removal of an adenoma from patients with primary hyperparathyroidism, amino-terminal immunoreactivity disappeared with a half-life of approximately 2 min (Papapoulos, Hendy, Manning, Lewin and O'Riordan, 1978). Thus, if a discrete amino-terminal fragment is generated by cleavage of the intact hormone it is almost certainly short-lived in the circulation.

Silverman and Yalow (1973) have suggested that the parathyroid glands, in addition to secreting intact hormone, may also secrete significant amounts of hormonal fragments, thus contributing to the heterogeneity in the circula-tion. They emphasised that because of the much longer half-lives of the carboxyl-terminal fragment(s) secretion of only a small amount of fragment relative to intact hormone could account for the predominance of carboxyl-terminal immunoreactivity in peripheral plasma. In support of this, Flueck, DiBella, Edis, Kehrwald and Arnaud (1977), have recently reported that patients with primary hyperparathyroidism secrete significant amounts of carboxyl-terminal fragments of PTH.

The secretion of fragments of PTH would be consistent with a calcium-regulated intracellular degradation of the hormone (see Section B). Preliminary studies (Mayer, Keaton, Hurst and Habener, 1977; Hanley, Takasuki Sulton, Schneider and Sherwood, 1978) have indicated that the plasma calcium concentration has an effect on the relative proportion of intact hormone and carboxyl-terminal fragment secreted; the higher the calcium the greater the proportion of fragment secreted. However it is to be emphasised that the existence of such a mechanism remains to be properly established.

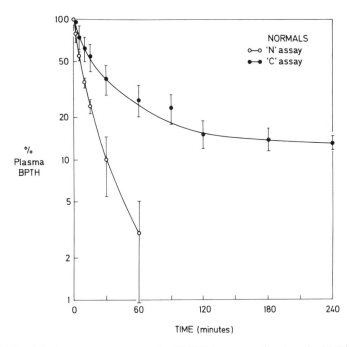

Fig. 7. After infusion of exogenous bovine PTH into man amino-terminal (○) immunoreactive bovine PTH is cleared rapidly from the circulation whereas carboxyl-terminal (●) immunoreactive material persists in the circulation for some hours. The concentration of plasma bovine PTH (M. ± S. E.M.; $n = 5$) is expressed as a percentage of the value obtained at the end of the infusion. (Reproduced with permission from Papapoulos *et al.*, 1977.)

Thus, the immunological heterogeneity of PTH in plasma probably arises by both secretion of fragments and generation of fragments by peripheral metabolism. The relative contribution of these factors in both normal and disease states has yet to be determined.

Both the kidney and the liver have been implicated in the metabolism of PTH. Berson and Yalow (1968a) showed that the clearance of immunoreactive PTH, after parathyroidectomy, was slower in patients with hyperparathyroidism secondary to renal insufficiency than in patients with primary hyperparathyroidism. Nephrectomy in both animals and man prolongs the survival of ^{125}I-labelled bovine PTH in the circulation (Melick and Martin, 1969; Martin, Melick and DeLuise, 1969). Slatopolsky and his colleagues have investigated the metabolism of exogenous bovine PTH in dogs, and reported that the kidney could clear both intact hormone and its amino-terminal and carboxyl-terminal fragments by a combination of glomerular filtration and peritubular uptake (Martin, Hruska, Lewis, Anderson and Slatpolsky, 1977).

In man after infusion of bovine PTH, patients with chronic renal failure, as a group, metabolised the amino-terminal region of the hormone less effectively than normal subjects (Fig. 8; Papapoulos et al., 1977). However,

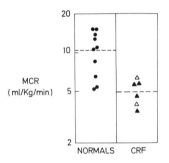

Fig. 8. Comparison of the metabolic clearance rate (MCR) of amino-terminal immuno-reactive PTH after infusion of exogenous bovine PTH in normal subjects (●) and in patients with chronic renal failure: with intact kidneys (▲) and without kidneys (△). Although the mean values for each group (represented by the dotted lines) are significantly different, there is some overlap. (Reproduced with permission from Papapoulos et al., 1977.)

as some anephric subjects could metabolise amino-terminal PTH as well as normals, organs other than the kidney must be important for the metabolism of PTH in man.

The liver has been suggested as a site of metabolism of PTH (Fang and Tashjian, 1972; Fischer et al., 1972) and the perfused rat liver can certainly metabolise bovine PTH (Canterbury, Bricker, Levey, Kozlorkis, Ruiz, Zull and Reiss, 1975). In vivo studies in dogs indicated that the liver selectively takes up and cleaves bovine PTH, but that it does not take up and metabolise the fragments further in contrast to the kidney (Martin, Hruska, Greenwalt, Klahr and Slatopolsky, 1976). Further investigations are required to evaluate the relative importance of the kidney and the liver (and possibly other organs) in the metabolism of PTH in man.

In order to investigate the cleavage sites on the PTH molecule the metabolism of ^{125}I-labelled bovine PTH has been studied in dogs by gel filtration of plasma and sequence analysis of the fragments generated to locate the iodotyrosyl residue at position 43 (Segre, Niall, Sauer and Potts, 1977). Time-course studies indicated that the initial cleavage occurred between residues 33 and 34, and that secondary cleavages occurred between residues 36–37, 40–41 and 42–43. A synthetic peptide comprising the 28–48 sequence of bovine PTH inhibited *in vivo* cleavage of the native bovine hormone (Rosenblatt, Segre and Potts, 1977).

The role of the metabolism of PTH has yet to be precisely defined. It could be entirely catabolic, representing the degradation of biologically active material. However, if biologically active, amino-terminal, fragments of the hormone are present in the circulation as suggested by both *in vivo* and *in vitro* experiments (Canterbury *et al.*, 1975) then it is possible that the initial cleavage of the hormone could represent an activation step.

The extremely rapid clearance of the amino-terminal region of the hormone from the circulation (Papapoulos *et al.*, 1977; 1978) argues against this, as does the fact that the intact bovine hormone is biologically active (to the extent of stimulating cAMP production) and is not cleaved further, in renal cortical adenyl cyclase preparations of bovine, chick and canine origin (Moseley, Martin, Robinson, Reit and Tregear, 1975: Goltzmann, Peytremann, Callahan, Segre and Potts, 1976).

D. MEASUREMENT: ASSAYS FOR PARATHYROID HORMONE

1. Biological Assays

(a) Conventional bioassays

The first bioassay for PTH was developed by Collip (1925) who showed that parathyroid gland extracts had a hypercalcaemic effect when given to intact dogs. Since then a number of bioassay systems have been described in which the hormonal activity is measured either *in vivo* or *in vitro* (Zanelli and Parsons, 1977). However, these bioassays are not suitable for measuring PTH in blood but have provided a method of determining the potency of different hormone preparations and of assessing the biological activity of various fragments of the PTH molecule.

The most widely used *in vivo* bioassay is that of Munson (1961) utilising young adult rats which had been placed on a low calcium diet for five days before use. The animals are then parathyroidectomised by electrocautery and are injected subcutaneously with standard or unknown doses of PTH.

Five hours after the injection, serum calcium is measured and the dose of the hormone required to prevent or antagonise the fall of calcium, produced by parathyroidectomy, is assessed. This assay has been proved practical and reliable but is relatively insensitive and requires considerable skill especially at the stage of parathyroidectomy. Various modifications of this procedure have been reported but none seems superior to the original method.

More recently, Dacke and Kenny (1973) and Parsons, Reit and Robinson (1973) used young birds to develop a bioassay for PTH. These assays measured the hypercalcaemic response produced in either Japanese quails or chicks after injections of standard or unknown preparations of PTH. These assays appear to be more sensitive and more practical as, for example, there is no need for parathyroidectomy.

Bioassays which assess the phosphaturic response to PTH injections in animals have been proved unreliable mainly because of the variability of urinary phosphate excretion in control animals and the non-specific induction of phosphaturia by interfering substances in partially purified extracts of parathyroid glands.

Apart from these *in vivo* approaches to bioassaying PTH, a number of *in vitro* systems have been developed. Raisz (1963) used mouse calvaria pre-labelled with ^{45}Ca and measured the release of radioactivity into the medium after addition of PTH to the preparation. Zanelli, Lea and Nisbet (1969) used a similar method without prelabelling and measured directly the calcium release into the medium. Isolated bone cells from rat or mouse calvaria have also been used and the effect of PTH on stimulating intracellular cAMP accumulations measured as an index of hormonal activity (Peck, Carpenter, Messinger and De Bra, 1974). Marcus and Aurbach (1969) developed a sensitive *in vitro* system which determined the effect of PTH on rat renal cortical adenyl cyclase and measured the production of cAMP from ATP. This is one of the most widely used *in vitro* assays and more recently similar assays for PTH have been described using renal cortical membranes preparations from many other species.

Apart from the problems of insensitivity and reproducibility of the bioassays, the lack, until recently, of a formal reference preparation of PTH also made the interpretation of results difficult. Most laboratories have expressed their results in terms of USP units of PTH calibrated against a Parathyroid Extract prepared by the Eli Lilly Company, which served as a working standard for many years. One USP unit is one-hundredth of the amount required to raise the serum calcium content of 100 ml of blood serum of normal dogs by 1 mg within 16–18 hr after administration. Robinson, Berryman and Parsons (1972) reported on the preparation of the first international standard which was established by the WHO in 1974 as the first

International Reference Preparation of Bovine Parathyroid Hormone for Bioassay.

(b) *Cytochemical bioassay*

The cytochemical assay is a relatively new bioassay technique for the measurement of very low concentrations of circulating peptide hormones. It is based on the principle that a hormone causes a specific biochemical effect on its target cells which may be quantitated by microdensitometry (Chayen, Daly, Loveridge and Bitensky, 1976). Measurement of very low concentrations of a peptide hormone, which otherwise could not be detected by other methods, can be achieved. Cytochemical assays have been used extensively for various peptide hormones. Chayen and Bitensky and their group who have pioneered the development of cytochemical bioassays have recently applied the technique to the measurement of parathyroid hormone (Chambers, Dunham, Zanelli, Parsons, Bitensky and Chayen, 1978; Fenton, Somers and Heath, 1978). They measured the activity of glucose-6-phosphate dehydrogenase in the distal convoluted tubules of guinea pigs and they were able to detect as little as 5 fg/ml of PTH in human plasma; this is approximately 20,000 times less than the concentration detected by conventional immuno-assays. In these preliminary reports the normal range of bioassayable PTH was between 1 and 15 pg/ml. Further validation of this technique is necessary but it is hoped that the cytochemical assay will provide useful information about parathyroid hormone secretion and its regulation especially in normal man where it is not always possible to detect any hormone with the radioimmunoassay technique.

2. Immunological Assays

The first immunoassay for PTH was reported by Berson and coworkers in 1963, using an antiserum raised against bovine PTH and ^{131}I-labelled bovine PTH as tracer (Berson, Yalow, Aurbach and Potts, 1963). Three years after this first description of the assay Berson and Yalow (1966) reported the first measurements of PTH in man. They showed that patients with primary hyperparathyroidism had high concentrations of immunoassayable hormone but, perhaps surprisingly, a considerable overlap was found between the values obtained in patients and those of normal subjects. Since then a number of laboratories have developed immunological assays for plasma PTH in man, all of which, with one exception (Reiss and Canterbury, 1968), showed various degrees of overlap between the values for hyperparathyroid patients and healthy normal subjects.

Until recently the development of immunoassays for PTH in man has

depended upon antisera raised against either the porcine or bovine molecule, because of the lack of sufficient human hormone for immunisation.
Antisera showing good cross-reactivity with human PTH have been produced by immunising several animal species including guinea-pigs, chickens
and goats. However, because of the known immunological differences between the parathyroid hormones of different species which are due to differences in primary structure, antisera raised against the bovine and porcine
molecules may lack the required specificity and affinity for the human hormone. Recently, human PTH has become available in sufficient quantities
to raise antisera and subsequently homologous immunoassays for the
measurement of PTH in man have been developed (Fisher, Binswanger and
Dietrich, 1974; Manning, Hendy and O'Riordan, 1977; Desplan, Jullienne,
Moukhtar and Milhaud, 1977; Papapoulos et al., 1978). It is hoped that the
application of these immunoassays to clinical practice will give further insight into the mechanism of secretion and metabolism of PTH in health and
disease.

The immunoassays currently in use utilise antisera raised against
the intact PTH molecule. These antisera are polyvalent containing antibody
populations which react with multiple antigenic sites within the PTH
molecule. They are therefore unselective assays, that is, they do not specifically detect a defined region of the hormone. As discussed in the previous
section, PTH in the circulation is heterogeneous comprising mainly fragments derived from the carboxyl terminus which are immunologically active,
but not biologically active. Antisera which recognise mainly the carboxyl-
terminal region of the molecule may be more useful in clinical practice, for
example in discriminating patients with primary hyperparathyroidism from
normals, than antisera directed predominantly against the biologically
active amino-terminal region (Arnaud, Goldsmith, Bordier and Sizemore,
1974). The need to resolve such questions has led to the development of
immunoassays specific for defined regions of the PTH molecule, so-called
region-specific assays. The main approaches used for the development of
such assays are outlined in Table 2. The potential usefulness of region-specific
assays for PTH is obviously great but the scarcity of the appropriate PTH
fragments has prevented their wide application.

The radioimmunoassay method itself has some disadvantages. For
example, PTH is susceptible to damage during labelling and is unstable
when labelled. PTH also readily adsorbs to glass and although this can be
overcome in the assay by incubating in diluted serum, this causes further
damage to the tracer, which may impair the affinity of the antibody for the
antigen. In order to overcome some of the difficulties, the immunoradiometric (labelled antibody) assay technique which had already been described
for insulin and growth hormone was applied to PTH (Addison, Hales, Wood-

Table 2

Development of region-specific immunoassay for PTH.

Radioimmunoassay

  Antiserum: raised against intact PTH 1–84; presaturated with either PTH 1–34 or 53–84. *Tracer*: intact hormone, ^{125}I-PTH 1–84

  Antiserum: raised against intact PTH 1–84. *Tracer*: fragment e.g. ^{125}I-PTH 1–34

  Antiserum: raised against PTH fragment e.g. PTH 1–34. *Tracer*: ^{125}I-PTH 1–34

Immunoradiometric (Labelled antibody) assay

  Antiserum: raised against intact PTH 1–84 or PTH fragment. Antibodies extracted with *fragment immunoadsorbent* (ImAd) consisting of either PTH 1–34 or PTH 53–84 coupled to cellulose. Labelled with ^{125}I.

---

head and O'Riordan, 1971). In this system PTH reacts directly with specific radioactively-labelled antibodies in contrast to the radioimmunoassay in which labelled and unlabelled antigen compete for binding to specific antibodies. There are a number of theoretical as well as practical advantages of the labelled antibody assay over the conventional radioimmunoassay. This assay system has been used in our laboratory for a number of years and was used for our clinical studies which are described in the following section. Antiserum 199 (B/W 211/32) which was raised in a guinea pig against bovine PTH was used. Antibodies were extracted from this antiserum with an immunoadsorbent, consisting of bovine PTH coupled to cellulose, and then labelled with ^{125}I (Hendy and O'Riordan, 1977). An extract of human parathyroid adenomas, which had been calibrated for hormone content against a highly purified human PTH preparation, was used as the standard in the assay. Characterisation of the antiserum with fragments of the bovine PTH molecule showed that it recognised antigenic determinants in both the amino- and carboxyl-terminal regions of the molecule (Figs 9(a) and (b)). In characterising a large number of other antisera in this way we were unable to find a single antiserum, raised against intact PTH, which reacted exclusively with either the amino- or the carboxyl-terminal part of the molecule (Barling, Hendy, Evans and O'Riordan, 1975; Hendy and O'Riordan, 1977).

E. PARATHYROID HORMONE IN MAN

PTH immunoassays have been extremely useful in the study of conditions characterised by hypersecretion of PTH but less valuable in normal subjects and in conditions associated with PTH deficiency, mainly because of the relative insensitivity of many current assay systems.

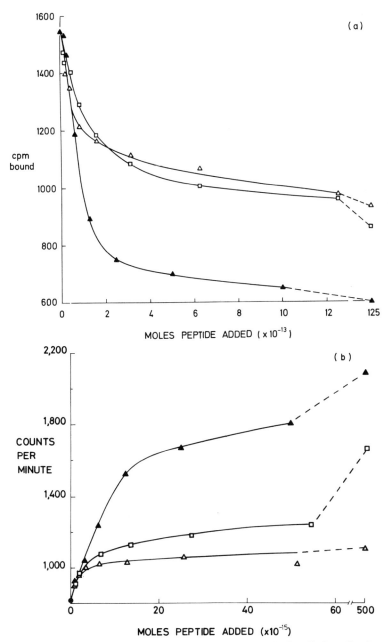

Fig. 9. Characterisation of (a) radioimmunoassay, and (b) labelled antibody assay (IRMA) with intact bovine parathyroid hormone (BPTH 1–84 ▲——▲), a carboxyl-terminal fragment derived from the native bovine hormone (BPTH 53–84 □——□) and a synthetic amino-terminal peptide (BPTH 1–34 △——△). Antiserum 199 (B/W 211/32) was used. Note the presence of amino acid carboxyl-terminal reacting antibodies in this antiserum.

1. Physiological Concentrations

(a) Normal adults

The serum PTH concentrations reported for normal man have varied widely, owing to differences in the reference preparations and the specificities of the antisera used by different laboratories. With the labelled antibody assay used in our own laboratory we have found that concentrations of circulating PTH in healthy adults range from <0.15 ng/ml (the detection limit of the assay) to 1.0 ng/ml (Fig. 10). Serum PTH levels measured in specific amino-terminal assays are lower than those found with unselective assays (Segre *et al.*, 1972; Papapoulos *et al.*, 1978).

(b) Diurnal variation

No seasonal or sex differences have been described for serum PTH levels but the existence of a diurnal variation has been reported (Jubitz, Canterbury, Reiss and Tyler, 1972; Sinha, Miller, Fleming, Khain, Edmondson, Johnston and Bell, 1975). Serum PTH concentrations appeared be be constant during the day but rose considerably after 20·00 hr reaching a peak between 2·00–4·00 hr. This nocturnal increase was not related to changes in serum calcium but could be abolished by hypercalcaemia. However, such diurnal variation has not been detected by some workers (Berson and Yalow, 1968b) and its significance is not understood.

(c) Concentrations in pregnancy

Albright and Reifenstein (1948) described pregnancy as a condition of "physiological secondary hyperparathyroidism" and more recently serum PTH concentrations have been reported to increase during pregnancy, particularly in the later part of the third trimester (Cushard, Creditor, Canterbury and Reiss, 1972). Serum PTH levels return to normal within 4–8 weeks of delivery in both lactating and non-lactating women.

(d) Concentrations in infancy and childhood

At birth PTH concentrations in cord blood have been reported to be either undetectable or very low (David and Anast, 1974), but start to rise after the first 48 hr of life. Between one and six years PTH levels are consistently lower than in adults but rise again between 8 and 10 years of age to reach adult levels (Clayton, Fairney, Flynn and Jackson, 1976).

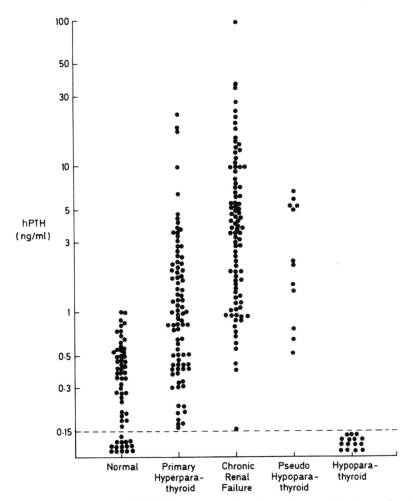

Fig. 10. Concentrations of PTH in serum as found in patients with primary hyperparathyroidism, chronic renal failure, pseudohypoparathyroidism and hypoparathyroidism compared with a group of normal controls. The detection limit of the assay, marked by the dotted line, is 0·15 ng/ml. Antiserum 199 (B/W 211/32) was used.

2. Disorders of Secretion

(a) Hyposecretion

(1) *Hypoparathyroidism.* Hypoparathyroidism is an uncommon condition, the majority of cases arising from damage to the parathyroid glands during neck surgery although occasional cases occur after radioactive iodine

treatment for thyrotoxicosis. Primary hypoparathyroidism is rare and may present at any age, sometimes being associated with absence of the thymus gland (Di George, 1965) and autoimmune endocrine disorders such as Addison's Disease. Serum PTH is undetectable by immunoassay in patients with hypoparathyroidism (Fig. 10).

(b) Hypersecretion

(1) Primary hyperparathyroidism. The prevalence of primary hyper-parathyroidism may be as high as 1 in 1000 (Boonstra and Jackson, 1971; Alveryd, 1968) the incidence being higher in women and increasing with age (Fig. 11(a)). Asymptomatic cases are now diagnosed more frequently as a result of routine biochemical screening and in a recent analysis of 100 consecutive cases 17% were diagnosed fortuitously and only 12% had symptoms of bone disease (Tomlinson and O'Riordan, 1978; Fig. 11(b)).

Primary hyperparathyroidism cannot be reliably diagnosed solely by measurement of serum immunoreactive PTH concentrations as in most assay systems there is considerable overlap with the normal range (Fig. 10). Better discrimination is obtained by relating serum PTH concentrations to levels of serum calcium (Arnaud, Goldsmith, Bordier and Sizemore, 1974). It has been suggested that serum PTH concentrations are less able to differ-entiate patients with primary hyperparathyroidism from normal subjects using antisera reactive with the amino-terminal rather than the carboxyl-terminal region (Arnaud *et al.*, 1974; Silverman and Yalow, 1973; Fischer *et al.*, 1974). However, using a homologous immunoassay system specific for the amino-terminal part of the human PTH molecule we have obtained a much better discrimination than with an unselective antiserum (Papa-poulos *et al.*, 1978).

A small percentage of patients with primary hyperparathyroidism have diffuse hyperplasia of the parathyroid glands rather than adenomata and Reiss and Canterbury (1969) have proposed that the changes in PTH con-centration in response to calcium infusion can be used to differentiate between these two groups. Calcium infusion suppressed PTH secretion in patients with hyperplasia but not with adenomata. However this was not confirmed by Murray, Peacock, Powell, Monchik and Potts (1972) who found PTH sup-pression to be similar in the two groups.

In patients with primary hyperparathyroidism elevated serum PTH levels return to normal soon after parathyroidectomy. Buckle (1969) calculated that the half-life of disappearance $(t_{\frac{1}{2}})$ of endogenous PTH after operation was approximately 20 min whereas Reiss and Canterbury (1974) reported a $t_{\frac{1}{2}}$ of 3 hr. We have found the $t_{\frac{1}{2}}$ to be as short as 2–5 min when PTH con-centrations are measured by an assay system specific for the amino-terminus

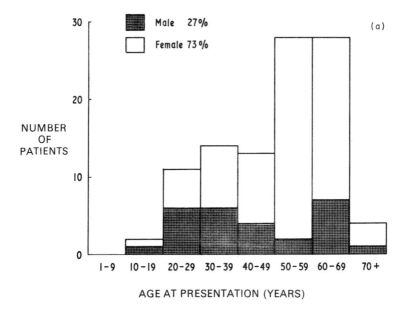

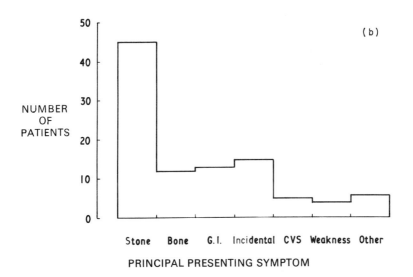

Fig. 11. Presentation of 100 consecutive patients with primary hyperparathyroidism. (a) The age of presentation: note that the incidence is two to three times higher in women than in men and increases with age; (b) the principal presenting symptom; only 12% had symptoms attributable to osteitis fibrosa cystica.

(Papapoulos *et al.*, 1978). Discrepancies in results obtained by different workers might be explained by the different properties of the antisera used and this possibility is supported by a study of calcium infusions into hyper-parathyroid patients. An apparently greater reduction in hormone concentrations occurred when PTH was measured with an antiserum directed predominantly towards the amino-terminal region than when measured with an antiserum thought to react mainly with the carboxyl-terminal region (Arnaud *et al.*, 1974).

Parathyroid venous sampling. Immunoassay of PTH is valuable in the preoperative localisation of parathyroid tumours by parathyroid venous sampling. PTH concentrations in the small veins of the thyroid plexus may be used to predict accurately the sites of abnormal parathyroid tissue in 85–90% of cases if the pattern of parathyroid venous drainage is also known (Fig. 12)

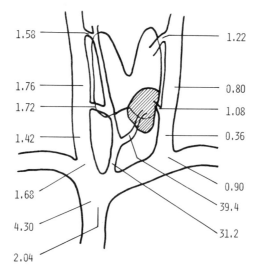

Fig. 12. Distribution of immunoreactive PTH after selective catheterisation to localise a parathyroid tumour. Note the peak hormone concentrations in the left superior, and the common inferior, thyroid veins which drained a parathyroid adenoma located at the left lower pole of the thyroid gland (shaded area). PTH is expressed in ng/ml.

(Tomlinson, Clements, Smith, Kendall and O'Riordan, 1974). If venous sampling is confined to larger veins accurate localisation is less reliable (O'Riordan, Kendall and Woodhead, 1971; Davies, Shaw, Ives, Thomas and Watson, 1973). Amino-terminal assays may be of greater value than carboxyl-terminal or unselective assays in localising abnormal parathyroid tissue when hormone concentrations are very high.

(2) Secondary hyperparathyroidism
Chronic renal failure. Hyperparathyroidism is a common and early complication of chronic renal failure (Reiss and Canterbury, 1969) and its aetiology is complex. Slatopolsky has suggested that phosphate retention indirectly stimulates the parathyroid glands by depressing plasma calcium (Slatopolsky, Caglar, Pennell, Taggart, Canterbury, Reiss and Bricker, 1971). However hyperparathyroidism might also occur because of defective renal 1α-hydroxylation of 25-hydroxycholecalciferol (Mawer, Taylor, Backhouse, Lumb and Stanbury, 1973; Haussler *et al.*, 1976) and the consequent decrease in intestinal calcium absorption, or because of end organ resistance to the action of the hormone (Massry, Coburn, Lee, Jowsey, and Kleeman, 1973; Lewin, Hendy, Papapoulos and O'Riordan, 1978). Impaired metabolism may also lead to increased PTH concentrations (see Section C3). Hyperparathyroidism usually resolves within a few months of renal transplantation but may persist for years (David, Saki, Brennen, Riggio, Cleigh, Stenzel, Rubin and Sherwood, 1973; Pletka, Strom, Hampers, Griffiths, Wilson, Bernstein, Sherwood and Merrill, 1976; Kleerekoper, Ibels, Ingham, McCarthy, Mahony, Stewart and Posen, 1975).

PTH immunoassay has been helpful in the assessment of treatments used in chronic renal failure, such as determination of optimal dialysate calcium (Goldsmith, Furszyfer, Johnson, Fournier, Arnaud, 1971) and magnesium concentrations (Pletka, Bernstein, Hampers, Merrill and Sherwood, 1974) and the use of 1α-hydroxylated derivatives of vitamin D in renal osteodystrophy (Brickman, Sherrard, Jowsey, Singer, Baylink, Maloney, Massry, Norman and Coburn, 1974; Brownjohn, Goodwin, Hately, Marsh, O'Riordan and Papapoulos, 1977). In most cases, these 1α-hydroxylated forms of vitamin D appear to suppress parathyroid secretion by elevating plasma calcium (Fig. 13), but in some a direct effect on the parathyroid glands may occur (Papapoulos, Brownjohn, Junor, Marsh, Goodwin, Hately, Lewin, Tomlinson, Hendy and O'Riordan, 1977).

Rickets and osteomalacia. Hyperparathyroidism occurs in chronic vitamin D deficiency (Preece, Tomlinson, Ribot, Pietrek, Korn, Davies, Ford, Dunnigan and O'Riordan, 1975; Lumb and Stanbury, 1974). However, as shown in Fig. 14 a number of hypocalcaemic patients have normal serum concentrations of PTH indicating that the glands have failed to respond to the hypocalcaemic stimulus. It seems, therefore, that in this condition serum calcium concentration is not the only modulator of PTH secretion and other factors are also involved, as for example, vitamin D metabolites which may directly affect the parathyroid glands (Care *et al.*, 1978). Secondary hyperparathyroidism can also be associated with some other forms of rickets and osteomalacia due to intestinal malabsorption of vitamin D and altered metabolism of vitamin D as it occurs in anticonvulsant osteomalacia or in

vitamin D dependent rickets, where there is failure of 1α-hydroxylation of
25-hydroxycholecalciferol (Arnaud, Maijer, Reade, Scriver and Whelan,
1970; Fanconi and Fischer, 1976). In familial hypophosphataemic vitamin
D resistance rickets which is characterised by normocalcaemia but low
plasma phosphate levels, PTH concentrations are normal or only slightly

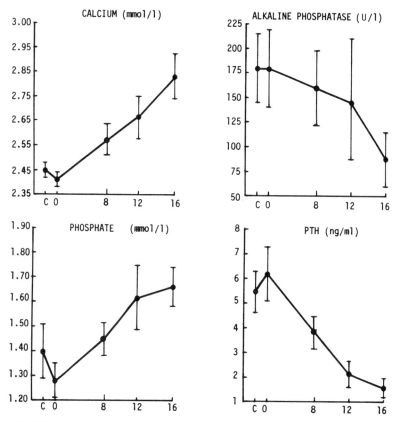

Fig. 13. Effect of 1α-dihydroxycholecalciferol on plasma calcium, alkaline phosphatase, phosphate and PTH in 10 patients treated for 16 months (M. ± S.E.M.) Horizontal
axis shows the time in months. Care additional control observations before treatment.
(Reproduced with permission from Papapoulos *et al.*, 1977.)

elevated (Arnaud, Glorieux and Scriver, 1971; Reitz and Weinstein, 1973;
Fanconi and Fischer, 1976).

Pseudohypoparathyroidism. End organ resistance to the action of PTH
results in hypocalcaemia and a consequent increase in PTH secretion (Fig. 10).
In the syndrome of pseudohypoparathyroidism described by Albright,

Burnett, Smith and Parsons (1942) both kidney and bone appear to be un-responsive to stimulation by PTH, but variants have been described (Drezner, Neelon and Lebovitz, 1973; Rodriguez, Villareal, Klahr and Slatopolsky, 1974; Stogmann and Fischer, 1975) in some of which only the kidney (Kolb and Steinbach, 1962; Cohen and Vince, 1969) or bone (Metz, Baylink, Hughes, Haussler and Robertson, 1977) appear to be unresponsive. Elevated PTH concentrations are generally reduced to normal by calcium infusion or Vitamin D treatment (See Lewin et al., 1978).

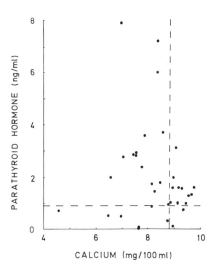

Fig. 14. Plasma PTH concentrations of 35 Asian patients with clinical vitamin D deficient osteomalacia or rickets, plotted as a function of the plasma calcium concentration. The horizontal dashed line represents the upper limit of normal for PTH and the vertical dashed line represents the lower limit of normal for plasma calcium. (Reproduced with permission from Preece et al., 1975.)

(3) *Ectopic PTH secretion.* Serum PTH concentrations in patients with malignancy-associated hypercalcaemia appear to depend upon the anti-sera and assay methods used. Some assay systems have detected elevated PTH concentrations in the majority of patients with hypercalcaemia of malignancy (Riggs, Arnaud, Reynolds and Smith, 1971) whilst others have only rarely detected high concentrations (Powell, Singer, Murray, Minkin and Potts, 1973).

The studies discussed in this chapter indicate that there are still many areas of controversy in parathyroid pathophysiology. However, much ground has been covered since the last edition of this volume and with the improved methodology now becoming available it seems likely that many apparent contradictions will soon be resolved.

ACKNOWLEDGEMENT

We would like to acknowledge the support of the MRC for our work on parathyroid hormone.

REFERENCES

Abe, M. and Sherwood, L. M. (1972). *Biochem. biophys. Res. Commun.* **48**, 396.
Addison, G. M., Hales, C. N., Woodhead, J. S. and O'Riordan, J. L. H. (1971). *J. Endocr.* **49**, 521.
Agus, Z. S., Gardner, L. B., Beck, L. H. and Goldberg, M. (1973). *Am. J. Physiol.* **224**, 1143.
Agus, Z. S., Puschett, J. B., Senesky, D. and Goldberg, M. (1971). *J. clin. Invest.* **51**, 2271.
Albright, F., Burnett, C. H., Smith, P. H. and Parsons, W. (1942). *Endocrinology*, **30**, 922.
Albright, F. and Reifenstein, A. C., Jr. (1948). "The Parathyroid Glands and Bone Disease." Williams and Wilkins, Baltimore.
Alveryd, A. (1968). *Acta chir. scand.* **9**, 389s.
Anast, C. S., Mohs, J. M., Kaplan, S. L. and Burns, C. W. (1972). *Science*, **177**, 606.
Andreatta, R. H., Hartmann, A., Johl, A., Kamber, B., Maier, R., Riniker, B., Rittel, W. and Sieber, P. (1973). *Helv. chim. Acta*, **56**, 470.
Arnaud, C. D., Glorieux, F. and Scriver, C. R. (1971). *Science*, **173**, 845.
Arnaud, C. D., Goldsmith, R. S., Bordier, P. J. and Sizemore, G. W. (1974). *Am. J. Med.*, **56**, 785.
Arnaud, C. D., Maijer, R., Reade, T., Scriver, C. R. and Whelan, D. T. (1970). *Pediatrics*, **46**, 871.
Aurbach, G. D. (1959). *J. biol. Chem.*, **234**, 3179.
Aurbach, G. D. and Potts, J. T., Jr. (1964). *Endocrinology*, **75**, 290
Barling, P. M., Hendy, G. N., Evans, M. C. and O'Riordan, J. L. H. (1975). *J. Endocr.* **66**, 307.
Benson, R. C., Riggs, B. L., Pickard, B. M. and Arnaud, C. D. (1974). *J. clin. Invest.* **54**, 175.
Berson, S. A. and Yalow, R. S. (1966). *Science*, **154**, 907.
Berson, S. A. and Yalow, R. S. (1968a). *J. clin. Endocr.* **28**, 1037.
Berson, S. A. and Yalow, R. S. (1968b). *Harvey Lecture*, **62**, 107.
Berson, S. A., Yalow, R. S., Aurbach, G. D. and Potts, J. T., Jr. (1963). *Proc. natn. Acad. Sci. USA*, **49**, 613.
Biddulph, D. M., Hirsch, P. F., Cooper, C. W. and Munson, P. L. (1970). *Endocrinology*, **87**, 1346.
Blobel, G. and Dobberstein, B. (1975). *J. Cell Biol.* **67**, 835.
Blum, J. W., Mayer, G. P. and Potts, J. T., Jr. (1974). *Endocrinology*, **95**, 84.

Boonstra, C. A. and Jackson, C. E. (1971). *Am. J. clin. Path.* **55**, 523.

Bordier, Ph. J., Tun Chot, S., Eastwood, J. B., Fournier, A. and de Wardener, H. E. (1973). *Clin. Sci.* **44**, 33.

Brewer, H. B. (1972). "Endocrinology, 1971" (S. Taylor, ed), p. 324. Heinemann, London.

Brewer, H. B., Fairwell, T., Ronan, R., Sizemore, G. W. and Arnaud, C. D. (1972). *Proc. natn. Acad. Sci. USA*, **69**, 3585.

Brewer, H. B. and Ronan, R. (1970). *Proc. natn. Acad. Sci. USA*, **67**, 1862

Brewer, H. B., Ronan, R., Fairwell, T., Rittel, W. and Arnaud, C. B. (1975). *In* "Calcium-regulating hormones" (R. V. Talmage, M. Owen and J. A. Parsons, eds), p. 23. Excerpta Medica, Amsterdam.

Brickman, A. S., Sherrard, D. J., Jowsey, J., Singer, F. R., Baylink, D. J., Maloney, N., Massry, S. G., Norman, A. W. and Coburn, J. W. (1974). *Arch. int. Med.* **134**, 883.

Brown, E. M., Carroll, R. J. and Aurbach, G. D. (1977). *Proc. natn. Acad. Sci. USA*, **74**, 4210.

Brown, E. M., Hurwitz, S. and Aurbach, G. D. (1976). *Endocrinology*, **99**, 1582.

Brownjohn, A. M., Goodwin, F. J., Hately, W., Marsh, F. P., O'Riordan, J. L. H. and Papapoulos, S. E. (1977). *Br. med. J.* ii, 721.

Brumbaugh, P. F., Hughes, M. R. and Haussler, M. R. (1975) *Proc. natn. Acad. Sci. USA*, **72**, 4871.

Buckle, R. M. (1969). *Br. med. J.* **ii**, 789.

Buckle, R. M., Care, A. D., Cooper, C. W. and Gittelman, H. J. (1968). *J. Endocr.* **42**, 529.

Campbell, P. N. and Blobel, G. (1976). *FEBS Lett.* **72**, 215.

Canterbury, J. M., Bricker, L. A., Levey, G. S., Kozlorkis, P. L., Ruiz, E., Zull, J. E. and Reiss, E. (1975). *J. clin. Invest.*, **56**, 1245.

Canterbury, J. M., Levey, G. S. and Reiss, R. E. (1973). *J. clin. Invest*, **52**, 524.

Canterbury, J. M. and Reiss, E. (1972). *Proc. Soc. exp. Biol. Med.*, **140**, 1393.

Care, A. D., Bates, R. F. L., Swaminathan, R., Scanes, C. G., Peacock, M., Mawer, E. B., Taylor, C. M., De Luca, H. F., Tomlinson, S. and O'Riordan, J. L. H. (1975). "Calcium Regulating Hormones" (R. V. Talmage, M. Owen and J. A. Parsons, eds), p. 100. Excerpta Medica, Amsterdam.

Care, A. D., Pickard, D. W., Papapoulos, S. E., O'Riordan, J. L. H. and Redel, J. (1978). *J. Endocr.* **78**, 303.

Chabardes, D., Imbert, M., Clique, A., Montegut, M. and Morel, F. (1975). *Pflugers Arch.* **354**, 229.

Chambers, D. J., Dunham, J., Zanelli, J. M., Parsons, J. A., Bitensky, L. and Chayen, J. (1978). *Clin. Endocr.* **9**, 375.

Chase, L. R. and Aurbach, G. D. (1967). *Proc. natn. Acad. Sci. USA*, **58**, 518.

Chase, L. R. and Aurbach, G. D. (1970). *J. biol. Chem.* **245**, 1520.

Chase, L. R., Melson, G. L. and Aurbach, G. D. (1969). *J. clin. Invest.* **48**, 1832.

Chayen, J., Daly, J. R., Loveridge, N. and Bitensky, L. (1976) *Rec. Prog. horm. Res.* **32**, 33.

Chertow, B. S., Baylink, D. J., Wergedal, M. H. H. S. and Norman, A. W. (1975). *J. clin. Invest.* **56**, 668.

Chou, P. Y. and Fasman, G. D. (1974). *Biochemistry*, **13**, 211.

Chu, L. L. H., Huang, W. Y., Littledike, E. T., Hamilton, J. W. and Cohn, D. V. (1975). *Biochemistry*, **14**, 3631.

Chu, L. L. H., MacGregor, R. R., Anast, C. S., Hamilton, J. W. and Cohn, D. V. (1973). *Endocrinology*, **93**, 915.

Chu, L. L. H., MacGregor, R. R., Hamilton, J. W. and Cohn, D. V. (1974). *Endocrinology*, **95**, 1431.

Clayton, B. E., Fairney, A., Flynn, D. and Jackson, D. (1976). "Inborn Errors of Calcium and Bone Metabolism" (H. Bickel and J. Stern, eds), p. 63. MTP, Lancaster.

Cohen, R. D. and Vince, F. P. (1969). *Arch. Dis. Child.* **44**, 96.

Cohn, D. V. and Hamilton, J. W. (1976) *Cornell Vet.* **66**, 271.

Cohn, D. V., MacGregor, R. R., Chu, L. L. H., Kimmel, J. R. and Hamilton, J. W. (1972). *Proc. natn. Acad. Sci. USA*, **69**, 1521.

Cohn, D. V., MacGregor, R. R., Chu, L. L. H., Huang, D. W. Y., Anast, C. S. and Hamilton, J. W. (1974) *Am. J. Med.* **56**, 767.

Cohn, D. V., MacGregor, R. R., Sinha, D., Huang, D. W. Y., Edelhoch, H. and Hamilton, J. W. (1974). *Arch. biochem. Biophys.* **164**, 669.

Collip, J. B. (1925). *J. biol. Chem.* **63**, 395.

Costello, J. M. and Dent, C. E. (1963). *Arch. Dis. Child.* **38**, 397.

Cushard, W. G. J., Creditor, M. A., Canterbury, J. M. and Reiss, E., (1972). *J. clin. Endocr. Metab.* **34**, 767.

Dacke, C. G. and Kenny, A. D. (1973). *Endocrinology*, **92**, 463.

David, D. S. Sakai, S., Brennen, B. L., Riggio, R. A., Cheigh, J., Stenzel, K. H., Rubin, A. L. and Sherwood, L. M. (1973). *New Engl. J. Med.* **289**, 398.

David, L. and Anast, C. S. (1974). *J. clin. Invest.* **54**, 287.

Davies, D. R., Shaw, D. G., Ives, D. R., Thomas, B. M. and Watson, L. (1973). *Lancet*, **i**, 1079.

Dayhoff, M. O. (1972). "Atlas of Protein Sequence and Structure", Vol. 5. National Biomedical Research Foundation, Silver Spring, MD.

Desplan, C. J., Jullienne, A., Moukhtar, M. S. and Milhaud, G. (1977). *Lancet*, **ii**, 198.

Dibella, F. P., Gilkinson, J. B., Flueck, J. A. and Arnaud, C. D. (1978). *J. clin. Endocr. Metab.* **46**, 604.

Dietrich, F. M., Binswanger, U., Hunziker, W. and Fischer, J. A. (1976). "Inborn Errors of Calcium and Bone Metabolism" (H. Bickel and J. Stern, eds), p. 39. MTP, Lancaster.

Di George, A. M. (1965). *J. Pediatr.* **67**, 907.

Drezner, M., Neelon, F. A. and Lebovitz, H. E. (1973). *New Engl. J. Med.* **289**, 1056.

Dufresne, L. R. and Gitelman, H. J. (1972), "Calcium, Parathyroid Hormone and the Calcitonins" Ed. (R. V. Talmage and P. L. Munson, eds), Int. Cong. Ser. No. 243, p. 202. Excerpta Medica Foundation, Amsterdam.

Fanconi, A. and Fischer, J. A. (1976). "Inborn Errors of Calcium and Bone Metabolism" (H. Bickel and J. Stern, eds), p. 52. MTP, Lancaster.

Fang, V. S. and Tashijan, A. H., Jr. (1972) *Endocrinology*, **90**, 1177

Fenton, S., Somers, S. and Heath, D. A. (1978). *Clin. Endocr.* **9**, 381.

Fischer, J. A., Oldham, S. B., Sizemore, G. W. and Arnaud, C. D. (1971). *Horm. Metab. Res.* **3**, 223.

Fischer, J. A., Oldham, S. B., Sizemore, G. W. and Arnaud, C. D. (1972) *Proc. natn. Acad. Sci. USA*, **69**, 2341.

Fischer, J. A., Binswanger, U. and Dietrich, F. M. (1974). *J. clin. Invest.* **54**, 1382.

Fischer, J. A., Blum, J. W. and Binswanger, U. (1973). *J. clin. Invest.* **52**, 2434.

Fiskin, A. M., Cohn, D. V. and Peterson, G. S. (1977). *J. biol. Chem.* **252**, 8261.

Flueck, J. A., Di Bella, F. P., Edis, A. J., Kehrwald, J. M. and Arnaud, C. D. (1977). *J. clin. Invest.* **60**, 1317.

Garabedian, M., Holick, M. F., DeLuca, H. F. and Boyle, I. T. (1972). *Proc. natn. Acad. Sci. USA*, **69**, 1673.

Goldberg, M., Agus, Z. S. and Goldfarb, S. (1976). "Int. Rev. Physiol" (K. Thurau, ed.), Vol. 11, Ch. 7, p. 221. University Park Press, Baltimore.

Goldsmith, R. S., Furszyfer, J., Johnson, W. J., Fournier, A. E. and Arnaud, C. D. (1971). *Am. J. Med.* **50**, 692.

Goltzmann, D., Peytremann, A., Callahan, E. N., Segre, G. V. and Potts, J. T., Jr. (1976). *J. clin. Invest.* **57**, 8.

Greenwald, I. and Gross, J. (1925). *J. biol. Chem.* **66**, 217.

Greenberg, P. B., Martin, T. J. and Sutcliffe, H. S. (1973). *Clin. Sci. mol. Med.* **45**, 183.

Habener, J. F., Chang, H. and Potts, J. T., Jr. (1977). *Biochemistry*, **16**, 3910.

Habener, J. F., Kemper, B. and Potts, J. T., Jr. (1975). *Endocrinology*, **97**, 431.

Habener, J. F., Kemper, B., Potts, J. T., Jr. and Rich, A. (1973). *Endocrinology*, **92**, 219.

Habener, J. F., Kemper, B., Potts, J. T., Jr., and Rich, A. (1975). *Biochem. biophys. Res. Commun.* **63**, 1114.

Habener, J. F., Kemper, B., Rich, A. and Potts, J. T. Jr., (1977). *Rec. Prog. horm. Res.* **33**, 249.

Habener, J. F. and Potts, J. T., Jr. (1976). *Endocrinology*, **98**, 197.

Habener, J. F., Potts, J. T. Jr. and Rich, A. (1976), *J. biol. Chem.* **251**, 3893.

Habener, J. F., Powell, D., Murray, T. M., Mayer, G. P. and Potts, J. T., Jr. (1971). *Proc. natn. Acad. Sci. USA*, **68**, 2986.

Habener, J. F., Segre, G. V., Powell, D., Murray, T. M. and Potts, J. T., Jr., (1972). *Nature, Lond.* **238**, 152.

Habener, J. F., Stevens, T. D., Tregear, G. W. and Potts, J. T., Jr. (1976). *J. clin. Endocr. Metab.* **42**, 520.

Hamilton, J. W., Hartman, C. R., MacGregor, D. H. and Cohn, D. V. (1977). *J. clin. Endocr. Metab.* **45**, 1023.

Hamilton, J. W., MacGregor, R. R., Chu, L. L. H. and Cohn, D. V. (1971). *Endocrinology*, **189**, 1440.

Hamilton, J. W., Niall, H. D., Jacobs, J. W., Keutmann, H. T., Potts, J. T., Jr., and Cohn, D. V. (1974). *Proc. natn. Acad. Sci. USA*, **71**, 653.

Hanley, D. A., Takatsuki, K., Sultan, J. M., Schneider, A. B. and Sherwood, L. M. (1978). *J. clin. Invest.* **62**, 1247.

Haussler, M. R., Baylink, D. J., Hughes, M. R., Brumbaugh, P. F., Wergedal, J. E., Shen, F. H., Nielsen, R. L., Counts, S. J., Bursac, K. M. and McCain, T. A. (1976). *Clin. Endocr.* **5**, 151S.

Heaton, F. W. and Pyrah, L. N. (1963). *Clin. Sci.* **25**, 475.

Hendy, G. N., Barling, P. M. and O'Riordan, J. L. H. (1974). *Clin. Sci. mol. Med.*, **47**, 567.

Hendy, G. N. and O'Riordan, J. L. H. (1976). "Handbook of Radioimmunoassay". (G. E. Abraham, ed.), p. 425. Marcel Dekker, New York.

Henry, H. L. and Norman, A. W. (1975). *Biochem. biophys. Res. Commun.* **62**, 781.

Henry, H. L., Weckster, W. R. and Norman, A. W. (1978). "Endocrinology of Calcium Metabolism" (D. H. Copp and R. V. Talmage, eds), p. 197. Excerpta Medica, ICS, 421, Amsterdam.

Hockaday, T. D. R., Wade, D. N. and Keynes, W. M. (1968). *Proc. R. Soc. Med.* **61**, 657.

Horton, J. E., Raisz, L. G., Simmons, H. A., Oppenheim, J. J. and Mergenhagen, S. E. (1972). *Science*, **177**, 793.

Huang, D. W. Y., Chu, L. L. H., Hamilton, J. W., MacGregor, R. R. and Cohn, D. V. (1975). *Arch. biochem. Biophys.* **166**, 67.

Hunt, N. H., MacNeil, S. and Martin, T. J. (1978) *Biochem. biophys. Res. Commun.* **81**, 581.

Jacobs, J. W., Kemper, B., Niall, H. D., Habener, J. F. and Potts, J. T., Jr. (1974). *Nature, Lond.* **249**, 155.

Jubitz, W., Canterbury, J. M., Reiss, E. and Tyler, F. H. (1972). *J. clin. Invest.* **51**, 2040.

Kalu, D. N., Pennock, J., Doyle, F. H. and Foster, G. V. (1970). *Lancet*, **i**, 1363.

Kaminsky, N. I., Broadus, A. E., Hardman, J. G., Jones, D. J. Jr., Ball, J. H., Sutherland, E. W. and Liddle, G. W. (1970). *J. clin. Invest*, **49**, 2387.

Kasemuth, R., Davies, S. J., Woodhead, J. S. and Peacock, M. (1977). *Calc. Tiss. Res.* **22S**, 442.

Kemper, B. (1976). *Nature, Lond.* **262**, 321.

Kemper, B., Habener, J. F., Ernst, M. D., Potts, J. T., Jr. and Rich, A. (1976). *Biochemistry*, **15**, 15.

Kemper, B., Habener, J. F., Mulligan, R. C., Potts, J. T., Jr. and Rich, A. (1974). *Proc. natn. Acad. Sci. USA*, **71**, 3731.

Kemper, B., Habener, J. F., Potts, J. T., Jr. and Rich, A. (1972). *Proc. natn. Acad. Sci. USA*, **67**, 643.

Kemper, B., Habener, J. F., Potts, J. T., Jr. and Rich, A. (1976). *Biochemistry*, **15**, 20.

Kemper, B., Habener, J. F., Rich, A. and Potts, J. T., Jr. (1974). *Science*, **184**, 167.

Kemper, B. and Stolarsky, L. (1976). Program. Abstr. 58th Ann. Meet. Endocr. Soc. Abst. No. 102.

Kemper, B. and Stolazsky, L. (1977). *Biochemistry*, **16**, 5.

Keutmann, H. T., Aurbach, G. D., Dawson, B. F., Niall, H. D., Deftos, L. J. and Potts, J. T., Jr. (1971). *Biochemistry*, **10**, 2779.

Keutmann, H. T., Barling, P. M., Hendy, G. N., Segre, G. V., Niall, H. D., Aurbach, G. D. Potts, J. T., Jr. and O'Riordan, J. L. H. (1974). *Biochemistry*, **13**, 1646.

Keutmann, H. T., Niall, H. D., O'Riordan, J. L. H. and Potts, J. T., Jr. (1975). *Biochemistry*, **14**, 1842.

Keutmann, H. T., Hendy, G. N., Boehnert, M., O'Riordan, J. L. H. and Potts, J. T., Jr. (1978a). *J. Endocr.* **78**, 49.

Keutmann, H. T., Sauer, M. M., Hendy, G. N., O'Riordan, J. L. H. and Potts, J. T., Jr., (1978b). *Biochemistry*, **17**, 5723.

King, R. G. and Stanbury, S. W. (1970). *Clin. Sci.* **39**, 281.

Kleerekoper, M., Ibels, L. S., Ingham, T. P., McCarthy, S. W., Mahony, J. F. Stewart, J. H. and Posen, S. (1975). *Br. med. J.* **3**, 680.

Klob, F. O. and Steinbach, H. L. (1962). *J. clin. Endocr.* **22**, 59.

Kronenberg, H. M., Roberts, B. E., Habener, J. F., Potts, J. T., Jr. and Rich, A. (1977). *Nature, Lond.* **267**, 804.

Kukreja, S. C., Johnson, P. A., Ayala, G., Bannerjee, P., Bowser, E. N., Hargis, G. K. and Williams, G. A. (1976). *Proc. Soc. exp. Biol. Med.* **151**, 326.

Lewin, I. G., Hendy, G. N., Papapoulos, S. E. and O'Riordan, J. L. G. (1978). *Clin. Sci. mol. Med.* **55**, 7 p.

Lewin, I. G., Papapoulos, S. E. Hendy, G. N., Tomlinson, S. and O'Riordan, J. L. H. (1978). *Clin. Sci. mol. Med.* **54**, 27 p.

Lewin, I. G., Papapoulos, S. E., Tomlinson, S., Hendy, G. N. and O'Riordan, J. L. H. (1978). *Quart. J. Med.* **47**, 533.

Lumb, G. A. and Stanbury, S. W. (1974). *Am. J. Med.* **56**, 833.

MacGregor, R. R., Chu, L. L. H., Hamilton, J. W. and Cohn, D. V. (1973). *Endocrinology.* **93**, 1387.

MacGregor, R. R., Chu, L. L. H. and Cohn, D. V. (1976). *J. biol. Chem.* **251**, 6711.

MacGregor, R. R., Hamilton, J. W. and Cohn, D. V. (1975). *Endocrinology*, **97**, 167.

Manning, R. M., Hendy, G. N. and O'Riordan, J. L. H. (1977). *J. Endocr.* **73**, 38p.

Marcus, R. and Aurbach, G. D. (1969). *Endocrinology*, **85**, 801.

Martin, K., Hruska, K., Greenwalt, A., Klahr, S., and Slatopolsky, E. (1976). *J. clin. Invest.* **58**, 781.

Martin, K., Hruska, K. A., Lewis, J., Anderson, C. and Slatopolsky, E. (1977). *J. clin. Invest.* **60**, 808.

Martin, T. J., Greenberg, P. B. and Melick, R. A. (1972). *J. clin. Endocr. Metab.* **34**, 437.

Martin, T. J., Melick, R. A. and De Luise, M. (1969). *Biochem. J.* **iii**, 509.

Massry, S. G., Coburn, J. W., Lee, D. B. N., Jowsey, J. and Keelman, C. R. (1973). *Ann. int. Med.* **78**, 357.

Mawer, E. B., Backhouse, J., Hill, L. F., Lumb, G. A., DeSilva, P., Taylor, C. M. and Stanbury, S. W. (1975). *Clin. Sci. mol. Med.* **48**, 349.

Mawer, E. B., Taylor, C. M. Backhouse, J., Lumb., G. A. and Stanbury, S. W. (1973). *Lancet*, **i**, 626.

Maxam, A. M. and Gilbert, W. (1977). *Proc. natn. Acad. Sci. USA*, **64**, 560.

Mayer, G. P., Habener, J. F. and Potts, J. T., Jr. (1976). *J. clin. Invest.* **57**, 678.

Mayer, G. P., Keaton, J. A., Hurst, J. G. and Habener, J. F. (1977). Prog. 59th Ann. Meet. Endocr. Soc. Abst. No. 355.

Melick, R. A. and Martin, T. J. (1969). *Clin. Sci.* **37**, 667.

Metz, S. A., Baylink, D. J., Hughes, M. R., Haussler, M. R. and Robertson, R. P. (1977). *New Engl. J. Med.* **297**, 1084.

Milstein, C., Brownlee, G. G., Harrison, T. M. and Matthews, M. B. (1972). *Nature, Lond.* **239**, 117.

Moseley, J. M., Martin, T. J., Robinson, C. J., Reit, B. W. and Tregear, G. W. (1975). *Clin. exp. Pharm. Phys.* **2**, 549.

Muldowney, F. P., Freaney, R. and McGeeney, D. (1968). *Quart. J. Med.* **37**, 517.

Munson, P. L. (1961). "The Parathyroids" (R. P. Greep and T. V. Talmage, eds), p. 94. C. C. Thomas, Springfield.

Murray, T. M., Muzaffer, S. A., Parsons, J. A. and Keutmann, H. T. (1975). *Biochemistry*, **14**, 2705.

Murray, T. M., Peacock, M., Powell, D., Monchik, J. M. and Potts, J. T. (1972). *Clin. Endocr.* **1**, 235.

Newman, W. F. and Ramp, W. K. (1972). "Cellular Mechanism for Calcium Transfer and Homeostasis" (G. Nichols, Jr. and R. H. Wasserman, eds). Academic Press, New York and London.

Niall, H. D., Keutmann, H. T., Sauer, R., Hogan, M., Dawson, B., Aurbach, G. D. and Potts, J. T., Jr. (1970). *Hoppe-Seyler's Z. Physiol. Chem.* **351**, 1586.

Niall, H. D., Sauer, R. T., Jacobs, J. W., Keutmann, H. T., Segre, G., O'Riordan, J. L. H., Aurbach, G. D. and Potts, J. T., Jr. (1974). *Proc. natn. Acad. Sci. USA*, **71**, 384.

Nordin, B. E. C. and Peacock, M. (1969). *Lancet*, **ii**, 1280.

O'Riordan, J. L. H., Kendall, B. E. and Woodhead, J. S. (1971). *Lancet*, **ii**, 1172.

O'Riordan, J. L. H., Tomlinson, S. and Hendy, G. N. (1976). "Calcium et Maladies Endocriniennes" (D. J. Hioco, ed.), p. 13. Sandoz Editions, Paris.

O'Riordan, J. L. H., Watson, L. and Woodhead, J. S. (1972). Clin. Endocr. 1, 149.

O'Riordan, J. L. H., Woodhead, J. S., Hendy, G. N., Parsons, J. A., Robinson, C. J., Keutmann, H. T., Dawson, B. F. and Potts, J. T., Jr., (1974). J. Endocr. 63, 117.

Papapoulos, S. E., Brownjohn, A. M., Junor, B. J. R., Marsh, F. P., Goodwin, F. J., Hately, W., Lewin, I. G., Tomlinson, S., Hendy, G. N. and O'Riordan, J. L. H. (1977). Clin. Endocr. 7, 59S.

Papapoulos, S. E., Hendy, G. N., Manning, R. M., Lewin, I. G., and O'Riordan, J. L. H. (1978). J. Endocr. 79, 33P.

Papapoulos, S. E., Hendy, G. N., Tomlinson, S., Lewin, I. G. and O'Riordan, J. L. H. (1977). Clin. Endocr. 7, 211.

Parsons, J. A. and Reit, B. (1974). Nature, Lond. 250, 254.

Parsons, J. A., Reit, B. and Robinson, C. J. (1973). Endocrinology, 92, 454.

Parsons, J. A. and Robinson, C. J. (1971). Nature, Lond. 230, 581.

Patt, H. M. and Luckhardt, A. B. (1942), Endocrinology, 31, 384.

Peck, W. A., Carpenter, J., Messinger, K. and De Bra, D. (1973). Endocrinology, 92, 692.

Pletka, P. G., Bernstein, D. S., Hampers, C. L., Merill, J. P. and Sherwood, I. L. M., (1974). Metabolism, 23, 619.

Pletka, P. G., Strom, T. B., Hampers, C. L., Griffiths, H., Wilson, R. E., Bernstein, D. S., Sherwood, L. M. and Merrill, J. P. (1976). Nephron. 17, 371.

Potts, J. T., Jr., Aurbach, G. D. and Sherwood, L. M. (1966). Rec. Prog. horm. Res. 22, 101.

Potts, J. T., Jr., Tregear, G. W., Keutmann, H. T., Niall, H. D., Sauer, R., Deftos, L. J., Dawson, B. F., Hogan, M. L. and Aurbach, G. D. (1971). Proc. natn. Acad. Sci. USA, 68, 63.

Powell, D., Singer, F. R., Murray, T. M., Minkin, C. and Potts, J. T., Jr., (1973). New Engl. J. Med. 289, 176.

Preece, M. A. Tomlinson, S., Ribot, C. A., Pietrek, J., Korn, H. T., Davies, D. M., Ford, J. A., Dunnigan, M. G. and O'Riordan, J. L. H. (1975). Quart. J. Med. 44, 575.

Raisz, L. G. (1963). Nature, Lond. 197, 1015.

Rasmussen, H. (1972). Clin. Endocr. Metab. 1, 3.

Rasmussen, H. and Craig, L. C. (1962). Rec. Prog. hormone Res. 18, 269.

Rasmussen, H., De Luca, H. F., Arnaud, C. D., Hawker, C. D. and Von Stedingk, M., (1963). J. clin. Invest. 42, 1940.

Rasmussen, H., Sze, Y. L. and Young, R. (1964). J. biol. Chem. 239, 2852.

Rasmussen, H., Wong, M., Bikle, D. and Goodman, D. B. P. (1972). J. clin. Invest. 51, 2502.

Reiss, E. and Canterbury, J. M. (1968). Proc. Soc. exp. Biol. 128, 501.

Reiss, E. and Canterbury, J. M. (1969). New Engl. J. Med. 280, 1381.

Reiss, E. and Canterbury, J. M. (1974). Rec. Prog. hormone Res. 30, 391.

Reitz, R. E. and Weinstein, R. L. (1973). New Engl. J. Med. 289, 941.

Riggs, B. L., Arnaud, C. D., Reynolds, J. C. and Smith, L. H. (1971). J. clin. Invest. 50, 2079.

Roberts, B. E. and Paterson, B. M. (1973). Proc. natn. Acad. Sci. USA, 70, 2320.

Robertson, W. G. (1976). "Calcium, Phosphate and Magnesium Metabolism", (B. E. C. Nordin, ed.), p. 250. Churchill Livingstone, London.

Robinson, C. J., Berryman, I. and Parsons, J. A. (1972). "Parathyroid Hormone and the Calcitonins" (R. V. Talmage and P. L. Manson, eds), p. 515. Excerpta Medica, Amsterdam.

Robinson, G. A., Butcher, R. W. and Sutherland, E. W. (1971). "Cyclic AMP." Academic Press, New York and London.

Rodriquez, H. J., Villareal, H., Klahr, S. and Slatopolsky, E. (1974). *J. clin. Endocr. Metab.* **39**, 693.

Rosenblatt, M., Callahan, E. N., Mahaffey, J. E., Pont, A. and Potts, J. T., Jr. (1977). *J. biol. Chem.* **252**, 5847.

Rosenblatt, M., Goltzman, D., Keutmann, H. T., Tregear, G. W. and Potts, J. T., Jr. (1976). *J. biol. Chem.* **251**, 159.

Rosenblatt, M., Segre, G. V. and Potts, J. T., Jr. (1977). *Biochemistry*, **16**, 2811.

Sauer, R. T., Niall, H. D., Hogan, M. L., Keutmann, H. T., O'Riordan, J. L. H. and Potts, J. T., Jr., (1974). *Biochemistry*, **13**, 1994.

Segre, G. V., Habener, J. F., Powell, D., Tregear, G. W. and Potts, J. T., Jr. (1972). *J. clin. Invest.* **51**, 3163.

Segre, G. V., Niall, H. D., Habener, J. F. and Potts, J. T., Jr. (1974). *Am. J. Med.* **56**, 774.

Segre, G. V., Niall, H. D., Sauer, R. T. and Potts, J. T., Jr. (1977). *Biochemistry*, **16**, 2417.

Segre, G. V. and Potts, J. T., Jr. (1976). *Endocrinology*, **98**, 1294.

Sherwood, L. M. and Abe, M. (1972). *J. clin. Invest.* **51**, 889.

Sherwood, L. M., Potts, J. T., Jr., Care, A. D., Mayer, G. P. and Aurbach, G. D. (1966) *Nature, Lond.* **209**, 52.

Sherwood, L. M., Mayer, G. P., Ramberg, C. F., Kronfield, D. S., Aurbach, G. D. and Potts, J. T., Jr. (1968). *Endocrinology*, **83**, 1043.

Sherwood, L. M., O'Riordan, J. L. H., Aurbach, G. D. and Potts, J. T., Jr. (1968). *J. clin. Endocr.* **27**, 140.

Silverman, R. and Yalow, R. S. (1973). *J. clin. Invest.* **52**, 1958.

Sinha, T. K., Miller, S., Fleming, J., Khain, R., Edmondson, J., Johnson, C. C., Jr., and Bell, N. H. (1975). *J. clin. Endocr. Metab.* **41**, 1009.

Slatopolsky, E., Caglar, S., Pennell, J. P., Taggart, D. D., Canterbury, J. M., Reiss, E., Bricker, N. W. (1971). *J. clin. Invest.* **50**, 492.

Stögmann, W. and Fischer, J. A. (1975). *Am. J. Med.* **59**, 140.

Stolazsky, L. and Kemper, B. (1978). *J. biol. Chem.* **253**, 7194.

Talmage, R. V. (1956). *Ann. N.Y. Acad. Sci.* **64**, 326.

Tan, C. M., Raman, A. and Sinnathyeay, T. A. (1972). *J. Obstet. Gynaec. Br. Commonw.* **79**, 694.

Targovnik, J. H., Rodman, J. S. and Sherwood, L. M. (1971). *Endocrinology*, **88**, 1477.

Tashjian, A. H., Jr. (1975). *New Engl. J. Med.* **293**, 1317.

Tomlinson, S., Barling, P. M., Albano, J. D. M., Brown, B. L. and O'Riordan, J. L. H. (1974). *Clin. Sci. mol. Med.* **47**, 481.

Tomlinson, S., Clements, V. R., Smith, M. J. G., Kendall, B. E. and O'Riordan, J. L. H. (1974). *Br. J. Surg.* **61**, 633.

Tomlinson, S., Hendy, G. N. and O'Riordan, J. L. H. (1976a). *Lancet.* **i**, 62.

Tomlinson, S., Hendy, G. N. and O'Riordan, J. L. H. (1976b). "Calcified Tissues, 1975" (S. Pors Nielsen and E. Hjørting-Hànsen, eds), p. 267. FADL'S Forlag.

Tomlinson, S., Hendy. G. N., Pemberton, D. M. and O'Riordan, J. L. H. (1976). *Clin. Sci. mol. Med.* **51**, 59.

Tomlinson, S. and O'Riordan, J. L. H. (1978) *Br. J. hosp. Med.* **19**, 40.

Tregear, G. W., van Reitschoten, J., Greene, E., Keutmann, H. T., Niall, H. D., Reit, B., Parsons, J. A. and Potts, J. T., Jr. (1973). *Endocrinology*, **93**, 1349.

Tregear, G. W., van Reitschoten, J., Greene, E., Niall, H. D., Keutmann, H. T., Parsons, J. A., O'Riordan, J. L. H. and Potts, J. T., Jr. (1974). *Hoppe-Seyler's Z. Physiol. Chem.* **355**, 415.

Williams, G. A., Hargis, G. K., Bowser, E. N., Henderson, W. J. and Martinez, N. (1973). *Endocrinology*, **92**, 687.

Woodhead, J. S., O'Riordan, J. L. H., Keutmann, H. T., Stoltz, M. L., Dawson, B. F., Niall, H. D., Robinson, C. J. and Potts, J. T., Jr. (1971). *Biochemistry*, **10**, 2787.

Zanelli, J. M., Lea, D. J. and Nesbit, J. A. (1969). *J. Endocr.* **43**, 33.

Zanelli, J. M. and Parsons, J. A. (1979). "Handbuch der Inneren Medizin, VI/1 Klinische Osteologie" (F. Kulencordt, ed.). Springer Verlag, Berlin.

II. Vitamin D

S. E. PAPAPOULOS, I. G. LEWIN, T. L. CLEMENS, G. N. HENDY
and J. L. H. O'RIORDAN

INTRODUCTION

Vitamin D is now regarded as the precursor of a hormone, namely 1,25-dihydroxyvitamin D. This is produced by the kidney and it circulates in the blood stream to act principally on gut and bone. An intermediate form also circulates, having been produced from the vitamin by 25-hydroxylation in the liver. The hormone acts, as do steroid hormones, in the nuclei of the receptor cells and its production is subject to feedback regulation. Thus, vitamin D and its metabolites fully justify recognition as the basis of an endocrine system which interacts with the parathyroid glands, and is of fundamental importance in the hormonal control of mineral metabolism.

This change in status, from vitamin to hormone, stemmed mainly from the work of Kodicek and his colleagues in Cambridge and of DeLuca and his colleagues in Madison. Progress initially depended on production of radio-labelled forms of vitamin D so that its metabolism could be studied. It was then found that the parent compound was converted into more polar derivatives, a number of which have been chemically characterised and some shown to be biologically more active than the parent compound. The time taken for these metabolites to be synthesised *in vivo* accounts for an early observation that there is a delay before vitamin D can stimulate intestinal absorption of calcium. Assays have now been developed for a number of vitamin D metabolites and have facilitated their study in man. Moreover, several hydroxylated derivatives of the vitamin have been synthesised and are proving valuable in clinical practice. In this chapter the main features of this newly recognised endocrine system will be reviewed.

A. CHEMISTRY

Vitamin D is a 9-10 secosterol with the A-ring rotated into the cis configuration. It differs, therefore, from a C_{21} steroid because of the disruption of the bond between C-9 and C-10 and the rotation of the A-ring. It has also an elongated side chain (Fig. 1). The natural form is vitamin D_3 (cholecalci-

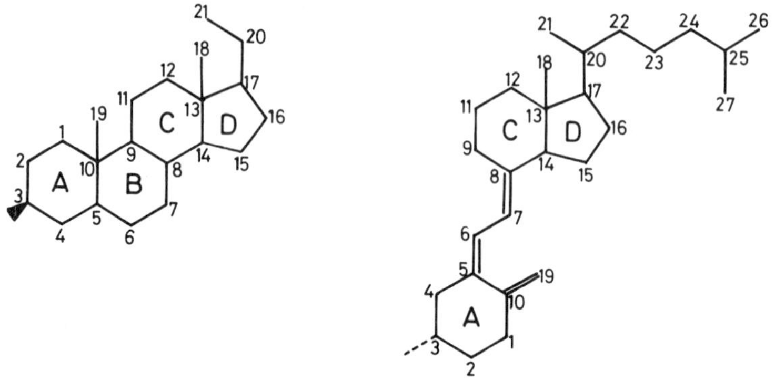

Fig. 1. General structure of a C_{21} steroid molecule (left) compared to a C_{27} 9–10 seco-sterol (right), such as vitamin D_3. The A-ring in the seco-sterol is in the cis-configuration about the 5–6 double bond.

ferol) which is a C_{27} compound; its precursor is 7-dehydrocholesterol which is present in the skin and irradiation of this compound with light of wavelength 230–313 nm leads to its conversion to vitamin D_3. Ultraviolet irradiation opens the B-ring at the 9–10 position to form previtamin D_3 and rearrangement of the molecule yields vitamin D_3. This rearrangement requires energy and its rate is temperature dependent. Two additional irradiation products of 7-dehydrocholesterol, namely lumisterol and tachysterol, are now known to be other derivatives of previtamin D_3 (Fig. 2), rather than intermediates in vitamin D_3 formation (see Campion, Pelc and Atkins, 1976). In addition to synthesis in the skin, vitamin D_3 can also be obtained by ingestion of foods which contain it naturally, or are enriched with it.

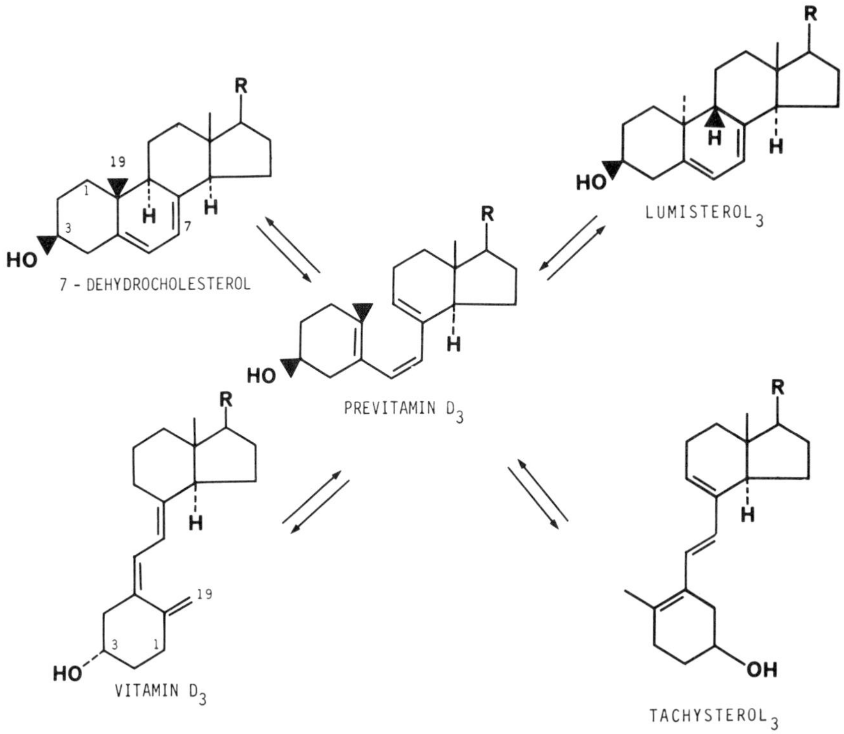

Fig. 2. Vitamin D_3 (cholecalciferol) is synthesised by irradiation of 7-dehydrocholesterol via the intermediate compound previtamin D_3. Lumisterol and tachysterol, formerly thought to be intermediates in vitamin D_3 formation, are now known to be other derivatives of previtamin D_3.

However, foods, such as milk and dairy products, are frequently fortified with vitamin D_2 (ergocalciferol) a synthetic compound prepared by irradiation of ergosterol obtained from yeasts and fungi. The side chain of ergocalciferol has a C-22 double bond and an extra methyl group attached to C-24, so that it is a C_{28} compound.

B. METABOLISM

Vitamin D undergoes two hydroxylation steps before it becomes biologically active: the first reaction occurring in the liver and the second in the kidney (Fig. 3). Vitamin D_3 produced either in the skin or absorbed from the small

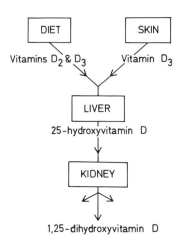

Fig. 3. Metabolic pathway of vitamin D. Metabolites other than 1,25-dihydroxy-vitamin D may be formed by hydroxylation of 25-hydroxyvitamin D (for example, 24,25- and 25,26-dihydroxyvitamin D).

intestine is rapidly accumulated in the liver where it is hydroxylated at C-25 of the side chain to form 25-hydroxycholecalciferol $[25(OH)D_3]$, the most abundant circulating form of the vitamin (Ponchon, Kennan and DeLuca, 1969). This reaction is catalysed by the enzyme 25-hydroxylase and requires NADPH, molecular oxygen and magnesium ions (Bhattacharyya and DeLuca, 1974). In mammals the 25-hydroxylation of vitamin D occurs exclusively in the liver and appears to take place in the microsomal fraction (Olson, Knutson, Bhattacharyya and DeLuca, 1976) but in the chick it also appears to take place in intestine and kidney (Tucker, Gagnon and Haussler, 1973). Vitamin D_2 is similarly metabolised in the liver to 25-hydroxyergocalciferol $[25(OH)D_2]$ (Suda, DeLuca, Schnoes and Blunt, 1969).

25(OH)D_3 is more effective than vitamin D_3 in curing rickets and also acts more rapidly in stimulating both intestinal calcium absorption and calcium mobilisation from bone. For these reasons it was believed to be the final active metabolite of vitamin D_3. However, further metabolism to a compound with still greater biological activity was then found to occur. In Kodicek's laboratory doubly-labelled vitamin D_3 with ^3H at C-1 and ^{14}C at position C-4 was administered to rachitic chicks. A metabolite which was more polar than $25(OH)D_3$ was then isolated from the cytosol of the intestinal mucosa. The ratio of $^3H/^{14}C$ had fallen, indicating that the metabolite had lost ^3H. This led to the suggestion that an oxygen function had been inserted (Lawson, Wilson and Kodicek, 1969) and that hydroxylation had occurred at C-1. This polar compound was identified as 1,25-dihydroxy-cholecalciferol $[1,25(OH)_2D_3]$ (see Fig 4; Lawson, Fraser, Kodicek, Morris

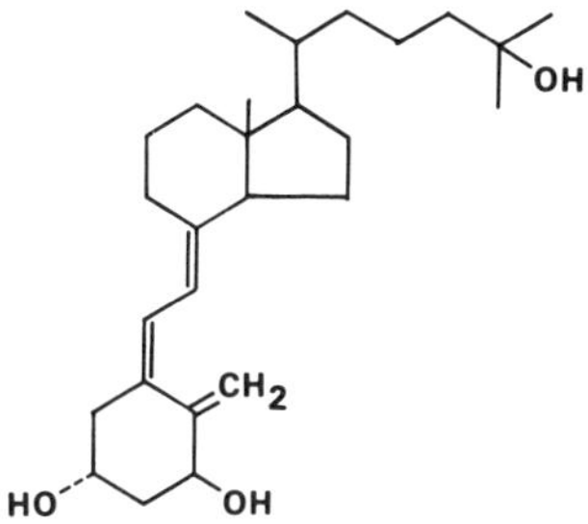

Fig. 4. Structure of 1,25-dihydroxyvitamin D_3 (1,25-dihydroxycholecalciferol).

and Williams, 1971; Holick, Schnoes, DeLuca, Suda and Cousins, 1971; Norman, Myrtle, Midgett, Nowicki, Williams and Popjak, 1971) and is the most biologically active metabolite of vitamin D_3 known. It is formed by further hydroxylation of $25(OH)D_3$ at C-1. This second hydroxylation stage occurs in kidney mitochondria (Fraser and Kodicek, 1970; Gray, Omdahl, Ghazarian and DeLuca, 1972) and involves a flavoprotein, an iron sulphur protein and cytochrome P-450. These components have been solubilised, isolated and reconstituted to form an active 1-hydroxylase system (Pedersen, Ghazarian, Orme-Johnson and DeLuca, 1976). 1α-hydroxylation of $25(OH)D_3$ occurs exclusively in the kidney and no $1,25(OH)_2D_3$ is synthesised in nephrectomised man (Mawer, Backhouse, Taylor, Lumb and Stanbury, 1973) or animals (Fraser and Kodicek, 1970).

Alternative metabolic pathways exist for $25(OH)D_3$ and lead to the formation of compounds other than $1,25(OH)_2D_3$. Hydroxylation at C-24 of the side chain yields 24,25-dihydroxycholecalciferol $[24,25(OH)_2D_3]$ (Holick, Schnoes, DeLuca, Gray, Boyle and Suda, 1972). This compound was initially, in error, thought to be 21,25-dihydroxycholecalciferol. The 24-

hydroxylation takes place in renal mitochondria (Knutson and DeLuca, 1974) but there is also evidence, both in man and animals, that it may occur in other tissues (Tanaka, Castillo, DeLuca and Ikekawa, 1977; Haddad, Min, Mendelsohn, Slatopolsky and Hahn, 1977). Two stereo-isomers of this compound can exist: 24**R**,25- and 24**S**,25$(OH)_2D_3$ but it is the former which probably occurs *in vivo* (Tanaka, DeLuca, Ikekawa, Morisaki and Koizumi, 1975). The exact role of 24,25$(OH)_2D_3$ is not yet clear and it appears to have only limited biological activity, although it has been reported to increase intestinal calcium absorption in man (Kanis, Cundy, Bartlett, Smith, Heynen, Warner and Russell, 1978).

Hydroxylation at C-26 in the side chain of 25$(OH)D_3$ occurs in experimental animals after injection of radiolabelled vitamin D_3, giving rise to 25,26-dihydroxycholecalciferol $[25,26(OH)_2D_3]$ (Suda, DeLuca, Schnoes, Tanaka and Holick, 1970b). Again there are two possible stereo-isomers; the natural form is probably 25,26**S**-dihydroxycholcalciferol. Kidney homogenates can carry out 26-hydroxylation (Tanaka and DeLuca, 1978) but the biological significance of this compound is not yet known.

In addition to the dihydroxylated compounds a trihydroxy form of the vitamin has also been identified. This is 1,24,25-trihydroxycholecalciferol $[1,24,25(OH)_3D_3]$ (Holick, Kleiner-Bossaler, Schnoes, Kasten, Boyle and DeLuca, 1973). It may be formed by renal 1-hydroxylation of 24,25$(OH)_2D_3$ or alternatively by 24-hydroxylation of 1,25$(OH)_2D_3$ (Tanaka *et al.*, 1977). 1,24,25$(OH)_3D_3$ is half as active as 1,25$(OH)_2D_3$ in stimulating intestinal calcium transport in rats and much less active in mobilising calcium from bone or stimulating intestinal phosphate transport (Holick *et al.*, 1973; Boyle, Omdahl, Gray and DeLuca, 1973). It therefore appears to have properties which are intermediate between 1,25$(OH)_2D_3$ and 24,25$(OH)_2D_3$.

The metabolic fate of 1,25$(OH)_2D_3$ has not been fully elucidated. The disappearance rate from plasma is rapid, only 14% of injected tritiated 1,25$(OH)_2D_3$ remaining in plasma 4 hr after injection (Mawer, Davies, Backhouse, Hill and Taylor, 1976; Gray, Caldas, Wilz, Lemann, Smith and DeLuca, 1978). In addition to the formation of 1,24,25$(OH)_3D_3$, oxidation of the side chain to carbon dioxide and water also occurs (Kumar, Harnden and DeLuca, 1976). Two products with acidic groups in the side chain and one with a lactone were recently identified (DeLuca and Schnoes, 1979).

Further studies of vitamin D metabolism are likely to reveal new compounds which will require detailed evaluation. Already Ghazarian and DeLuca (1977) have reported that a kidney microsomal fraction will metabolise 25$(OH)D_3$ to two as yet unidentified compounds which migrate on Sephadex LH20 between 24,25$(OH)_2D_3$ and 1,25$(OH)_2D_3$.

C. PHYSIOLOGY

1. Transport

After absorption from duodenum (Schachter, Finkelstein and Kowarski, 1964) and distal ileum (Kodicek, 1960), vitamin D is associated with chylomicrons (Blomstrand and Forsgren, 1967). It subsequently becomes bound by a specific vitamin D binding protein (DBP), presumably after mobilisation from tissue stores such as liver, muscle and fat. The nature of the DBP varies with the species (Hay and Watson, 1977). The chick appears to have two β-globulins which bind vitamin D_3 and 25(OH)D_3 (Edelstein, Lawson and Kodicek, 1973), whereas in the rat and in man the DBP is a single α-globulin. This has been isolated from human plasma and characterised. It has an approximate mw of 52,000, a sedimentation coefficient of 4·1S and an isoelectric point of 4·9 (Bouillon, Van Baelen and De Moor, 1976a; Haddad and Walgate, 1976a; Imawari, Kida and Goodman, 1976). It is identical with the globulin which was previously known as group specific component (Gc) of serum (Daiger, Schanfield and Cavalli-Sforza, 1975; Bouillon, Van Baelen, Rombauts and De Moor, 1976b. Imawari *et al.*, 1976). This DBP has a high affinity for 25(OH)D_3 ($K_d = 1·2 \times 10^{-10}$ M) and a single binding site per molecule (Bouillon and Van Baelen, 1977). Binding affinities are similar for 25(OH)D_3, 24,25(OH)$_2D_3$ and 25,26(OH)$_2D_3$ but lower for 1,25(OH)$_2D_3$ and vitamin D_3. It appeared that in the cytosol of kidney and muscle cells, there is a 6S protein with high affinity for 25(OH)D_3 (Haddad and Birge, 1975). However, this is produced by combination of the 4·1S plasma binding protein with another cytosolic protein which does not bind vitamin D or its metabolites (Van Baelen, Bouillon and De Moor, 1977).

Assays for the measurement of DBP in the circulation have been developed (Haddad and Walgate, 1976b; Bouillon, Van Baelen and DeMoor, 1977a). In normal subjects the mean concentration in plasma was found to be 525 $\pm$ 24 ng/ml, indicating that only 1–3% of binding sites are saturated with vitamin D ligands (Haddad and Walgate, 1976b). DBP concentrations do not appear to be influenced by vitamin D status, as no significant difference occurs in D-deficient or D-intoxicated patients. However, in conditions where other changes in plasma protein concentrations occur, such as in pregnancy and in women receiving oral contraceptives, the concentrations of DBP are increased, whereas in chronic liver disease and the nephrotic syndrome, they are decreased (Haddad and Walgate, 1976b; Imawari and Goodman, 1977; Bouillon, Van Baelen and DeMoor, 1977b).

2. Effects

Vitamin D compounds affect the gut and bone and may also influence other tissues such as kidney and muscle. In the small intestine, vitamin D and its metabolites increase calcium and phosphate absorption. Active calcium transport is stimulated and this is accompanied by passive movement of phosphate (Omdahl and DeLuca, 1973). In addition an active phosphate transport system is also stimulated; this is independent of calcium (Chen, Castillo, Korycka-Dahl and DeLuca, 1974) but requires sodium (Taylor, 1974). Estimated potencies with which vitamin D and its metabolites affect calcium and phosphate transport vary with experimental conditions. In the chick *in vivo*, a single dose of $1,25(OH)_2D_3$ was found to be 13–15 times as effective, and $25(OH)D_3$ was twice as effective as vitamin D_3 in increasing intestinal absorption of calcium. The response to $1,25(OH)_2D_3$ was also more rapid than that for the other two compounds (Myrtle and Norman, 1971). In the rat, $24,25(OH)_2D_3$ (Boyle *et al.*, 1973) and $25,26(OH)_2D_3$ (Suda *et al.*, 1970b) both produce small increases in calcium absorption. The effect of $24,25(OH)_2D_3$ is delayed in comparison with $1,25(OH)_2D_3$ and can be abolished by nephrectomy (Boyle *et al.*, 1973). However, Kanis *et al.* (1978) have reported that $24,25(OH)_2D_3$ increases calcium absorption in nephrecto-mised patients though others have not found such an effect. *In vitro,* $1,25(OH)_2D_3$ and $25(OH)D_3$ can both increase calcium absorption by a direct action on the gut whereas vitamin D_3 cannot (Parkes, 1978; Olson and DeLuca, 1969). Overall, it is clear, therefore, that $1,25(OH)_2D_3$ has the principal role in increasing calcium transport across the intestine although other vitamin D compounds may play a smaller part.

In bone, the anti-rachitic effect of vitamin D compounds is well known. Whether healing of rickets is measured by changes in total bone ash or by the line test anti-rachitic assay (US Pharmacopoeia, 1955), $1,25(OH)_2D_3$ is four to five times as effective in rats as $25(OH)D_3$ and 10 times as effective as vitamin D_3 (Tanaka, Frank and DeLuca, 1973). However, it has been difficult to show that vitamin D compounds have a direct effect on bone formation and it may be that calcification is being facilitated by maintenance of ade-quate calcium and phosphate concentrations. In contrast, vitamin D derivatives have been shown to mobilise bone mineral and also to potentiate the osteolytic action of parathyroid hormone (Rasmussen, DeLuca, Arnaud, Hawker and Von Stedingk, 1963). Parathyroid hormone (PTH) may also be necessary for the calcium mobilising effect of $1,25(OH)_2D_3$ (Garabedian, Tanaka, Holick and DeLuca, 1974). It has, therefore, been suggested that vitamin D compounds act on bone to facilitate remodelling and also to maintain plasma calcium and phosphate concentrations. *In vivo*, the effects of vitamin D compounds on bone have been compared by measuring the rise in serum calcium which they produce in rachitic animals maintained on low calcium diets. In the chick, $1,25(OH)_2D_3$ was found to be five to six times more potent and $25(OH)D_3$ one and a half times more potent than vitamin D_3 (Norman and Henry, 1974). In the rat, $1,25(OH)_2D_3$ and $25(OH)D_3$ were both ten times more potent than vitamin D_3 (Tanaka et al., 1973). The effect of $25(OH)D_3$ but not $1,25(OH)_2D_3$ was inhibited by nephrectomy (Holick, Garabedian and DeLuca, 1972). $24,25(OH)_2D_3$ was found to be as potent as $25(OH)D_3$ (Suda, DeLuca, Schnoes, Ponchon, Tanaka and Holick, 1970a) but $25,26(OH)_2D_3$ had no effect (Suda et al. 1970b).

In vitro, $1,25(OH)_2D_3$ and $25(OH)D_3$ both cause bone resorption, the effect of $1,25(OH)_2D_3$ being more rapid and at least 100 times more potent on a molar basis than that of $25(OH)D_3$ (Raisz and Trummel, 1972; Reynolds, Holick and DeLuca, 1973). Vitamin D_3, (even in large doses), $24,25(OH)_2D_3$ (Raisz and Trummel, 1972) and $25,26(OH)_2D_3$ (Suda et al., 1970b) have no significant effect on bone cultures. It therefore seems that the effects of vitamin D on bone are caused almost entirely by $1,25(OH)_2D_3$.

The effect of vitamin D and its metabolites upon renal excretion is still not entirely clear. Early studies which showed an increase in urinary calcium and a decrease in urinary phosphate excretion may have been demonstrating an indirect effect of vitamin D caused by changes in filtered load of calcium and suppression of parathyroid activity (see Goldberg, Agus and Goldfarb, 1976). More recent studies have suggested that there is a direct effect. Administration of vitamin D_3, $25(OH)D_3$ and $1,25(OH)_2D_3$ to parathyroidectomised dogs and rats caused a decrease in both calcium and phosphate excretion, probably by increasing proximal tubular reabsorption (Puschett, Moranz and Kurnick, 1972; Puschett, Fernandez, Boyle, Gray, Omdahl and DeLuca, 1972; Costanzo, Steele and Weiner, 1974). Other studies in the rat have suggested that the phosphate-conserving action, at least of $25(OH)D_3$, requires the presence of PTH (Popovtzer, Robinette, DeLuca and Holick, 1974). However, as $25(OH)D_3$ and $1,25(OH)_2D_3$ were found, to be equipotent in their effects on renal excretion (Puschett et al., 1972) the interpretation of these studies remains difficult.

The action of vitamin D compounds on muscle has not been studied in detail. However, proximal myopathy is common in vitamin D deficiency and resolves quickly on treatment. Radiolabelled vitamin D is known to localise in sarcolemma (Kodicek, 1963), and calcium uptake by sarcolemma from vitamin D-deficient rabbits is subnormal (Curry, Basten, Francis and Smith, 1974).

3. Mode of Action

The mode of action of steroid hormones, particularly androgens and oestrogens, has been extensively studied (see Chan and O'Malley, 1976) and the effects of $1,25(OH)_2D_3$ at a cellular level seem similar. Upon entering its target cells the sterol is bound by a specific cytoplasmic receptor. This hormone-receptor complex is then transported to the nucleus, where it interacts with the genome resulting in the stimulation of mRNA production (Fig. 5). The cytoplasmic receptor was first demonstrated in chick intestine

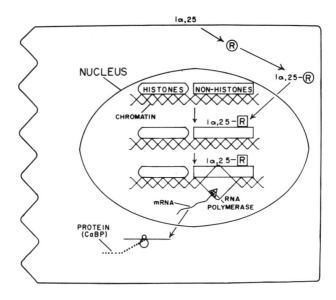

Fig. 5. Mode of action of 1,25-dihydroxyvitamin D in the intestinal mucosal cell. This proposed mechanism includes binding of the hormone to the cytoplasmic receptor protein (R), and migration of this complex to the nuclear chromatin. Here, specific genes are transcribed into new mRNA, which is translated into functional protein, such as calcium-binding protein (CaBP). (Reproduced with permission from Haussler *et al.*, 1977.)

by Brumbaugh and Haussler (1974b, 1975) and is a protein of mw 47,000 and sedimentation coefficient 3·7S (Kream, Reynolds, Knutson, Eisman and DeLuca, 1976; Haussler and McCain, 1977). It has high affinity for $1,25(OH)_2D_3$ $(K_d = 2 \times 10^{-9}$ M) but will also bind other vitamin D metabolites with lower affinity. $25(OH)D_3$ binds 1/500 as effectively as the hormone whereas $24,25(OH)_2D_3$ and $1,24,25(OH)_2D_3$ bind 1/800 and 1/3 as well respectively (Proscall, Okamura and Norman, 1975; Haussler and Brumbaugh, 1976).

Movement of the hormone-receptor complex to the nucleus occurs rapidly. Subcellular localisation studies in the chick have shown that nuclear accumulation of labelled $1,25(OH)_2D_3$ reaches half maximal saturation within 30 min after administration (Brumbaugh and Haussler, 1974a; Tsai, Wong and Norman, 1972). In the nucleus the hormone-receptor complex is bound to the chromatin fraction (Tsai *et al.*, 1972) but the exact sequence of events which follows is not fully established. It is thought that the nuclear binding is determined by non-histone proteins and that this activates specific genes leading to synthesis of mRNA, under the influence of RNA polymerase II. This mRNA is presumably translated into proteins which influence calcium and phosphate transport. This sequence of events is illustrated in Fig. 5.

In support of this scheme, it has been shown that $1,25(OH)_2D_3$ enhances RNA synthesis in the chick (Tsai and Norman, 1973). It also increases both RNA polymerase II activity (Zerwekh, Haussler and Lindell, 1974) and intestinal chromatin template capacity for RNA biosynthesis in rachitic chicks (Zerwekh, Lindell and Haussler, 1976). These effects occur 2–3 hr after injection of the hormone. The effect of $1,25(OH)_2D_3$ on mRNA has been demonstrated indirectly by the use of inhibitors of mRNA synthesis, such as α-amanatin and actinomycin D which blocked the $1,25(OH)_2D_3$-induced increase in calcium transport across chick intestine (Corradino, 1973).

Several specific proteins appear to be produced in response to stimulation by $1,25(OH)_2D_3$. The calcium-binding protein (CaBP) first described by Wasserman and Taylor (1966) is synthesised in response to $1,25(OH)_2D_3$ (Spencer, Charman, Emtage and Lawson, 1976a). Its production was studied in detail by extraction of polysomal RNA from the intestine of D-deficient chicks and translation of mRNA in cell free systems. CaBP was synthesised by the polysomes of chicks injected with $1,25(OH)_2D_3$ before sacrifice and was identified by precipitation with specific CaBP antibodies. It was not synthesised by the polysomes of untreated chicks (Spencer *et al.*, 1976a). It has been proposed that CaBP is involved in the transport of calcium across the intestinal wall (Wasserman, Taylor and Fulmer, 1974). However, increased calcium absorption in response to $1,25(OH)_2D_3$ may precede the formation of CaBP in rachitic chicks (Spencer, Charman, Wilson and Lawson, 1976b) whilst CaBP concentrations remain high after calcium transport has stopped (Fig. 6). This evidence, and the absence of CaBP from the membrane of the microvilli of intestinal cells (Wasserman, Corradino, Fulmer and Taylor, 1974) suggests that additional calcium transport mechanisms exist. Recently, two brush border proteins have been identified as being synthesised by chick intestine in response to $1,25(OH)_2D_3$. Their appearance correlates well with the onset of $1,25(OH)_2D_3$-induced calcium absorption but their direct involvement in calcium transport has yet to be established (Wilson and Lawson, 1977).

The mechanism of action of $1,25(OH)_2D_3$ has also been studied in other tissues but the evidence for specific $1,25(OH)_2D_3$ receptors in bone and

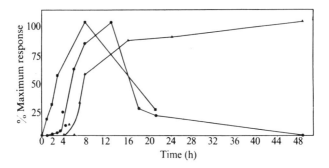

Fig. 6. Time-course of changes in intestinal calcium absorption (■), calcium binding protein mRNA activity (●) and calcium binding protein concentration (▲) in rachitic chicks after a single injection of 125 ng of 1,25-dihydroxycholecalciferol. (Reproduced with permission from Spencer *et al.*, 1976.)

kidney is still largely indirect. For example, in prelabelled bone cultures, vitamin D analogues are able to release ^{45}Ca with relative potencies which are similar to their binding affinities to intestinal receptor protein (Stern, Mavreas, Trummel, Schnoes and DeLuca, 1976). It has also been reported that $1,25(OH)_2D_3$ localises preferentially in the nuclei of bone cells (Weber, Pons and Kodicek, 1971) and that a specific $3 \cdot 2S$ binding protein occurs in the cytosol (DeLuca and Schnoes, 1978). In kidney, $1,25(OH)_2D_3$ stimulates RNA biosynthesis and a vitamin D-dependent calcium-binding protein has also been found (Wasserman *et al.*, 1974; Morrissey and Rath, 1974). Specific high affinity receptors for $1,25(OH)_2D_3$ have been detected in parathyroid tissue and they closely resemble those found in the intestine (Brumbaugh, Hughes and Haussler, 1975; Cloix, Ulmann, Bachelet and Funck Brentano, 1976; Haddad, Walgate, Min and Hahn, 1976). More detailed study of these tissues and a search for specific high affinity receptors in other tissues may further define the role of $1,25(OH)_2D_3$.

4. Regulation of Metabolism

Dietary intake and endogeneous synthesis of vitamin D are both very variable. There is, therefore, a need for regulation of the production of more active derivatives. This is feasible at the stages of hepatic and renal hydroxylation.

The activity of the 25-hydroxylase enzyme in the liver is not affected by calcium or phosphate but is subject to product inhibition by $25(OH)D_3$ itself (Bhattacharyya and DeLuca, 1973). Tucker *et al.*, (1973), were not, however, able to confirm this observation in the chick, reporting that 25-hydroxylation is not affected by the vitamin D status of the animal. Further studies, in animals, and man after administration of vitamin D or 25(OH)D$_3$ and measurement of circulating 25-hydroxy vitamin D, suggest that the 25-hydroxylation step is not tightly controlled since any suppression of the enzyme can be overcome when large amounts of substrate are provided.

It was thought that treatment with a synthetic form of vitamin D, namely 1α-hydroxycholecalciferol [1α(OH)D$_3$] might be safer than with 1,25(OH)D$_3$ because 1α(OH)D$_3$ requires hepatic hydroxylation in the side chain at C-25 to become active (Holick, Tanaka, Holick, Schnoes, DeLuca and Gallagher, 1976; Holick, DeBlanco, Clark, Henley, Neer, DeLuca and Potts, 1977). This might give a safety factor if there was product inhibition of 25-hydroxylase but in fact hypercalcaemia can be produced with 1α(OH)D$_3$ even in μg doses, and careful monitoring of therapy with this drug is needed (Brownjohn, Goodwin, Hateley, Marsh, O'Riordan and Papapoulos, 1977).

More important therefore than regulation of 25-hydroxylation is the control of 1- and 24-hydroxylase systems in the kidney. These two enzymes have not been separated yet but it is unlikely that the one is a modification of the other as the change from one to the other requires new protein synthesis. There is a switching mechanism which determines the activity of these two enzyme systems and which is regulated by a number of modulators, particularly PTH, calcium, phosphate and 1,25(OH)$_2$D$_3$ itself.

(a) Calcium and parathyroid hormone

The relationship between serum calcium and the further hydroxylation of 25(OH)D$_3$ was first demonstrated by Boyle, Gray and DeLuca (1971). In hypocalcaemia, 25(OH)D$_3$ is preferentially converted to 1,25(OH)$_2$D$_3$, whereas in normo- and hypercalcaemia it is mainly metabolised to 24,25(OH)$_2$D$_3$ (Fig. 7). It therefore appears that there is a reciprocal relationship between the 1-hydroxylase and 24-hydroxylase enzymes. The regulatory effects of calcium and PTH concentrations on these enzymes have been studied extensively. Thyroparathyroidectomised rats fed on a low calcium diet were found to synthesise only 24,25(OH)$_2$D$_3$ when examined 48 hr after operation. Administration of a small dose of PTH was followed by 1,25(OH)$_2$D$_3$ production but small increases in serum calcium also occurred (Garabedian, Holick, DeLuca and Boyle, 1972). Studies by MacIntyre and coworkers have suggested that PTH has only an indirect or permissive effect on 1-hydroxylase activity (Galante, MacAuley, Colston and MacIntyre, 1972; Galante, Colston, Evans, Byfield, Matthews and Mac-Intyre, 1973; Larkins, MacAuley, Colston, Evans, Galante and Mac-Intyre, 1973) and there has been much controversy on this subject. *In vitro*

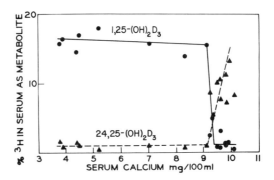

Fig. 7. Relationship between serum calcium and the amount of radioactive 1,25- and 24,25-dihydroxycholecalciferols in the circulation of rats 12 hr after injection of tritiated 25-hydroxycholecalciferol. (Reproduced with permission from Boyle *et al.*, 1972.)

studies in chick kidney have shown that PTH increases 1-hydroxylase activity when calcium levels are kept constant (Fraser and Kodicek, 1973; Henry, 1977). Furthermore, the increase in circulating $1,25(OH)_2D_3$ concentrations which occur in rats fed low calcium diets has been shown to be dependent upon the presence of intact parathyroid glands (Hughes, Brumbaugh, Haussler, Wergedal and Baylink, 1975). These studies indicate that PTH plays an important role in the regulation of 1-hydroxylase activity, but the mechanism by which this occurs is not fully known though PTH has been reported to stimulate $1,25(OH)_2D_3$ formation via cAMP production (Horiuchi, Suda, Takahashi, Shimazawa and Ogata, 1977).

(b) *Phosphate*

Phosphate depletion causes an increase in circulating $1,25(OH)_2D_3$ levels in intact pigs (Haussler, Hughes, Baylink and McCain 1977) and rats (Hughes *et al.*, 1975). In thyroparathyroidectomised rats on a low phosphate diet, 1-hydroxylase activity is increased (Tanaka and DeLuca, 1973) and plasma $1,25(OH)_2D_3$ concentrations are elevated (Hughes *et al.*, 1975). In parathyroidectomised chicks, renal 1-hydroxylase activity is not reduced unless plasma phosphate is elevated (Galante *et al.*, 1973). Some *in vitro* studies in chick kidney have shown that phosphate depletion has no effect on 1-hydroxylase activity (Henry, Midgett and Norman, 1974) but this has not been confirmed (Baxter and DeLuca, 1976). It therefore appears that low phosphate concentrations stimulate and high phosphate concentrations inhibit renal 1-hydroxylase activity and that these effects are independent of PTH.

(c) 1,25-Dihydroxyvitamin D

It is possible for $1,25(OH)_2D_3$ to control its own synthesis and this may be very important (Larkins, MacAuley and MacIntyre, 1974). Vitamin D deficiency increases 1-hydroxylase activity (Henry et al., 1974) whereas administration of $1,25(OH)_2D_3$ decreases 1-hydroxylase and stimulates 24-hydroxylase activity (Cork, Haussler, Pitt, Rizzardo, Hesse and Pechet, 1974; Tanaka, Lorenc and DeLuca, 1975). This switch in enzyme activity has been investigated in vitamin D-deficient chicks. When they are given physiological doses of $1,25(OH)_2D_3$ the decline in 1-hydroxylase and the increase in 24-hydroxylase activity occurs over several days. However, when larger doses of $1,25(OH)_2D_3$ are given, the switch in enzyme activity occurs more rapidly and this can be prevented by actinomycin D (MacIntyre, Colston, Evans, Lopez, MacAuley, Piegnour-Deville, Spanos and Szelke, 1976). These and other observations (Colston, Evans, Spelsberg and MacIntyre, 1977) suggest that $1,25(OH)_2D_3$ regulates its own production by the synthesis of new protein. Indirect regulation may also occur via the effect of $1,25(OH)_2D_3$ on the parathyroid glands and the consequent changes in serum calcium and phosphate.

(d) Other regulators

Calcium requirements are increased in physiological states such as growth, pregnancy, lactation and egg-laying and the hormonal changes occurring during these conditions might be expected to influence vitamin D metabolism. The effects of various hormones on $1,25(OH)_2D_3$ synthesis have therefore been examined. Egg-laying birds were shown to have increased 1-hydroxylase activity (Tanaka, Castillo and DeLuca, 1976) with a consequent increase in production rate (Kenny, 1976) and high circulating levels of $1,25(OH)_2D_3$ (Spanos, Pike, Haussler, Colston, Evans, Goldner, McCain and MacIntyre, 1976). Since oestrogen concentrations are also elevated during egg-laying the effect of oestradiol on 1-hydroxylase activity was studied. Injections of oestradiol valerate into mature male chickens and quails cause a marked increase in 1-hydroxylase activity (Castillo, Tanaka, DeLuca and Sunde, 1977). Studies in mature or castrated birds indicate that this effect is dependent upon the presence of testosterone and/or progesterone (Tanaka et al., 1976) and that treatment with all three hormones produces an increase in plasma concentrations of $1,25(OH)_2D_3$ (Tanaka, Castillo and DeLuca, 1977). However, MacIntyre (1977) found that testosterone and progesterone were not necessary for oestrogens to increase $1,25(OH)_2D_3$ production.

Prolactin concentrations are increased during pregnancy and lactation and concentrations of $1,25(OH)_2D_3$ are also high in these conditions (Pike, Toverud, Boass, McCain and Haussler, 1977; Boass, Toverud, McCain, Pike and Haussler, 1977). Prolactin injected into chicks causes an increase in 1-hydroxylase activity and elevates plasma $1,25(OH)_2D_3$ concentrations (Spanos, Colston, Evans, Galante, MacAuley and MacIntyre, 1976; Spanos *et al.*, 1976).

Growth hormone (Pike *et al.*, 1977), cortisol (Luckert, Stanbury, and Mawer, 1973), insulin (Schneider, Omadhl and Schedl, 1976) and calcitonin (MacIntyre, Evans and Larkins, 1977) have also been implicated in the control of $1,25(OH)D_3$ production but their relative importance is unknown. The mechanisms by which they exert their effect requires further investigation, though in the case of calcitonin it has been suggested that its action is mediated via PTH (Lorenc, Tanaka, DeLuca and Jones, 1977).

It should be noted here that the regulation of renal hydroxylation in mammals has been relatively little studied, partly because mammalian blood and tissue homogenates contain an inhibitor of 1-hydroxylase. The significance of this inhibitor is not yet known (Botham, Ghazarian, Kream and DeLuca, 1976a, b). Moreover in many of the studies referred to above, relatively extreme conditions have been used. Clearly regulation of renal metabolism of vitamin D is very important as are the interactions of vitamin D and parathyroid hormone, though much remains to be learnt, especially in man.

D. MEASUREMENT OF VITAMIN D AND ITS METABOLITES

1. Extraction and Purification

In many studies the initial extraction and subsequent purification of the various forms of vitamin D, from biological fluids, has been critical. An initial lipid extraction is necessary; one of the most commonly used methods has been based on that of Bligh and Dyer (1959) with chloroform/methanol/water. An alternative is to use dichloroethane and acetone (1:3), which has the advantage of avoiding a phase split. Acetone or ether can also be used. An extract with less lipid is obtained with dichloromethane, which efficiently extracts $1,25(OH)_2D_3$ but is less effient for $25(OH)D_3$.

The extracts then have to be fractionated chromatographically. The choice of system will depend on which metabolites are to be studied, the degree of purity required, and the number of samples to be processed. Silicic acid is widely used; vitamin D and vitamin D esters are eluted with ether and light petroleum (1:2); 25(OH)D can then be eluted with ether followed by 24,25-

and $25,26(OH)_2D_3$ with 10% methanol in ether. Liquid-gel partition chromatography with Sephadex LH-20 is very useful, with a solvent system such as hexane/chloroform $(1:1)$ or hexane/chloroform/methanol $(9:1:1$ or $1\cdot4)$. This separates $25(OH)D_3$ from $24,25(OH)_2D_3$. On LH-20, however, it is difficult to separate $1,25(OH)_2D_3$ from $25,26(OH)_2D_3$. Chromatography on celite (with a water-organic solvent partition) has a very high resolving power but is technically laborious.

A major advance has been the use of high pressure liquid chromatography (Fig. 8) which can be used either preparatively or analytically (see Vol. 3, Ch. II). The technical advances that make this possible include the use of improved pumping systems giving continuous flow, with improved injection systems of low dead space coupled to UV flow-through detectors of high sensitivity (with full scale deflection down to $0\cdot005$ optical density units). Particularly important, of course, has been the improved quality and

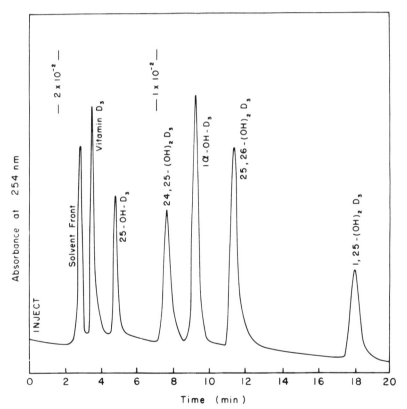

Fig. 8. Separation of a mixture of vitamin D_3 derivatives using high pressure liquid chromatography. (Reproduced with permission from Jones and De Luca, 1975.)

consistency of the packing materials and the techniques used for packing. Support materials are of silicic acid (particle size 5 or 10μ). Modified silicic acids may be useful in some circumstances. For example octadecyl silane (C-18) bonded to silicic acid gives a "reverse phase" system so that more polar compounds elute earlier than the less polar compounds, in contrast to the standard system. The elution pattern in high pressure liquid chromatography is extremely reproducible if the conditions are standardised. Highly purified glass distilled solvents have to be used and they should be kept dry, degassed and filtered through PTFE (polytetrafluorethylene). The elution pattern can be modified by changing the solvent system; for example, decreasing the proportion of isopropanol in hexane delays the elution of $1,25(OH)_2D_3$ and can increase its separation from other metabolites. With high pressure liquid systems, it is possible to separate vitamin D_2 and vitamin D_3 and their derivatives and also to separate stereo-isomers, which is not feasible with other systems.

2. Synthesis of Reference and Radiolabelled Compounds

The preparations of vitamin D_3 and vitamin D_2 are relatively easy because suitable starting compounds are available. These are 7-dehydrocholesterol and ergosterol respectively. They are irradiated at low temperature to produce the previtamin and then the reaction mixture is warmed to induce thermal rearrangement and so form the vitamin. Preparation of hydroxylated derivatives of vitamin D has been much more difficult, because suitable hydroxylated precursors are not readily available. Nevertheless, $25(OH)D_3$, $1,25(OH)_2D_3$ and $24,25(OH)_2D_3$ have all been prepared. For these, appropriate intermediate compounds have to be synthesised namely, 25-hydroxy-cholesterol, 1,25-dihydroxycholesterol and 24,25-dihydroxycholesterol. These compounds are prepared with protected hydroxyl groups and then irradiated to open the B-ring; thermal rearrangement is induced before the protective ester groups are removed. A variety of methods have been used, with a variety of starting compounds (see, for example, Campbell, Squires and Babcock, 1969; Barton, Hesse, Pechet and Rizzardo, 1974; Narwid, Blount, Iacobelli and Uskokovic, 1974). Introduction of the 1-hydroxyl group was particularly difficult: the preparation therefore of mg quantities of 1,25-dihydroxycholecalciferol represents a major achievement, particularly since the synthesis involves 20–30 steps with losses accruing at each stage. An analogue containing the 1α-hydroxyl group but not the 25 hydroxyl group has also been synthesised: this is 1α-hydroxycholecalciferol which has been used extensively in clinical studies. The **R** and **S** stereo-isomers of $24,25(OH)_2D_3$ have been prepared separately either from a racemic mixture of by "directed" or "stereo-specific" synthesis. Another natural derivative of vitamin D, namely $1,24,25(OH)_3D_3$ has also been synthesised chemically (Partridge, Shiuey, Baggiolini, Hennessy and Uskokovic, 1977). These synthetic derivatives of vitamin D_3 with hydroxyl groups at the 1α position are extremely potent: for example, only $1-2\,\mu g$ of $1,25(OH)_2D_3$ or $1(OH)D_3$ are sufficient to restore normocalcaemia in hypoparathyroid patients compared to $1-2$ mg of vitamin D_2 or D_3 which are needed to produce the same effect.

An interesting natural source of $1,25(OH)_2D_3$ is the plant *Solanum malacoxylon*. This plant contains the glycoside of the dihydroxy form of vitamin D_3 and produces a hypercalcaemic syndrome in cattle (Bassude and Humphreys, 1976; Napoli, Reeve, Eisman, Schnoes and DeLuca, 1977; Haussler, Hughes, McCain, Zerwerkh, Brumbaugh, Jubiz and Wasserman, 1977. This, however, has not proved to be a practical source of $1,25(OH)_2D_3$.

Hydroxylated derivatives of vitamin D_2 have not been synthesised because all these chemical syntheses are laborious and different techniques would be needed to incorporate the side chain of the derivatives of vitamin D_2. The lack of a convenient source of hydroxylated forms of vitamin D_2 has resulted in less extensive investigations of the reactivity of these compounds and important quantitative differences from the corresponding forms of vitamin D_3 may have been overlooked.

A number of other analogues have been prepared, for example, 3-deoxy-1α-hydroxycholecalciferol as well as a number of compounds with the triene structure in the 5,6 trans configuration to give analogues of dihydrotachysterol. These structural differences affect the proportion of the A-ring that is in the axial rather than the equatorial form and they have been valuable for analysis of structure–function relationships (Norman, Johnston, Osborne, Proscal, Carey, Hammond, Mitra, Pirio, Rego, Wing and Okamura, 1976).

Although radioactive forms of vitamin D were valuable in the early studies of the metabolism of the vitamin, they were of relatively low specific activity. ^3H-(26,27)-25-hydroxycholecalciferol (specific activity of $1-12$ c/mmol) has been prepared chemically. More recently ^3H(23,24)-25-hydroxycholecalciferol with specific activity up to 90 c/mmol has been prepared: the theoretical maximum specific activity of this compound is 116 c/mmol. Chemical synthesis of radioactive forms of dihydroxy-derivatives of cholecalciferol has not been possible. This is because the radioactive moiety would have to be introduced early in the synthesis and therefore large amounts of radioactivity would have to be used since the subsequent losses are great. Instead, tritiated $1,25(OH)_2D_3$ and $24,25(OH)_2D_3$ have been prepared biologically, by incubation of labelled $25(OH)D_3$ with homogenates of renal cortex from vitamin D deficient chicks. When tracer of specific activity up to 12c/mmol is used, it is relatively easy to work on a scale that allows direct assessment of the specific activity of the final product, measuring the final amount of $1,25(OH)_2D_3$ spectroscopically. However when higher specific activity tracer is used, this becomes impracticable. Preparation of labelled $24,25(OH)_2D_3$ is also possible and the best yield is obtained if the vitamin D deficient chicks are given $1,25(OH)_2D_3$ 24 hr before being killed. This inhibits 1-hydroxylase activity and activates the 24-hydroxylase system, and seems more satisfactory than using normal chick kidneys. This compound can also be made using kidneys from animals fed on a high calcium diet.

3. Assay Methods

(a) Vitamin D

Early techniques for measurement of vitamin D_3 were either bioassays (Bills, Honeywell, Wirick and Nussmeier, 1931; Kodicek and Lawson, 1967) or physico-chemical methods such as gas-liquid chromatography (Avioli and Lee, 1966), absorptiometry (Nield, Russell and Zimmerli, 1960) and fluorimetry (Chen, Terepka and Lane, 1964). Bioassays were barely sensitive enough to measure normal plasma concentrations. However, by using gas-liquid chromatography Avioli and Lee (1966) were able to measure as little as 5 ng of vitamin D_3 but extensive purification was required. Similar problems hampered other physico-chemical methods, but greater sensitivity has recently been achieved using gas-liquid chromatography and selected ion-monitoring (GC/MS) (Cruyl and De Leenheer, 1977). High pressure liquid chromatography (HPLC) apparatus coupled to sensitive UV detectors has also recently been used to measure separately vitamin D_3 and vitamin D_2 in plasma extracts (Jones, 1978)*.

(b) 25-Hydroxyvitamin D

The most useful techniques devised to measure $25(OH)_2D$ in plasma have been competitive protein-binding assays which use the naturally occurring binding proteins. These have been obtained from several sources such as vitamin D-deficient rat plasma (Belsey, DeLuca and Potts, 1971; Preece, O'Riordan, Lawson and Kodicek, 1974; Edelstein, Charman, Lawson and Kodicek, 1974) or normal rat serum (Bouillon, van Kerkhove and De Moor, 1976c), human plasma (Bayard, Bec and Louvet, 1972) or rat kidney cytosol (Haddad and Chyu, 1971). These assays all require preliminary purification of plasma extracts either by silicic acid, Sephadex LH-20 or thin layer

---

* Subsequently in this chapter if the metabolites of vitamin D_2 and D_3 have not been measured separately, they are referred to collectively e.g. as $25(OH)D$, $1,25(OH)_2D$. It is possible that quantitative errors may occur in these combined measurements, as metabolites of vitamin D_2 and D_3 may react differently in the systems used.

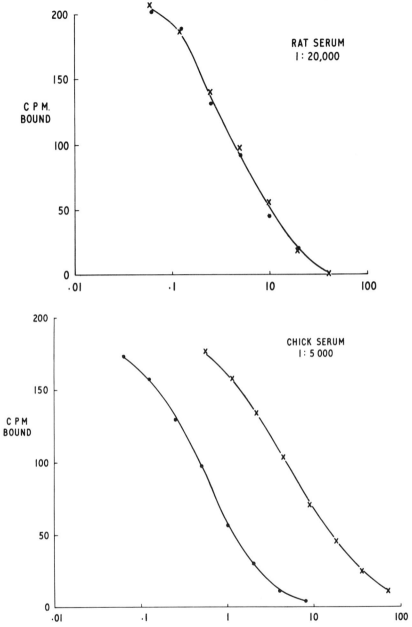

Fig. 9. Four standard curves as used for the differential assay of 25-hydroxychole-calciferol (●) and 25-hydroxyergocalciferol (×) (concentration in pmol). In the assay using rat serum (top) the two 25-hydroxy-compounds reacted identically, whereas when chick serum was used (bottom) 25-hydroxycholecalciferol was 10 times more reactive than 25-hydroxyergocalciferol, although the curves were parallel. (Reproduced with permission from Preece *et al.*, 1975.)

chromatography. Careful standardisation of the reference preparations of 25(OH)D_3 is necessary. The molar extinction coefficient in 100% ethanol at 265 nm is 18,300; thus a solution containing $10\mu g/ml$ (equivalent of 400 u/ml) has an absorption of 0·476. The most sensitive assay (Preece *et al.*, 1974) has a detection limit of 0·03 pmol (12·5 pg) of 25(OH)D_3 per tube—equivalent to 2·0 nmol/l (0·8 ng/ml) of plasma. A number of workers have described assays for 25(OH)D_3 which omit chromatography (Belsey, DeLuca and Potts, 1974; Garcia-Pascual, Peutremann, Courvoisier and Lawson, 1976; Offerman and Dittmar, 1974). However, if samples are assayed without chromatography, consistently higher values are obtained than if chromatography is used (Graham, Preece and O'Riordan, 1977). This is partly due to cross-reactivity of 24,25(OH)$_2$D$_3$ and 25,26(OH)$_2$D$_3$ with the binding-protein (Haddad, Min, Walgate and Hahn, 1976; Taylor, Hughes and De Silva, 1976; O'Riordan, Graham and Dolev, 1977). These assays are less time consuming and may therefore be useful as screening tests, but for more detailed pathophysiological studies, chromatography is essential.

A differential assay for 25(OH)D_3 and 25(OH)D_2 has been developed using binding-proteins from two different species. The binding protein in rat plasma has equal affinity for 25(OH)D_3 and 25(OH)D_2 whereas the binding-protein from the chick has higher affinity for 25(OH)D_3 than for 25(OH)D_2. By separately assaying the same plasma sample using both rat and chick binding-protein and the same tracer [^{3}H-25(OH)D_3] the differential concentrations of 25(OH)D_3 and 25(OH)D_2 may be calculated (Preece, Tomlinson, Ribot, Pietrek, Korn, Davies, Ford, Dunnigan and O'Riordan, 1975) (Fig. 9).

In addition to competitive protein-binding assays a number of sensitive physico-chemical methods for the measurement of 25(OH)D are now available. These include gas-liquid chromatography (Skiah, Budowski and Katz, 1973), mass fragmentography (Bjorkhem and Holmberg, 1976) and high pressure liquid chromatography (Eisman, Shepard and DeLuca, 1977; Kosh and Van Der Slik, 1976). HPLC may also be used to measure both 25(OH)D_3 and 25(OH)D_2 in the same sample (Lambert, Syverson, Arnaud and Spelsberg, 1977; Jones, 1978).

(c) 24,25- and 25, 26-Hydroxyvitamin D

Interest in the physiological role of 24,25(OH)$_2$D$_3$ has stimulated the development of assays for this metabolite. A number of assays for 24,25(OH)$_2$D have been reported (Haddad *et al.*, 1977; Taylor *et al.*, 1976; O'Riordan *et al.*, 1977; Weisman, Reiter and Root, 1977). They all use the same binding-proteins which are employed in assays for 25(OH)D. If silicic acid chromatography is used, 24,25- and 25,26-dihydroxyvitamin D elute together but if

LH-20 chromatography is used they are separated and could be measured individually. The circulating binding protein in the rat has higher affinity for $24,25(OH)_2D_3$ than it has for $25(OH)D_3$ but rather lower affinity for $25,26$-$(OH)_2D_3$.

(d) 1,25-Dihydroxyvitamin D

The measurement of this metabolite has been difficult because of its low concentration in plasma. Brumbaugh, Haussler, Bursac and Haussler (1974) reported a radioreceptor assay for $1,25(OH)_2D$ which used the natural receptor system obtained from chick intestine (see Fig. 5). In this system $1,25(OH)_2$-D_3 is initially bound to the high affinity cytoplasmic receptor and the hormone receptor complex subsequently binds to chromatin. The association with chromatin stabilises the hormone-receptor complex and allows separation of bound from free hormone by filtration. As described in the original report, a fresh receptor preparation was required for each assay and three successive chromatographic steps are needed to purify $1,25(OH)_2D$ from plasma extracts. A modification of this method has been devised by Eisman, Hamstra, Kream and DeLuca (1976a,b) who showed that the receptor protein could be stabilised and lyophilised at $-70°$. They used polyethylene glycol to precipitate the $1,25(OH)_2D$. Addition of globulin to give a larger precipitate is helpful (J. Mallon, personal communication). Prepurification with LH-20 and high pressure liquid chromatography is necessary. These radioreceptor assays have contributed greatly to our understanding of vitamin D metabolism but their application has been restricted for technical reasons.

Bioassays have also been used to measure $1,25(OH)_2D$ in plasma. The method of Hill, Mawer and Taylor (1975) quantitates $1,25(OH)_2D$ by measuring its effect on intestinal calcium transport in the rat. Large volumes of plasma are required for that, but Stern, Hamstra, DeLuca and Bell (1978) have developed a bioassay which measures $1,25(OH)_2D$ by its ability to release ^{45}Ca from prelabelled foetal bone cultures and this method is extremely sensitive with a limit of detection of 0.0025 pmol (1 pg). However, skill in organ culture techniques is required and the number of samples which can be processed simultaneously is very limited.

In addition to these methods, a radioimmunoassay for $1,25(OH)_2D_3$ has been described which uses antibodies raised against a $1,25(OH)_2D$ hemisuccinate derivative coupled to bovine serum albumin. These antibodies bind $1,25(OH)_2D_3$ and other dihydroxy metabolites of vitamin D_3 with similar degree and for this reason plasma extracts have to be purified prior to assay. Separation of antibody-bound from free hormone is accomplished by a simple dextran-coated charcoal step. The sensitivity of this method is 10 pg tube which is similar to the radioreceptor assays (Clemens, Hendy, Graham, Baggiolini, Uskokovic and O'Riordan, 1978a, b).

4. Concentrations in Plasma

(a) Vitamin D

Remarkably little is known of the concentration of vitamin D in the circulation. Jones (1978), using high pressure liquid chromatography, reported that the combined concentration of vitamin D_2 and D_3 in 25 adults in winter was 5.7 ± 2.9 nmol/l (2.2 ± 1.1 (S.D.) ng/ml) (roughly 15% of the concentration of 25(OH)D in these subjects).

(b) 25-Hydroxyvitamin D

The concentration of 25(OH)D in plasma has been extensively studied and shown to be a valuable index of vitamin D status in man. It is greater than that of any other metabolite and is easily measured but is readily altered by exposure to sunlight (so that there is a seasonal variation in the normal range) and by dietary supplementation.

The normal concentration varies in different parts of the world. In the UK, Preece *et al.*, (1974) found the range to be between 8.8 and 75 nmol/l (3.5 and 30 ng/ml) with a mean value of 30 nmol/l (12 ng/ml). This is similar to that found by Stamp, Round, Rowe and Haddad (1972) and by Edelstein *et al.*, (1974). Using a differential assay, only 25(OH)D_3 was found and there was no 25(OH)D_2 (Preece *et al.*, 1975). The mean 25(OH)D in France was similar, 37.5 nmol/l (15 ng/ml) (Bayard, Beck, Thon That and Louvet, 1973), and in Belgium where Bouillon *et al.* (1976c) found a mean value of 35.0 nmol/l (14 ng/ml). In contrast, in the USA, the concentrations of 25(OH)D are higher: Haddad and Chyu (1971) found a mean of 68.3 ± 29.5 (S.D) nmol/l (27.3 ± 11.8 ng/ml) and Belsey *et al.*, (1971) found 83.3 ± 9.0 nmol/l (33.3 ± 3.6 ng/ml). These higher values reflect in large part the American practice of fortifying foods with vitamin D: sometimes vitamin D_3 is used for this purpose in the USA but more commonly vitamin D_2 is added, for example, to milk; then 25(OH)D_2 is found in plasma (Haddad and Hahn, 1973). The higher concentrations of 25(OH)D in American subjects are in part also due to greater exposure to sunshine; in lifeguards, for example, the concentration was as high as 175 nmol/l (70 ng/ml) (Haddad and Chyu, 1971).

The importance of sunlight in the formation of 25(OH)D has been demonstrated in studies in nuclear submariners in the UK, in whom concentrations of 25(OH)D fell significantly after a two month patrol, during which time they had a diet adequate in vitamin D but were completely deprived of the UV light of the sun (Preece *et al.*, 1975). Exposure to UV light is therefore the principal factor responsible for the seasonal variation in circulating 25(OH)D. Mean serum concentrations are at their nadir in late winter and at their peak in late summer. McLaughlin, Raggat, Fairney, Brown, Lester and Wills (1974) found a rise in mean 25(OH)D concentration in normal British subjects from 46·5 ± 19·8 (s.d.) nmol/l (18·6 ± 7·9 ng/ml) in December to 90·5 ± 23·3 nmol/l (36·2 ± 9·3 ng/ml) the following September. Conversely, Stamp and Round (1974) noted a fall in mean 25(OH)D concentrations in young English people from 53·3 nmol/l (21·3 ng/ml) in autumn to 33·3 nmol/l (12·9 ng/ml) in the following spring.

There appears to be no significant differences in 25(OH)D concentrations between males and females. In neonates, concentrations of 25(OH)D are generally below maternal concentrations, but the reported ratios have varied between 57 % and 108 % (Hillman and Haddad, 1974; Rosen, Roginsky, Natherson and Finberg, 1974; Bouillon et al., 1977b).

An area in which assays for circulating 25(OH)D have been very valuable is in the investigation of rickets and osteomalacia. Low serum concentrations of 25(OH)D are indicative of vitamin D deficiency as the cause of the disease, while normal concentrations point towards other diagnostic possibilities.

Human vitamin D deficiency has been particularly studied in the UK because of the high incidence of clinical rickets or osteomalacia in the Asian immigrant population (Holmes, Enoch, Taylor and Jones, 1973; Dunnigan, Paton, Hease, McNicoll, Gardner and Smith, 1962; Swan and Cooke 1971). This must be attributed to vitamin D deficiency; in all subjects with clinically proven disease (Fig. 10), serum concentrations of 25(OH)D were found to be less than 7 nmol/l (3 ng/ml) (Preece, Ford, McIntosh, Dunnigan, Tomlinson and O'Riordan, 1973; Preece et al., 1975). Subclinical disease can also occur and it was shown that a significant proportion (nearly 50%) of the apparently healthy Indian population had serum 25(OH)D concentrations below the lower limit of normal (Preece et al., 1975). These low values of 25(OH)D were generally associated with high serum alkaline phosphatase concentrations, indicating that the apparent vitamin D deficiency was associated with other biochemical evidence of rickets or osteomalacia. It seems likely that in these subjects, if these low concentrations are maintained, overt disease will develop.

There has been much speculation as to the aetiology of vitamin D deficiency in Asians. It has been suggested that the phytate content of their diet (chapatti flour) may induce the disease by binding calcium in the gut. However,there is no good evidence to support this hypothesis. It seems that the disease is probably multi-factorial in origin, due partly to a poor vitamin D intake and partly to limited exposure to sunlight. Diet probably plays the most important role as vitamin D deficiency is variable amongst different ethnic groups of Indians with different dietary intake of vitamin D (Hunt,

D

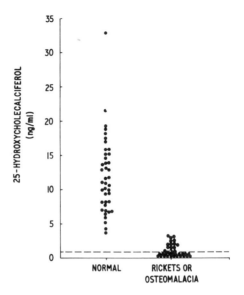

Fig. 10. Serum concentrations of 25-hydroxycholecalciferol in normal subjects and in patients with clinical osteomalacia or rickets. The broken line represents the limit of detection of the assay (0·8 ng/ml serum) (1 ng/ml = 2·5 nmol/l). (Reproduced with permission from Preece *et al.* 1975.)

O'Riordan, Windo and Trusswell, 1976), but limited exposure to sunlight may well be contributory. The deficiency can be easily treated with small doses of vitamin D or by supplementation of the chapatti flour with the vitamin (Pietrek, Preece, Windo, O'Riordan, Dunnigan, McIntosh and Ford, 1976). Long-term fortification of food is necessary however to prevent recurrence of the deficiency.

Vitamin D deficiency can also occur in the elderly, in whom circulating 25(OH)D concentrations may be very low (Preece *et al.*, 1975). This can lead to the development of severe osteomalacia, though in many the deficiency is subclinical. Again the deficiency is probably multi-factorial in origin, being partly due to poor vitamin D intake and partly to lack of exposure to UV light. The elderly do respond well, however, to UV light which can raise circulatory levels of 25(OH)D (Corless, Gupta, Switala, Barragry, Boucher, Cohen and Diffey, 1978). It has also been suggested that there is resistance to vitamin D in the elderly and that oral administration does not raise the concentration of 25(OH)D to the same extent as in younger people, because of malabsorption of vitamin D (Barragry, France, Corless, Gupta, Switala, Boucher and Cohen, 1978). However it has been our practice to treat elderly patients with 3000 u of vitamin D_3 daily, which raises the concentration of 25(OH)D_3 and heals the osteomalacia.

Evidence of vitamin D deficiency may occur in gastro-intestinal disorders such as coeliac disease (Stamp, 1974), blind loop syndrome and gastric and small bowel resections. Jejuno-ileal bypass for obesity is associated with a fall in 25(OH)D concentrations and although concentrations may rise again in some cases, possibly owing to improved diet and adaptive intestinal changes (Teitelbaum, Halverson, Bates, Wise and Haddad, 1977). Vitamin D deficiency may, however, persist and in one series osteomalacia was present in a third of cases (Compston and Creamer, 1977). In hepatic disease there can be an osteodystrophy composed of porotic- and malacic-components, to varying degrees. The histological features of this are still poorly defined and the condition is probably multi-factorial in origin (Long and Wills, 1978). 25(OH)D concentrations tend to be subnormal in both chronic cholestatic and hepatocellular disease and are lowest in patients with the most severe disease (Long, Skinner, Wills and Sherlock, 1976). In primary biliary cirrhosis a mean 25(OH)D concentration of 17·8 nmol/l (7·1 ng/ml), compared with a normal value of 44·3 nmol/l (17·7 ng/ml) has been reported (Compston and Thompson, 1977).

Many factors may account for the vitamin D deficiency observed in gastro-intestinal diseases. In conditions such as extensive ileal resection and primary biliary cirrhosis there may be malabsorption of dietary vitamin D; in addition the enterohepatic circulation of 25(OH)D may be disturbed (Compston and Thompson, 1977). Decreased 25-hydroxylation of vitamin D might also occur in severe liver disease, but studies with radiolabelled vitamin D suggest that this function is usually well preserved (Krawitt, Grundman and Mawer, 1977).

Epileptic patients on anticonvulsant drugs, especially phenytoin, may have hypocalcaemia and raised serum alkaline phosphatase concentrations and some develop rickets or osteomalacia (Kruse, 1968; Richens and Rowe, 1970; Dent, Richens, Rowe and Stamp, 1970) which may be partly resistant to the action of vitamin D. In a number of studies, the concentration of 25(OH)D in anticonvulsant-treated epileptics without overt bone disease has been lower than in control groups (Stamp et al., 1972; Hahn, Hendin, Scharp and Haddad, 1972; Bouillon et al., 1967c). However, there are remarkably few recordings of the concentration of 25(OH)D in patients with treated epilepsy who have developed rickets or osteomalacia; Stamp (1976) reported three such patients, with values of 3·5–6·5 nmol/l (1·4–2·6 ng/ml). The cause of the lower levels is not entirely clear: in some patients it may be due to dietary deficiency and avoidance of sunlight. It has been suggested, however, that the enzyme-inducing effects of the anti-epileptic drugs are important (Dent et al., 1970). It has been reported that in patients on phenobarbitone, conversion of vitamin D_3 to $25(OH)D_3$ is accelerated (Hahn, Birge, Scharp and Avioli, 1972) but that a further metabolism of this is also accelerated. Biliary excretion of metabolites of vitamin D may also be accelerated and contribute to the development of the vitamin deficiency.

In primary hyperparathyroidism the concentration of 25(OH)D is usually normal but it may be low in patients with osteitis fibrosa cystica. This might contribute to the osteomalacic component of this condition though it might in part be a result of the bone disease of hyperparathyroidism causing pain and thus limiting the mobility of the patient and therefore exposure to sunlight.

Renal osteodystrophy is a common complication of chronic renal failure and its aetiology appears to be multi-factorial (see Ch. I). In normal subjects, the proportion of circulating 25(OH)D which is metabolised to $1,25(OH)_2D$ is small and it would be surprising if a disturbance of this pathway would, in chronic renal failure, affect the serum concentrations of the 25-hydroxylated metabolite. In agreement with this postulate, is the finding of normal concentrations of circulating 25(OH)D in patients with chronic renal failure (Shen, Baylink, Sherrard, Shen, Maloney and Wergedal, 1975) though high (Lund, Sorensen, Nielsen, Munk, Bärenholdt and Petersen, 1975) and low concentrations have also been reported (Bayard *et al.*, 1973).

Low circulating 25(OH)D in some patients with chronic renal failure has been attributed to the restricted diet that these patients are taking or to their limited exposure to sunlight. However, it has also been proposed that uraemia *per se* may have an effect on the 25-hydroxylation of vitamin D by inducing hepatic microsomal enzyme activity (Wake and Maddocks, 1975). In this way, apparent vitamin D deficiency might be produced.

Although the major disturbance of vitamin D metabolism in chronic renal failure lies in the defective production of $1,25(OH)_2D$ by the kidney, it has been suggested that low 25(OH)D concentrations may also play some role in the development of the osteomalacic component of renal osteodystrophy (Eastwood, Harris, Stamp and de Wardener, 1976).

(c) 24,25- and 25,26-Dihydroxyvitamin D

There have been very few reports about the circulating concentrations of $24,25(OH)_2D$ in man and no direct measurements of $25,26(OH)_2D$. Haddad *et al.*, (1977) reported that the mean serum concentration of $24,25(OH)_2D$ in healthy American adults is 8.8 ± 0.5 (S.E.) nmol/l (3.7 ± 0.2 ng/ml). Similarly Weisman *et al.* (1977) found a mean concentration of 7.9 ± 3.1 (S.D.) nmol/l (3.3 ± 1.3 ng/ml) in American children. Taylor *et al.*, (1976), in the UK, found a mean of only 4.03 ± 1.97 (S.D.) nmol/l (1.68 ± 0.82 ng/ml). The reason for this apparent difference in the concentrations of $24,25(OH)_2D$ reported for the American and British populations is not entirely clear. Using a simplified system which measures the total concentration of 24,25-

$(OH)_2D$ and $25,26(OH)_2D$ (Graham *et al.*, 1977) we have found that the combined concentration of these metabolites in healthy British subjects was $4\cdot75 \pm 1\cdot70$ nmol/l ($1\cdot98 \pm 0\cdot7$ ng/ml). It was therefore very similar to that reported by Taylor *et al.* (1976) for $24,25(OH)_2D$ on its own and on this basis it may be that $25,26(OH)_2D$ circulates in low concentrations. The combined concentrations (Fig. 11) of $24,25(OH)_2D$ and $25,26(OH)_2D$ were

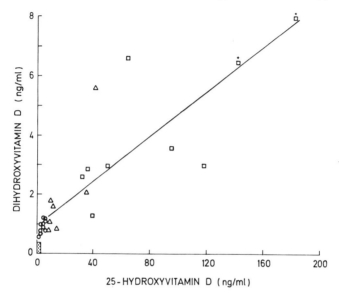

Fig. 11. Relationship between serum 25(OH)D concentration and the combined concentrations of $24,25(OH)_2D$ and $25,26(OH)_2D$ in normal subjects ($\triangle$), patients with chronic renal failure ($\bigcirc$) and vitamin D-treated patients ($\square$) ($n = 26$, $r = 0\cdot85$, $p < 0\cdot001$). * = Samples taken at different times from the same patient. Values for five patients with dietary vitamin D deficiency lie in the bottom left hand corner.

positively correlated with those of 25(OH)D over a wide range of vitamin D intake (Dolev, E. and O'Riordan, J. L. H., unpublished observation). They were high on large doses of vitamin D and undetectable in vitamin D deficiency. Thus, in man at least, it seems that a major determinant for the formation of these dihydroxy metabolites of vitamin D is the concentration of circulating 25(OH)D itself. In patients with impaired renal function the combined concentrations of 24,25- and $25,26(OH)_2D$ were lower than in normal subjects. Whilst this finding may be attributed to defective renal 24-hydroxylation of 25(OH)D, it could also be the result of the lower 25(OH)D concentrations which were found in these patients (Fig. 11). Haddad *et al.* (1977) reported that the concentrations of $24,25(OH)_2D$ in anephric patients were within the normal range, suggesting that extrarenal sites for the 24-hydroxylation reaction exist. However, Taylor (1977) was unable to detect any 24,25-$(OH)_2D$ in the sera of anephric patients even after four days of treatment with $25(OH)D_3$, which caused an increase in circulating $25(OH)D_3$. Again, the reason for this discrepancy is not clear and further studies of the production of $24,25(OH)_2D$, and its regulation in various diseases, are needed in order to understand its significance.

(d) 1,25-Dihydroxyvitamin D

As assays for this metabolite become more widely available, its measurement may prove to be more useful than 25(OH)D in a variety of clinical situations. Normal serum concentrations are far lower than for both 25(OH)D and $24,25(OH)_2D$ and this has made it a difficult substance to measure. Using the radioreceptor assay, Brumbaugh *et al.* (1974) initially reported a mean $1,25(OH)_2D$ concentration in normal adults to be $153·6 \pm 29·0$ (s.d.) pmol/l (64 ± 12 pg/ml) (range $98·4$–204 pmol/l, 41–85 pg/ml), but more recently the same group have quoted a mean normal concentration of $79·2 \pm 14·4$ (s.d.) pmol/l (33 ± 6 (s.d.) pg/ml) (range $50·4$–108 pmol/l, 21–45 pg/ml) (Haussler, Hughes, Pike and McCaine, 1977). Eisman *et al.* (1976a, b), using their competitive protein binding method, have reported a mean concentration in normal subjects of $69·6 \pm 4·8$ (s.e.m.) pmol/l ($29 \pm 2·0$ pg/ml) and Stern *et al.* (1978), with their bioassay, found a normal mean of $59·4 \pm 4·8$ (s.e.m.) pmol/l ($24·8 \pm 2·0$ pg/ml). Clemens, Hendy, Papapoulos, Lewin, Fraher, Care and O'Riordan (1978c) found, by means of a radioimmunoassay, a mean concentration in healthy subjects in UK of $98·4 \pm 7·2$ (s.e.m.) pmol/l ($41 \pm 3·0$ pg/ml) (range $52·8$–$141·6$ pmol/l, 22–59 pg/ml).

Circulating $1,25(OH)_2D$ seems to be uninfluenced to any major degree by exposure to sunlight (Haussler *et al.*, 1977) or by a wide range of vitamin D intake (Hughes, Baylink, Gonnerman, Toverud, Ramp and Haussler, 1977). It seems, however, that $1,25(OH)_2D$ production is age-related, as higher concentrations have been found in a small number of children (Haussler *et al.*, 1977; Eisman *et al.*, 1976a). Further studies are required to establish this.

A significant increase in circulating $1,25(OH)_2D$ has also been observed in pregnant women towards the end of pregnancy ($175·2 \pm 45·6$ pmol/l, 73 ± 19 pg/ml compared to $93·6 \pm 40·8$ pmol/l, 39 ± 17 pg/ml which was the mean concentration in non-pregnant females) (Pike *et al.*, 1977). This increase in serum $1,25(OH)_2D$ concentrations may be responsible for the enhanced intestinal absorption of calcium which is known to occur in pregnancy.

Studies of circulating $1,25(OH)_2D$ in pathological conditions have been limited. However, in recent years sufficient information has been obtained to provide further insight into the pathophysiology of many clinical disorders of mineral metabolism. The most extensively studied condition is chronic renal disease. The kidney is the sole site of production of $1,25(OH)_2D$ and patients with chronic renal failure have markedly reduced serum concentrations of $1,25(OH)_2D$.

In the majority of them the concentrations fall below the sensitivity of the assay (Fig. 12). Also, all anephric patients studied had undetectable levels,

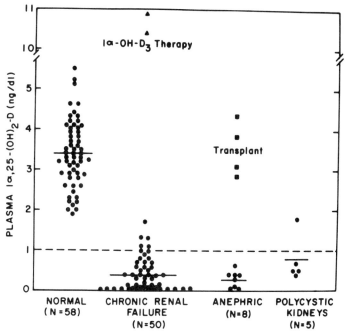

Fig. 12. Circulating 1,25-dihydroxyvitamin D concentrations, measured by a radioreceptor assay, in normal patients and patients with renal disease (1 ng/100 ml = 24 pmol/l). (Reproduced with permission from Haussler *et al.*, 1977.)

as would be expected (Haussler, Baylink, Hughes, Brumbaugh, Wergedal, Shen, Nielsen, Counts, Bursac and McCain, 1976; Haussler *et al.*, 1977; Kream, Eisman and DeLuca, 1977; Clemens *et al.*, 1978c) and after successful renal transplantation circulating concentrations of $1,25(OH)_2D$ rise. Deficient 1-hydroxylation in chronic renal failure is thought to be one of the important factors leading to the development of renal osteodystrophy. It can be treated by long-term therapy with nearly physiological doses of either $1,25(OH)_2D_3$ or $1\alpha(OH)D_3$ (Brickman, Sherrard, Jowsey, Singer,

Baylink, Maloney, Massry, Norman and Coburn, 1974; Papapoulos, Brownjohn, Junor, Marsh, Goodwin, Hateley, Lewin, Tomlinson, Hendy and O'Riordan, 1977).

Assays for $1,25(OH)_2D$ have been useful in the elucidation of the pathogenesis of other vitamin D-resistant conditions as, for example, sex-linked hypophosphataemic rickets or vitamin D dependent rickets in which serum 25(OH)D concentrations are normal. In sex-linked hypophosphataemic rickets there is marked hypophosphataemia, probably as a result of defective phosphate transport in the kidney and the intestine (Glorieux and Scriver, 1972; Short, Binder and Rosenberg, 1973). The very low serum phosphate concentrations might be expected to stimulate $1,25(OH)_2D$ production but surprisingly the concentrations of $1,25(OH)_2D$ are apparently normal (Haussler *et al.*, 1976). It may be that patients with hypophosphataemic rickets have a more generalised renal tubular defect which may also involve a defect in the ability of renal 1-hydroxylase to respond to the hypophosphataemic stimulus.

Vitamin D-dependent rickets or pseudo D deficiency is a form of vitamin D resistant rickets (Prader, Illig and Heierli, 1961), which is inherited as an autosomal recessive trait. This condition has all the clinical, radiological and biochemical features of vitamin D-deficient rickets but pharmacological doses of vitamin D or $25(OH)D_3$ are needed for the complete healing of the rachitic lesions (Scriver, 1970; Balsan and Garabedian, 1972). Fraser, Kooh, Kind, Holick, Tanaka and DeLuca, (1973) reported that only small doses of $1,25(OH)_2D_3$ (namely 1–2 µg/d) are sufficient to heal the rickets in such patients. A similar response was also observed when the condition was treated with $1\alpha(OH)D_3$ (Balsan, Garabedian, Sorgniard, Holick and DeLuca, 1975; Reade, Scriver, Glorieux, Nogrady, Delvin, Poirier, Holick and DeLuca, 1975). These observations suggested that in vitamin D-dependent rickets there is deficient 1-hydroxylase activity and this was supported by the finding of low circulating concentrations of $1,25(OH)_2$ in such patients (Scriver, Reade, DeLuca and Hamstra, 1978).

Anticonvulsant osteomalacia has also been considered as a vitamin D-resistant state, but in epileptic patients receiving enzyme-inducing drugs, serum concentrations of $1,25(OH)_2D$ have been found to be within the normal range (Jubiz, Haussler, McCain and Tolman, 1977). However, the concentrations of $1,25(OH)D$ had not been measured in epileptic patients with overt bone disease. PTH, as discussed in Section C4(a), stimulates the renal production of $1,25(OH)_2D$ in animals.

In patients with primary hyperparathyroidism who had elevated serum calcium concentrations, there were high concentrations of $1,25(OH)_2D$ in serum. Haussler *et al.* (1976) reported a mean of $129·6 \pm 50·4$ pmol/l (54 ± 21 pg/ml) in 26 patients with primary hyperparathyroidism and Kream *et al.* (1977) a range of 108–348 pmol/l (45–145 pg/ml) in a further eight patients. A significant correlation between serum 1,25(OH)$_2$D and rate of intestinal absorption of calcium was demonstrated in such patients which suggests that the effect of PTH on intestinal calcium transport is indirect and is mediated through increased production of 1,25(OH)$_2$D by the kidney (Kaplan, Haussler, Deftos, Bone and Pak, 1977). In contrast, in hypoparathyroid hypocalcaemic patients, serum concentrations of 1,25(OH)$_2$D tend to be low (Haussler *et al.*, 1976; Haussler *et al.*, 1977; Kream *et al.*, 1977). Interestingly, in patients with pseudohypoparathyroidism, a condition in which there is parathyroid overactivity and end-organ resistance to the action of the hormone, serum 1,25(OH)$_2$D concentrations also tend to be low (Drezner, Neelon, Haussler, McPherson and Lebovitz, 1976; Haussler *et al.*, 1977). Whether this is due to suppression of 1-hydroxylase by high serum phosphate, which occurs in this condition, or whether there is a generalised renal tubular defect is not known.

Idiopathic hypercalciuria is a condition of obscure aetiology characterised by excessive urinary calcium output and formation of renal stones. In the majority of cases there is tendency for hypophosphataemia which may be due to renal leak of phosphate. Mean circulating 1,25(OH)$_2$D concentrations have been found to be elevated in this condition 120 $\pm$ 38·4 pmol/l (50 $\pm$ 16 pg/ml) and a number of patients had concentrations well above the upper limit of normal (Haussler *et al.*, 1977). It has been suggested that this increase in circulating 1,25(OH)$_2$D is the result of the low serum phosphate and it may also be responsible for the increased intestinal calcium absorption which occurs in the majority of these patients.

Osteoporosis is the most common metabolic bone disease, but its aetiology is unknown. In a group of women with post-menopausal osteoporosis the mean serum concentration of 1,25(OH)$_2$D (60 pmol/l; 25 pg/ml) was found to be significantly lower than in age-matched controls (84 pmol/l; 35 pg/ml), though in a large proportion of the patients the concentrations were within the normal range. It was suggested that the lower concentrations of 1,25(OH)$_2$-D may contribute to the development of the disease by reducing intestinal absorption of calcium (Gallagher, Riggs, Eisman, Arnaud and DeLuca, 1976; DeLuca, 1977). The cause of these lower concentrations are not known though it has been suggested that reduced synthesis due to oestrogen deficiency, low serum parathyroid hormone concentrations and a tendency to hyperphosphataemia might be implicated (Riggs and Gallagher, 1978). However, these findings, although attractive, were not confirmed by Haussler *et al.* (1977) who found normal concentrations of circulating 1,25(OH)$_2$D in women with post-menopausal osteoporosis. Clearly more studies are needed to evaluate the role of 1,25(OH)$_2$D in the pathogenesis of this condition.

Changes in circulating 1,25(OH)$_2$D have been studied in patients with

Paget's disease who became hypocalcaemic after treatment with mithramycin. A significant increase in serum $1,25(OH)_2D$ occurred when serum calcium decreased, indicating fine control of this hormone in man *in vivo* (Bilezikian, Canfield, Jacobs, Polay, D'Adamo, Eisman and DeLuca, 1978). Interesting observations have also been made in a small number of patients with various other metabolic diseases. For example, high concentrations of $1,25(OH)D$ have been found in tumoural calcinosis in negroes, an unusual condition associated with hyperphosphataemia (Prince, Schaefer, Goldsmith and Chaussmer, 1978). In patients with sarcoidosis the development of hypercalcaemia has been attributed to high serum $1,25(OH)_2D$ concentrations (Papapoulos, Clemens, Fraher, Lewin, Sandler and O'Riordan, 1979).

In vitamin D intoxication hypercalcaemia may occur with serum $25(OH)D$ concentrations above 875 nmol/l (350 ng/ml) (Preece *et al.*, 1975) but, surprisingly, $1,25(OH)_2D$ levels appear to be normal or only minimally elevated. Hughes, Baylink, Jones and Haussler (1976) reported two patients who became hypercalcaemic on high doses of vitamin D. Serum $25(OH)D$ concentrations were 1480 nmol/l (592 ng/ml) and 1295 nmol/l (518 ng/ml) but serum $1,25(OH)_2D$ levels were only 124·8 pmol/l (52 pg/ml) and 134·4 pmol/l (56 pg/ml) respectively. Similarly, in experimental animals made hypercalcaemic with vitamin D, large increases in $25(OH)D$ concentrations occurred but were not associated with significant increases in $1,25(OH)_2D$ levels (Hughes *et al.*, 1977). These findings raise the possibility that hypercalcaemia in vitamin D intoxication may be largely due to a direct action of $25(OH)D$. In support of this is an observation by Counts, Baylink, Shen, Sherrard and Hickman (1975) that hypercalcaemia occurred in an anephric child treated with vitamin D in whom the concentration of $25(OH)D$ was 1587·5 nmol/l (635 ng/ml). There is no information at present on serum $1,25-(OH)_2D$ concentrations in patients who have become hypercalcaemic during treatment with either $1,25(OH)_2D_3$ or $1\alpha(OH)D_3$.

Many other problems may be solved by the techniques now available and further study of vitamin D metabolism will continue to increase understanding of the aetiology of disorders of calcium and phosphate metabolism and thus allow a rational approach to their treatment.

ACKNOWLEDGEMENT

We acknowledge with pleasure the generous support of the Wellcome Trust for our studies on vitamin D.

REFERENCES

Avioli, L. V. and Lee, S. W. (1966). *Anal. Biochem.* **16**, 193.

Balsan, S. and Garabedian, M. (1972). *J. clin. Invest.* **51**, 749.

Balsan, S., Garabedian, M., Sorgniard, R., Holick, M. F. and DeLuca, H. F. (1975). *Paediat. Res.* **9**, 586.

Barragry, J. M., France, M. W., Corless, D., Gupta, S. P., Switala, S., Boucher, B. J. and Cohen, R. D. (1978). *Clin. Sci. mol. Med.* **55**, 213.

Barton, D. H. R., Hesse, R. H., Pechet, M. M. and Rizzardo, E. (1974). *J. chem. soc. Chem. Comm.* 203.

Bassude, C. D. K. and Humphreys, D. J. (1976). *Clin. Endocr.* **5**, 109S.

Baxter, L. A. and DeLuca, H. F. (1976). *J. biol. Chem.* **351**, 3158.

Bayard, F., Bec, P. and Louvet, J. P. (1972). *Eur. J. clin. Invest.* **2**, 195.

Bayard, F., Bec, P., Thon That, H. and Louvet, J. P. (1973). *Eur. J. clin. Invest.* **3**, 447.

Belsey, R., DeLuca, H. F. and Potts, J. T., Jr., (1971). *J. clin. Endocr. Metab.* **33**, 554.

Belsey, R., DeLuca, H. F. and Potts, J. T., Jr. (1974). *J. clin. Endocr. Metab.* **38**, 1046.

Bhattacharyya, M. and DeLuca, H. F. (1973). *J. biol. Chem.* **248**, 2969.

Bhattacharyya, M. and DeLuca, H. F. (1974). *Arch. biochem. Biophys.* **160**, 58.

Bilezikian, J. P., Canfield, R. E., Jacobs, T. P., Polay, J. S., D'Adamo, A. P., Eisman, J. A. and DeLuca, H. F. (1978). *New Engl. J. Med.* **299**, 437.

Bills, C. E., Honeywell, E. M., Wirick, A. M. and Nussmeier, M. (1931). *J. biol. Chem.* **90**, 619.

Bjorkhem, I. and Holmberg, I. (1976). *Clin. chim. Acta,* **68**, 215.

Bligh, E. G. and Dyer, W. J. (1959). *Can. J. Biochem. Physiol.* **37**, 911.

Blomstrand, R. and Forsgren, L. (1967). *Acta chem. scand.* **21**, 1662.

Boass, A., Toverud, S. U., McCain, T. A., Pike, J. W. and Haussler, M. R. (1977). *Nature, Lond.* **267**, 630.

Botham, K. M., Ghazarian, J. G., Kream, B. E. and DeLuca, H. F. (1976a). *Biochemistry,* **15**, 2130.

Botham, K. M., Ghazarian, J. G., Kream, B. E. and DeLuca, H. F. (1976b). *Biochemistry,* **15**, 4961.

Bouillon, R. and Van Baelen, H. (1977). *In* "Vitamin D: Biochemical, Chemical and Clinical Aspects Related to Calcium Metabolism" (A. W. Norman, K. Schaefer, J. W. Coburn, H. F. DeLuca, D. Frazer, H. G. Grigoleit and D. von Herrath, eds), p. 97. Walter de Gwyter, Berlin and New York.

Bouillon, R., Van Baelen, H. and De Moor, P. (1976a). *Biochem. J.,* 159, 463.

Bouillon, R., Van Baelen, H. and De Moor, P. (1977a). *J. clin. Endocr. Metab.* **45**, 225.

Bouillon, R., Van Baelen, H. and De Moor, P. (1977b). *J. clin. Endocr. Metab.* **45**, 679.

Bouillon, R., Van Baelen, H., Rombauts, W. and De Moor, P. (1976b). *Eur. J. Biochem.* **66**, 285.

Bouillon, R., Van Keckhove, P. and De Moor, P. (1976c). *Clin. Chem.* **22**, 364.

Boyle, I. T., Gray, R. W. and DeLuca, H. F. (1971). *Proc. natn. Acad. Sci. USA,* **68**, 2131.

Boyle, I. T., Omdahl, J. L., Gray, R. W. and DeLuca, H. F. (1973). *J. biol. Chem.* **248**, 4174.

Brickman, A. S., Sherrard, D. J., Towsey, T., Singer, F. R., Baylink, D. J., Maloney, N., Massry, S. G., Norman, A. W. and Coburn, J. W. (1974). *Arch. int. Med.*, **134**, 883.

Brownjohn, A. M., Goodwin, F. J., Hately, W., Marsh, F. R., O'Riordan, J. L. H. and Papapoulos, S. E. (1977). *Br. med. J.* **2**, 721.

Brumbaugh, P. F. and Haussler, M. R. (1974a). *J. biol. Chem.* **249**, 1251.

Brumbaugh, P. F. and Haussler, M. R. (1974b). *J. biol. Chem.* **249**, 1258.

Brumbaugh, P. F. and Haussler, M. R. (1975). *Life Sci.* **16**, 353.

Brumbaugh, P. F., Haussler, D. G., Bursac, K. M. and Haussler, M. R. (1974). *Biochemistry*, **13**, 4091.

Brumbaugh, P. F., Hughes, M. R. and Haussler, M. R. (1975). *Proc. natn. Acad. Sci. USA*, **72**, 4871.

Cambell, J. A., Squires, D. M. and Babcock, J. C. (1969). *Steroids*, **13**, 567.

Campion, H., Pelc, B. and Atkins, D. (1976). Vitamin D. *In* "Calcium, Phosphate and Magnesium Metabolism. Clinical, Physiological and Diagnostic Procedures" (B. E. C. Nordin, ed.), p. 444. Churchill Livingstone, London.

Castillo, L., Tanaka, V., DeLuca, H. F. and Sunde, M. L. (1977). *Arch. biochem. Biophys.* **179**, 211.

Chan, L. and O'Malley, B. W. (1976). *New Engl. J. Med.* **294**, 1322, 1372, 1430.

Chen, P. S., Jr., Terepka, A. R. and Lane, K. (1964). *Anal. Biochem.* **8**, 34.

Chen, T. C., Castillo, L., Korycka-Dahl, M. and DeLuca, H. F. (1974). *J. Nutr.* **104**, 1056.

Clemens, T. L., Hendy, G. N., Graham, R. F., Baggiolini, E. G., Uskokovic, M. R. and O'Riordan, J. L. H. (1978a). *Clin. Sci. mol. Med.* **54**, 329.

Clemens, T. L., Hendy, G. N., Graham, R. F., Baggiolini, E. G., Uskokovic, M. R. and O'Riordan, J. L. H. (1978b). *J. Endocr.* **77**, 49P.

Clemens, T. L., Hendy, G. N., Papapoulos, S. E., Fraher, L. J., Care, A. D. and O'Riordan, J. L. H. (1978c). *Clin. endocr.* (in press).

Cloix, J. F., Ulmann, A., Bachelef, M. and Funck-Brentano, J. L. (1976). *Steroids*, **28**, 743.

Colston, K. W., Evans, I. M. A., Spelsberg, T. C. and MacIntyre, I. (1977). *Biochem. J.* **164**, 83.

Compston, J. E. and Creamer, B. (1977). *Gut*, **18**, 171.

Compston, J. E. and Thompson, R. P. H. (1977). *Lancet*, **i**, 721.

Cork, D. J., Haussler, M. R., Pitt, M. J., Rizzardo, E., Hesse, R. H. and Pechet, M. M. (1974). *Endocrinology*, **94**, 1337.

Corless, D., Gupta, S. P., Switala, S., Barragry, J. M., Boucher, B. J., Cohen, R. D. and Diffey, B. L. (1978). Lancet, **ii**, 649.

Corradino, R. A. (1973). *Nature, Lond.* **243**, 41.

Costanzo, L. S., Steele, P. R. and Weiner, I. M. (1974). *Am. J. Physiol.* **226**, 1490.

Counts, S. J., Baylink, D. J., Shen, F. H., Sherrard, D. J. and Hickman, R. O. (1975). *Ann. int. Med.* **82**, 196.

Cruyl, A. A. M. and De Leenheer, A. P. (1977). *In* "Vitamin D: Biochemical, Chemical and Clinical Aspects Related to Calcium Metabolism" (A. W. Norman, K. Schaefer, J. W. Coburn, H. F. DeLuca, D. Frazer, H. G. Grigoleit and D. von Herrath, eds), p. 455. Walter de Gruyter, Berlin and New York.

Curry, O. B., Basten, J. F., Francis, M. J. O. and Smith, R. (1974). *Nature, Lond.* **249**, 83.

Daiger, S. P., Shanfield, M. S. and Cavalli-Sforza, L. L. (1975). *Proc. natn. Acad. Sci. USA*, **72**, 2076.

DeLuca, H. F. (1977). *Clin. Endocr.* **7**, 1S.

DeLuca, H. F. and Schnoes, H. K. (1978). *In* "Endocrinology of Calcium Metabolism" (D. H. Copp and R. V. Talmage, eds), p. 178. Excerpta Medica, Amsterdam and Oxford.

DeLuca, H. F. and Schnoes, H. K. (1979). *In* "Proceedings of the Forth Workshop on Vitamin D". (In press.)

Dent, C. E., Richens, A., Rowe, D. J. F. and Stamp, T. C. B. (1970). *Br. med. J.* **4**, 69.

Drezner, M. K., Neelon, F. A., Haussler, M. R., McPherson, H. T. and Lebovitz, H. E. (1976). *J. clin. Endocr. Metab.* **42**, 621.

Dunnigan, M. G., Paton, J. P. L., Haase, S., McNicol, G. W., Gardner, M. D. and Smith, C. M. (1962). *Scott. Med. J.* **10**, 1.

Eastwood, J. B., Harris, E. Stamp, T. C. B. and De Wardener, H. E. (1976). *Lancet*, **ii**, 1209.

Edelstein, S., Charman, M., Lawson, D. E. M. and Kodicek, E. (1974). *Clin. Sci. mol. Med.* **46**, 231.

Edelstein, S., Lawson, D. E. M. and Kodicek, E. (1973). *Biochem. J.* **135**, 417.

Eisman, J. A., Hamstra, A. J., Kream, B. E. and DeLuca, H. F. (1976a). *Arch. biochem. Biophys.* **176**, 235.

Eisman, J. A., Hamstra, A. J., Kream, B. E. and DeLuca, H. F. (1976b). *Science*, **193**, 1021.

Eisman, J. A., Shephard, R. M. and DeLuca, H. F. (1977). *Anal. Biochem.* **80**, 298.

Ford, J. A., Colhoun, E. M., McIntosh, W. B. and Dunnigan, M. G. (1972). *Br. med. J.* **2**, 677.

Fraser, D., Kooh, S. W., Kind, H. P., Holick, M. F., Tanaka, Y. and DeLuca, H. F. (1973). *New Engl. J. Med.* **289**, 817.

Fraser, D. R. and Kodicek, E. (1970). *Nature, Lond.* **228**, 764.

Fraser, D. R. and Kodicek, E. (1973). *Nature New Biol.* **241**, 163.

Galante, L., Colston, K. W., Evans, I. M. A., Byfield, P. G. H., Matthews, E. W. and MacIntyre, I. (1973). *Nature, Lond.* **244**, 438.

Galante, L., MacAuley, S. J., Colston, K. W. and MacIntyre, I. (1972). *Lancet*, **ii**, 985.

Gallagher, C., Riggs, L., Eismann, J., Arnaud, S. and DeLuca, H. F, (1976). *Clin. Res.* **24**, 360A.

Garabedian, M., Holick, M. F., DeLuca, H. F. and Boyle, I. T. (1972). *Proc. natn. Acad. Sci. USA*, **69**, 1673.

Garabedian, M., Tanaka, V., Holick, M. F. and DeLuca, H. F. (1974). *Endocrinology*, **94**, 1022.

Garcia-Pascual, B., Peytremann, A., Courvoisier, B., and Lawson, D. E. M. (1976). *Clin. chim. Acta*, **68**, 99.

Ghazarian, T. G. and DeLuca, H. F. (1974). *Arch. biochem. Biophys.* **160**, 63.

Ghazarian, T. G. and DeLuca, H. F. (1977). *Biochem. biophys. Res. Commun.* **75**, 550.

Glorieux, F. and Scriver, C. R. (1972). *Science*, **175**, 997.

Goldberg, M., Agus, Z. S. and Goldfarb, S. (1976). Renal Handling of Calcium and Phosphate. *In* "Kidney and Urinary Tract Physiology II" (K. Tharau, ed.), Vol. 11, p. 211. University Park Press, Baltimore.

Graham, R. F., Preece, M. A. and O'Riordan, J. L. H. (1977). *Calc. Tiss. Res.* **22S**, 416.

Gray, R. W., Caldas, A. E., Wilz, D. R., Lemann, J., Jr., Smith, G. A. and DeLuca, H. F. (1978). *J. clin. Endocr. Metab.* **46**, 756.

Gray, R. W., Omdahl, T. L., Ghazarian, T. G. and DeLuca, H. F. (1972). *J. biol. Chem.* **247**, 7528.

Haddad, J. G. and Birge, S. J. (1975). *J. biol. Chem.* **250**, 299.

Haddad, J. G. and Chyu, K. J. (1971). *J. clin. Endocr. Metab.* **33**, 992.

Haddad, J. G. and Hahn, T. J. (1973). *Nature, Lond.* **244**, 515.

Haddad, J. G. and Walgate, J. (1976a). *J. biol. Chem.* **251**, 4803.

Haddad, J. G. and Walgate, J. (1976b). *J. clin. Invest.* **58**, 1217.

Haddad, J. G., Min, C., Mendelsohn, M., Slatopolsky, E. and Hahn, T. J. (1977). *Arch. biochem. Biophys.* **182**, 390.

Haddad, J. G., Min, C., Walgate, J. and Hahn, T. J. (1976). *J. clin. Endocr. Metab.* **43**, 712.

Haddad, J. G., Walgate, J., Min, C. and Hahn, T. J. (1976). *Biochem. biophys. Acta*, **444**, 921.

Hahn, T. J., Birge, S. J., Scharp, C. R. and Avioli, L. (1972). *J. clin. Invest.* **51**, 741.

Hahn, T. J., Hendin, B. A., Scharp, C. R. and Haddad, J. G. (1972). *New Engl. J. Med.* **287**, 900.

Haussler, M. R. and Brumbaugh, P. F. (1976). *In* "Hormone Receptor Interactions. Molecular Aspects of Modern Pharmacology–Toxicology" (G. S. Levy, ed.), Vol. 9, p. 301. Marcell Dekker, New York.

Haussler, M. R. and McCain, T. A. (1977). *New Engl. J. Med.* **297**, 974, 1041.

Haussler, M. R., Baylink, D. J., Hughes, M. R., Brumbaugh, P. F., Wergedal, J. E., Shen, F. H., Nielsen, R. L., Counts, S. J., Bursac, K. M. and McCain, T. A. (1976). *Clin. Endocr.* **7**, 151S.

Haussler, M. R., Hughes, M. R., Baylink, D. and McCain, T. A. (1977). *Adv. exp. med. Biol.* **81**, 233.

Haussler, M. R., Hughes, M. R., McCain, T. A., Zerwekh, P. F., Brumbaugh, W., Jubiz, W. and Wasserman, R. H. (1977). *Calc. Tiss. Res.* **22S**, 1.

Haussler, M. R., Hughes, M. R., Pike, J. W., and McCain, T. A. (1977). *In* "Vitamin D: Biochemical, Chemical and Clinical Aspects Related to Calcium Metabolism" (A. W. Norman, K. Schaefer, J. W. Coburn, H. F. DeLuca, D. Frazer, H. G. Grigoleit and D. von Herrath, eds), p. 473. Walter de Gruyter, Berlin and New York.

Hay, A. W. M. and Watson, G. (1977). *In* "Vitamin D: Biochemical, Chemical and Clinical Aspects Related to Calcium Metabolism" (A. W. Norman, K. Schaefer, J. W. Coburn, H. F. DeLuca, D. Frazer, H. G. Grigoleit and D. von Herrath, eds), p. 483. Walter de Gruyter, Berlin and New York.

Henry, H. (1977). *In* "Vitamin D: Biochemical, Chemical and Clinical Aspects Related to Calcium Metabolism" (A. W. Norman, K. Schaefer, J. W. Coburn, H. F. DeLuca, D. Frazer, H. G. Grigoleit and D. von Herrath, eds), p. 125. Walter de Gruyter, Berlin and New York.

Henry, H. L., Midgett, R. J. and Norman, A. W. (1974). *J. biol. Chem.* **249**, 7584.

Hill, L. F., Mawer, E. B. and Taylor, C. M. (1975). *In* "Vitamin D and Problems Related to Uraemic Bone Disease" (A. W. Norman, K. Schaefer, H. G. Grigoleit, eds), p. 755. Walter de Gruyter, Berlin and New York,

Hillman, L. S. and Haddad, J. G. (1974). *J. Pediat.* **84**, 742.

Holick, M. F., DeBlanco, M. C., Clark, M. B., Henley, J. W., Neer, R. M., DeLuca, H. F. and Potts, J. T., Jr. (1977). *J. clin. Endocr. Metab.* **44**, 595.

Holick, M. F., Garabedian, M. and DeLuca, H. F. (1972). *Science*, **176**, 1146.

Holick, M. F., Kleiner-Bossaler, A., Schnoes, H. K., Kasten, P. M., Boyle, I. T., and DeLuca, H. F. (1973). *J. biol. Chem.* **248**, 6691.

Holik, M. F., Schnoes, H. K., DeLuca, H. F., Gray, R. W., Boyle, I. T. and Suda, T. (1972). *Biochemistry*, **11**, 4251.

Holick, M. F., Schnoes, H. K., DeLuca, H. F., Suda, T. and Cousins, R. J. (1971). *Biochemistry*, **10**, 2799.

Holick, M. F., Tavela, T. E., Holick, S. A., Schnoes, H. K., DeLuca, H. F. and Gallagher, B. M. (1976). *J. biol. Chem.* **251**, 1020.

Holmes, A. M., Enoch, B. A., Taylor, J. L. and Jones, M. E. (1973). *Quart. J. Med.* **42**, 125.

Horiuchi, N., Suda, T., Takahashi, H., Shimazawa, E. and Ogata, E. (1977). *Endocrinology*, **101**, 969.

Hughes, M. R., Baylink, D. J., Gonnerman, W. A., Toverud, S. U., Ramp., W. K. and Haussler, M. R. (1977). *Endocrinology*, **100**, 799.

Hughes, M. R., Baylink, D. J., Jones, P. G. and Haussler, M. R. (1976). *J. clin. Invest.* **58**, 61.

Hughes, M. R., Brumbaugh, P. F., Haussler, M. R., Wergedal, J. E. and Baylink, D. J. (1975). *Science*, **190**, 578.

Hunt, S., O'Riordan, J. L. H., Windo, J. and Trusswell, A. S. (1976). *Br. med. J.* **2**, 1351.

Imawari, M. and Goodman, D. S. (1977). *J. clin. Invest.* **59**, 432.

Imawari, M., Kida, K. and Goodman, D. S. (1976). *J. clin. Invest.* **58**, 514.

Jones, G. (1978). *Clin. Chem.* **24**, 287.

Jubiz, W., Haussler, M. R., McCain, T. A. and Tolman, K. G. (1977). *J. clin. Endocr. Metab.* **44**, 379.

Kanis, J. A., Cundy, T., Bartlett, M., Smith, R., Heynen, G., Warner, G. T. and Russell, R. G. G. (1978). *Br. med. J.* **i**, 1382.

Kaplan, R. A., Haussler, M. R., Deftos, L. J., Bone, H. and Pak, C. V. C. (1977). *J. clin. Invest.* **59**, 756.

Kenny, A. D. (1976). *Am. J. Physiol.* **230**, 1604.

Kida, K. and Goodman, D. S. (1976). *J. Lipid Res.* **17**, 485.

Knutson, J. C. and DeLuca, H. F. (1974). *Biochemistry*, **13**, 1543.

Kodicek, E. (1960). Vitamin Metabolism. *In* "Fourth International Congress of Biochemistry", p. 198. Pergamon Press, London.

Kodicek, E. (1963). *In* "Transfer of Calcium and Strontium Across Biological Membranes" (R. H. Wasserman, ed.), p. 185. Academic Press, New York and London.

Kodicek, E. and Lawson, D. E. M. (1967). *In* "The Vitamins" (P. Gyorgy and W. N. Pearson, eds), p. 211. Academic Press, New York and London.

Kosh, K. T. and Van Der Slik, A. L. (1976). *Anal. Biochem.* **74**, 282.

Krawitt, E. L., Grundman, M. J. and Mawer, E. B. (1977) *Lancet*, **ii**, 1246.

Kream, B. E., Eisman, J. A. and DeLuca, H. F. (1977). *In* "Vitamin D: Biochemical, Chemical and Clinical Aspects Related to Calcium Metabolism" (A. W. Norman, K. Schaefer, J. W. Coburn, H. F. DeLuca, D. Frazer, H. G. Grigoleit and D. von Herrath, eds), p. 501. Walter de Gruyter, Berlin and New York.

Kream, B. E., Reynolds, R. D., Knutson, J. C., Eisman, J. A. and DeLuca, H. F. (1976). *Arch. biochem. Biophys.* **176**, 779.

Kruse, R. (1968). *Monatschr. Kinderkeilkd.* **116**, 378.

Kumar, R., Harnden, D. and DeLuca, H. F. (1976). *Biochemistry*, **15**, 2420.

Lambert, P. W., Syverson, B. J., Arnaud, C. D. and Spelsberg, T. C. (1977). *J. Ster. Biochem.* **8**, 929.

Larkins, R. G., MacAuley, S. J., Colston, K. W., Evans, I. M. A., Galante, L. S. and MacIntyre, I. (1973). *Lancet*, **ii**, 289.

Larkins, R. G., MacAuley, S. J. and MacIntyre, I. (1974). *Nature, Lond.* **252**, 412.

Lawson, D. E. M., Fraser, D. R., Kodicek, E., Morris, H. R. and Williams, D. H. (1971). *Nature, Lond.* **230**, 228.

Lawson, D. E. M., Wilson, P. W. and Kodicek, E. (1969). *Biochem. J.* **115**, 269.

Long, R. G., Skinner, R. K., Wills, M. R. and Sherlock, S. (1976). *Lancet*, **ii**, 650.

Long, R. G. and Wills, M. R. (1978). *Br. J. hosp. Med.* **20**, 312.

Lorenc, R., Tanaka, V., DeLuca, H. F. and Jones, G. (1977). *Endocrinology*, **100**, 468.

Luckert, B. P., Stanbury, S. W. and Mawer, E. B. (1973). *Endocrinology*, **93**, 718.

Lund, B., Sorensen, O. H., Nielsen, S. P., Munck, O., Bärenholdt, O. and Petersen, K. (1975). *Lancet*, **ii**, 372.

MacIntyre, I. (1977). *In* "Vitamin D: Biochemical, Chemical and Clinical Aspects Related to Calcium Metabolism" (A. W. Norman, K. Schaefer, J. W. Coburn, H. F. DeLuca, D. Frazer, H. G. Grigoleit and D. von Herrath, eds), p. 155. Walter de Gruyter, Berlin and New York.

MacIntyre, I., Colston, K. W., Evans, I. M. A., Lopez, E., MacAuley, S. J., Piegnour-Deville, J., Spanos, E. and Szelke, M. (1976). *Clin. Endocr.* **5**, 85S.

MacIntyre, I., Evans, I. M. A. and Larkins, R. C. (1977). *Clin. Endocr.* **6**, 65.

Mawer, E. B., Backhouse, J., Taylor, C. M., Lumb, C. A. and Stanbury, S. W. (1973). *Lancet*, **ii**, 626.

Mawer, E. B., Davies, M., Backhouse, J., Hill, L. F. and Taylor, C. M. (1976) *Lancet*, **i**, 1203.

McLaughlin, M., Raggat, P. R., Fairney, A., Brown, D. J., Lester, A and Wills, M. R. (1974). *Lancet*, **i**, 536.

Morrissey, R. L. and Rath, D. F. (1974). *Proc. Soc. exp. biol. Med.*, **145**, 699.

Myrtle, J. F. and Norman, A. W. (1971). *Science*, **171**, 79.

Napoli, J. L., Reeve, L. E., Eisman, J. A., Schnoes, H. K. and DeLuca, H. F. (1977). *In* "Vitamin D: Biochemical, Chemical and Clinical Aspects Related to Calcium Metabolism" (A. W. Norman, K. Schaefer, J. W. Coburn, H. F. DeLuca, D. Frazer, H. G. Grigoleit and D. von Herrath, eds), p. 29. Walter de Gruyter, Berlin and New York.

Narwid, T. A., Blount, J. F., Iacobelli, J. and Uskovic, M. R. (1974). *Helv. chim. Acta*, **57**, 781.

Nield, C. H., Russell, W. C. and Zimmerli, A. (1960). *J. biol. Chem.* **136**, 73.

Norman, A. W. and Henry, H. (1974). *Rec. Prog. horm. Res.* **30**, 431.

Norman, A. W., Johnson, R. L., Osborn, T. W., Proscal, D. A., Carey, S. C., Hammond, M. L., Mitra, M. N., Pirio, M. R., Rego, A., Wing, R. M. and Okamura, W. H. (1976). *Clin. Endocr.* **5**, 121S.

Norman, A. W., Myrtle, J. F., Midgett, R. J., Nowicki, H. G., Williams, V. and Popjak, G. (1971). *Science*, **173**, 51.

Norman, A. W., Schaefer, K., Coburn, J. W., DeLuca, H. F., Frazer, D., Grigoleit, H. G. and von Herrath, D. (eds) (1977). "Vitamin D: Biochemical, Chemical and Clinical Aspects Related to Calcium Metabolism." Walter de Gruyter, Berlin and New York.

Norman, A. W., Wong, R. G., Reddy, C., Brickman, A. S. and Coburn, J. W. (1973). "Proc. 9th Eur. Symp. Cal. Tissue" (H. Czitober and J. Eschberger, eds), p. 249. Facla Publication, Vienna.

Offerman, G. and Dittmar, F. (1974). *Horm. Metab. Res.* **6**, 534.

Olson, E. B. and DeLuca, H. F. (1969). *Science*, **176**, 1146.

Olson, E. B. Jr., Knutson, J. C., Bhattacharyya, M. H. and DeLuca, H. F. (1976). *J. clin. Invest.* **57**, 1213.

Omdahl, J. L. and DeLuca, H. F. (1973). *Physiol. Rev.* **53**, 327.

O'Riordan, J. L. H., Graham, R. F. and Dolev, E. (1977). *In* "Vitamin D: Biochemical, Chemical and Clinical Aspects Related to Calcium Metabolism" (A. W. Norman,

K. Schaefer, J. W. Coburn, H. F. DeLuca, D. Frazer, H. G. Grigoleit and D. von Herrath, eds), p. 519. Walter de Gruyter, Berlin and New York.

Papapoulos, S. E., Brownjohn, A. M., Junor, B. J. R., Marsh, F. P., Goodwin, F. J., Hately, W., Lewin, I. G., Tomlinson, S., Hendy, G. N. and O'Riordan, J. L. H. (1977). *Clin. Endocr.* 7, 59S.

Papapoulos, S. E., Clemens, T. L., Fraher, L. J., Lewin, I. G., Sandler, L. M. and O'Riordan, J. L. H. (1979), *Lancet*, i, 627.

Parkes, C. O. (1978). *In* "Endocrinology of Calcium Metabolism" (D. H. Copp and R. V. Talmage, eds), p. 165. Excerpta Medica, Amsterdam and Oxford.

Partridge, J. J., Shieuy, S. J., Baggiolini, F. G., Hennessy, B. and Uskokovic, M. R. (1977). *In* "Vitamin D: Biochemical, Chemical and Clinical Aspects Related to Calcium Metabolism" (A. W. Norman, K. Schaefer, J. W. Coburn, H. F. DeLuca, D. Frazer, H. G. Grigoleit and D. von Herrath, eds), p. 47. Walter de Gruyter, Berlin and New York.

Pedersen, J. I., Ghazarian, J. B., Orme-Johnson, N. R. and DeLuca, H. F. (1976). *J. bid. Chem.* 251, 3933.

Pietrek, J., Preece, M. A., Windo, J., O'Riordan, J. L. H., Dunnigan, M. G., McIntosh, W. B. and Ford, J. A. (1976). *Lancet*, i, 1145.

Pike, W. J., Toverud, S., Boass, A., McCain, T. and Haussler, M. R. (1977). *In* "Vitamin D: Biochemical, Chemical and Clinical Aspects Related to Calcium Metabolism" (A. W. Norman, K. Schaefer, J. W. Coburn, H. F. DeLuca, D. Frazer, H. G. Grigoleit and D. von Herrath, eds), p. 187. Walter de Gruyter, Berlin and New York.

Ponchon, G., Kennan, A. L. and DeLuca, H. F. (1969). *J. clin. Invest.* 48, 2032.

Popovtzer, M. M., Robinette, J. B., DeLuca, H. F. and Holick, M. F. (1974). *J. clin. Invest*, 53, 913.

Prader, A., Illig, R. and Heierli, E. (1961). *Helv. paediat. Acta*, 16, 452.

Preece, M. A., Ford, J. A., McIntosh, W. B., Dunnigan, M. G., Tomlinson, S., and O'Riordan, J. L. H. (1973). *Lancet*, i, 1145.

Preece, M. A., O'Riordan, J. L. H., Lawson, D. E. M., Kodicek, E. (1974). *Clin. chim. Acta*, 54, 235.

Preece, M. A., Tomlinson, S., Ribot, C. A., Pietrek, J., Korn, H. T., Davies, D. M., Ford, J. A., Dunnigan, M. G. and O'Riordan, J. L. H. (1975) *Quart. J. Med.* 44, 575.

Prince, M. J., Schaefer, P. C., Goldsmith, R. S. and Chaussmer, A. B. (1978). 60th Meet. Am. Endocr. Soc., Abst. No. 322.

Proscal, D. A., Okamura, W. H. and Norman, A. W. (1975). *J. biol. Chem.* 250, 8382.

Puschett, J. B., Fernandez, P. C., Boyle, I. T., Gray, R. W., Omdahl, J. L. and DeLuca, H. F. (1972). *Proc. Soc. exp. Biol. Med.* 141, 379.

Puschett, J. B., Moranz, J. and Kurnick, W. S. (1972). *J. clin. Invest.* 51, 373.

Raisz, L. G. and Trummel, C. L. (1972). *In* "Endocrinology, 1971" (S. Taylor, ed.), p. 480. Heinemann, London.

Rasmussen, H., DeLuca, H. F., Arnaud, C., Hawker, C. and von Stedingk, M. (1963). *J. clin. Invest.* 42, 1940.

Reade, T. M., Scriver, C. R., Glorieux, F. H., Nogrady, B., Delvin, E., Poirier, R., Holick, M. F. and DeLuca, H. F. (1975). *Paediat. Res.* 9, 593.

Reynolds, J. J., Holick, M. F. and DeLuca, H. F. (1973). *Calc. Tiss. Res.* 12, 295.

Richens, A. and Rowe, D. J. F. (1970). *Br. med. J.* 4, 73.

Rosen, J. F., Roginsky, M., Nathenson, G. and Finberg, L. (1974). *Am. J. Dis. Child.* 127, 220.

Riggs, B. L. and Gallagher, J. C. (1978). *In* "Endocrinology of Calcium Metabolism" (D. H. Copp and R. V. Talmage, eds), p. 43. Excerpta Medica, Amsterdam and Oxford.

Schachter, D., Finkelstein, F. D. and Kowarski, S. (1964). *J. clin. Invest.* **43**, 787.
Schneider, L. E., Omdahl, J. and Schedl, H. P. (1976). *Endocrinology*, **99**, 793.
Scriver, C. R. (1970). *Pediatrics*, **45**, 361.
Scriver, C. R., Reade, T. M., DeLuca, H. F. and Hamstra, A. J. (1978). *New Engl. J. Med.* **299**, 976.
Shen, F. H., Baylink, D. J., Sherrard, D. J., Shen, L., Maloney, N. A. and Wergedal, J. E. (1975). *J. clin. Endocr. Metab.* **40**, 1009.
Short, E. M., Binder, H. J. and Rosenberg, L. F. (1973). *Science*, **179**, 700.
Skiah, D., Budowski, P. and Katz, M. (1973). *Anal. Biochem.* **56**, 606.
Spanos, E., Pike, J. W., Haussler, M. R., Colston, K. W., Evans, I. M. A., Goldner, A. M., McCain, T. A. and MacIntyre, I. (1976). *Life Sci.* **19**, 1751.
Spanos, E., Colston, K. W., Evans, I. M. A., Galante, L., MacAuley, S. J. and MacIntyre, I., (1976). *Mol. cell. Endocr.* **5**, 163.
Spencer, R., Charman, M., Emtage, S. and Lawson, D. E. M. (1976a). *Eur. J. Biochem.* **71**, 399.
Spencer, R., Charman, M., Wilson, P. and Lawson, D. E. M. (1976b). *Nature, Lond.* **263**, 16.
Stamp, T. C. B. (1974). *Lancet*, **ii**, 121.
Stamp, T. C. B. (1976). *In* "Inborn Errors of Calcium and Bone Metabolism (H. Bickel and J. Stern, eds), p. 256. MTP Press, Lancaster.
Stamp, T. C. B. and Round, J. M. (1974). *Nature, Lond.* **247**, 563.
Stamp, T. C. B., Round, J. M., Rowe, D. J. F. and Haddad, J. G. (1972). *Br. med. J.* **4**, 9.
Stern, P. H., Hamstra, A. H., DeLuca, H. F. and Bell, N. H. (1978). *J. clin. Endocr. Metab.* **46**, 891.
Stern, P. H., Mavreas, T., Trummel, C. L., Schnoes, H. K. and DeLuca, H. F. (1976). *Mol. Pharmacol.* **12**, 879.
Suda, T., DeLuca, H. F., Schnoes, H. K. and Blunt, J. W. (1969). *Biochem. biophys. Res. Commun.* **35**, 182.
Suda, T., DeLuca, H. F., Schnoes, H. K., Ponchon, G., Tanaka, Y. and Holick, M. F. (1970a). *Biochemistry*, **9**, 2917.
Suda, T., DeLuca, H. F., Schnoes, H. K., Tanaka, Y. and Holick, M. F. (1970b). *Biochemistry*, **9**, 4776.
Swan, G. H. J. and Cooke, W. T. (1971). *Lancet*, **ii**, 456.
Tanaka, Y., Castillo, L. and DeLuca, H. F. (1976). *Proc. natn. Acad. Sci. USA*, **73**, 2701.
Tanaka, Y., Castillo, L. and DeLuca, H. F. (1977). *In* "Vitamin D: Biochemical, Chemical and Clinical Aspects Related to Calcium Metabolism" (A. W. Norman, K. Schaefer, J. W. Coburn, H. F. DeLuca, D. Frazer, H. G. Grigoleit and D. von Herrath, eds), p. 215. Walter de Gruyter, Berlin and New York.
Tanaka, Y., Castillo, L., DeLuca, H. F. and Ikekawa, N., (1977). *J. biol. Chem.* **252**, 1421.
Tanaka, Y. and DeLuca, H. F. (1973). *Arch. biochem. Biophys.* **154**, 566.
Tanaka, Y. and DeLuca, H. F. (1978). *Biochem. biophys. Res. Commun.* **83**, 7.
Tanaka, Y., DeLuca, H. F., Ikekawa, N., Morisaki, M. and Koizumi, N. (1975). *Arch. biochem. Biophys.* **170**, 620.
Tanaka, Y., Frank, H. and DeLuca, H. F. (1973). *Endocrinology*, **92**, 417.
Tanaka, Y., Lorenc, R. S. and DeLuca, H. F. (1975). *Arch. biochem. Biophys.* **171**, 521.
Taylor, A. N. (1974). *J. Nutr.* **104**, 489.

Taylor, C. M. (1977). *In* "Vitamin D: Biochemical, Chemical and Clinical Aspects Related to Calcium Metabolism" (A. W. Norman, K. Schaefer, J. W. Coburn. H. F. DeLuca, D. Frazer, H. G. Grigoleit and D. von Herrath, eds), p. 541. Walter de Gruyter, Berlin and New York.

Taylor, C. M., Hughes, S. E. and de Silva, P. (1976) *Biochem. biophys. Res. Commun.* **70**, 1243.

Teitelbaum, S. L., Halverson, J. D., Bates, M., Wise, L. and Haddad, J. G. (1977). *Ann. int. Med.* **86**, 289.

Tsai, H. C. and Norman, A. W. (1973). *Biochem. biophys. Res. Commun.* **54**, 622.

Tucker, G., Gagnon, R. E. and Haussler, M. R. (1973). *Arch. biochem. Biophys.* **155**,

Tucker, G., Gagnon, R. E. and Haussler, M. R. (1973). *Arch. biochem. Biophys.* **155**, 47.

U.S. Pharmacopoeia (1955). 14th Revision, p. 809. Mack Easton, PA.

Van Baelen, H., Bouillon, R. and De Moor, P. (1977). *J. biol. Chem.* **25**, 4501.

Wake, C. J. and Maddocks, J. L. (1975). *Lancet*, **i**, 516.

Wasserman, R. H., Corradino, R. A., Fulmer, C. S. and Taylor, R. (1974). *Vit. Horm.* **32**, 299.

Wasserman, R. H. and Taylor, A. N. (1966). *Science*, **152**, 791.

Wasserman, R. H. and Taylor, A. N. (1973). *J. Nutr.* **103**, 586.

Wasserman, R. H., Taylor, A. N. and Fulmer, C. S. (1974). *Biochem. Soc. Spec. Publ.* **3**, 55.

Weber, J. C., Pons, V. and Kodicek, E. (1971). *Biochem. J.* **125**, 147.

Weisman, Y., Reiter, E. and Root, A. (1977). *J. Pediat.* **91**, 904.

Wilson, P. W. and Lawson, D. E. M. (1977). *Biochem. biophys. Acta.* **497**, 805.

Zerwerkh, J. E., Haussler, M. R. and Lindell, T. J. (1974). *Proc. natn. Acad. Sci. USA*, **71**, 2337.

Zerwerkh, J. E., Lindell, T. J. and Haussler, M. R. (1976). *J. biol. Chem.* **251**, 2388.

III. Calcitonin

L. J. DEFTOS

A. CALCITONIN

1. History

In 1962, during perfusion studies with blood high in calcium of the thyroid-parathyroid apparatus of the dog, Copp and his colleagues (Copp, Cameron, Cheney, Davidson and Henze, 1962) discovered a hypocalcaemic factor that caused a greater decline in blood calcium than that produced by para-thyroidectomy. Since the hypocalcaemia could not be ascribed to inhibition of parathyroid hormone secretion by the hypercalcaemic perfusion, Copp proposed the existence of a hypocalcaemic hormone that was secreted by the parathyroid gland and named it calcitonin. During parathyroidectomy studies in rats, Hirsch, Gauthier and Munson (1963) made the astute observation that parathyroidectomy by electrocautery produced a greater fall in calcium than did surgical parathyroidectomy. They concluded that cautery of the adjacent thyroid gland released a calcium-lowering factor from the thyroid gland. A hypocalcaemic factor was extracted from the thyroid gland and it was named thyrocalcitonin to distinguish it from calcitonin. This initial controversy regarding the source of this hormone was resolved in 1964 by Foster, Baghdianjz, Kumar, Slack, Soliman and MacIntyre (1964a) and Foster, MacIntyre and Pearse (1964b) who demonstrated its thyroid origin and suggested that the source of calcitonin in the dog was the cell population corresponding to the parafollicular cells of Nonidez (1932) and the parenchymatous cells of Baber (1876). Further histochemical and immunochemical studies established a discrete population of cells—the C-cells—of the thyroid gland as the source of calcitonin in man and other mammals (Solcia and Sampietro, 1968; Kalina, Foster, Clark and Pearse, 1970; Kracht, Hachmeister and Christ, 1970; McMillan, Hooker and Deftos, 1974; Wolfe, Voelkel and Tashjian, 1974). In sub-mammals, calcitonin is produced by the ultimobranchial glands (Copp, Cockroft and Kueh, 1977).

2. Biochemistry

The amino acid sequences of nine calcitonins from seven different species have been determined (Fig. 1). Examination of the naturally occurring calcitonins reveals certain common structural features, together with a considerable amount of apparent variability. The common features include the 1,7 amino-terminal disulphide bridge and the carboxyl-terminal prolinamide residue. Seven of the amino-terminal nine residues are identical in all calcitonins. Residues 28 (glycine) and 32 (prolinamide) are the only other sequence positions completely conserved. In general, there is also considerable homology in the 10–27 region among porcine, bovine, and ovine calcitonin, between human and rat calcitonin, and between salmon and eel calcitonin, respectively (Byfield, McLoughlin, Matthews and MacIntyre, 1976; Raulais, Merle and Milhaud, 1974; Noda and Narita, 1976; Otani, Yamauchi, Meguro, Kitazawa, Watanabe and Orimo, 1976). It is also likely that there is considerable homology between salmon and chicken calcitonin since radioimmunoassays based on the former can be used to measure the latter (Cutler, Habener, Dee and Potts, 1974a; Cutler, Habener and Potts, 1974b).

Calcitonins from ultimobranchial glands isolated from Chum, Sockeye, Pink and Cohoe salmon species reveal that each species secretes two forms of calcitonin, I and either II or III. Salmon II differs from salmon I in positions 15, 22, 29 and 31. Salmon III is identical to salmon II in these positions,

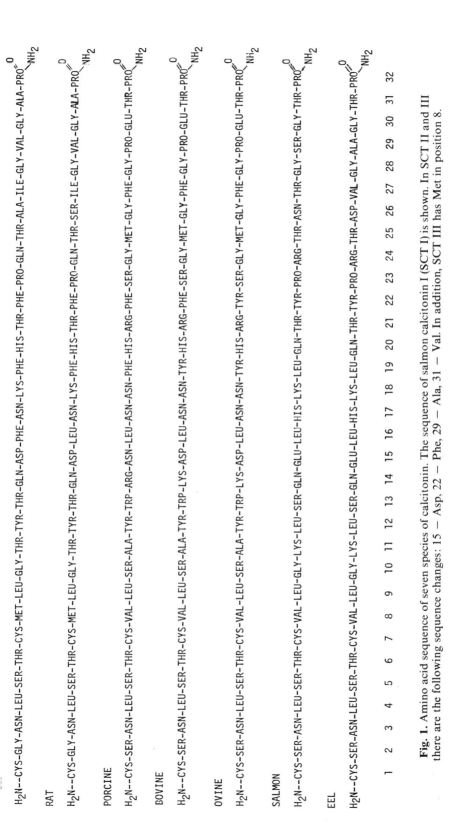

Fig. 1. Amino acid sequence of seven species of calcitonin. The sequence of salmon calcitonin I (SCT I) is shown. In SCT II and III there are the following sequence changes: 15 — Asp, 22 — Phe, 29 — Ala, 31 — Val. In addition, SCT III has Met in position 8.

but differs from salmon I in an additional position (residue 8) where methionine replaces valine (Keutmann, Lequin, Habener, Singer, Niall and Potts, 1972).

The sequence variability of the middle region of calcitonin (residues 10–27 inclusive) is perhaps more apparent than real. Though no single amino acid in this region is constant in all seven calcitonins, there is considerable similarity when the comparison is based on the chemical properties of the amino acid side chains. Acidic residues (aspartic or glutamic acid) are found only at position 15. (The only other acidic residue is found at position 30 in porcine, bovine, and ovine calcitonins.) Basic residues are also confined to a relatively few positions. Where substitutions are found for basic residues, asparagine or glutamine is the most common replacement. This is a conservative change since the amides are regarded as possessing weakly basic properties and the basic amino acid-amide exchange is extremely common in other groups of related proteins and peptides. Hydrophobic residues (leucine, phenylalanine or tyrosine) are distributed almost regularly along the peptide chain, occupying positions 4, 9, 12, 16, 19 and 22.

All calcitonins contain at least one acidic residue at positions 15 and/or 30. Moderate conservation regarding the distribution of basic residues has been observed, as discussed above. Positions 14, 17, 18 and 20 are occupied by either a basic residue (arginine, lysine or histidine) or an amide. All calcitonins contain at least two basic residues. Methionine is usually found at two positions in the calcitonins, 8 and 25. Methionine is not required, however, for biological activity since salmon and eel calcitonins lack methionine. Tryptophan is present in porcine, bovine and ovine calcitonins at position 13, but salmon, human, rat and eel calcitonins lack tryptophan. The number of tyrosines present in the calcitonins varies from zero (in salmon II and III) to three (in ovine calcitonin). When present, tyrosines occupy positions 12, 19 and/or 22. Though tyrosine is plainly not essential for biological activity, it is always replaced by a hydrophobic residue at these positions as mentioned above.

In view of the loss of activity associated with omission of only one or two amino acids, while retaining constant the amino-terminal sequence and the carboxyl-terminal prolinamide, it is hardly surprising that the search for "active fragments" of calcitonin has not been rewarding (Potts, Niall and Deftos, 1971). These limited observations suggest strongly that the whole peptide chain is involved in the biological activity of the hormone, the overall size and chain length and the chemical groupings at either end of the chain being particularly critical for binding to receptor sites.

3. Biological Effects

Calcitonin exerts its biologic effects by acting on three primary target organs—bone, kidney, and the gastro-intestinal (GI) tract. Like many other peptide hormones, calcitonin seems to mediate its effects via adenylate cyclase (Care, Bates and Gitelman, 1970; Heersche, Marcus and Aurbach, 1974; Marx and Aurbach, 1975). The effect of calcitonin in blood—to decrease plasma calcium and phosphate concentrations—is the summation of these multiple actions of the hormone.

(a) Bone

The major biologic effect of calcitonin is to decrease bone resorption by inhibiting osteoclastic activity. It has also been suggested that calcitonin promotes bone formation but this has been difficult to establish (Potts and Deftos, 1974; Singer, Woodhouse, Parkinson and Joplin. 1969; Lutwak, Singer and Urist, 1974). Calcitonin acts on both the mineral and organic phases of bone. By inhibiting the resorption of the mineral phase, calcitonin prevents the translocation of calcium and phosphorus from bone. In those situations in which bone turnover is sufficiently high, calcitonin will produce hypocalcaemia and hypophosphataemia. By inhibiting the resorption of the organic phase of bone, calcitonin decreases the excretion of urinary hydroxy-proline.

(b) Kidney

Calcitonin increases the urinary excretion of calcium and phosphorus (Potts and Deftos, 1974). Calcitonin also promotes the renal excretion of sodium and potassium (Bijvoet, van der Sluys Veer, de Vries and van Koppen, 1971). The physiologic significance of these renal effects of calcitonin is not fully defined (Ardaillou, 1975).

(c) Gastro-intestinal tract

The effects of calcitonin on the tract are not well established. There is evidence to suggest that it inhibits the absorption of calcium (Olson, DeLuca and Potts, 1972) and, alternatively, that is has no effect on the absorption of calcium (Gray, Bieberdorf and Fordtran, 1973). Further studies are clearly necessary to resolve this controversy. The effects of calcitonin on the secretory activity of the GI tract seem better established. Calcitonin inhibits gastric secretion (Becker, Konturek, Reeder and Thompson, 1973; Fahrenkrug, Hornum and Rehfeld, 1975) and bile flow (Dangoumau, Bussiere, Noel and Balabaud, 1976), has a variable effect on secretin (Iwatsuki and Hashimoto,

1976; Tarnawski, Bogdal, Dura, Marszalek and Jedrychowski, 1974), and promotes water and electrolyte secretion by the small intestine (Gray et al., 1973) and salivary gland secretion (Koelz, Drack and Blum, 1976).

(d) Other effects

A variety of other effects have been observed for calcitonin. It has been reported to be antiflammatory (Abdullahi, Arrigoni-Martelli, Gramm, Franco and Velo, 1977; Velo, DeBastiani, Nogarin and Abdullahi, 1976), to promote fracture (Adachi, Abe, Tanaka, Miyakawa and Kumaoaka, 1974) and wound (Lupulescu, 1975) healing, to be uricosuric (Blahos, Osten, Mertl, Kotas, Gregor and Reisenauer, 1975), to inhibit lipolysis (Werner and Low, 1974), and to have pituitary (Leicht, Biro and Weinges, 1974) and CNS (Pecile, Ferri, Braga and Olgiati, 1975) effects. The importance of these effects will be decided by future studies.

4. Secretion

(a) Calcium and related minerals

Calcium is the best-studied secretagogue for calcitonin (Tashjian, Howland, Kenneth, Melvin and Hill, 1970; Deftos, Powell, Parthemore and Potts, 1973; Parthemore and Deftos, 1975). The secretion of calcitonin is directly related to blood calcium concentration. An acute increase in blood calcium results in a proportional increase in plasma calcitonin and an acute decrease in blood calcium produces a corresponding decrease in plasma calcitonin. Although the effects of acute changes in blood calcium concentration on plasma calcitonin are well-established, the effects of chronic hypercalcaemia and hypocalcaemia are not fully defined. Although differing results have been reported, there seems to be a compensatory increase in plasma calcitonin in patients with primary hyperparathyroidism, especially males (Parthemore, Moriguchi and Deftos, 1977a; Tashjian et al., 1970; Silva, Snider and Becker, 1974). Patients with non-parathyroid hypercalcaemia can also have elevated plasma calcitonin (Lee, Catanzaro, Parthemore, Roach and Deftos, 1977; Silva, Becker, Primack, Doppman and Snider, 1975; Coombes, Hillyard, Greenberg and MacIntyre, 1974) but in such patients it is difficult to establish if the hypercalcitoninaemia is due to hypercalcaemia, ectopic calcitonin production, or other causes (see Section C.1(a)). These variable responses of plasma calcitonin in patients with hypercalcaemia may reflect a limited capacity of C-cells to respond to chronic stimulation. Animal studies suggest that the C-cells can become "exhausted" during prolonged exposure to elevated blood calcium (Ericson, 1968); however, these experiments have many limitations and their applicability to humans is not clear. Studies in humans suggest that females may have such a decreased calcitonin reserve compared with males (Parthemore and Deftos, 1978).

Similarly, there are no definitive studies on the effect of chronic hypocalcaemia on calcitonin secretion. It might be inferred from some studies that chronic hypocalcaemia suppresses calcitonin secretion (Deftos et al., 1973). Calcium and pentagastrin infusion in hypocalcaemic patients produces a considerably greater increase in plasma calcitonin than that seen in normal subjects. The chronic hypocalcaemia in these subjects may result in increased storage of calcitonin in C-cells, which is released by the secretagogues. Direct studies of secretion are necessary to establish this hypothesis (Parthemore and Deftos, 1975).

Minerals related to calcium also seem to have an acute stimulatory effect or calcitonin secretion. In animal studies the administration of magnesium and strontium stimulates secretion of calcitonin but to a lesser degree than does calcium (Pento, Glick, Kagan and Gorfein, 1974). Magnesium also stimulates the secretion of calcitonin in normal human subjects but it is interesting to note that in some patients with medullary thyroid carcinoma, magnesium seems to suppress calcitonin secretion (Anast, David, Winnacker, Glass, Baskin, Brubaker and Burns, 1975).

(b) Gastro-intestinal factors

Several GI factors can also regulate the secretion of calcitonin. In humans as well as experimental animals, the intravenous administration of pentagastrin (and the closely related cholecystokinin (Barlet and Garel, 1976) and caerulin (Passeri, Carapezzi, Seccato, Monica, Storzzi and Palummeri, 1975)) and glucagon produce a brisk increase in plasma calcitonin (Deftos, Bury, Mayer, Habener, Singer, Powell, Krook, Watts and Potts, 1972; Deftos, Goodman, Engelman and Potts, 1971). In these studies, however, the doses of both hormones were sufficiently great to increase their blood concentration to abnormally high levels (Hennessey, Wells, Ontjes and Cooper, 1974). Although the studies by Munson, Cooper, Gray, Peng, Toverud, Harper and Ontjes (1973) suggest a physiological role for gastrin in the regulation of calcitonin secretion, further studies are necessary to test this hypothesis for humans (see Section A.5).

Recent studies have demonstrated that both pentagastrin and glucagon can stimulate calcitonin secretion in normal subjects (Fig. 2). However, it is not clear if the relationship with GI hormones such as gastrin or glucagon is physiologically important. The doses of gastrin (and glucagon) used to stimulate calcitonin secretion produce blood levels of the GI hormones that are probably higher than seen in the postprandial state. Furthermore, is has been possible to demonstrate an increase in plasma calcitonin related to eating and/or an oral calcium load in only a few clinical and experimental studies (Nozaki, Noda, Obi, Nishizawa, Morii and Wada, 1976; Garel, 1978).

However, studies in animals suggest a functional link between the GI tract and calcitonin secretion. In suckling rats and goats, there is a post-prandial increase in calcitonin which is apparently not related to changes

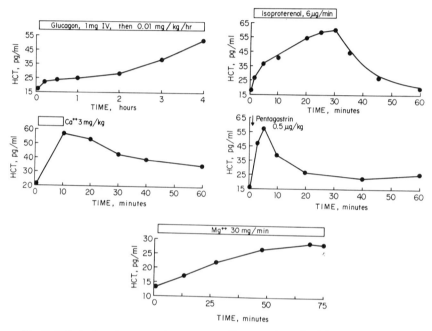

Fig. 2. Effect of various secretagogues on the secretion of calcitonin in humans.

in calcium (Talmage, Doppelt and Cooper, 1975; Garel, Care and Barlet, 1974; Toverud, Harper and Munson, 1976). Similar changes take place in the feeding mother. Also, a feedback relationship exists between calcitonin and GI function since high levels of exogenous or endogenous calcitonin can suppress certain aspects of GI function (Bolman, Cooper, Garner, Munson and Wells, 1977). The latter studies have demonstrated the complex interaction among GI hormones and other factors in the regulation of calcitonin secretion (Roos, Bundy, Bailey and Deftos, 1974; Roos, Bundy, Miller and Deftos, 1975; Roos and Deftos, 1976). In the mature rat, plasma calcitonin is higher in the fed state than in the fasted state, again independent of calcium (Roos, Parthemore, Lee and Deftos, 1977). The signal for this relationship in the rat is not obvious since the effects of pentagastrin on plasma calcitonin have been variable (Roos, Cooper, Frelinger and Deftos, 1978).

Thus, there is considerable clinical and experimental data to suggest a functional relationship between the GI tract and C-cells. However, the physiological significance of this relationship awaits further study.

(c) Neuroendocrine factors

There is accumulating data to indicate that neuro-endocrine hormones can influence the secretion of calcitonin. A series of experimental studies have demonstrated that adrenergic agents stimulate and suppress the secretion of calcitonin (Care *et al.*, 1970; Bates, Bruce and Care, 1970a; Bates, Phillippo and Lawrence, 1970b; Phillippo, Bruce and Lawrence, 1970; Hsu and Cooper, 1975). Similar effects have been observed in clinical studies in normal human subjects and in patients with primary and secondary abnormalities in calcitonin secretion (Metz, Deftos, Baylink and Robertson, 1978; Vora, Williams, Hargis, Bowser, Kawahara, Jackson, Henderson and Kukreja, 1978). An effect on calcitonin secretion of another neuro-endocrine agent, somatostatin, has not been firmly established. In high doses in animal studies, calcitonin suppression has been observed (Hargis, Williams, Reynolds, Chertow, Kukreja, Bowser and Henderson) whereas it is not apparent in lower doses in human studies (Metz *et al.*, 1978). The possibility of an effect of somatostatin on calcitonin secretion is intriguing since somatostatin-containing cells have been demonstrated by immunohistology in the thyroid gland (Hokfelt, Efendic, Hellerstrom, Johansson, Luft and Arimura, 1975). As with the GI hormones, the physiological significance of the relationship between neuroendocrine factors and calcitonin secretion remains to be established.

(d) Age and sex

The effect of age and sex on plasma calcitonin appears to be complicated. In the salmon species, plasma calcitonin is greater in females than in males (Watts, Copp and Deftos, 1974). In the bovine species the opposite is true but age and dietary factors are also important in that calcitonin is decreased in older animals and increased in those on high-calcium diets (Deftos, Habener, Krook and Mayer, 1972). In the murine species females have higher levels of plasma calcitonin and in both sexes hormone concentration increases as a function of age (Deftos, Roos and Parthemore, 1975; Roos *et al.*, 1977).

Preliminary studies in humans suggest that age and sex also influence calcitonin secretion. Higher than normal plasma levels have been reported in pregnant females and newborn infants and this has been supported by histological studies in the latter group (Samaan, Hill, Beceiro and Schultz, 1973; Hesch, Woodhead, Huefner and Wolf, 1973; Dirksen and Anast, 1976; Anast, 1977; Pearse, 1969). Peliminary studies suggested that plasma calcitonin decreases as a function of age in females (Davidson, Frumar, Judd, Shamonki, Tatoryn, Meldrum and Deftos, 1979). However, it seems reasonably well-established that calcitonin secretion and calcitonin reserve are decreased in females (Heath and Sizemore, 1977; Parthemore, 1977; Parthemore *et al.*, 1977; Parthemore and Deftos, 1978). Thus, although age and sex influence calcitonin secretion, other factors, some of them species specific, also modulate these effects.

(e) Other factors

A surprising relationship has been observed between calcitonin secretion and iodine metabolism; surprising since C-cells have not been classically regarded as participating in iodine metabolism. In rats made iodine-deficient, C-cells become hyperplastic and plasma calcitonin increases; this effect may be more clearly related to T_4 than TSH (Peng, Cooper, Pterusz and Volpert, 1975; Clark, Rollo, Stroop, Castner, Rehfeld, Loken and Deftos, 1977). This effect can be blocked or reversed by iodine replacement and perhaps by thyroxine (Deftos, Roos, Knecht, Lee, Pavlinac, Bone and Parthemore, 1978). In some instances the effect of iodine deficiency on calcitonin may be due to the development of hypercalcaemia (Clark, Rehfeld, Deftos, Castner, Stroop and Loken, 1978). By contrast, athyreotic cretins may have a decreased calcitonin secretion (Carey, Jones, Parthemore and Deftos, 1978). Prostaglandins in high doses stimulate plasma calcitonin in the rat but this effect is difficult to reproduce consistently in humans (Metz, Deftos, Baylink and Robertson, 1977a; Metz, Deftos, Baylink and Robertson, 1977b). Some studies suggest that calcitonin may exert an auto-regulatory effect on its own secretion (Bell, 1970).

5. Calcitonin in Human Physiology

The role of calcitonin in human biology was naturally difficult to define until sensitive and specific procedures were developed for the accurate measurement of the hormone (Fig. 3). Based largely on negative or inadequate data, no clear significance was ascribed to human calcitonin for almost a decade after its discovery. Although animal studies offered some clues, there were enough species differences in calcitonin to preclude convincing extrapolations to humans. However, in the last several years data has been accumulating regarding the role of calcitonin in human physiology.

The first step in studying calcitonin in human physiology was to provide convincing evidence that the hormone circulates in the peripheral plasma of normal humans (Deftos, 1978a). Because of the low concentrations of hormone found in human plasma by most but not all laboratories, extremely sensitive radioimmunoassays were developed in several laboratories for clinical studies (Parthemore and Deftos, 1978; Heath and Sizemore, 1977).

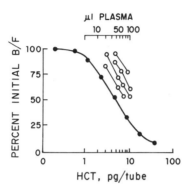

Fig. 3. Radioimmunoassay for human calcitonin. This standard curve demonstrates that antiserum LJ-1 can be used to detect less than 1 pg of the hormone. Also shown is the linear displacement produced by increasing aliquots of plasma from normal human subjects (○).

Application of these assays have uncovered some potentially important characteristics of the secretion of human calcitonin. Perhaps the most important to date is the observation that the concentration of plasma calcitonin is less in females than in males both in the basal state and during provocative tests of calcitonin secretion (Parthemore and Deftos, 1978; Heath and Sizemore, 1977). This has led to speculation that a relative deficiency of calcitonin, which acts to inhibit bone resorption, in females may play some role in the pathogenesis in this sex of osteoporosis, a disease characterised by increased bone resorption. Extensive studies are necessary to test this hypothesis but the general concept receives some support from studies in males and females with primary hyperparathyroidism (Section C.2(a). In addition, there is some preliminary data to suggest that, at least in females, plasma calcitonin decreases as a function of age (Davidson et al., 1979).

It is difficult to conclude that calcitonin plays a role in preventing postprandial hypercalcaemia in humans as it seems to in experimental animals (Munson, 1971; Roos, Frelinger, Yoon, Bergeron, Knecht, Lee and Deftos, 1978; Roos et al., 1978). While it is true that athyreotic patients may have decreased calcium tolerance, only a few studies have been able to demonstrate any prandial-related changes in plasma calcitonin (Section A.4(b)).

However, animal studies and preliminary clinical studies suggest the possibility that a prandially-related role for calcitonin may exist in the perinatal period. An increase in maternal plasma calcitonin may attenuate the skeletal resorption which occurs in the mother to provide calcium for the developing foetus and the feeding infant. And, an increase in foetal and infant calcitonin may help in the assimilation of maternal and/or dietary calcium (Toverud, et al., 1976; Taylor, Lewis and Balderstone, 1975). It has also been suggested that there is some diurnal variation of plasma calcitonin (Hillyard, Cooke, Coombes, Evans and MacIntyre, 1977). Additionally, plasma calcitonin has been reported to vary with menstruation in females (Pitkin, Reynolds, Williams and Hargis, 1978).

Thus, a variety of physiological variables—such as sex, feeding, growth and development, and perhaps age—which influence human calcitonin secretion in humans have been defined. These factors are discussed in more detail throughout this chapter. Additional studies will undoubtedly present a more complete picture of the physiological role of calcitonin. To these considerations must be added novel implications of the presence of an immunoreactive, calcitonin-like substance in the pituitary gland of several species (Deftos, Burton, Catherwood, Bone, Parthemore, Guillemin, Watkins and Moore, 1978).

B. DISORDERS OF CALCITONIN SECRETION AND METABOLISM

Primary as well as secondary disorders of calcitonin secretion have been defined. The best described primary disorder of calcitonin secretion is medullary thyroid carcinoma. However, ectopic calcitonin production by non-thyroidal tumours is being identified with increasing frequency and may become epidemiologically more important in this respect than medullary thyroid carcinoma. Abnormalities of calcitonin secretion also seem to occur in other malignant states. Secondary hypercalcitoninaemia seems to occur in primary hyperparathyroidism although this is disputed. In renal disease there appear to be disorders of calcitonin secretion as well as metabolism and disorders of calcitonin secretion have been demonstrated and postulated for several bone diseases (Table 1).

1. Medullary Thyroid Carcinoma

(a) History

Medullary thyroid carcinoma (MTC) is a tumour of the calcitonin-producing cells (C-cells) of the thyroid gland. In contrast to the follicular cells of the

Table 1

Conditions reported or postulated to be associated with abnormalities of calcitonin secretion and/or metabolism. Adapted from Deftos, 1978a.

Condition	Possible mechanism
Medullary thyroid carcinoma	Genetic/functional
C-cell hyperplasia	
Pre-hyperplasia	
Ectopic calcitonin production	Malignancy
Hypocalcaemia	Calcium
Hypercalcaemia/hypercalciuria	Calcium/gastrin
Hyperparathyroidism	Calcium/PTH/GI hormones
Malignancy	Possible factors
	Calcium
	Bone resorption
	Prostaglandins
	CT secretagogues
Pancreatitis	Glucagon/non-thyroidal calcitonin
Pregnancy	Calcium/bone resorption
Neonatal hypocalcaemia	Calcium/bone resorption
Renal disease	Metabolism/bone resorption/vitamin D
Bone disease	Bone resorption/CT secretagogues
Hyperostotic states	
Pycnodysostosis	
Engelman's disease	
Osteopetrosis	
Hyper-resorptive states	
Osteitis fibrosa cystica	
Osteoporosis	
Renal osteodystrophy	

thyroid, the presence of C-cells within the human thyroid gland has been established only relatively recently (Baber, 1876; Nonidez, 1932). This population of cells had attracted little attention until the discovery of (thyro)calcitonin in the early 1960's. Williams (1966) suggested that C-cells might be the cellular origin of medullary carcinoma of the thyroid. This tumour had been recognised by Hazard, Hawk and Crile (1959) as a distinct pathological entity that could be distinguished from other thyroid tumours. Williams' hypothesis was proved correct when several investigators demonstrated by bioassay the presence of abnormal calcitonin concentrations in the plasma and tumour of patients with medullary thyroid carcinoma (Meyer and Abdel-Bari, 1968; Melvin and Tashjian, 1968; Milhaud, Tubiana, Parmentier and Coutris, 1968; Cunliffe, Black, Hall, Johnston, Hudgson, Shuster, Gudmundsson, Joplin, Williams, Woodhouse, Galante and MacIntyre, 1968). These findings were confirmed by specific radioimmunoassays of

E

human calcitonin in tumour and blood (Clark, Byfield, Boyd and Foster, 1969) and by histochemical studies (Kalina *et al.*, 1970). Subsequently, the tumour was also shown to produce a wide variety of bioactive substances including: calcitonin, amyloid, ACTH, histaminase, catecholamines, serotonin, dopa decarboxylase, prostaglandins, bradykinin, kallikrein, carcinoembryonic antigen and somatostatin. The unique histologic and biochemical features of medullary thyroid carcinoma were soon complemented by its unique clinical associations with other endocrine and non-endocrine neoplasms (Table 2). A series of studies established the association

Table 2

Multiple endocrine neoplasia. Adapted from Deftos, 1978a.

Type I	
Parathyroid	Adenoma or hyperplasia
Pancreas	Adenoma (islet cells)
Pituitary	Adenoma
Type II	
Thyroid	Medullary thyroid carcinoma
Adrenal	Pheochromocytoma
Parathyroid	Hyperplasia or adenoma
Type III	
Thyroid	Medullary thyroid carcinoma
Adrenal	Phaeochromocytoma
Neural tissue	Neurogangliomas
Somatic	Marfanoid habitus

between medullary thyroid carcinoma and pheochromocytomas, parathyroid neoplasms and multiple endocrine neuromata. Most, if not all, of these associated neoplasms share with medullary thyroid carcinoma a common embryologic origin—the neural crest (LeDourain and LeLievre, 1970).

(b) *Embryology*

It is now generally accepted that the thyroidal C-cells, which become neoplastic in medullary thyroid carcinoma, are neural crest in origin. These cells migrate to the ultimobranchial bodies from the neural crest. In sub-mammals the cells form a distinct organ, the ultimobranchial organ, which becomes the site of the C-cells and their secretory product, calcitonin. In mammals the C-cells become incorporated into the thyroid gland and perhaps other sites. The neural crest origin of C-cells offers an explanation for the association of medullary thyroid carcinoma with other tumours of neural crest origin and also explains the production by these tumours of a wide variety of bioactive substances (Deftos, 1978).

(c) Pathology

Medullary thyroid carcinoma is usually a firm, rounded tumour located in the middle or upper lobes of the thyroid gland (Williams, 1966). It is commonly bilateral and multifocal, especially in familial cases. The histological features of the tumour can vary in appearance. The cells usually are polyhedral or polygonal in shape and are arranged in a variety of patterns. The arrangement of the cells can be influenced by the distribution of stromal elements, which can be scanty or predominant. Calcification commonly is found in the tumour. The areas of calcification are more dense and irregular than the homogeneous psammoma bodies occurring in other thyroid cancers. Dense calcifications may be visible on X-ray. A common feature of medullary thyroid carcinoma is the presence of amyloid. The amyloid has the histochemical characteristics of the immune amyloids, but immunochemical and immunohistological studies suggest that it is also secreted by the C-cells and is structurally related to calcitonin. Amyloid occurs with such regularity in medullary thyroid carcinoma that its absence, if a large enough area is surveyed, must be considered a strong point against the diagnosis. However, the importance of amyloid in the diagnosis of medullary thyroid carcinoma has been replaced by specific immunochemical staining procedures, which demonstrated the abnormal C-cells (McMillan, Hooker and Deftos, 1974).

(*1*) *C-cell hyperplasia.* Williams (1966) observed that foci of hyperplastic C-cells occurred in the rat form of this tumour and that it was difficult to distinguish between such hyperplastic areas and true tumours. Ljungberg (1972) described increased C-cell population remote from the tumour in medullary thyroid carcinoma. Wolfe and his colleagues defined C-cell hyperplasia as a distinct pathological entity (Wolfe, Melvin, Cervi-Skinner, Al Saadi, Juliar, Jackson and Tashjian, 1973). They were studying three patients at risk for medullary thyroid carcinoma because of their family history. These patients had small but progressive increases in plasma calcitonin during calcium infusion and consequently underwent thyroidectomy. The extirpated thyroid glands did not reveal the presence of medullary thyroid carcinoma. However, they observed clusters of hyperplastic parafollicular cells which were calcitonin-positive by immunohistological studies. The presence of increased calcitonin in these cells was confirmed by bioassay and immunoassay. The distribution of these hyperplastic parafollicular cells was in the area where C-cells are usually most prominent, the upper and middle portions of the lateral thyroid lobes. These observations suggested that, at least in familial cases of medullary thyroid carcinoma, the frank malignancy is preceded by a progressive hyperplasia of C-cells. These cells exhibited no atypical nuclei or other invasive tendencies. Although cellular hyperplasia has been suggested to be a precursor for many forms of malignancy, this progression has seldom been so well documented as it is for medullary thyroid carcinoma. The variable behaviour of medullary thyroid carcinoma is reflected in this predecessor of the tumour in that it can become manifest in early childhood or as late as the second decade (Carney, Sizemore and Lovestedt, 1976; Keiser, Beaven, Doppman, Wells and Buja, 1973; Wolfe *et al.*, 1973). More recent studies indicate that there may be even more subtle histological antecedents to medullary thyroid carcinoma.

The findings of these early stages of medullary thyroid carcinoma, in addition to their fundamental importance for cancer pathogenesis, is of considerable clinical significance. The early stages of medullary thyroid carcinoma, when the neoplastic process is confined to the thyroid gland, are the most amenable to surgery; C-cell hyperplasia and even more subtle histological changes are below the threshold of clinical detection but may be identifiable with the calcitonin assay. Such early identification offers the best hope for effective therapy and even cure. Provocative testing is especially valuable in such patients who may have normal basal levels of plasma calcitonin (McKenna, Lorber, Parthemore, Bone and Deftos, 1978).

(2) *C-cell adenoma.* An adenoma of thyroid C-cells has only rarely been reported (Beskid, 1975; Milhaud, 1976). In Beskid's case, the cells of one of 12 non-toxic thyroid adenomata were identified as C-cells on the basis of their staining characteristics. The adenoma did not concentrate radioactive iodine *in vivo* and an extract of it produced hypocalcaemia in the rat. These results must be considered as only preliminary evidence for the existence of adenoma of C-cells. Definitive evidence must await specific immunohisto-chemical studies which demonstrate the presence of calcitonin in tumour and perhaps in peripheral blood.

(d) Incidence

Medullary thyroid carcinoma has been estimated to comprise 4–12% of all thyroid cancer, itself a relatively uncommon tumour (Hill, Ibanez, Samaan, Ahearn and Clark, 1973). The ratio of female to male involvement is closer to unity than in other thyroid tumours. Although the majority of cases reported in the earlier literature appeared to be sporadic, an appreciation of the familial incidence of the tumour is resulting in an increasing identification of familial cases. Despite its rarity, the tumour has assumed a clinical importance that far outweighs its incidence. This has happened because:

(i) the tumour commonly occurs in a familial distribution in an autosomal dominant pattern;

(ii) its presence can be established by measuring its secretory product, calcitonin;

(iii) it is associated with an intriguing constellation of clinical features. Since the tumour is inherited as an autosomal dominant characteristic, the search for it in the family of an affected individual often is fruitful. In fact, by biochemical testing, the tumour can be diagnosed even when there has been no clinical evidence of its presence. This early diagnosis can lead to effective therapy and even to the cure of the cancer (Tashjian *et al.*, 1970).

(e) Natural history

Medullary thyroid carcinoma generally is regarded to be intermediate to the aggressive behaviour of anaplastic thyroid carcinoma and the more prolonged course of papillary and follicular thyroid carcinoma. However, the natural history of a given tumour can vary greatly and this can make decisions regarding therapy difficult. The tumour can be rapidly progressive, widely metastatic, and lead to death within weeks of diagnosis. By contrast, it can be indolent and compatible with decades of life (Hill *et al.*, 1973). Medullary thyroid carcinoma commonly spreads to regional lymphatics, a complication present in the majority of tumours reported. Distant metastases can involve any organ; lung, liver, bone, and adrenal gland are relatively common sites (Ibanez, Cole, Russell and Clark, 1967).

(f) Calcitonin secretion

As a neoplastic disorder of the C-cells of the thyroid gland, medullary thyroid carcinoma produces abnormally high amounts of calcitonin. The calcitonin content of the tumour can exceed that of the normal thyroid by orders of magnitude. As a result, patients with this tumour have abnormal concentrations of calcitonin in peripheral blood and urine. In many patients basal concentrations of the hormone are sufficiently elevated to be diagnostic of the tumour. Therefore, the radioimmunoassay for calcitonin can diagnose the presence of medullary thyroid carcinoma with an exceptional degree of accuracy and specificity when applied to measurements in random plasma samples. However, in an increasing percentage of patients with this tumour, basal levels of the hormone are indistinguishable from normal (Deftos, 1974). Many of these cases represent early stages of C-cell neoplasia or perhaps even hyperplasia, and these early stages are most amenable to surgical cure. Thus, provocative tests have been developed for the diagnosis of medullary thyroid carcinoma and its histological antecedents (Melvin, Tashjian and Miller, 1972). These tests have led to the identification of the tumour in patients in whom the diagnosis could have been missed by only basal calcitonin determinations.

(1) Provocative testing

(i) Glucagon—Although glucagon can stimulate calcitonin secretion, its clinical use as a diagnostic agent has been abandoned for several reasons. Glucagon is not a reliable calcitonin secretagogue since its effect is variable. Also, glucagon can release catecholamines; since patients with medullary thyroid carcinoma can have associated pheochromocytomas, and adrenergic crises can be precipitated by its administration (Deftos, 1978).

(ii) Calcium—Calcium by intravenous infusion has been the most widely used secretagogue for calcitonin in medullary thyroid carcinoma. In early studies calcium was infused at doses ranging from 3–5 mg/1 kg/hr for 2–4 hr. The increase in plasma calcium levels produced by such infusions, usually several mg/dl, consistently produced an abnormal increase in plasma calcitonin in patients with medullary thyroid carcinoma (Tashjian *et al.*, 1970; Deftos, 1974). The abnormal increase in plasma calcitonin occurred even in tumour patients who had basal concentrations of the hormone that were indistinguishable from normal (Deftos, 1974). Thus, the measurement of calcitonin after calcium infusion served to identify patients with medullary thyroid carcinoma who had non-diagnostic concentrations of basal calcitonin (Tashjian *et al.*, 1970; Deftos, 1974; McKenna *et al.*, 1978).

There are several disadvantages with the prolonged calcium infusions. The length of the procedure was inconvenient and the dose of calcium often necessitated hospitalisation in research wards under continual professional supervision. Also, the calcium rose to levels sufficient to produce hypertension, nausea, and even vomiting in the recipients. For these reasons, shorter infusions of calcium have been developed which are more convenient and safer than the longer procedures and yet seem to be as reliable in stimulating calcitonin secretion (Parthemore, Bronzert, Roberts and Deftos, 1974). In these procedures, the increase in plasma calcium usually is less than 1 mg/dl (0·25 mmol/l), but calcitonin is reliably stimulated. The procedure can be completed in several min and is well tolerated (Deftos, 1974; Parthemore *et al.*, 1974).

(iii) Pentagastrin—Pentagastrin is another widely used provocative agent for calcitonin secretion in patients with medullary thyroid carcinoma (Hennessey *et al.*, 1974). When administered as an intravenous bolus at a dose of 0·5 µg/kg, pentagastrin produces a rapid increase in plasma calcitonin. This pattern of calcitonin response, however, is probably a function of the dose and rapidity of administration of pentagastrin rather than any innate properties of this secretagogue. When calcium is given as a similar IV bolus over a few seconds, a calcitonin response similar to that seen with pentagastrin infusion is observed; and when pentagastrin is infused over several minutes, a response similar to that produced by calcium infusion is seen (McKenna *et al.*, 1978; Deftos, 1978a; Rude and Singer, 1977). Although the

rapidity of the pentagastrin infusion is advantageous, this provocative test does have some drawbacks. The administration of pentagastrin produces an unpleasant but poorly described sensation in the recipient. Also, at this time of writing, the use of pentagastrin as a diagnostic test in medullary thyroid carcinoma suspects is not approved by the Food and Drug Administration; therefore, an institutionally approved protocol may be required for its administration.

An interesting modification of the pentagastrin test has been described by Wells *et al.* (1975). They administered gastrin to patients with medullary thyroid carcinoma while an indwelling catheter was located in the inferior thyroid vein. During this procedure, they were able to demonstrate a dramatic increase in thyroidal vein as well as peripheral calcitonin concentration. In some patients there was an increase in thyroid vein calcitonin while the increase in peripheral calcitonin was not diagnostic. The localising capabilities of such venous catheterisation procedures is further demonstrated by studies performed during surgery and during patient follow-up (Goltzman, Potts, Ridgeway and Maloof, 1974). These investigators were able to localise precisely a recurrence of medullary thyroid carcinoma and thus institute more effective surgical treatment. However, such procedures cannot be considered routine and they require considerable expertise. The improved diagnostic potential of these catheterisation procedures is certainly diminished by their technical difficulty and may be further obviated by the increased sensitivity of newer calcitonin radioimmunoassays. These newer assays have better defined normal and abnormal ranges of basal as well as stimulated calcitonin concentrations in peripheral human plasma. Accordingly, patients in whom provocative testing was necessary for establishing the diagnosis of medullary thyroid carcinoma can now be identified by basal calcitonin measurements with assays of improved sensitivity. Not only is the concentration of thyroidal venous calcitonin not well established, but it can be influenced by a small change in the position of the indwelling catheter used to collect the sample for assay. A more practical use of selective venous catheterisation is in the evaluation of the location and extent of medullary thyroid carcinoma (Wells, Ontjes, Cooper, Hennessey, Ellis, McPherson and Sabiston, 1975) or an ectopic calcitonin-producing tumour (Goltzman *et al.*, 1974; Wells *et al.*, 1975). Knowledge of the presence of metastatic disease can greatly influence therapy.

(iv) *Pentagastrin vs calcium*—Debate has appeared in the literature regarding the relative clinical value of pentagastrin and calcium infusion in the diagnosis of medullary thyroid carcinoma (Hennessey *et al.*, 1974; Wells *et al.*, 1975). The most important point to keep in mind is that most tumours respond to both agents and that both infusion procedures can produce false negative results; i.e. some tumours respond to calcium but not gastrin and vice versa (Gagel, Melvin, Tashjian, Miller, Feldman, Wolfe, DeLellis, Cervi-Skinner and Reichlin, 1975). In general, both the sensitivity and specificity of the calcitonin assay probably is as important a factor as the choice between calcium and gastrin in provocative testing of a medullary thyroid carcinoma suspect. With a sensitive assay (of the appropriate specificity), either pentagastrin or calcium will identify the patient with tumour in most instances. Therefore, if one procedure gives negative results in a medullary thyroid carcinoma suspect, the alternative procedure should be used before excluding the diagnosis (Deftos, 1978a). There is some preliminary evidence to suggest that calcium infusion may be more valuable in diagnosing early forms of the tumour (McKenna et al., 1978). Preliminary results of combined calcium–pentagastrin infusions have not been consistent (Wells et al., 1975; McKenna et al., 1978).

(v) *Whisky*—Another agent recently introduced as a provocative test for calcitonin in Scotch whisky (Dymling, Ljungberg, Hillyard, Greenberg, Evans and MacIntyre, 1976). When 50 ml is administered orally to a patient with medullary thyroid carcinoma, there is an increase in plasma calcitonin comparable to that produced by some calcium infusions. The diagnostic increase usually occurs within 15 min. Whisky has the advantage that unlike other provocative agents it can be administered orally; it is, therefore, more convenient to administer, especially in resting patients in other than a hospital setting. However, more experience is necessary to establish the reliability of whisky and the amounts recommended for use in this procedure may produce side effects. And, as with the other provocative agents, false negative results have been observed. In this respect, it should be kept in mind that alcohol can produce diarrhoea and flushing in medullary thyroid carcinoma, perhaps stimulating the production of substances by the tumour which are responsible for these symptoms (Cohen, MacIntyre, Grahame-Smith and Walker, 1973); thus, the possibility of additional untoward whisky effects in patients with medullary thyroid carcinoma exists.

(vi) *Magnesium*—A surprising feature of the secretion of calcitonin in medullary thyroid carcinoma is the effect of magnesium (Anast et al., 1975). In experimental animals and normal humans magnesium infusion increases circulating calcitonin (Deftos, 1978a). By contrast, magnesium infusion was observed by Anast et al. (1975) to suppress the secretion of calcitonin in three patients with medullary thyroid carcinoma. These results seem to reflect a basic difference between normal and malignant C-cells in their secretory response to magnesium.

(2) *Venous catheterisation procedures.* Calcitonin assay can be used in conjunction with selective venous catheterisation to define the location as well as presence of medullary thyroid carcinoma. A gradient of hormone concentration in a specific vein may localise the tumour to the site draining

that vein. To do so, of course, requires accurate catheter placement and confirmation of location by appropriate dye studies. Several factors limit the usefulness of catheterisation procedures. Since the high incidence of bilateral medullary thyroid carcinoma dictates bilateral neck surgery in any case, the procedure has limited use in primary diagnosis. If recurrence or persistence after surgical treatment is being evaluated, this will be done in an area in which the venous pattern has been distorted by the surgery. Therefore, accurate correlation between venous sample and anatomical sites necessitates arterial studies to establish blood flow patterns. Arterial studies and considerable risk, time, and expense to venous catheterisation. Therefore, the greatest potential value of catheterisation studies is probably in the location of tumour metastases (or ectopic calcitonin production). Prior knowledge of the presence of metastatic or ectopic disease could greatly influence therapy.

(3) *Calcitonin measurements in the evaluation of therapy.* Serial measurements of plasma calcitonin in patients with calcitonin-producing tumours can be useful in monitoring the effectiveness of therapy (Deftos, McMillan, Sartiano, Abuid and Robinson, 1976). This application of the calcitonin assay pertains to surgical as well as chemotherapeutic treatment. In addition to determining the relatively acute effects of a given treatment regimen, a periodic surveillance with appropriate provocative testing can be conducted for recurrence of tumour (Silva *et al.*, 1975; Deftos *et al.*, 1976; Gagel *et al.*, 1975).

(4) *Immunochemical heterogeneity.* There are multiple immunochemical forms of calcitonin in tumours and in plasma (Deftos, Roos, Bronzert and Parthemore, 1975). Plasma or tumour of a patient with medullary thyroid carcinoma exhibit, after gel filtration chromatography, multiple peaks of immunoreactive calcitonin. The number of peaks is influenced by the size of the column, the nature of the matrix gel, and the elution conditions. Under such influences calcitonin shows dimerisation, polymerisation or hetero-aggregation (e.g. with other proteins) which may influence the elution profile. Thus, some peaks are produced by the conditions used to study them. However, some of the peaks may also reflect the biosynthesis, secretion, and metabolism of calcitonin. Since a metabolic precursor for calcitonin has been described (Roos, Okano and Deftos, 1974) and a pre-pro-calcitonin is likely to exist, these species may be represented in plasma. And, since calcitonin is metabolised at least after secretion and perhaps intracellularly, such metabolic derivatives may also be represented in plasma. Therefore, the multiple forms of immunoassayable plasma calcitonin represent a complex mixture of actual as well as operatively created species of calcitonin, its biosynthetic precursors, and its metabolites (Singer and Habener, 1974; Fig. 4).

The immunochemical profile of calcitonin may vary among certain disease
states. This variation has been suggested for the calcitonin-producing
tumours and has been established for renal disease (Lee, Parthemore and
Deftos, 1977a). In both conditions most of the elevated calcitonin is in the
form of species with a molecular weight greater than calcitonin monomer.
In renal disease the calcitonin elutes at or near the void volume of the

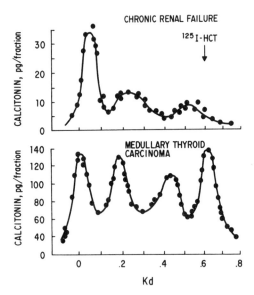

Fig. 4. Immunochemical heterogeneity of plasma calcitonin (Bio Gel P-10 chromatography).

columns used (Lee, Parthemore and Deftos, 1977b); ectopically produced
calcitonin may also elute at or near the position of the biosynthetic pre-
cursor(s) of calcitonin (Roos, *et al.*, 1974; Deftos *et al.*, 1975; Deftos *et al.*,
1977); in other malignancies, calcitonin monomer may predominate. Therefore, it may be possible to use the immunochemical pattern of plasma
calcitonin in the differential diagnosis of hypercalcitoninaemic states.
Because of this, specificity as well as sensitivity must be considered in
evaluating the diagnostic value of a calcitonin assay system (Deftos *et al.*,
1975a).
    Certain characteristics of the immunochemical heterogeneity of plasma
calcitonin are also conferred by the immunochemical specificity of the antiserum used to make hormone measurements. Antibodies of a given specificity for the calcitonin molecule will react with (and therefore detect)

preferentially species of the hormone which have that specificity. For example, if calcitonin is metabolised to a fragment which contains amino acids 24–32, an antiserum with specificity for the 24–32 region of calcitonin will detect that fragment whereas an antiserum with specificity for another region of the molecule may not. Therefore, immunochemical heterogeneity is a function of the hormone species being measured as well as the procedure used for measuring (Deftos et al., 1976).

Assessment of the immunochemical heterogeneity of plasma calcitonin can provide fundamental information about C-cell function (Roos, et al., 1977). In addition to this basic knowledge, information of clinical importance may result. The use of antisera of differing specificities for calcitonin to measure species of hormone in the same specimens of plasma can give varying results. Thus, some antisera may be more specific for identifying the presence of calcitonin precursors, such as procalcitonin, in plasma whereas others may be more specific for measuring calcitonin monomer and calcitonin metabolites. The same antiserum may give differing patterns of elevated plasma calcitonin found in eutopic versus ectopic abnormalities of calcitonin secretion (Deftos et al., 1975a). Thus, some antisera may be more specific for identifying thyroidal calcitonin whereas others may be more specific for identifying non-thyroidal calcitonin. Certain non-malignant disease states such as renal failure are characterised by elevated levels of plasma calcitonin with immunochemical profiles that are distinctly different from that seen in, for example, medullary thyroid carcinoma. Perhaps the most dramatic clinical implication of calcitonin heterogeneity will be for screening patients for the early diagnosis of medullary thyroid carcinoma or other calcitonin-producing tumours. Some assay procedures may identify better than other assay systems the slightly increased basal concentrations of calcitonin which occur in early medullary thyroid carcinoma. Furthermore, different provocative agents may stimulate the secretion (or release) of different species of calcitonin (Silva, Snider, Becker and Moore, 1977; Heath and Sizemore, 1975). Thus, the optimal diagnostic combination may depend on the correct provocative test for a given assay system and the correct assay system for a given provocative test (Deftos, 1978; Hennessey et al., 1974; Rude and Singer, 1977; Silva et al., 1977; Heath and Sizemore, 1975).

(g) Treatment

Surgery is the treatment of choice for medullary thyroid carcinoma. The surgery must be tailored to each individual patient (Hill et al., 1973). Optimal treatment is afforded by an experienced neck surgeon since many decisions regarding the procedure have to be made during surgery. In tumour confined to the thyroid gland, total thyroidectomy should be performed. This procedure is advocated even if there is apparent involvement of only one lobe, since involvement of the other lobe is so likely. This is especially true in familial medullary thyroid carcinoma, but bilateral tumours occur often enough in sporadic cases to warrant total thyroidectomy. When even a rim of apparently normal thyroid tissue is left behind, the malignancy is likely to recur locally or appear at a metastatic site (Keiser et al., 1973).

Surgical treatment should be aggressive if there is regional lymph node involvement. Since the tumour can behave in an indolent manner, removal of regional lymphatics may retard the complications of locally invasive tumour. Therefore, the surgeon should be prepared to remove as many lymph nodes as possible. To do so, a central dissection of lymph nodes may be indicated (Hill, et al., 1973); neck dissection may be performed if the lateral cervical nodes are involved. The neck dissection may be radical or a modified radical procedure (Nathaniels, Nathaniels and Wang, 1970; Kaplan, 1973). The sternum may be split for more extensive node removal if indicated by the findings at surgery (Block, Horn, Miller, Barrett and Brush, 1967; Block, Xavier and Brush, 1975).

Although ^{131}I and suppressive doses of T_4 have been reported to be useful in some patients (Didolkar and Moore, 1974), this form of treatment generally cannot be recommended on either clinical or theoretical grounds. The C-cells do not concentrate iodine as do the follicular cells of the thyroid and the secretory activity of the tumour does not respond to either T_4 or TSH (Melvin et al., 1972). Chemotherapy has not been evaluated extensively in the treatment of medullary thyroid carcinoma since surgery is beneficial in a majority of treatable patients. However, chemotherapy must be considered in patients with metastatic disease and recurrent disease after optimal surgical treatment. In such instances, adriamycin alone or in combination with other agents may be useful (Gottlieb and Hill, 1975).

2. Multiple Endocrine Neoplasia (MEN)

Medullary thyroid carcinoma occurs in association with phaeochromocytomas, mucosal neuromas, and hyperparathyroidism. As such, this thyroid tumour is part of a MEN syndrome that can be distinguished from MEN, Type I (Steiner, Goodman and Powers, 1968) which is associated with pancreatic islet cell and pituitary adenomata and hyperparathyroidism. When the thyroid tumour occurs with these other endocrine tumours, two distinct patterns can be defined. One of them, MEN Type II (or IIa), includes medullary thyroid carcinoma, phaeochromocytomas, and hyperparathyroidism. The other, MEN Type III (or IIb), includes medullary thyroid carcinoma, phaeochromocytomas, and mucosal neuromas. (These tumours also called ganglioneuromas to indicate the presence of ganglion cells, but they probably are most accurately referred to as neurogangliomas, since neural tissue predominates.) Also, these patients can have features of Marfan's disease (Table 2).

There is an embryological as well as a genetic basis for the association of medullary thyroid carcinoma with these other tumours. The cells of medullary thyroid carcinoma, pheochromocytomas, and the neurogangliomas are all of neural crest origin. The associated hyperparathyroidism does not fit into this unitary concept of embryogenesis, since parathyroid cells are not classically considered to be of neural crest origin, although, Pearse and Takor (1976) have suggested such an origin. An alternative explanation to the hyperparathyroidism is a functional relationship between it and medullary thyroid carcinoma. According to this hypothesis, the abnormal concentrations of calcitonin produce hyperparathyroidism that is secondary to the hypocalcaemic actions of the calcitonin. Although this type of functional relationship between the neoplasias may exist, the most convincing evidence supports a genetic relationship between medullary thyroid carcinoma and hyperparathyroidism (Melvin, Tashjian and Miller, 1971).

These associations of medullary thyroid carcinoma with other tumours have important clinical consequences. When they occur, the mucosal neurogangliomas may be the first manifestations of the MEN. These lesions thus provide an early warning of the presence of two potentially lethal tumours—medullary thyroid carcinoma and pheochromocytoma. Additionally, the existence of pheochromocytoma or medullary thyroid carcinoma should suggest the possible coexistence of the other tumour. Hyperparathyroidism can be similarly regarded. It is, therefore, important for physicians to recognise that the presence of medullary thyroid carcinoma in their patients should stimulate a search for other tumours in the patient and his family. If diagnosed early, all of the serious features of MEN are treatable and even curable.

(a) Phaeochromacytoma

(1) History. Sipple (1961) presented evidence that supported the association between phaeochromocytoma and thyroid tumour. He reported the case of a 33-yr-old male with bilateral phaeochromocytoma and a poorly differentiated, invasive thyroid tumour thought to be a follicular adenocarcinoma. Sipple reviewed the literature and presented five other cases with phaeochromocytoma and thyroid tumour. The phaeochromocytomas were bilateral in four of the cases and the thyroid tumours were variously described as follicular adenocarcinoma, papillary adenocarcinoma, adenocarcinoma and anaplastic carcinoma.

In the early 1960's there were also additional case reports of the simultaneous occurrence of a phaeochromocytomas and medullary thyroid carcinoma (reviewed in Deftos, 1978). Williams (1967) reported two cases of phaeochromocytomas and thyroid cancer and reviewed 15 others. He was able to establish that at least 11 of the total of 17 cases of thyroid tumour actually were medullary thyroid carcinoma. In the same year Schimke and Hartmann (1965) also reviewed the previous reports of the simultaneous occurrence of a phaeochromocytoma and medullary thyroid carcinoma and added studies of their own of two families in which these two tumours occurred simultaneously in five patients. Thus, the association between phaeochromocytomas and medullary thyroid carcinoma has been well established in previous and recent literature (Deftos, 1978a).

(2) *Incidence.* Since different reports have emphasised different aspects of the MEN, it is difficult to determine how commonly phaeochromocytomas occur in association with medullary thyroid carcinoma. It has become apparent that the incidence of phaeochromocytomas is much higher than previously appreciated. In MEN III, the incidence of phaeochromocytomas usually approaches 50% (Khairi, Dexter, Burzynski and Johnston, 1975) whereas in the MEN II syndrome it usually is less than 20% (Hill *et al.*, 1973). However, it is likely that these are underestimations, especially in MEN Type III, since most recent studies suggest a much higher incidence (Deftos, 1978a).

Phaeochromocytomas occurring in association with medullary thyroid carcinoma have several distinct features. Bilateral and multifocal phaeochromocytomas are very common and have an incidence of greater than 70%. This contrasts with a bilateral incidence of usually less than 10% for sporadic phaeochromocytomas. Phaeochromocytomas are much more likely to occur in patients with familial rather than sporadic medullary thyroid carcinoma (Steiner *et al.*, 1968; Khairi, *et al.*, 1975). When phaeochromocytomas and medullary thyroid carcinoma occur together in the same patient, the medullary thyroid carcinoma is likely to be diagnosed first (Hill *et al.*, 1973; Steiner *et al.*, 1968; Khairi, *et al.*, 1975). The thyroid tumour may antedate the phaeochromocytomas by as much as 21 years (Nathaniels *et al.*, 1970). Many instances have been reported in which a phaeochromocytoma did not become clinically manifest until years after surgical removal of a medullary thyroid carcinoma; when this occurs, the medullary thyroid carcinoma may not be recognised as part of MEN. Furthermore, a second phaeochromocytoma may become manifest after removal of the first (Hill *et al.*, 1973). This sequence of events results in a greater incidence of phaeochromocytomas in older patients with medullary thyroid carcinoma. Less often, the thyroid and adrenal tumour may be discovered contemporaneously and, in some cases, phaeochromocytomas may be diagnosed before medullary thyroid carcinoma. If hyperparathyroidism also exists, it, too, is likely to antedate phaeochromocytoma (Hill *et al.*, 1973; Steiner *et al.*, 1968; and Khairi *et al.*, 1975).

(*3*) *Adrenal medullary hyperplasia.* Just as C-cell hyperplasia may be a predecessor of medullary thyroid carcinoma, so may adrenal medullary hyperplasia be a predecessor of the phaeochromocytomas seen with medullary thyroid carcinoma (Ljungberg, 1972; Carney, Sizemore and Tyce, 1975). Although cases of adrenal medullary hyperplasia had been reported in the literature, none of them were patients with medullary thyroid carcinoma (Bialestock, 1961; Drukker, Formijne and Schoot, 1957; Montalbano, Baronofsky and Ball, 1962: Sherwin, 1964; Visser and Axt, 1975). DeLellis, Wolfe, Gagel, Feldman, Miller, Gang and Reichlin (1976) described the adrenal glands of 10 patients from a large kindred with familial medullary thyroid carcinoma. There is an increase in the medullary volume of adrenal glands when compared to controls. The increase in medullary mass results from diffuse and/or multifocal proliferation of adrenal medullary cells, primarily those found within the head and body of the glands. The multifocal proliferation can give an adenomatous appearance (Ljungberg, 1972). There is hypertrophy as well as hyperplasia of the cells and they show increased mutotic activity and increased total catecholamine content (Carney *et al.*, 1975). In addition, the ratio of adrenal to noradrenaline was increased in the tumour (DeLellis *et al.*, 1976). These findings suggest that a sequence of events similar to those postulated for medullary thyroid carcinoma and hyperparathyroidism take place in the development of phaeochromocytomas —hypertrophy develops into hyperplasia; multifocal hyperplasia develops into nodularity; neoplastic transformation to phaeochromocytoma is the final stage of the sequence in most cancers, but malignancy can also be seen.

(*b*) *Hyperparathyroidism*

(*1*) *History.* Cushman (1962) described the simultaneous occurrence of a parathyroid adenoma in a patient with medullary thyroid carcinoma who also had a phaeochromocytoma. Additional reports of the association of hyperparathyroidism and medullary thyroid carcinoma appeared and the two additional cases of Steiner *et al.* (1968) brought the literature total to 13 at that time (Steiner *et al.*, 1968). In the intervening years, other reports have clearly established the association between medullary thyroid carcinoma and hyperparathyroidism.

(*2*) *Incidence.* As with phaeochromocytomas, it is difficult to establish the exact incidence of hyperparathyroidism in patients with medullary thyroid carcinoma. The most recent literature suggests that hyperplasia is more common than adenoma. Melvin *et al.* (1972) made the diagnosis of hyperparathyroidism in 10 of 12 patients of a kindred with medullary thyroid carcinoma whereas Hill *et al.* (1973) could establish the diagnosis of hyper-parathyroidism in only two of 73 patients with medullary thyroid carcinoma. Additional series record an intermediate incidence. There are several possible explanations for this disparity. There is diagreement regarding the criteria necessary to distinguish between a normal and abnormal parathyroid gland and the criteria to classify parathyroid abnormalities (Block *et al.*, 1975). Another explanation for the reported incidence of hyperparathyroidism in medullary thyroid carcinoma is the developing appreciation of the differing incidence of hyperparathyroidism in MEN II and MEN III. At this time the concurrence of hyperparathyroidism and medullary thyroid carcinoma is well established and, although it cannot be quantitated, the presence of one tumour should always make the presence of the other suspect.

(3) *Pathology.* When Steiner *et al.* (1968) reviewed the literature of MEN, they recorded 10 cases with parathyroid adenoma and three cases with para-thyroid hyperplasia. In later reports, the incidence of parathyroid hyperplasia in patients with medullary thyroid carcinoma has increased and has even approached 100% (Melvin, Miller and Tashjian, 1971; Keiser *et al.*, 1973). This controversy regarding parathyroid pathology in patients with medullary thyroid carcinoma is only reflective of the general difficulties in this area of histological diagnosis (Potts and Deftos, 1969). There are no standardised histology criteria to distinguish the hyperfunctioning parathyroid gland from normal. In fact, it has even been suggested that light microscopy may be inadequate for the purpose and that EM studies might be necessary, at least in some cases (Birge, Haddad, Teitlebaum and Avioli, 1970). There is, additionally, a lack of uniform criteria to distinguish between parathyroid hyperplasia and parathyroid adenoma (Keiser *et al.*, 1973; Block *et al.*, 1975).

(4) *Relationship between medullary thyroid carcinoma and hyperpara-thyroidism.* Two theories prevail regarding the link between hyperpara-thyroidism and medullary thyroid carcinoma. One possibility is that the hyperparathyroidism is a functional disorder representing a compensatory response of the parathyroid glands to a hypocalcemic effect of the calcitonin. This view does have some additional clinical and experimental support. There are also, however, equally convincing data that the hyperparathy-roidism is an inherited rather than functional component of medullary thyroid carcinoma. The high incidence of hyperparathyroidism in patients with medullary thyroid carcinoma is just as compatible with this view as with the previously discussed functional hypothesis. The genetic view would be more attractive if the embryologic origin of the parathyroid gland was neural crest, as is the embryologic origin of the other prominent features of the syndrome—phaeochromocytoma, medullary thyroid carcinoma, and mucosal neuromas. Most evidence suggests that the parathyroid glands are

of endodermal origin, arising from the third and fourth branchial pouches. However, there are data to suggest that the parathyroid glands may, indeed, be of neutral crest origin (Pearse and Takor, 1976). If this is confirmed, it would provide a more unifying genetic basis for MEN II and III.

(c) Multiple mucosal neuromas (MMN)

(1) History. Williams and Pollock (1966) described two patients with medullary thyroid carcinoma and phaeochromocytomas who had neuromas involving the mucous membrane of the lips, tongue, and eyes. Schimke, Hartmann, Prout and Rimoin (1968) described three additional patients with this syndrome and recorded the presence of megacolon in each patient. In one patient rectal biopsy was consistent with ganglioneuromatosis of the submucous and myenteric plexuses. In the same year Gorlin, Sedano, Vickers and Cervenka (1968) re-emphasised the association between multiple mucosal neuromas, phaeochromocytomas, and medullary thyroid carcinoma by reviewing 17 published cases. In several patients the neuromas were either congenital or noticed within the first few years of life, thus becoming manifest before the other features of the syndrome. These authors also commented on the presence of a Marfanoid habitus, intestinal ganglioneuromatosis and medullated corneal nerve fibres in this group of patients and thus described the features of this syndrome as it is appreciated currently—medullary thyroid carcinoma, phaeochromocytomas, diffuse neurogangliomatosis involving the mucosa of the gastrointestinal tract, and a Marfanoid habitus (Khairi et al., 1975).

(2) Mucosal neuromas. The most consistent component of this syndrome is the presence of neuromas with a centrofacial distribution. The most common location of neuromas is in the oral cavity. The most prominent microscopic feature of the neuromas is an increase in the size and number of nerves. The nerves are tortuous and highly branched and often surrounded by a thickened perineurium. Both medullated and unmedullated fibres are involved. Ganglion cells and connective tissue may be present, but the latter often is not prominent. This latter feature usually distinguishes these neuromas from the neurofibromas of von Recklinghausen's neurofibromatosis.

Oral mucosal neuromas are found most commonly on the lips, tongue, and buccal mucosa and are usually the first components of the syndrome to appear. Almost invariably they are present by the first decade and can even be present at birth (Khairi et al., 1975). The mucosal neuromas along with the subsequently described ocular findings give the patients a very characteristic facial appearance. Because of this there is striking similarity in appearance of different subjects with the syndrome even though they may be unrelated and of the opposite sex.

(3) *Ocular findings.* Mucosal neuromas can be present in the eyelids, conjunctiva and cornea. The tarsal neuromas result in thickened eyelids and retracted eyelashes, which give the eye a hooded, sleepy look. In addition to the neuromas, a variety of other ocular abnormalities has been reported. The medullated corneal nerves are thickened and traverse the cornea and anastomose in the pupillary area. These hypertrophied nerve fibres are seen readily with the slit lamp but occasionally may be evident on funduscopic examination (Khairi *et al.*, 1975).

(4) *Gastro-intestinal abnormalities.* Gastro-intestinal abnormalities are prominent features of MEN (Hill *et al.*, 1973; Carney *et al.*, 1976). Diarrhoea is one of the most common symptoms of affected patients (Hill *et al.*, 1973). Its aetiology is multifactorial. The diarrhoea seen in these patients often can be ascribed to one of the many substances produced by medullary thyroid carcinoma (Section B.1(a)). Most of these agents have been variably described to increase either directly or indirectly gastro-intestinal motility. Some of the gastro-intestinal symptoms of diarrhoea and constipation additionally can be ascribed to those gastro-intestinal abnormalities that are part of the mucosal neuroma syndrome. The most common of these is gastro-intestinal ganglioneuromatosis. The lesions of gastro-intestinal ganglioneuromatosis are reminiscent of those that occur in the facial mucosal neuromas. In fact, all cases of diffuse gastro-intestinal ganglioneuromatosis occur in association with mucosal neuromas, and isolated intestinal ganglio-neuromatosis is not associated with medullary thyroid carcinoma (Carney *et al.*, 1976). The ganglioneuromatosis is best studied in the small and large intestine but has also been observed in the oesophagus and stomach (Carney *et al.*, 1976). There is a proliferation of the neural elements of the myenteric and submucosal plexuses. The anatomic lesions can be associated with the functional problems of swallowing difficulties, megacolon, diarrhoea, and constipation, respectively (Khairi *et al.*, 1975). It is likely that the neurological lesions play some role in these functional GI abnormalities. Another common gastro-intestinal finding which may contribute to the diarrhoea is the presence of diverticulosis.

(5) *Marfanoid habitus.* A Marfanoid habitus is seen commonly in the MMN syndrome (Khairi *et al.*, 1975). The Marfanoid habitus refers to a tall, slender body with an abnormal upper to lower body segment ratio and poor muscle development. The extremities are thin and long and there may be lax joints and hypotonic muscles. Associated with the Marfanoid habitus may be dorsal kyphosis, pectus excavatum, pectus carinaturm, pes cavus and a high-arched palate. In contrast to true Marfan's syndrome no patients with MMN have been reported who have aortic abnormalities, ectopic lentis, homocystinuria, or mucopolysaccharide abnormalities.

C. DIFFERENTIAL DIAGNOSIS OF
HYPERCALCITONINAEMIA (see Table 1)

1. Hypercalcitoninaemia and Non-thyroidal Cancer

It is now well established that a wide variety of cancers are associated with an elevated plasma level of immunoassayable calcitonin (Coombes et al., 1974; Milhaud, Calmette, Taboulet, Julleinne and Moukhtar, 1974; Silva, Becker, Primack, Doppman and Snider, 1974; David, Cohn and Anast, 1975; Ellison, Woodhouse, Hillyard, Dowsett, Coombes, Gilby, Greenberg and Neville, 1975; Hillyard, Coombes, Greenberg and MacIntyre, 1975; Silva et al., 1975; Hillyard, Coombes, Greenberg, Galante and MacIntyre, 1976; Silva and Becker, 1976a; Silva, Becker, Primack, Doppman and Snider, 1976b; Deftos, 1978). Several hypotheses have been advanced to explain these associations:

(a) Ectopic calcitonin production

(1) Calcitonin production by the tumour. This hypothesis is usually supported only by the concurrence of hypercalcitoninemia and malignancy (Coombes et al., 1974; Milhaud et al., 1974; Silva et al., 1974; Hillyard et al., 1975; Hillyard et al., 1976; Silva et al., 1976). Such an association obviously does not establish causality and it leaves open many explanations other than calcitonin production by the tumour. However, it seems fairly certain that some tumours do produce calcitonin even when strict criteria are applied, such as demonstration of calcitonin in the tumour by assay and immuno-histology, demonstration of a calcitonin gradient across the vascular bed of the tumour *in situ*, and demonstration *in vitro* of calcitonin biosynthesis and secretion by the tumour (Coombes et al., 1974; Milhaud et al., 1974; Silva et al., 1974; David et al., 1975; Ellison et al., 1975; Hillyard et al., 1975; Hillyard et al., 1976; Silva et al., 1976a; Silva et al., 1976b).

(2) Production of calcitonin-related substances by the tumour. There is considerable evidence that hormone-secreting tumours may produce biological variants of their "native" hormones. For example, insulinomas seem to produce abnormal amounts of pro-insulin, oat-cell carcinoma of the lung may produce abnormal ACTH fragments, and some cancers may produce immunochemically altered forms of PTH (Deftos, Keutmann, Niall, Tregear, Habener, Murray, Powell and Potts, 1971; Riggs, Arnaud, Reynolds and Smith, 1971; Abe, Adachi, Miyakawa, Tanaka, Yamaguchi, Tanaka, Kameya and Shimosato, 1977; Himsworth, Bloomfield, Coombes, Ellison, Gilkes, Lowry, Setchell, Slavin and Rees, 1977). It is, therefore, possible that calcitonin-producing tumours may produce abnormal amounts

of calcitonin precursors, such as pro- (or pre-) calcitonin or calcitonin peptides. There is, in fact, a possible conceptual framework for this hypothesis. Many of the tumours that ectopically secrete calcitonin are of neural crest origin and therefore embryologically related (Weichert, 1970; Singer and Habener, 1974; Hazard, 1977; Tischler, Dichter, Biales and Green, 1977; Deftos, 1978a) to each other. (This, of course, raises questions about the distinction between eutopic and ectopic calcitonin production.) Calcitonin and its precursor molecules may be part of a large "neural crest" molecule and immunoreactive calcitonin has been demonstrated in the pituitary gland of several species (Deftos et al., 1978; Deftos, Catherwood, Bone, Parthemore, Minick and Guillemin, 1978).

(b) Eutopic (thyroidal) calcitonin production

(1) Tumour-associated hypercalcaemia. An acute increase in blood calcium has long been known to be a potent calcitonin secretagogue (Potts and Deftos, 1969). Recent studies indicate that chronic hypercalcaemia can also stimulate thyroidal calcitonin secretion in humans (Lee et al., 1977; Pathemore et al., 1977). Since a variety of malignant disorders is associated with hypercalcaemia, hypercalcaemia, per se, may account for some of the instances of the hypercalcitoninemia of malignancy (Deftos, 1978a).

(2) Tumour-associated calcitonin secretagogue. This intriguing hypothesis is supported by the observation that in patients with some tumours (not associated with hypercalcaemia), the thyroid gland seems to be the source of the elevated plasma calcitonin (Silva et al., 1975). Several candidates for such a secretagogue exist. They include prostaglandins which are produced by a variety of tumours and which can stimulate calcitonin secretion and gastrin which can also be an ectopic product of tumours and which can stimulate calcitonin secretion (Hennessey, Gray, Cooper and Ontjes, 1973; Seyberth, Segre, Morgan, Sweetman, Potts and Oates, 1975; Roos and Deftos, 1976). Other as-yet-unidentified calcitonin secretagogues would have to be considered in this hypothesis.

(3) Tumour metastases to bone. This could result from hypercalcaemia due to the metastases of tumour to bone and/or the production by the tumour of a bone-resorbing agent such as PTH, prostaglandin, a vitamin D-like sterol, or osteocyte activating factor (OAF) (Gordan, Cantino, Erhardt, Hansen and Lubich, 1966; Powell, Singer, Murray, Minkin and Potts, 1973; Deftos and Neer, 1974; Mundy, Raisz, Cooper, Schechter and Salmon, 1974; Seyberth et al., 1975). An equally interesting possibility is the release of a calcitonin secretagogue from bone cells perturbed by either the tumour or by a bone resorptive product of the tumour (Deftos et al., 1975; Deftos, 1978). This would imply that bone cells had the capacity to "protect"

themselves against increased bone resorption by stimulating the secretion of calcitonin, which would act to inhibit the bone resorption (Deftos, 1977; Deftos, Parthemore and Bone, 1977). If so, a new regulatory axis between bone cells and calcitonin, and perhaps other calcaemic hormones, might be uncovered. This would have important implications for metastatic bone disease (Deftos, 1978).

(c) Abnormal metabolism of endogenous calcitonin

This may result from some direct metabolic effect of the tumour itself or from some general metabolic consequence of the malignant state. Although it is unlikely that this mechanism by itself could lead to the elevations of plasma calcitonin seen in malignancy, it may contribute to the thyroidal or tumoural hypercalcitoninaemia and to calcitonin heterogeneity (Roos et al., 1978).

(d) Artifactural elevations in plasma calcitonin

Although it is now established that true hypercalcitoninaemia occurs in a variety of cancers, in some patients the apparent hypercalcitoninaemia may be due to a non-specific effect of the malignant state on calcitonin measurement (Deftos, 1971; Deftos et al., 1971; David et al., 1975). Possible examples of this would include the presence of either abnormal immunoglobulins or other proteins (especially in myelomas and lymphomas) which would interfere with the immunology of the radioimmunoassay or the presence of enzymes which might affect in a non-specific manner either plasma calcitonin or the labelled calcitonin or antibody used in the RIA (David et al., 1975; Straus and Yalow, 1976; Baylin, Bailey, Hsu and Foster, 1977; Rossier, Bayon, Vargo, Ling, Guillemin and Bloom, 1977; Deftos and O'Riordan, 1978).

Our studies and those of others indicate that many of these hypotheses are plausible in at least some instances of the hypercalcitoninaemia of malignancy. These studies have demonstrated that non-thyroidal malignancies produce calcitonin (Coombes et al., 1974; Milhaud et al., 1974; Baylin, 1975; Hillyard et al., 1975; Deftos et al., 1976; Hillyard et al., 1976; Silva et al., 1976a), that tumour-associated hypercalcaemia increases plasma calcitonin (Deftos, 1977; Lee et al., 1977; Deftos, 1978), that tumour-associated factors can act as calcitonin secretagogues (Seyberth et al., 1975; Deftos, 1978b), that calcitonin associated with malignancy exists in "abnormal" forms (Parthemore, Roos and Deftos, 1975; Deftos et al., 1976; Silva et al., 1976a; Silva et al., 1976b; Roos et al., 1977), and that non-specific factors in malignant disease can influence calcitonin assays (Deftos, 1971; Deftos et al., 1971; Riggs et al., 1971). Thus, there are several hypotheses which can be tested regarding the hypercalcitoninaemia of malignancy. The evaluation of these hypotheses could have considerable practical importance as well as potential functional importance. The practical importance will result from the development of improved procedures for the diagnosis and management of the patient with calcitonin-associated cancer. There are at least two possible conceptual hypotheses for the hypercalcitoninemia of malignancy:

(i) that ectopic calcitonin production by some tumours reflects their common embryological origin (neural crest) and their primitive hormonal precursors (Lips, van der Sluys Veer, van der Donk, van Dam and Hackeng, 1978);

(ii) that eutopic (thyroidal) hypercalcitoninemia in malignancy is due to the stimulation of CT secretion by bone cells which have been perturbed (resorbed) by the malignancy (Deftos, 1978).

2. Other Hypercalcitoninaemic States

Several other hypercalcitoninemic states have been described that should be considered in evaluating the patient with possible medullary thyroid carcinoma. Hypercalcitoninemia, found commonly in renal disease (Heynen and Franchimont, 1974; Lee et al., 1977), is probably due to abnormal metabolism as well as secretion of the hormone. Less well-established is the increased plasma calcitonin variably reported in pregnancy and pancreatitis (Samaan et al., 1973; Canale and Donabedian, 1975; Weir, Lesser, Drop, Fischer and Warshaw, 1975). These three conditions are not likely to be confused with medullary thyroid carcinoma or other malignancies.

(a) Hypercalcaemia

Acutely induced hypercalcaemia is a well-documented stimulus for calcitonin secretion (Clark et al., 1969; Tashjian et al., 1970; Deftos, 1971a; Deftos et al., 1971b, c, 1978). It is now becoming evident that chronic hypercalcaemic and hypercalciuric states may also be associated with increased calcitonin secretion (Lee et al., 1977; Parthemore, 1977; Parthemore et al., 1977). This presumably represents a homeostatic response of the C-cells to defend against the challenge to calcium homeostasis. Provocative testing of calcitonin secretion may be necessary to demonstrate fully the hypersecretory state of calcitonin which exists in chronic hypercalcaemic states such as primary hyperparathyroidism (Silva et al., 1974; Parthemore, 1977; Parthemore et al., 1977). It is of note that females with primary hyperparathyroidism, like normal females, have less calcitonin reserve than males (Parthemore et al., 1975).

(b) Renal disease

Elevated levels of plasma calcitonin have been observed in both clinical
and experimental forms of renal disease (Kanis, Earnshaw, Heynen, Russell
and Woods, 1977; Lee *et al.*, 1977a, b). The immunochemical form of calcitonin in renal disease is quite characteristic. It has not been established
if this represents an abnormality of calcitonin secretion, calcitonin metabolism, or a combination of the two. The calcitonin abnormality may play
some role in the pathogenesis of renal osteodystrophy. The greatest
elevations, perhaps compensatory to the increased bone resorption, are
reported to occur in patients with lesser bone disease (Kanis *et al.*, 1977).
Although the absolute levels of plasma calcitonin are elevated, there is
decreased calcitonin reserve in experimental forms of renal disease and the
metabolism of the hormone is abnormal (Lee *et al.*, 1977a) and there may be
decreased calcitonin responsiveness (Lee *et al.*, 1977b). Thus, neither the
biological or pathophysiological significance of the calcitonin abnormalities
of renal disease have been established (Fig. 4).

(c) Bone disease

Abnormalities in calcitonin secretion may occur in several bone diseases.
Hormone concentrations in renal osteodystrophy have been discussed
above. The secretion of calcitonin is abnormal in one hyperostotic state,
pycnodysostosis, and may also be abnormal in others (Baker, Wallach
and Tashjian, 1973; see Table 1). The decreased calcitonin reserve in females
may play some role in the greater severity of osteitis fibrosa cystica in women
with primary hyperparathyroidism and in the pathogenesis of osteoporosis
(Milhaud *et al.*, 1974; Heath and Sizemore, 1977; Pathemore, 1977; Parthemore *et al.*, 1977).

(d) Pancreatitis

Glucagon-stimulated calcitonin secretion has been implicated in the pathogenesis of the hypocalcaemia of pancreatitis. Although this view is supported
by some radioimmunoassay studies, others cannot demonstrate any calcitonin abnormalities in pancreatitis (Canale and Donabedian, 1975;
Robertson, Moore, Switz, Sizemore and Estep, 1976). It is intriguing to
speculate that the pancreas or adjacent gastro-intestinal cells may be a
source of calcitonin-like activity (Takaoka, Takamori, Ichinose, Schikaya,
Igawa, Kikutani and Yamamoto, 1969; Sowa, Appert and Howard, 1977).
Plasma artifacts affecting radioimmunoassay performance may be exaggerated in pancreatitis and this problem must be overcome before an accurate

assessment can be made of calcitonin secretion in pancreatitis (Straus and Yallow, 1976; Deftos, 1978; Deftos and O'Riordan, 1978).

D. THERAPEUTIC APPLICATIONS OF CALCITONIN

Calcitonin has been used as an effective therapeutic agent in several disease states (Singer, 1975). The therapeutic applications of calcitonin utilise its major biological actions to inhibit bone resorption and to lower blood calcium. Three forms of calcitonin have been used—porcine, salmon, and human. Porcine calcitonin has been most widely used in continental Europe, human calcitonin in England, and salmon calcitonin in the United States. Salmon calcitonin has the advantage of being the most potent form of the hormone. Unlike human calcitonin, it is a foreign protein and since it must be given parenterally, it can produce antibodies. These antibodies may neutralise the biological effect of the hormone (Bijvoet, van der Sluys Veer and Jansen, 1968; Woodhouse, Bordier, Fisher, Joplin, Reiner, Kalu, Foster and MacIntyre, 1971; DeRose, Singer, Avramides, Flores, Dziadiw, Baker and Wallach, 1974; Greenberg, Doyle, Fisher, Hillyard, Joplin, Pennock and MacIntyre, 1974; Singer, 1975).

1. Bone Diseases

(a) Paget's disease

Calcitonin, which acts to inhibit bone resorption, has been an effective agent in treating patients with Paget's disease (Bijvoet et al., 1968). The recommended parenteral dose of calcitonin is 100 u/day. Smaller doses may be effective also (Avramides, Flores, DeRose and Wallach, 1975). The drug results in improvement of the clinical and biochemical parameters of the disease. Bone pain usually is improved or relieved within several weeks of starting therapy, but this effect has not been evaluated in a double-blind study. Skin temperature can be decreased toward normal and there can be a dramatic improvement in neurological complications of the illness. If cardiac output is elevated as a complication of Paget's disease, it can be returned toward normal by calcitonin (Singer, 1975). The biochemical abnormalities of Paget's disease are also improved by the administration of calcitonin. Elevated plasma and urinary hydroxyproline levels fall within hours of administration of calcitonin, reflecting inhibition by the hormone of osteoclast activity. Plasma alkaline phosphatase also drops, but this effect takes several days (Avramides, Baker and Wallach, 1974; Singer, 1975). The bio-chemical parameters may return to normal in patients with mild Paget's disease. However, if they are markedly elevated, alkaline phosphatase and hydroxyproline may decline only to a plateau above normal levels. Despite this failure to reverse completely the biochemical abnormalities, there can be continued improvement in the X-rays and the histology of bone. Therefore, in some patients, the persistence of elevated alkaline phosphatase and hydroxyproline actually may be associated with bone healing (DeRose et al., 1974; Greenberg et al., 1974). However, it is clear that some patients with Paget's disease become resistant to the therapeutic effects of the hormone. This refractoriness may or may not be associated with the development of antibodies to the calcitonin (Haddad and Caldwell, 1972; Singer, Aldred, Neer, Krane, Potts and Bloch, 1972). An advantage of calcitonin over other forms of treatment for Paget's disease is relative freedom from side-effects. In addition to its effectiveness, calcitonin is the least toxic agent for the treat-ment of Paget's disease (Singer and Habener, 1974). Nausea may occur after administration of the drug but is usually mild and transient (Singer and Habener, 1974).

Mithramycin and the diphosphonates, the former on an investigational basis, are available for the treatment of Paget's disease. Their use has been discussed in several reviews (Ryan, Schwartz and Perlia, 1969; Smith. Russell and Bishop, 1971; Singer and Habener, 1974).

(b) Osteopenic states

Calcitonin has been used in the treatment of patients with a variety of osteopenic states including generalised and localised osteoporosis and osteogenesis imperfecta. Results have been variable and further evaluation is necessary (Milhaud, Talbot and Coutris, 1975; Liskova, 1976; August, Shapiro and Hung, 1977; Martin, 1978).

2. Hypercalcaemic States

Treatment of the patient with hypercalcaemia utilises another of the biolo-gical actions of calcitonin, the lowering of blood calcium. Calcitonin mani-fests its hypocalcaemic effect primarily by inhibiting bone resorption; it is also weakly calciuretic (Bijvoet et al., 1968; Deftos and Neer, 1974). Thus, at least acutely, calcitonin commonly is effective in producing a rapid decrease of 1–2 mg/100 ml (0·25—0·5 mmol/l) in blood calcium in the hypercalcaemic patient. In some patients the results can be more dramatic but in others there may be little effect. A primary advantage of calcitonin in treating hypercalcaemia is its ease of administration and its freedom from toxicity. Calcitonin is especially useful in the treatment of the hypercalcaemic patient who is also hyperphosphatemic, since the hormone can lower the concentration of both minerals (Deftos and Neer, 1974).

ACKNOWLEDGEMENTS

This work was supported by the American Cancer Society, the Veterans Administration, the National Institutes of Health, and CIBA–GEIGY. Susan Murphy provided secretarial assistance.

REFERENCES

Abe, K., Adachi, I., Miyakawa, S., Tanaka, M., Yamaguchi, K., Tanaka, N., Kameya, T. and Shimosato, T. (1977). *Cancer Res.* 37, 4190.

Abdullahi, S. E., Arrigoni-Martelli, E., Gramm, E., Franco, L. and Velo, G. P. (1977). *Ag. Act.* 7, 488.

Adachi, I., Abe, K., Tanaka, M., Miyakawa, S. and Kumaoka, S. (1974). *Endocr. jap.* 27, 317.

Anast, C. S. (1978). "Proceedings of the Sixth Parathyroid Conference." Excerpta Medica, Amsterdam.

Anast, C. S., David, L., Winnacker, J., Glass, R., Baskin, W., Brubaker, L. and Burns, T. (1975). *J. clin. Invest.* 56, 1615.

Ardaillou, R. (1975). *Nephron.* 15, 250.

August, G. P., Shapiro, J. and Hung, W. (1977). *J. Pediatr.* 91, 1001.

Avramides, A., Baker, R. K. and Wallach, S. (1974). *Metabolism,* 23, 1037.

Avramides, A., Flores, A., DeRose, J. and Wallach, S. (1975). *Br. med. J.* 3, 632.

Baber, E. C. (1876). *Phil. Trans. R. Soc. Lond.* 166, 557.

Barlet, J. P. and Garel, J. M. (1976). *J. Endocr.* 70, 151

Baker, R. K., Wallach, S. and Tashjian, A. H. (1973). *J. clin. Endocr. Metab.* 37, 46.

Bates, R. F., Bruce, J. B. and Care, A. D. (1970a). *J. Endocr.* 46, 11.

Bates, R. F., Phillippo, M. and Lawrence, C. B. (1970b). *J. Endocr.* 48, 8.

Baylin, S. B. (1975). *Hosp. Prac.* 10, 117.

Baylin, S. B., Bailey, A. L., Hsu, T. H. and Foster, G. V. (1977). *Metabolism,* 26, 1345.

Becker, H. D., Konturek, S. J., Reeder, D. D. and Thompson, J. C. (1973). *Am. J. Pathol.* 225, 277.

Bell, N. H. (1970). *J. clin. Invest.* 49, 1368.

Beskid, M. (1975). *Acta histochem.* 54, 313.

Bialestock, D. (1966). *Arch. dis. Child.* 36, 465.

Bijvoet, O. L. M., van der Sluys Veer J. and Jansen, A. P. (1968). *Lancet,* i, 876.

Bijvoet, O. L. M., van der Sluys Veer, J., de Vries, H. H. and van Koppen, A. T. J. (1971). *New Engl. J. Med.* **284**, 681.

Birge, S. J., Haddad, J., Teitlebaum, S. and Avioli, L. V. (1970). *Proc. 52nd Meet. Endocr. Soc.,* A23.

Blahos, J., Osten, J., Mertl, L., Kotas, J., Gregor, O. and Reisenauer, R. (1975). *Horm. Metab. Res.* **7**, 445.

Block, M. A., Horn, R. C., Jr., Miller, J. M., Barrett, J. L. and Brush, B. E. (1967). *Ann. Surg.* **166**, 403.

Block, M. A., Xavier, A. and Brush, B. E. (1975). *J. Am. Geriatr. Soc.* **23**, 385.

Bolman, R. M., III, Cooper, C. W., Garner, S. C., Munson, P. L. and Wells, S. A., Jr. (1977). *Endocrinology,* **100**, 1014.

Byfield, P. G. H., McLoughlin, J. L., Matthews, E. W. and MacIntyre, I. (1976). *FEBS Lett.* **65**, 242.

Canale, D. D. and Donabedian, R. K. (1975). *J. clin. Endocr. Metab.* **40**, 738.

Care, A. D., Bates, R. F. L. and Gitelman, H. J. (1970). *J. Endocr.* **48**, 1.

Carey, D., Jones, K. L., Parthemore, J. G. and Deftos, L. J. (1978). *Clin. Res.* **26**, 72A.

Carney, A. J., Sizemore, G. W. and Lovestedt, S. A. (1976). *Oral Surg.* **41**, 739.

Carney, A. J., Sizemore, G. W. and Tyce, G. M. (1975). *Mayo Clinic Proc.* **50**, 3.

Clark, M. B., Byfield, P. G. H., Boyd, G. W. and Foster, G. V. (1969). *Lancet,* ii, 74.

Clark, O. H., Rollo, D., Stroop, J., Castner, B., Rehfeld, S. J., Loken. H. F. and Deftos. L. J. (1978). *Surgery,* **83**, 626.

Cohen, S. L., MacIntyre, I., Grahame-Smith, D. and Walker, J. G. (1973). *Lancet,* 2, 1172.

Coombes, R. C., Hillyard, C., Greenberg, P. B. and MacIntyre, I. (1974). *Lancet,* 2, 164.

Copp, D. H., Camerson, E. C., Cheney, B. A., Davidson, A. G. F. and Henze, K. G. (1962). *Endocrinology,* **70**, 638.

Copp, D. H., Cockroft, D. W. and Kueh, Y. (1977). *Science,* **158**, 924.

Cunliffe, W. J., Black, M. M., Hall, R., Johnston, I. D. A., Hudgson, P., Shuster, S., Gudmundsson, T. V., Joplin, G. F., Williams, E. D., Woodhouse, N. J. Y., Galante, L. and MacIntyre, I. (1968). *Lancet.* ii, 63.

Cushman, P., Jr. (1962). *Am. J. Med.* **32**, 352.

Cutler, G. B., Jr., Habener, J. F., Dee, P. C. and Potts, J. T., Jr. (1974). *FEBS Lett.* **38**, 209.

Cutler, G. B., Jr., Habener, J. F. and Potts, J. T., Jr. (1977). *Endocrinology,* **100**, 537.

Dangoumau, J., Bussiere, C., Noel, M. and Balabaud, C. (1976). *J. Pharmacol.* **7**, 69.

David, L., Cohn, D. V. and Anast, C. S. (1975). *Pathol. Biol.* **22**, 833.

Davidson, D. J., Frumer, A. M., Judd, H. L., Shamonki, I. M., Tataryn, I. V., Meldrun, D. R. and Deftos, L. J. (1979). *Proc. 61st Ann. Meet. Endocr. Soc.*

Deftos, L. J. (1971). *Metabolism,* **20**, 1122.

Deftos, L. J. (1974). *J. Am. med. Assoc.* **227**, 403.

Deftos, L. J. (1978a). "Advances in Internal Medicine", p. 159. Year Book Medical Publishers, New York.

Deftos, L. J. (1978b). *Clin. Res.* **26**, 528.

Deftos, L. J., Bone, H. G. and Parthemore, J. G. (1977). *Curr. Conc. Bone Dis.* **2**, 1.

Deftos, L. J., Bury, A. W., Habener, J. F., Singer, F. R. and Potts, J. T., Jr. (1971a). *Metabolism,* **20**, 1129.

Deftos, L. J., Burton, D., Catherwood, B. D., Bone, H. G., Parthemore, J. G., Guillemin. R., Watkins, W. and Moore, R. Y. (1978). *J. clin. endocr. Metab.* **47**, 457.

Deftos, L. J., Goodman, A. D., Engelman, K. and Potts, J. T., Jr. (1971c). *Metabolism*, **20**, 428.

Deftos, L. J., Habener, J. F., Krook, L. and Mayer, G. P. (1972). *Clin. Res.* **20**, 544.

Deftos, L. J., McMillan, P. J., Sartiano, G. P., Abuid, J. and Robinson, A. G. (1976). *Metabolism*, **25**, 543.

Deftos, L. J. and Neer, R. (1974). "Annual Review of Medicine", Vol. 25. Annual Reviews, Inc., New York.

Deftos, L. J. and O'Riordan, J. L. H. (1978). "Endocrinology of Calcium Metabolism" (D. H. Copp and R. V. Talmadge, eds), p. 345, Exerpta Medica, Amsterdam.

Deftos, L. J., Powell, D., Parthemore, J. G. and Potts, J. T., Jr. (1973). *J. clin. Invest.* **52**, 3109.

Deftos, L. J., Roos, B. A., Bronzert, D. and Parthemore, J. G. (1975a). *J. clin. Endocr. Metab.* **40**, 407.

Deftos, L. J., Roos, B. A., Knecht, G. L., Lee, J., Pavlinac, D., Bone, H. G. and Parthemore, J. G. (1978). "Proceedings of the Sixth Parathyroid *Conference*." Excerpta Medica, Amsterdam.

Deftos, L. J., Roos, B. A. and Parthemore, J. G. (1975b). *West. J. Med.* **123**, 447.

DeLellis, R. A., Wolfe, H. J., Gagel, R. F., Feldman, Z. T., Miller, H. H., Gang, D. L. and Reichlin, S. (1976). *Am. J. Pathol.* **83**, 177.

DeRose, J., Singer, F. R., Avramides, A., Flores, A., Dziadiw, R., Baker, R. K. and Wallach, S. (1974). *Am. J. Med.* **56**, 867.

Didolker, M. S. and Moore, G. E. (1974). *Am. J. Surg.* **128**, 100.

Dirksen, M. C. and Anast, C. S. (1976). *Pediatr. Res.* **10**, 408.

Drukker, W., Formijne, P. and Schoot, J. B. (1957). *Br. med. J.* **1**. 186.

Dymling, J. F., Ljungberg, O., Hillyard, C. J., Greenberg, P. B., Evans, I. M. A. and MacIntyre, I. (1976). *Acta endocr., Copenh.* **82**, 500.

Ellison, M., Woodhouse, D., Hillyard, C., Dowsett, M., Coombes, R. C., Gilby, E. D. Greenberg, P. B. and Neville, A. M. (1975). *Br. J. Cancer*, **32**, 373.

Ericson, L. E. (1968). *J. Ultrastruct. Res.* **24**, 145.

Fahrenkrug, J., Hornum, I. and Rehfeld, J. F. (1975). *J. clin. Endocr. Metab.* **41**, 149.

Foster, G. V., Baghdiantz, A., Kumar, M. A., Slack, E., Soliman, H. A. and MacIntyre. I. (1964a). *Nature, Lond.* **202**, 1303.

Foster, G. V., MacIntyre, I. and Pearse, A. G. E. (1964b). *Nature, Lond.* **203**, 1029.

Garel, J. M. (1978). *C.r. Acad. Sci.* **286**, 643.

Garel, J. M., Care, A. D. and Barlet, J. P. (1974). *J. Endocr.* **62**, 497.

Gagel, F. R., Melvin, K. E. W., Tashjian, A. H., Jr., Miller, H. H., DeLellis, R. A., Cervi-Skinner, S. and Reichlin, S. (1975). *Trans. Assoc. Am. Phys.* **88**, 177.

Goltzman, D., Potts, J. T., Jr., Ridgeway, E. C. and Maloof, F. (1974). *New Engl. J. Med.* **290**, 1035.

Gordan, G. S., Cantino, T. J., Erhardt, L., Hansen, J. and Lubich, W. (1966). *Science*, **151**, 1226.

Gorlin, R. J., Sedano, H. O., Vickers, R. A. and Cervenka, J. (1968). *Cancer*, **22**, 293.

Gottlieb, J. A. and Hill, C. S., Jr. (1975). *Cancer Chemother. Rep.* **6**, 283.

Gray, T. K., Bieberdorf, F. A. and Fordtran, J. S. (1973). *J. clin. Invest.* **52**, 3084.

Greenberg, P. B., Doyle, E. H., Fisher, M. T., Hillyard, C. J., Joplin, G. F., Pennock, J. and MacIntyre, I. (1974). *Am. J. Med.* **56**, 867.

Haddad, J. G., Jr. and Caldwell, J. G. (1972). *J. clin. Invest.* **51**, 3133.

Hargis, G. K., Williams, G. A., Reynolds, W. A., Chertow, B. S., Kukreja, S. C., Bowser, E. N. and Henderson, W. J. (1978). *Endocrinology*, **102**, 745.

Hazard, J. B. (1977). *Am. J. Pathol.* **88**, 213.

Hazard, J. B., Hawk, W. A. and Crile, G. (1959). *J. clin. Endocr. Metab.* **19**, 152.

Heath, H. and Sizemore, G. W. (1977). *J. clin. Invest.* **60**, 1135.

Heersche, J. N. M., Marcus, R. and Aurbach, G. D. (1974). *Endocrinology*, **94**, 241.

Hennessey, J. F., Gray, T. K., Cooper, C. W. and Ontjes, D. A. (1973). *J. clin. Endocr. Metab.* **36**, 200.

Hennessey, J. F., Wells, S. A., Jr., Ontjes, D. A. and Cooper, C. W. (1974). *J. clin. Endocr. Metab.* **39**, 487.

Hesch, R. D., Woodhead, S., Huefner, M. and Wolf, H. (1973). *Horm. Metab. Res.* **5**, 235.

Heynen, G. and Franchimont, P. (1974). *Eur. J. clin. Invest.* **4**, 213.

Hill, C. S., Jr., Ibanez, M. L., Samaan, N. A., Ahearn, M. J. and Clark, R. L. (1973). *Medicine*, **52**, 141.

Hillyard, C. J., Cooke, T. J. C., Coombes, R. C., Evans, I. M. A. and MacIntyre, I. (1977). *Clin. Endocr.* **6**, 291.

Hillyard, C. J., Coombes, R. C., Greenberg, P. B., Galante, L. S. and MacIntyre, I. (1976). *Clin. Endocr.* **5**, 1.

Hillyard, C. J., Coombes, R. C., Greenberg, P. B. and MacIntyre, I. (1975). *J. Endocr.* **66**, 2p.

Hirsch, P. F., Gauthier, G. F. and Munson, P. L. (1963). *Endocrinology*, **73**, 244.

Hokfelt, T., Efendic, S., Hellerstrom, C., Johansson, O., Luft, R. and Arimura, A. (1975). *Acta endocr., Copenh.* **80**, 5.

Hsu, W. H. and Cooper, C. W. (1975). *Calc. Tiss. Res.* **19**, 125.

Ibanez, M. L., Cole, V. W., Russell, W. O. and Clark, R. I. (1967) *Cancer*, **20**, 706.

Iwatsuki, K. and Hashimoto, K. (1976). *Clin. Exp. Pharmacol. Physiol.* **3**, 159.

Kalina, M., Foster, G. V., Clark, M. B. and Pearse, A. G. E. (1970) "Calcitonin, 1969", p. 268. William Heinemann Medical Books, Ltd, New York.

Kabis, J. A., Earnshaw, M., Heynen, G., Russell, R. G. G. and Woods, C. G. (1977). *Calc. Tiss. Res.* **22**, 147.

Kaplan, E. L. (1973). *Surg. Annu.* **5**, 97.

Keiser, J. R., Beaven, M. A., Doppman, J., Wells, S. and Buja, L. M. (1973). *Ann. int. Med.* **78**, 561.

Keutmann, H. T., Lequin, R. M., Habener, J. F., Singer, F. R., Niall, H. D. and Potts, J. T., Jr (1972), "Endocrinology, 1971", p. 316. William Heinemann Medical Books, Ltd., New York.

Khairi, M. R. A., Dexter, R. N., Burzynski, N. J. and Johnston, C. C., Jr. (1975), *Medicine*, **54**, 89.

Koelz, H. R., Drack, G. T. and Blum, A. L. (1976). *Schweiz. med. Wschr.* **106**, 298.

Kracht, J., Hachmeister, U. and Christ, U. (1969). "Calcitonin, 1969", p. 274. William Heinemann Medical Books, Ltd, New York.

LeDourain, N. and LeLievre, C. (1970). *C. r. Acad. Sci.* **270**, 2857.

Lee, J. C., Catanzaro, A., Parthemore, J. G., Roach, B. and Deftos, L. J. (1977a). *New Engl. J. Med.* **297**, 431.

Lee, J. C., Larsen, M. A., Roos, B. A. and Deftos, L. J. (1977b). *Clin. Res.* **25**, 394A.

Lee, J. C., Parthemore, J. G. and Deftos, L. J. (1977c). *Calc. Tiss. Res.* **22S**, 154.

Lee, J. C., Parthemore, J. G. and Deftos, L. J. (1977d). *J. clin. Endocr. Metab.* **45**, 528.

Leicht, E., Biro, G. and Weinges, K. F. (1974). *Horm. Metab. Res.* **6**, 410.

Lips, C. J. M., van der Sluys Veer, J., van der Donk, J. A., van Dam, R. H. and Hackeng. W. H. L. (1978). *Lancet*, **i**, 16.

Liskova, M. (1976). *Calc. Tiss. Res.* **22**, 207.

Ljungberg, O. (1972). *Acta pathol. microbiol. scand.* **231**, 1.

Lupulescu, A. (1975). *Proc. Soc. exp. Biol. Med.* **150**, 703.

Lutwak, L., Singer, F. R. and Urist, M. R. (1974). *Ann. int. Med.* **80**, 630.

Martin, T. J. (1978). *Scot. med. J.* **23**, 161.

Marx, S. J. and Aurbach, G. D. (1975). *Endocrinology*, **97**, 448.

McKenna, T. J., Lorber, D. L., Parthemore, J. G., Bone, H. G. and Deftos, L. J. (1978). *Clin. Res.* **26**, 34A.

McMillan, P. J., Hooker, W. M. and Deftos, L. J. (1974). *Am. J. Anat.* **140**, 73.

Melvin, K. E. W., Miller, H. H. and Tashjian, A. H., Jr. (1971a). *New Engl. J. Med.* **285**, 1115.

Melvin, K. E. W. and Tashjian, A. H., Jr. (1968). *Proc. natn. Acad. Sci., USA*, **59**, 1216.

Melvin, K. E. W. and Tashjian, A. H., Jr. (1972). *Rec. Prog. horm. Res.* **28**, 399.

Melvin, K. E. W., Tashjian, A. H., Jr. and Miller, H. H. (1971b). *Trans. Assoc. Am. Phys.* **84**, 144.

Metz, S. A., Deftos, L. J., Baylink, D. and Robertson, R. P. (1977). *Clin. Res.* **25**, 161A.

Metz, S. A., Deftos, L. J., Baylink, D. and Robertson, R. P. (1978). *J. clin. Endocr. Metab.* **47**, 151.

Meyer, J. S. and Abdel-Bari, W. (1968). *New Engl. J. Med.* **278**, 530.

Milhaud, G. (1976). *Biomedicine*, **24**, 159.

Milhaud, G., Calmette, C., Taboulet, J., Julleinne, A. and Moukhtar, M. S. (1974). *Lancet*, **i**, 462.

Milhaud, G. and Moukhtar, M. S. (1966). *Proc. Soc. exp. Biol. Med.* **123**, 207.

Milhaud, G., Talbot, J. N. and Coutris, G. (1975). *Biomedicine*, **22**, 223.

Milhaud, G., Tubiana, M., Parmentier, C. and Coutris, G. (1968). *C.r. Acad. Sci.* **266**, 608.

Montalbano, F. P., Baronofsky, I. D. and Ball, H. (1962). *J. Am. med. Assoc.* **182**, 264.

Mundy, G. R., Raisz, L. G., Cooper, R. A., Schechter, G. P. and Salmon, S. E. (1974). *New Engl. J. Med.* **291**, 1041.

Munson, P. L. (1971). *Am. J. med. Sci.* **262**, 310.

Munson, P. L., Cooper, C. W., Gray, T. K., Pen, T. C., Toverud, S. U., Harper, C. and Ontjes, D. A. (1972). "Endocrinology 1973", p. 131. William Heinemann Medical Books, Ltd, New York, London.

Nathaniels, E. K., Nathaniels, A. M. and Wang, C. A. (1970). *Ann. Surg.* **171**, 165.

Noda, T. and Narita, K. (1976). *J. Biochem.* **79**, 353.

Nonidez, J. F. (1932). *Am. J. Anat.* **49**, 479.

Nozaki, K., Noda, S., Obi, S., Nishizawa, Y., Morii, H. and Wada, M. (1976). *Endocr. jap.* **23**, 83.

Otani, M., Yamauchi, H., Meguro, T., Kitazawa, S., Watanabe, S. and Orimo, H. (1976). *J. Biochem.* **79**, 345.

Parthemore, J. G., Bronzert, D., Roberts, G. and Deftos, L. J. (1974). *J. clin. Endocr. Metab.* **39**, 108.

Parthemore, J. G. and Deftos, L. J. (1975). *J. clin. Invest.* **56**, 385.

Parthemore, J. G. and Deftos, L. J. (1978). *J. clin. Endoc. Metab.* **47**, 184.

Parthemore, J. G., Moriguchi, M. and Deftos, L. J. (1977). *Clin. Res.* **25**, 498A.

Parthemore, J. G., Roos, B. A. and Deftos, L. J. (1975). *Clin. Res.* **23**, 113.

Passeri, M., Carapezzi, C., Seccato, S., Monica, C., Storzzi, D. and Palummeri, E. (1975). *Experientia*, **31**, 1234.

Pearse, A. G. E. (1969). "Calcitonin", p. 125. William Heinemann Medical Books, Ltd, New York.

Pearse, A. G. E. and Takor, T. T. (1976). *Clin. Endocr.* **5**, 229.

Pecile, A., Ferri, S., Braga, P. C. and Olgiati, V. R. (1975). *Experientia*, **31**, 332.

Peng, T. C., Cooper, C. W., Pterusz, P. and Volpert, E. M. (1975). *Endocrinology*, **97**, 1537.

Pento, J. T., Glick, S. M., Kagen, A. and Gorfein, P. C. (1974). *Endocrinology*, **94**, 1176.

Phillippo, M., Bruce, J. B. and Lawrence, C. B. (1960). *J. Endocr.* **46**, xii.

Pitkin, M., Reynolds, W. A., Williams, G. A. and Hargis, G. K. (1979) *J. clin. Endocr. Metab.* (in press).

Potts, J. T., Jr. and Deftos, L. J. (1969). "Duncan's Diseases of Metabolism", p. 904. 6th edition. W. B. Saunders Co., Philadelphia.

Potts, J. T., Jr. and Deftos, L. J. (1974). "Duncan's Diseases of Metabolism", p. 1225. 7th edition. W. B. Saunders Co., Philadelphia.

Potts, J. T., Jr., Niall, H. D. and Deftos, L. J. (1971). "Current Topics in Experimental Endocrinology", p. 151. Academic Press, New York and London.

Powell, D., Singer, F. R., Murray, T. M., Minkin, C. and Potts, J. T., Jr. (1973). *New Engl. J. Med.* **289**, 176.

Raulais, D., Merle, M. and Milhaud, G. (1974). "Endocrinology 1973", p. 117. William Heinemann Medical Books, Ltd, New York.

Riggs, B. L., Arnaud, C. D., Reynolds, J. C. and Smith, L. H. (1971). *J. clin. Invest.* **50**, 2079.

Robertson, G. M., Jr., Moore, E. W., Switz, D. M., Sizemore, G. W. and Estep, H. L. (1976). *New Engl. J. Med.* **294**, 512.

Roos, B. A., Bergeron, G., Guggenheim, K. and Deftos, L. J. (1977a). *Clin. Res.* **25**, 398A.

Roos, B. A., Bundy, L. L., Bailey, R. and Deftos, L. J. (1974a). *Endocrinology*, **95**, 1142.

Roos, B. A., Bundy, L. L., Miller, E. A. and Deftos, L. J. (1975). *Endocrinology*, **97**, 39.

Roos, B. A., Cooper, C. W., Frelinger, A. L. and Deftos, L. J. (1978). *Endocrinology*, **103**, 2180.

Roos, B. A. and Deftos, L. J. (1976). *Clin. Endocr.* **5**, 217s.

Roos, B. A., Frehlinger, A. L., Yoon, M. J., Bergeron, G., Knecht, G., Lee, J. and Deftos, L. J. (1978). *Clin. Res.* **26**, 131A.

Roos, B. A., Okano, K. and Deftos, L. J. (1974b). *Biochem. biophys. Res. Commun.* **60**, 1134.

Roos, B. A., Parthemore, J. G., Lee, J. and Deftos, L. J. (1977b). *Calc. Tiss. Res.* **22S**, 298.

Rossier, J., Bayon, A., Vargo, T. M., Ling, N., Guillemin, R. and Bloom, F. (1977). *Life Sci.* **21**, 847.

Rude, R. K. and Singer, F. R. (1977). *J. clin. Endocr. Metab.* **44**, 980.

Ryan, W. G., Schwartz, T. B. and Perlia, C. P. (1969). *Ann. int. Med.* **70**, 549.

Samaan, N. A., Hill, C. S., Jr., Beceiro, J. R. and Schultz, P. N. (1973). *J. Lab. Clin. Med.* **81**, 671.

Schimke, R. N. and Hartmann, W. H. (1965). *Ann. int. Med.* **63**, 1207.

Schimke, R. N., Hartmann, W. H., Prout, T. E. and Rimoin, D. L. (1968). *New Engl. J. Med.* **279**, 1.

Seyberth, H. W., Segree, G. V., Morgan, J. L., Sweetman, B. J., Potts, J. T., Jr. and Oates, J. A. (1975). *New Engl. J. Med.* **293**, 1278.

Sherwin, R. P. (1964). *Am. J. Surg.* **107**, 136.

Silva, O. L. and Becker, K. L. (1976). *Br. med. J.* **1**, 460.

Silva, O. L., Becker, K. L., Primack, A., Doppman, J. and Snider, R. H. (1974a). *New Engl. J. Med.* **290**, 1122.

Silva, O. L., Becker, K. L., Primack, A., Doppman, J. L. and Snider, R. H. (1975a). *J. Am. med. Assoc.* **234**, 183.

Silva, O. L., Becker, K. L., Primack, A., Doppman, J. L. and Snider, R. H. (1976). *Chest*, **69**, 495.

Silva, O. L., Snider, R. H. and Becker, K. L. (1974b). *Clin. Chem.* **20**, 337.

Silva, O. L., Becker, K. L., Primack, A. and Snider, R. H. (1973). *Pharmacologist*, **15**, 252.

Silva, O. L., Snider, R. H., Becker, K. L. and Moore, C. F. (1975b). *Fed. Proc.* **34**, 761.

Silva, O. L., Snider, R. H., Becker, K. L. and Moore, C. F. (1977). *J. Endocr.* **73**, 183.

Singer, F. R. (1975). *Medicine*, **57**, 117.

Singer, F. R. and Habener, J. F. (1974). *Biochem. biophys. Res. Commun.* **61**, 660.

Singer, F. R., Woodhouse, N. J. Y., Parkinson, D. K. and Joplin, G. F. (1969). *Clin. Sci.* **37**, 181.

Singer, F. R., Aldred, J. P., Neer, R. M., Krane, S. M., Potts, J. T., Jr. and Bloch, K. J. (1972). *J. clin. Invest.* **51**, 2331.

Sipple, J. H. (1961). *Am. J. Med.* **31**, 163.

Smith, R., Russell, R. G. and Bishop, M. (1971). *Lancet*, **i**, 945.

Solcia, E. and Sampietro, R. (1968). "Calcitonin." William Heinemann Medical Books, Ltd, New York.

Sowa, M., Appert, H. E. and Howard, J. M. (1977). *Surg. Gynec. Obstet.* **144**, 365.

Steiner, A. L., Goodman, A. D. and Powers, S. R. (1968). *Medicine*, **47**, 371.

Strauss, E. and Yalow, R. S. (1976). *J. Lab. clin. Med.* **87**, 292.

Takaoka, Y., Takamori, M., Ichinose, M., Shikaya, T., Igawa, N., Kikutani, M. and Yamamoto, T. (1969). *Acta med. nagasaki*, **13**, 28.

Talmage, R. V., Dopelt, S. H. and Cooper, C. W. (1975). *Proc. Soc. exp. Biol. Med.* **149**, 885.

Tarnawski, A., Bofdal, J., Dura, K., Marszalek, Z. and Jedrychowski, A. (1974). *Gut*, **15**, 703.

Tashjian, A. H., Jr., Howland, B. G., Kenneth, B. A., Melvin, K. E. W. and Hill, C. S., Jr. (1970). *New Engl. J. Med.* **283**, 890.

Taylor, T. G., Lewis, P. E. and Balderston, O. (1975). *J. Endocr.* **66**, 297.

Tischler, A. S., Dichter, M. A., Biales, D. and Green, L. G. (1977). *New Engl. J. Med.* **296**, 919.

Toverud, S. U., Harper, C. and Munson, P. L. (1976). *Endocrinology*, **99**, 371.

Velo, G. P., DeBastiani, G., Nogarin, L. and Abdullahi, S. E. (1976). *Agents Actions*, **6**, 284.

Visser, J. W. and Axt, R. (1975). *J. clin. Pathol.* **28**, 298.

Vora, N. M., Williams, G. A., Hargis, G. K., Bowser, E. N., Kawahara, W., Jackson, B. L., Henderson, W. J. and Kukreja, S. C. (1978). *J. clin. Endocr. Metab.* **46**, 567.

Watts, E. G., Copp, D. H. and Deftos, L. J. (1974). *Endocrinology*, **96**, 214.

Weichert, R. F., III (1970). *Am. J. Med.* **49**, 232.

Weir, G. C., Lesser, P. B., Drop, L. J., Fischer, J. E. and Warshaw, A. L. (1975). *Ann. int. Med.* **83**, 185.

Wells, S. A., Jr., Ontjes, D. A., Cooper, C. W., Hennessey, J. F., Ellis, G. J., MacPherson, H. T. and Sabiston, D. C., Jr. (1975). *Ann. Surg.* **182**, 362.

Werner, S. and Low, H. (1974). *Horm. Metab. Res.* **6**, 30.

Williams, E. D. (1966). *J. clin. Pathol.* **19**, 114.

Williams, E. D. (1967). *J. clin. Pathol.* **20**, 395.

Williams, E. D and Pollock, D. J. (1966). *J. Pathol. Bacteriol.* **91**, 71.

Wolfe, H. J., Melvin, K. E. W., Cervi-Skinner, S. J., Al Saadi, A. A., Juliar, J. F., Jackson, C. E. and Tashjian, A. H., Jr. (1973). *New Engl. J. Med.* **289**, 437.

Wolfe, H. J., Voelkel, E. F. and Tashjian, A. H., Jr. (1974). *J. clin. Endocr. Metab.* **38**, 688.

Woodhouse, N. J. Y., Bordier, P., Fisher, M., Joplin, G. F., Reiner, M., Kalu, D. N., Foster, G. V. and MacIntyre, I. (1971). *Lancet*, **i**, 1139.

F

IV. The Catecholamines.
Adrenaline; Noradrenaline; Dopamine

B. A. CALLINGHAM and M. A. BARRAND

A. SOME CHEMICAL AND PHYSICAL PROPERTIES OF ADRENALINE, NORADRENALINE AND DOPAMINE

1. General Properties

There is now clear evidence that the circulating blood of man and other animals contains not only adrenaline (A) and noradrenaline (NA), but also a third catecholamine, dopamine (DA). In the last edition of this book, the presence of dopamine could only be suspected. The formulae and some physical properties of these amines are given in Table 1.

Armstrong and Barlow (1976), state that the pK_a values of the catecholamines at 37° are within one log unit of physiological pH. This would indicate that there are normally significant proportions of the ions, zwitterions and of the uncharged amines. Factors that modify the proportions and their importance are discussed by Ganellin (1977). Quantum chemical methods (see Green, Johnson and Kang, 1974) have been used in attempts to determine the physiologically preferred conformers of the catecholamines, with special attention paid recently to DA (Horn, Post and Kennard, 1975; Grol and Rollema, 1977).

2. Stability

Although the catecholamines are relatively stable in aqueous solutions at pH 4 or below, their stability declines as the pH rises. Destruction is very rapid in alkaline solution, an effect catalysed by the presence of heavy metals.

Problems concerned with the instability of the catecholamines frequently arise when they are added to oxygenated physiological saline solutions at 37°. Iversen (1964) showed that ^{3}H-NA was best preserved in Kreb's solution by a combination of ascorbic acid and EDTA (see Callingham, 1967a). Recently, Hughes and Smith (1978) have confirmed these results, but have also found that these preservatives may reduce the amount of NA taken up by tissues. However, the presence of animal tissues alone may limit the degree of non-enzymatic decomposition of catecholamines (Häggendal and Svedmyr, 1967; Hughes and Smith, 1978).

The catecholamines are relatively stable in plasma, but they disappear more rapidly in whole blood. This appears to be caused by the slow uptake of the amines into the erythrocytes (Schanker, Nafpliotis and Johnson, 1961; Zimon, Sheps, Hazelrig, Schirger and Owen, 1966; Roston, 1967). Danon and Sapira (1972a) have shown that this uptake is temperature-dependent and saturable, but has little in common with the neuronal and smooth muscle uptake systems for catecholamines. The presence of catechol-O-methyl transferase (COMT) in the red blood cell (Horst, Gattanell, Urbano and Sheppard, 1969; Axelrod and Cohn, 1971) only partially accounts for the uptake.

A small amount of catecholamine is taken up by the blood platelets (Born, Hornykiewicz and Stafford, 1958; Abrams and Solomon, 1969; Born and Smith, 1970), limited presumably by their small total mass.

Table 1

Naturally occurring DA, NA and A bases.

	DA	L-NA	L-A
	4-(2-aminoethyl)-1,2-benzenediol $C_8H_{11}NO_2$	L-4-(2-amino-1-hydroxyethyl) 1,2-benzenediol $C_8H_{11}NO_3$	L-4-[1-hydroxy-2-(methylamino)-ethyl] 1,2-benzenediol $C_9H_{13}NO_3$
Molecular weight	153·18	169·18	183·20
Melting point	hydrochloride 241° (decomposition)	base 216·5°–218° (decomposition)	base 211°–221° (decomposition)
Optical rotation $[\alpha]_D^{25}$ in dilute HCl	—	−37·3°	−50° to −53·5°
	free base highly sensitive O_2 rapidly discolours hydrochloride freely soluble in water	hydrochloride freely soluble in water	free base gradually turns brown in air hydrochloride freely soluble in water

3. Binding to Plasma Proteins

There is dispute concerning the importance and implications of the binding of catecholamines to plasma proteins (see Callingham and Barrand, 1976). Antoniades, Goldfein, Zileli and Elmadjian (1958) showed that A bound to human plasma albumin in preference to NA, the side-chain being important in this interaction (Zia, Cox and Luzzi, 1971). DA is also bound (Franksson and Änggård, 1970). At least two components in plasma are involved in the binding (Danon and Sapira, 1972b), and Russell and Doty (1973) report that there are two distinct sites that are selective for the catechols, since besides DA, NA and A, they also bind dihydroxyphenylalanine (DOPA).

Powis (1973, 1974, 1975) has reported that the binding can be antagonised, as can the binding of the catecholamines to collagen, by oxytetracycline. He suggests, from evidence that shows that oxytetracycline can potentiate the biological actions of catecholamines, that binding of this nature could be a major mechanism for their inactivation. However, Branco, Fleming Torrinha and Osswald (1974) were unable to antagonise the binding to proteins with oxytetracycline. Moreover, Kalsner (1976) has found that, in the perfused arteries of the rabbit's ear, oxytetracycline does not increase the magnitude or duration of the responses to either catecholamines or stimulation of the adrenergic nerves. Much needs to be resolved.

B. BIOLOGICAL OCCURRENCE AND METABOLISM

1. Distribution

There is much evidence to show that the catecholamines are distributed throughout the tissues of a wide range of species (von Euler, 1956; Iversen, 1967; Holzbauer and Sharman, 1972).

The chromaffin cells of the adrenal medulla contain large quantities of catecholamines, made up of mixtures of NA and A with much smaller amounts of DA. The proportions of NA and A in the adrenal medulla depend on the species, being about 80% A in man, for example. Not all the cells of the adrenal medulla are able to convert NA to A, thus leading to the storage of these amines in separate cells (Pohorecky and Wurtman, 1971).

The organs of Zuckerkandl and extramedullary chromaffin tissue contain appreciable amounts of the catecholamines, particularly during foetal and early post-natal life, when NA is usually the predominant amine (Coupland, 1965; Pohorecky and Wurtman, 1971).

The NA content of other tissues is associated almost entirely with their postganglionic sympathetic adrenergic innervation; the greater the density of nerves, the greater the content of NA. The highest concentrations are found in the vas deferens, ciliary body, salivary glands, heart and spleen. Low amounts are found in skeletal muscle and none in bone marrow and placenta. The small amounts of A that can be found in tissues are mainly in the scattered chromaffin cells (Iversen, 1967). In the periphery, DA has been found in high concentrations in special mast cells in ruminants, and in many other tissues, including spleen, splenic nerves, pancreas, kidney, lung and the gut (see Holzbauer and Sharman, 1972). It has also been found in the glomus cells of the carotid body and in sympathetic ganglia. It is associated with the small intensely fluorescent cells of the ganglia (Eränkö and Härkönen, 1965) and may be concerned with ganglionic transmission (Libet and Tosaka, 1970).

In the brain, the highest amounts of NA are found in the hypothalamus, while DA is concentrated in the basal ganglia (Glowinski and Iversen, 1966; Brownstein, Saavedra and Palkovits, 1974). There are also small amounts of A in brain tissue (see Holzbauer and Sharman, 1972; Hökfelt, Fuxe, Goldstein and Johansson, 1974).

2. Biosynthesis

By far the most important route for the biosynthesis of catecholamines (see Fig. 1) is that first proposed by Blaschko (1939). Although several alternative routes of synthesis are possible, including for example one in which DOPA could be β-hydroxylated to produce dihydroxyphenylserine (DOPS) as a direct precursor of NA, none appears to contribute significantly to the tissue stores of catecholamines (Iversen, 1967; Kirshner, 1975).

The enzymes responsible for each step in the synthetic pathway have been identified and characterised. Nagatsu, Levitt and Udenfriend (1964) described the properties of tyrosine hydroxylase, the enzyme responsible for the conversion of tyrosine to DOPA. This enzyme, located in adrenergic and dopaminergic nerves, and exhibiting a very high degree of stereospecificity towards L-tyrosine, is mainly found in the soluble fractions of tissue homogenates. However, the possibility that the enzyme may associate with the storage vesicles or form aggregates makes it difficult to resolve its subcellular localisation *in vivo*.

The hydroxylation of tyrosine to DOPA is generally believed to be the rate-limiting step in the biosynthesis of catecholamines. The rate of this reaction can be altered by a variety of factors, such as, feedback inhibition both by product and by the catecholamines, nerve impulse activity, the effects of some hormones and the integrity of the nerve itself (see Nagatsu, 1975; Reis and Joh, 1977; Weiner, Lee, Barnes and Dreyer, 1977). The interaction between the factors that may influence this particular step is very complicated and not fully understood.

Dopa decarboxylase (aromatic L-amino acid decarboxylase), which decarboxylates DOPA to DA is widely distributed in animal tissues, and its presence cannot be used to identify adrenergic neurons. Lovenberg, Weissbach and Udenfriend (1962) showed that this enzyme would decarboxylate a wide variety of aromatic, L-amino acids, including α-methyl-DOPA, 5-hydroxytryptophan and to a lesser extent, histidine. Tyrosine is a rather poor substrate, which helps to limit the endogenous synthesis of tyramine.

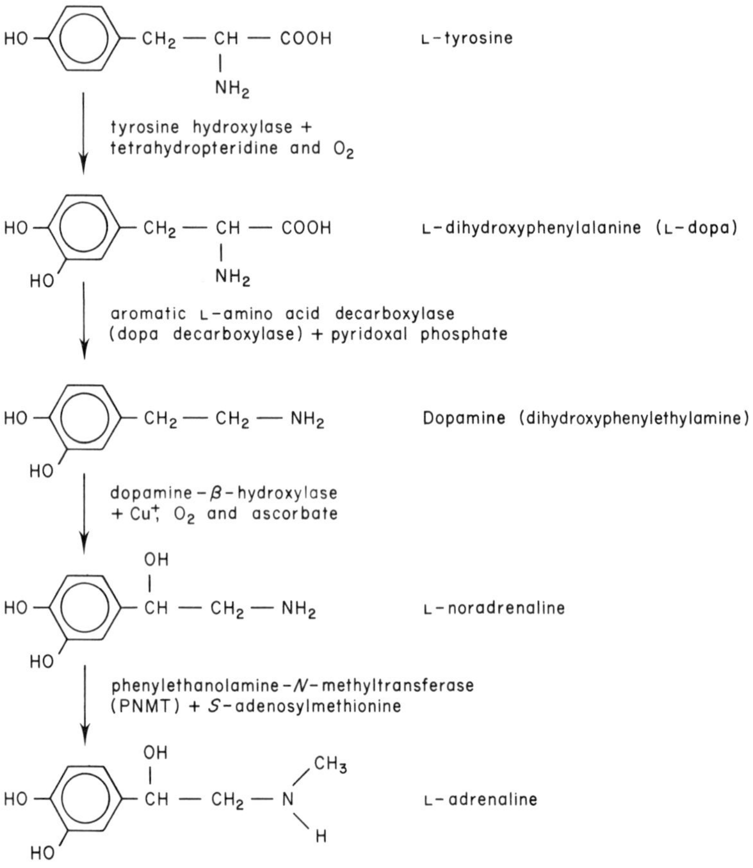

Fig. 1. Biosynthesis of catecholamines.

Dopamine-β-hydroxylase (dopamine-β-oxidase), which converts DA to NA, appears to be contained entirely within the catecholamine storage vesicles. Again this enzyme is not specific for DA but will hydroxylate many other β-phenylethylamines such as tyramine to octopamine and α-methyl-DA to α-methyl-NA. This enzyme is subject to various controlling influences

including naturally occurring inhibitors, that may have important consequences for the synthesis of NA and A (Molinoff, Orcutt, Nelson and Harden,
1977).

The final enzyme phenylethanolamine-N-methyl transferase, catalyses the
conversion of NA to A. In mammals, the enzyme is only found in the adrenal
medulla, extramedullary chromaffin tissue, and, in small amounts in the
brain (Ciaranello, 1977). Axelrod (1962) showed that the enzyme required
S-adenosylmethionine as the methyl donor. This enzyme is notable for its
dependence upon very high concentrations of glucocorticoid (Pohorecky
and Wurtman, 1971; Weiner, 1975).

3. Uptake, Storage and Release

(a) Tissue uptake

Although Elliott (1905) had suggested that A disappeared in the tissues it
excited, it was Burn (1932) who first put forward the idea that A was taken
up into tissue stores. With the advent of radiolabelled catecholamines,
Axelrod, Weil-Malherbe and Tomchick (1959) were able to show that this
uptake could take place from the circulation. The short half-life of NA and A
in the circulation, of about 20 sec (Vane, 1969) is not due to their catabolism
in the blood but is the result of systems that take up the amines into the body
tissues (Iversen, 1975).

The characteristics of the process responsible for the uptake of catecholamines into the adrenergic neurons of the rat heart were first described by
Iversen (1963). This neuronal uptake process, often called "uptake$_1$," is,
in the rat heart and in many other tissues, a saturable process that obeys
Michaelis–Menten kinetics. It has a high affinity for the naturally occurring
catecholamines (see Table 2), which it can accumulate against a considerable
concentration gradient. The degree of stereospecificity for the optical
enantiomers of NA appears to depend on the particular species and organ
(see Ross, 1976). The amount of amine taken up by this system from the
circulation will depend, not only on the relative abundance of the adrenergic
innervation but also on the distance which the amines must travel to reach
the vicinity of the nerves. In certain tissues, such as the heart with a rich
sympathetic innervation in close proximity to the receptors, uptake$_1$ plays a
vital part in the conservation of released NA. Uptake$_1$ will take up a variety
of catecholamines, β-phenylethylamines and related compounds, and is
inhibited by cocaine and many other drugs, including tricyclic antidepres-
sants (Callingham, 1967b; Iversen, 1967; Maxwell, Ferris and Burcsu, 1976).

In addition to neuronal uptake, there is a second system that can be found
in the cell membranes of smooth muscles and glands for example (Iversen,

Table 2

Kinetic constants for the neuronal and extraneuronal accumulation of catecholamines by the perfused rat heart.

Catecholamine	K_m (μM)	V_{max} (nmol/g/ min)	References
Neuronal accumulation			
DA	0·69	1·45	Hellman *et al.* (1971)
(−)-NA	0·27	1·18	Iversen (1963)
(±)-A	1·4	1·04	Iversen (1965a)
(±)-Isoprenaline	not a substrate		Callingham and Burgen (1966)
Extraneuronal accumulation			
DA	590	140	Hellman *et al.* (1971)
NA	252	100	Iversen (1965b)
A	51·6	64·4	Iversen (1965b)
Isoprenaline	23·4	15·5	Callingham and Burgen (1966)

1965b; Gillespie, 1973, 1974). This uptake system, which is often called "uptake$_2$," differs in several respects from uptake$_1$. It has a much lower affinity for NA (Table 2), is not stereoselective, but due to the relative abundance of the sites the V_{max} of the system greatly exceeds that of uptake$_1$. It has a greater affinity for the N-substituted amines such as A and isoprenaline.

Unlike uptake$_1$, which allows the amines to be returned to the neuronal storage vesicles, uptake$_2$ delivers the amines into cells that have no storage vesicles but only the catabolic enzymes, COMT and monoamine oxidase (MAO). After exposure to high concentrations of catecholamines, or if the enzymes are inhibited, it is possible to demonstrate their accumulation in the tissue (Iversen, 1965b; Callingham and Burgen, 1966; Lightman and Iversen, 1969). Uptake$_2$ is inhibited by several compounds, including the O-methylated catabolites, normetanephrine and metanephrine, by certain steroids and by clonidine (Salt, 1972). Recent evidence would indicate that uptake$_2$ is probably associated with at least two extraneuronal compartments (Bönisch and Trendelenburg, 1974; Bönisch, Uhlig and Trendelenburg, 1974; Uhlig, Fiebig and Trendelenburg, 1976).

In the circulation, the catecholamines may be exposed to both uptake systems in the walls of the blood vessels. Although the NA released from the adrenergic vasomotor nerves can be taken back and conserved by uptake$_1$ (Bevan and Osher, 1970; Su and Bevan, 1970), it is difficult to assess the relative importance of the uptake systems in terminating the effects of both released and circulating NA in blood vessels. As the distance between effector cell and neuron increases, less of the neuronally-released NA will return by uptake$_1$, and the ability of cocaine to potentiate the actions of NA will also decline (Verity, 1971). When the gap is very large or the amines are delivered from the lumen of the blood vessels, the importance of extraneuronal uptake must increase. Distances of the order of 4000 Å have been reported in coronary arteries (Malor, Griffen and Taylor, 1973). Neuronal uptake of circulating catecholamines has been shown, together with uptake into the smooth muscle of the blood vessels and absorption on to collagen (Gillespie and Muir, 1970; Bevan, Bevan, Osher and Su, 1972; De la Lande, Harvey and Holt, 1974). The amount of neuronal uptake varies considerably in the various blood vessels (Rolewicz, Whitmore and Zimmermann, 1969; Bevan, Hosmer, Ljung, Pegram and Su, 1974). Moreover, blockade of uptake$_1$ may have little or no effect on the responses of vascular tissues to NA (Kalsner and Nickerson, 1969a, b, c; Nishioka, 1971; De la Lande et al., 1974; Kalsner, 1974). Inhibition of uptake$_2$ will often lead to potentiation of NA and of isoprenaline in particular (Kalsner, Frew and Smith, 1975; Cornish, Goldie and Miller, 1978). There is also some evidence that high circulating concentrations of cholesterol, which has been shown to inhibit uptake$_2$ (Salt and Iversen, 1972), and of low-density lipoprotein, can also potentiate the actions of NA (Rosendorff, Bloom and Stein, 1976).

In the lung, NA is taken up from the circulation in preference to A (Vane, 1969), by a process that shares some of the properties of both neuronal and non-neuronal uptake (Gillis, 1976; Gillis and Roth, 1976). The non-innervated human umbilical arteries can also remove catecholamines from the circulation (Burnstock, McLean and Wright, 1971). In man, it has been shown that ^{3}H-NA is more effectively taken up from the circulation in the forearm than in the lung (Stjärne, Kaijser, Mathé and Birke, 1975). Kinetic models for the removal of circulating catecholamines have been devised (Maas, 1970).

The activity of the various uptake mechanisms may modify the concentrations and proportions of the catecholamines measured in blood samples taken from a particular vessel (Iversen, 1974; Berkowitz and Spector, 1976).

(b) Storage

In 1953, Blaschko and Welch, and Hillarp, Lagerstedt and Nilson showed that the catecholamine content of the bovine adrenal medulla was associated with a subcellular granule fraction. The granules, or vesicles, from both the adrenal medulla and from adrenergic nerves contain not only the catecholamines but also dopamine-β-hydroxylase, acidic proteins (the chromagranins) and ATP (Smith, 1972; Winkler and Smith, 1975; Perlman and Chalfie, 1977). Several other constituents, including a Mg^{++}-dependent ATPase have also been identified.

The vesicles represent the major site of catecholamine storage. They are retained, complexed with the chromagranins and ATP, by the action of uptake systems located in the vesicle membrane (Philippu, 1976). At low temperatures the complexes are stable, but at $37°$ active uptake is essential, both to maintain the vesicle content of catecholamine and to deliver the DA from the cytoplasm for conversion to NA. ATP and Mg^{++} are required for the uptake system to operate efficiently (Kirshner, 1962; Da Prada, Obrist and Pletscher, 1975). Inhibition of the vesicle uptake by drugs, such as reserpine will cause a loss of vesicle stores, but the mechanisms involved are not simple (see Phillippu, 1976).

(c) Release

Although the precise mechanisms are not fully resolved, there is a considerable weight of evidence to show that the physiological release of catecholamines is brought about by exocytosis (Smith, 1973; Viveros, 1975; Kopin, 1977; Perlman and Chalfie, 1977). Thus the contents of the vesicle are released through a pore in the neuronal membrane that appears to be made as a result of fusion with the vesicle. Besides the catecholamines, the dopamine-β-hydroxylase, chromagranins and ATP find their way into the synaptic gap. In common with many other secretory processes, calcium is essential (Douglas, 1975). In the absence of calcium there is virtually no exocytosis possible.

The output of NA elicited by the stimulation of adrenergic nerves can be modified by several naturally occurring substances including NA itself. The site of action of NA appears to be on α-receptors located on the presynaptic nerve membrane (Langer, 1977). Pretreatment with α-receptor antagonists causes an increase in the output of NA (Starke, Montel and Schümann, 1971), while α-receptor agonists lead to a reduction. There is evidence that the presynaptic α-receptors differ slightly from those on the postsynaptic membrane. For example clonidine, and α-methyl-NA are more potent agonists on the presynaptic α-receptors than they are on the post-synaptic α-receptors (Starke, Endo and Taube, 1975). A difference in potency is also shown by some antagonists. In isolated human blood vessels α-receptor antagonists were found to be able to increase the release of NA from the vasomotor nerves, while exposure to added NA reduced the release (Stjärne and Brundin, 1975).

Evidence also exists to indicate the presence of presynaptic β-receptors responsible for a positive feedback on release, as well as specific receptors for DA (for a detailed discussion see Langer, 1977).

When NA is released by the action of indirectly-acting sympathomimetic amines such as tyramine, calcium is not involved in the release process and the presynaptic receptors are largely without effect. Under these circumstances it would seem that the NA escapes from the neuron by some degree of passive diffusion augmented by a carrier-facilitated efflux (Paton, 1976). These processes of efflux, which are normally obscured, can be revealed by pretreatment with MAO inhibitors to allow the cytoplasmic concentration of NA to increase considerably.

4. Catabolism

For many years it was thought that the main route of catabolism was by the action of MAO. However, the discovery that the urine of man and other animals contained metabolites with 4-hydroxy-3-methoxy groups showed that at least another enzyme was involved (see Sharman, 1973, 1975). The particular enzyme responsible was found to be catechol-O-methyltransferase (COMT) (Axelrod, 1957), which required S-adenosylmethionine as the methyl donor.

Most evidence supports the view that both enzymes are primarily located within cells; MAO in the outer membrane of the mitochondrion (Blaschko, 1974) while COMT is probably in the cytoplasm (Guldberg and Marsden, 1975). The precise distribution of COMT is not completely resolved. As a result of the location of these enzymes within the cell, the catabolism of the catecholamines depends upon their delivery by the systems of uptake into the enzyme-containing cells. Drugs that modify uptake will therefore have profound effects on the amounts and proportions of the metabolites.

Some of the major routes of catabolism are shown in Fig. 2, but for extensive maps of many routes see Sharman (1973, 1975).

Circulating catecholamines are mainly O-methylated before deamination, especially since the action of COMT increases the affinity of the amines for MAO (Tipton, 1973). The several O-methylated aldehydes that are formed are then converted to either the corresponding acid or alcohol by the actions of aldehyde dehydrogenase and aldehyde reductase respectively. In the case of NA and A the common metabolite, 4-hydroxy-3-methoxymandelic acid (HMMA, "vanilmandelic acid" or VMA) is produced. From DA, 4-hydroxy-3-methoxyphenylacetic acid (homovanillic acid, HVA) is produced. The products of COMT and MAO acting on their own are also to be found in the urine (Fig. 2).

Besides relatively small amounts of the free catecholamines, their conjugates can also be found. The pattern of conjugation appears to vary with the particular species (Sharman, 1973, 1975).

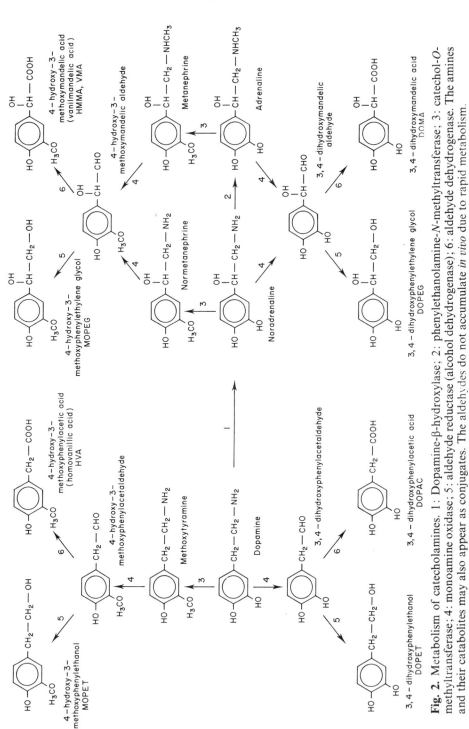

Fig. 2. Metabolism of catecholamines. 1: Dopamine-β-hydroxylase; 2: phenylethanolamine-*N*-methyltransferase; 3: catechol-*O*-methyltransferase; 4: monoamine oxidase; 5: aldehyde reductase (alcohol dehydrogenase); 6: aldehyde dehydrogenase. The amines and their catabolites may also appear as conjugates. The aldehydes do not accumulate *in vivo* due to rapid metabolism.

C. METHODS OF DETERMINATION

Since the concentrations of DA, NA and A in the blood plasma are normally very low, assay techniques of great sensitivity are needed to measure them. Almost all the assay methods currently available must be used at or very near to their limits of sensitivity. In consequence there is a multiplicity of methods incorporating small modifications to a limited number of basic techniques, in the hope of improving the sensitivity, specificity or convenience.

1. Extraction and Purification

Ten years ago, the most commonly used assay methods were based on the conversion of the catecholamines to highly fluorescent derivatives. Since that time others, such as radioenzymatic and gas and liquid chromatographic methods have appeared. Most methods require the extraction of the catecholamines from the plasma before assay, not only to concentrate the amines but also to isolate them from substances liable to interfere. The presence of interfering substances was a serious problem with some of the earlier fluorimetric methods (Callingham, 1967a).

There are many methods designed to extract the catecholamines from tissue samples and blood plasma (Callingham and Cass, 1963; Sharman, 1971; Anton and Sayre, 1972; Atack, 1977), but nearly all now depend on the use of alumina or ion-exchange resins.

(a) Adsorption on alumina

In most of the current methods, the alumina is activated before use by heating at 90–100° in 2 M HCl followed by decanting to remove the finest particles, and thorough washing and drying. With fluorimetric assays, this procedure is essential to avoid high blank values and quenching (Sharman, Vanov and Vogt, 1962). The catecholamines may be adsorbed on alumina from either the native plasma (Price and Price, 1957) or after precipitation of the plasma proteins with an agent such as perchloric acid (Anton and Sayre, 1962).

By adsorption on alumina, catecholamines can be separated successfully from the O-methylated amines, methoxytyramine, normetanephrine and metanephrine.

(b) Ion-exchange resins

The use of the strongly acidic cation-exchange resin, Dowex 50, for the extraction of catecholamines from tissues was introduced by Bertler, Carls-son and Rosengren (1958). Vendsalu (1960) adapted the method for the extraction of NA and A from deproteinised plasma. By a suitable choice of concentrations of HCl, strong cation-exchange resins allow the separate elution of NA plus A; DA; DOPA plus tyrosine and the O-methylated amines (Häggendal, 1962a, b; Iversen, 1963; Atack, 1977). Both free and conjugated catecholamines in the same sample can be assayed by passing the plasma through a Dowex 50 column to extract the free amines. The conjugated amines that pass through the column in the original effluent are then hydro-lysed and extracted on a second column (Häggendal, 1963b).

There are, however, problems associated with resins, including the occasional presence of fluorescent contaminants. Thorough washing of the resin is essential before elution of the amines (Häggendal, 1963a).

Although, for tissues, there are several elaborate extraction methods, based on the use of alumina together with ion-exchange resins, for plasma, alumina alone is the most widely used.

(c) Paper chromatography

Paper chromatography has been used mainly before bioassay. The tech-nique used by Vogt (1952) with a few modifications has become a standard method (McEwen, 1967). The catecholamines are extracted from heparinised plasma by acid-ethanol, evaporated to dryness and the residue taken up in acetone-ethanol. The extract is applied to acid-washed, ascorbate-sprayed chromatography paper and run in phenol-HCl. After removal of all traces of phenol with benzene, the amines are eluted for assay.

2. Biological Methods

Until a quarter of a century ago, the only methods available for the assay of catecholamines in tissue extracts were biological (Gaddum, 1959; Calling-ham and Cass, 1963; Callingham, 1967a; Vane, 1969). Bioassays were often of great sensitivity and capable of detecting less than 5·9 pmol (1 ng) of NA or 5·5 pmol (1 ng) of A. They were comparatively insensitive towards DA.

The blood pressure of the pithed rat was widely used. Pretreatment with a β-receptor antagonist made it more sensitive to the pressor effects of A (Vanov and Vogt, 1963). A sensitivity of 1·2–2·4 pmol (0·2–0·4 ng) of NA was achieved by inhibition of uptake$_1$ by imipramine or cocaine (Haefely, Hürlimann and Thoenen, 1965). The isolated rat uterus stimulated to con-tract with either acetylcholine or carbachol provided a reliable and very sensitive assay for A in blood (Poole and Watts, 1969; Holzbauer and Vogt, 1954, 1955). With electrical stimulation measurable antagonism could be obtained with 5·5 fmol (1) pg of A or less: NA was several thousand times less active (Harvey and Pennefather, 1962a, b). Many other bioassays were developed, but all were very time-consuming and required the rigorous separation of the catecholamines except where they were present in high concentrations.

Bioassay experienced a revival in the hands of Vane (1969). Blood from either the experimental animal or human subject was superfused directly over a series of isolated assay organs capable of detecting and identifying several blood borne agents. The rat stomach strip and hen rectal caecum were used for the detection of NA and A. This technique made extraction of the agents unnecessary and undesirable.

3. Chemical and Biochemical Methods

Chemical and biochemical methods can be divided into three groups: (a) fluorimetric, (b) gas and liquid chromatographic and (c) radioenzymatic methods.

(a) Fluorimetric methods

Although fluorimetric methods are no longer universally employed, due to the attractions of more recently developed methods, fluorimetry has some advantages of its own, such as its relative economy and ease of automation. Fluorimetric methods are available that are sensitive enough to detect reliably the catecholamine concentrations of normal human plasma, provided attention is paid to the need to control any variation in the fluorescence of the blanks and the presence of contaminants.

Nearly all fluorimetric methods are based on the trihydroxyindole (THI) method for NA and A (Atack, 1977). When A for example is gently oxidised under controlled conditions, it produces adrenochrome which in strong alkali in the presence of an antioxidant rearranges to form the highly fluorescent adrenolutine (von Euler, 1959; Callingham, 1967a; Atack, 1977). NA yields the corresponding noradrenolutine, with characteristically different activation and emission spectra, enabling both amines to be measured in the same extract. NA and A can also be discriminated from each other by the assay at two different pH values, one where both amines are oxidised and one where only the A is oxidised. DA can be assayed by a similar method to produce the fluorescent dihydroxyindole (Carlsson and Waldeck, 1958; Atack, 1973).

Most of the measurements of plasma NA and A were, until a few years ago, obtained by the use of the THI method (Callingham, 1975). Improvements in the method have continued to appear. For example, the method of Diamant and Byers (1975) is capable of measuring the catecholamine content of rat as well as human plasma with a high degree of precision. Other methods depend on a two-column procedure for the prior extraction and concentration of the amines (Valori, Brunori, Renzini and Corea, 1970; Jiang, Machacek and Wadel, 1976; Miura, Campese, DeQuattro and Meijer, 1977).

Methods based on the condensation of the amines with ethylene diamine (EDA) are now rarely used. This is probably the result of their bad reputation for lack of specificity, which they soon acquired (see Callingham, 1967a). Even though this fault was finally corrected, they never recovered to be serious rivals of the THI-based methods again. The EDA method was exploited most successfully, however, by Laverty and Sharman (1965) who assayed all three amines after conversion to their acetyl derivatives and separation by paper chromatography. Fluorimetric assays are critically reviewed by Atack (1977).

(b) Chromatographic methods

There have been several reports of the use of gas-liquid chromatography (GLC) for the purification and isolation of catecholamines and their metabolites from a variety of tissues. Although the sensitivity of the method is adequate for most purposes, a reliable and sensitive method for blood plasma has proved elusive. Flame ionisation (Fales and Pisano, 1962; Maruyama and Takemori, 1971, 1972) and electron capture detectors (Karoum, Cattabeni, Costa, Ruthven and Sandler, 1972) have been used, but do not as yet appear able to reach the necessary sensitivity. The sensitivity of the method has been increased to some degree by the prior adsorption of the amines on to alumina followed by evaporation of the subsequent eluate to dryness (Wang, Imai, Yoshioka and Tamura, 1975), a method used successfully to assay the DA and DOPA in the plasma of L-DOPA-treated patients with Parkinson's disease (Mizuno, 1977). No attempt was made to measure the much lower concentrations of plasma NA and A. Claims to have measured red cell catecholamine content by GLC with a flame ionisation detector (Lovelady, 1976) are intriguing, but have recently been challenged (Benedict and Boutagy, 1977).

An important but albeit expensive extension of the GLC method to achieve the required sensitivity involves the GLC procedure followed by mass spectrometry (Costa, Koslow and LeFevre, 1975: Vol. 3 Ch. 3). Sensitivities of the order of 1 pg are possible by this technique (Koslow, Cattabeni and Costa, 1972). Wang *et al.* (1975) argued that this method was sensitive enough, when the triacetyl derivatives of the catecholamines were used, to need only 1 ml of normal plasma.

A promising development is the use of high performance liquid chromatography followed by electrochemical detection (Refshauge, Kissinger, Dreiling, Blank, Freeman and Adams, 1974; Vol. 3, Ch. 2). At present, the method has proved successful for the assay of brain DA and NA (Keller,

Oke, Mefford and Adams, 1976). So far, this technique has not achieved that combination of sensitivity and stability needed for the assay of plasma catecholamines, but it is clearly capable of further development.

(c) Radioenzymatic methods

Radioenzymatic methods involve the conversion of the catecholamines to their O-methylated derivatives by the action of COMT, or in the case of NA alone, to its N-methylated derivative by the action of PNMT. In both instances, the radioactive methyl donor is labelled S-adenosyl-methionine (SAM). The radioactive derivatives are then extracted and counted by liquid scintillation (see Fig. 3).

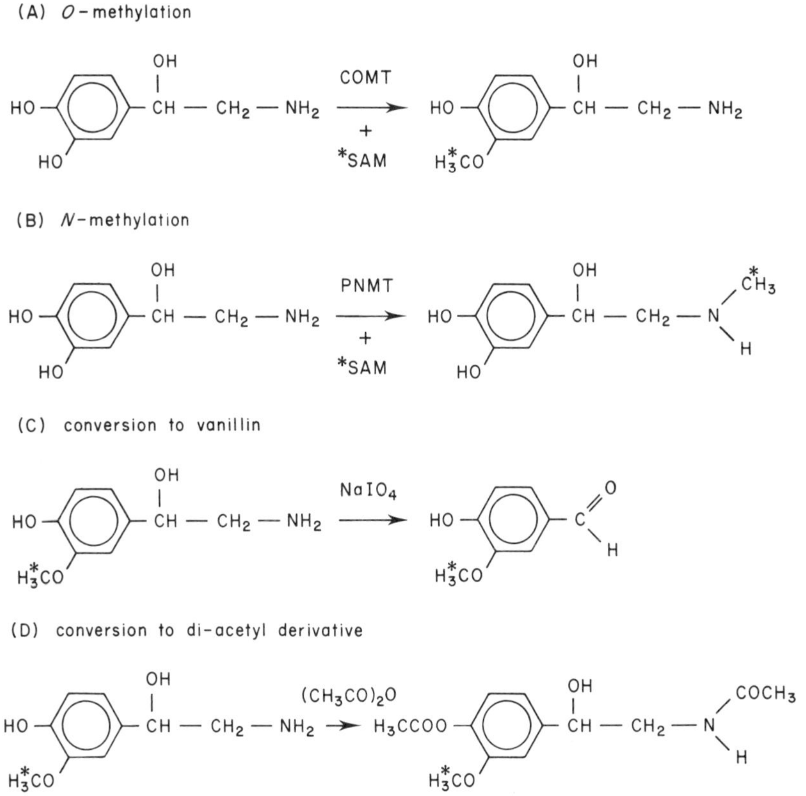

(A) O-methylation

(B) N-methylation

(C) conversion to vanillin

(D) conversion to di-acetyl derivative

Fig. 3. Reactions employed in the radioenzymatic assay of catecholamines. (A) attachment of labelled methyl group to the 3-hydroxyl; (B) attachment of labelled methyl group to the terminal nitrogen of NA; (C) conversion of the 3-methoxy-amines to vanillin by periodate; (D) conversion of the 3-methoxy-amines to their di-acetyl derivatives by acetic anhydride.

(*1*) *Methods based on incubation of COMT with plasma extracts.* Engelman, Portnoy and Lovenberg (1968) were the first to measure catecholamines in plasma by the use of COMT. After concentration of the amines by ion exchange chromatography and lyophilisation of the eluate, incubation was done in the presence of ^{14}C-SAM. The ^{14}C-labelled methylated derivatives were extracted and converted to ^{14}C-vanillin for counting to measure the content of A and NA together. Recoveries through the procedure were measured by the addition to the plasma sample of ^{3}H-NA. The method was then modified by the addition of a thin-layer chromatography step prior to the conversion to vanillin, to separate the methylated derivatives to enable NA and A to be measured separately (Engelman and Portnoy, 1970). Cellulose gel electrophoresis was also used to separate the metanephrines which were then counted without conversion to vanillin (Siggers, Salter and Toseland, 1970). Concentration of the catecholamines was also done with alumina followed by freeze-drying (Christensen, 1973a). Christensen (1973b) also modified the method so that DA could be assayed. The solution that remained from the conversion of the normetanephrine and metanephrine to vanillin and its extraction, was re-extracted with a mixture of toluene and amyl alcohol to recover the methoxytyramine.

Coyle and Henry (1973) modified the method further to measure the catecholamines in perchloric acid extracts of tissues. Unlabelled standards were used to dispense with the need for double isotope counting facilities. and ^{3}H-SAM of high specific activity replaced ^{14}C-labelled SAM to yield more dpm/mol of amine methylated. Unfortunately this method was unsuitable for plasma, due to the presence of some inhibitor of COMT. However, De Champlain, Farley, Cousineau and van Ameringen (1976) were able to show that calcium was a major factor in this inhibition. Chelation of the calcium while maintaining the essential magnesium largely restored the COMT activity. Da Prada and Zürcher (1976) found that the addition of sodium tetraphenylborate to the methylated amines facilitated their extraction into diethylether. With the inclusion of chromatography to enable the separate estimation of NA and A, sensitivities of the order of 1–1·5 pg in 100 µl samples of deproteinised plasma, were reported. Deproteinised plasma in 50 µl samples has proved adequate in the recent method of Sole and Hussain (1977), with a sensitivity of 1 pg. Benzyloxyamine was included to inhibit the decarboxylation of DOPA.

In all these methods, significant interference is caused if the samples contain either α-methyl-NA or isoprenaline.

(*2*) *Methods based on incubation of COMT with native plasma.* There are several methods that carry out the methylation step directly in the plasma with little or no pretreatment of the sample. Passon and Peuler (1973) demonstrated the feasibility of this approach, which also does not require the addition of labelled standards. Tris buffer was used instead of phosphate. It has been confirmed that phosphate buffers can reduce the activity of COMT (Gauchy, Tassin, Glowinski and Cheramy, 1976). The sensitivity claimed for this method varies considerably. For example, Cryer, Santiago and Shah (1974) reported that they could measure 59 fmol (10 pg) of NA added to 1 ml of plasma, but Moerman, Bogaert and De Schaepdryver (1976) quoted between 296 and 591 pmol/l (50 and 100 pg/ml). Hörtnagl, Benedict, Grahame-Smith and McGrath (1977) reported sensitivities of 148–177 pmol/l (25–30 pg/ml), by the use of 300 μl plasma samples, ^{3}H-SAM of very high specific activity, and by saturating the reaction mixture with solid potassium phosphate before extraction of the methylated amines. Peuler and Johnson (1977) have reduced the sample volume to 50 μl, and with the addition of benzyloxyamine and a modified extraction system, claim sensitivities of 1 pg for NA (5·9 fmol) and A (5·5 fmol) and 6 pg (39·2 fmol) for DA. However, both α-methyl-NA and isoprenaline were still found to interfere. A double-isotope assay for use directly in plasma has been developed, which employs two-dimensional chromatography for the separation of the methylated amines (Ben-Jonathan and Porter, 1976).

In assay methods where COMT is used it is necessary to replace ascorbate as a preservative by reduced glutathione. Blaschke and Hertting (1971) showed that ascorbate could serve as a substrate for the enzyme and thus reduce the methylation of catecholamines.

(3) *Methods based on PNMT.* Henry, Starman, Johnson and Williams (1975) described a method in which NA was converted to ^{3}H-A by incubation with ^{3}H-SAM and the enzyme, PNMT. The NA was extracted on alumina from 2 ml plasma samples. The resulting ^{3}H-A was also extracted on alumina, and the eluate treated with phosphotungstic acid to remove any remaining SAM. The assay appears to be specific for NA, since PNMT is much more active against NA than other possible substrates. Non-catechol substrates are removed at the alumina stages. A sensitivity of about 148 fmol/100 μl (25 pg/100 μl) of eluate was reported. This specific assay for NA was used as the basis for a differential assay of all three catecholamines (Weise and Kopin, 1976).

(4) *Method of Barrand and Callingham.* From the number of slightly different radioenzymatic methods, it is apparent that there are still many difficulties inherent in the assay of the very small amounts of catecholamines in normal plasma. Table 3 summarises some of their key details.

In our laboratory we have attempted to develop an assay method (Callingham and Barrand, 1976) that overcomes most of the problems, but is relatively simple and quick. Plasma samples containing 4 mmol/l reduced glutathione and 5 nmol/l EGTA are used in 250 μl volumes. With normal plasma, even samples of this size will only contain about 177 fmol (30 pg) of

Table 3

Radioenzymatic methods for the assay of plasma catecholamines: some characteristics and claimed sensitivities.

References	Catecholamines measured	Sample volume	Methyl donor[b]	Radioactivity recovered/ng of added catecholamine	Sensitivity
a. Double isotope COMT methods					
Engelman et al. (1968)	DA + NA + A[a]	lyophilised eluate from 10 ml plasma	^{14}C-SAM	370 dpm	250 pg
Engelman and Portnoy (1970)	NA, A	lyophilised eluate from 10 ml plasma	^{14}C-SAM	44 cpm	250 pg
Christensen (1973a, b)	DA, NA, A	lyophilised eluate from 10 ml plasma	^{14}C-SAM	103 cpm	250 pg
b. Single isotope COMT methods in deproteinised plasma					
De Champlain et al. (1976)	NA + A[c]	300 μl of supernatant	^{3}H-SAM	3660 cpm	80 pg/ml plasma
Da Prada and Zürcher (1976)	DA, NA, A	100 μl of supernatant = 50 μl of plasma	^{3}H-SAM	24,000 dpm	1-1·5 pg/sample = 20–30 pg/ml plasma
Sole and Hussain (1977)	DA, NA, A	50 μl of supernatant	^{3}H-SAM	DA; 30,000 cpm NA; 13,000 cpm A; 20,000 cpm	1 pg/sample = 20 pg/ml plasma
c. COMT methods in native plasma: single isotope					
Passon and Peuler (1973)	NA, A	250–750 μl	^{3}H-SAM	1343 dpm	—

Reference	Amines assayed	Sample volume	Substrate	Radioactivity	Sensitivity
Hörtnagl et al. (1977)	NA, A	300 µl	^{3}H-SAM	DA; 30,000 cpm NA; 20,000 cpm A; 20,000 cpm	20 pg/ml plasma 20 pg/ml plasma 20 pg/ml plasma
Callingham and Barrand (1976) (as described here)	DA, NA, A	250 µl	^{3}H-SAM	DA; 18,000–80,000 dpm NA; 10,000–30,000 dpm A; 15,000–45,000 dpm	40–100 pg/ml plasma 40–80 pg/ml plasma 15–80 pg/ml plasma
d. Double isotope Ben-Jonathan and Porter (1976)	DA, NA, A	25–100 µl	^{3}H-SAM	DA; 24,053 dpm NA; 4817 dpm A; 7710 dpm	10–30 pg for all three amines = 300 pg/ml plasma
e. PNMT method Henry et al. (1975)	NA	100 µl of 750 µl of eluate from 2 ml of plasma	^{3}H-SAM	7500 cpm	25 pg/100 µl eluate
f. Combined PNMT and COMT method Weise and Kopin (1976)	DA, NA, A	150 µl of 700 µl of eluate from 3 ml of plasma	^{3}H-SAM	DA; 6700 dpm NA; 7500–10,000 dpm A; 7500–10,000 dpm NA by PNMT; 14,500 dpm	127 pg/ml plasma 17 pg/ml plasma 17 pg/ml plasma 20 pg/ml plasma

[a] The catecholamines are assayed together as total amine, but only normetanephrine is added as carrier.
[b] SAM is S-adenosylmethionine.
[c] NA and A are assayed together as total amine with DA treated as a contaminant.

DA 1 pg/ml = 6·53 pmol/l
NA 1 pg/ml = 5·91 pmol/l
A   1 pg/ml = 5·46 pmol/l

NA and less of DA and A. Internal standards consisting of 200 pg each of unlabelled DA (1·31 pmol), NA (1·18 pmol) and A (1·09 pmol) are added to a replicate sample of the plasma to be assayed.

To each plasma sample is added 25 μl of 0·01 M HCl, with or without the internal standards, followed by a mixture containing: 0·5 mM dithiothreitol, 2×10^{-4} M benzyloxyamine, 10^{-4} M pargyline, 20 mM MgCl$_2$, 3·9 mM EGTA, 40 mM tris buffer, 2 μCi ³H-SAM and COMT to give a final pH of 8·8. After incubation at 37° in a shaking water bath for 50 min, the reaction is stopped by the addition of 250 μl of 2 M borate buffer at pH 11.

Blank values are obtained by incubating plasma samples that have previously been treated with alumina to remove their content of catecholamines. We believe that blanks obtained this way approach more closely to the real blank value than do those obtained by omitting any component of the reaction, or by suppressing enzyme activity by removal of Mg^{++}, or by the addition of borate before incubation.

Excess NaCl is added to assist extraction of the methylated amines into toluene/amyl alcohol (3:2 v/v). They are then back-extracted into 650 μl of 0·1 M HCl, followed by the addition of 100 μg of methoxytyramine, normetanephrine and metanephrine as carriers.

Descending paper chromatography can now be used to separate the metabolites of the three catecholamines (Cuello, Hiley and Iversen, 1973), but the process is slow. To hasten this part of the assay, a modification of the system by Laverty and Sharman (1965) is used (see also Sharman, 1971). The methylated amines are converted to their acetyl-derivatives (Fig. 3) by treating the acid extracts twice with 50 μl quantities of acetic anhydride and excess NaHCO$_3$ to neutralise the acid and allow the amines to remain in their most readily acylable form (Welsh, 1952). The stable acetylated derivatives are extracted into 500 μl of ethyl acetate, spotted on Whatman No. 1 paper, for descending chromatography. The solvent system is toluene/methanol/water/ethyl acetate (10:5:5:4 by vol). After equilibration against the aqueous phase of the solvent for 1·5 hr, the chromatograms are run in the organic phase at 27° for 2 hr. The spots corresponding to the derivatives of the three catecholamines are revealed by spraying with Folin-Ciocalteu reagent and ammonia. They are then cut directly into scintillation vials for elution and counting.

With this method sensitivities of: DA, 65–131 fmol (10–20 pg); NA, 59–118 fmol (10–20 pg) and A, 27–55 fmol (5–10 pg), with good linearity up to about 1 ng are achieved. However, variations in sensitivity are seen, which appear to depend on the particular plasma sample.

D. LEVELS IN PERIPHERAL PLASMA

1. Normal Resting Conditions

As outlined earlier, A and some NA enter the circulation by release from the adrenal medulla, while NA also originates from the adrenergic neurons. The exact source of the circulating DA is still uncertain. Once in the blood, the catecholamines are then subject to the uptake processes in the various vascular beds. Thus the concentrations measured in blood samples from any particular point in the circulation represent the resultant of all these different processes.

Most estimates of the normal concentrations of catecholamines in the plasma have been done on blood samples obtained from the arm veins of resting supine subjects, under conditions designed to minimise the stress involved in the collection procedure. Some values for the resting DA, NA and A levels in venous plasma, obtained by radioenzymatic methods are shown in Table 4. The mean values from this table of 1·65 nmol/l (0·28 ng/ml) and 0·44 nmol/l (0·08 ng/ml) for NA and A respectively compare with values of 1·77 nmol/l (0·3 ng/ml) and 0·27 nmol/l (0·05 ng/ml) obtained by the TH1 method (see Callingham, 1975). Although slight differences in plasma catecholamine levels between males and females are sometimes seen, they do not appear to be significant.

There are significant differences in catecholamine content in blood samples drawn from various regions of the body. For example Vendsalu (1960) found that the concentrations of A were highest in blood from the renal veins and vena cava, and Turton and Deegan (1973) found lower levels of A in the anticubital vein compared with the pulmonary artery. Lake, Ziegler and Kopin (1976) assayed blood from the superior vena cava and brachial artery of patients undergoing open heart surgery, and found that the levels of NA were lower in the arterial blood, presumably due to removal of NA during passage through the lungs.

Miura, Haneda, Sato, Miyazawa, Sakuma, Kobayashi, Minai, Shirato, Honna, Takishima and Yoshinaga (1976) assayed blood samples from the coronary sinus, aorta and femoral vein taken during cardiac catheterisation. In agreement with earlier findings, the A content in the aorta was higher than that in the femoral vein. NA levels were highest in the coronary sinus both at rest and during handgrip exercise. This exercise caused elevation of NA and A in all three areas sampled, but the increment in NA was greater in the coronary sinus than in the aorta or in the femoral vein. In fact in conditions of increased sympathetic activity, NA levels in the coronary sinus failed to correlate with levels in the aorta or femoral vein. From this these authors suggested that cardiac tissue is not a major contributor to

Table 4

Mean resting levels of catecholamines in peripheral venous plasma of normal human subjects, determined by radioenzymatic methods.

Method[a]	Number of subjects	Plasma concentrations in ng/ml ± S.E.M.			Reference
		DA	NA	A	
a	22	—	0·20 ± 0·017	0·05 ± 0·006	Engelman and Portnoy (1970)
a	16	—	0·22 ± 0·023	0·05 ± 0·013	Christensen (1973a)
a	6	0·20 ± 0·024	—	—	Christensen (1973b)
b	15	—	0·218 ± 0·014[b]		De Champlain et al. (1976)
b	7	0·127 ± 0·02	0·20 ± 0·023	0·047 ± 0·007	Da Prada and Zürcher (1976)
b	3	0·053 ± 0·001	0·282 ± 0·004	0·096 ± 0·002	Sole and Hussain (1977)
c	8	—	0·223 ± 0·092	0·041 ± 0·023	Cryer et al. (1974a)
c	8	—	0·16 ± 0·02	0·16 ± 0·05	Moerman et al. (1976)
c	11 ♂	—	0·44 ± 0·129	0·124 ± 0·076	Hörtnagl et al. (1977)
c	7 ♀	—	0·55 ± 0·087	0·13 ± 0·071	
c	15	0·034 ± 0·008	0·279 ± 0·043	0·023 ± 0·005	Peuler and Johnson (1977)
c	10 ♂	0·20 ± 0·07	0·29 ± 0·05	0·17 ± 0·02	Callingham and Barrand (1976)[c]
c	6 ♀	0·19 ± 0·04	0·41 ± 0·05	0·13 ± 0·01	
c	14 ♀	0·169 ± 0·016	0·312 ± 0·025	0·046 ± 0·005	Barrand and Callingham (unpub.)
e	7	—	0·254 ± 0·029	—	Henry et al. (1975)
f	13	0·033 ± 0·008	0·208 ± 0·017	0·067 ± 0·009	Weise and Kopin (1976)

[a] See Table 3.
[b] NA and A assayed as total amine.
[c] Blood samples taken from volunteers around the laboratory without any previous rest period.

DA 1 ng/ml = 6·53 nmol/l
NA 1 ng/ml = 5·91 nmol/l
A 1 ng/ml = 5·46 nmol/l

the levels of catecholamines in the circulation. Work by Yamaguchi, De Champlain and Nadeau (1975) lends support to this suggestion. They measured total plasma catecholamine levels in samples taken from the coronary sinus and aorta of dogs during electrical stimulation of the heart. At rest, the concentrations were higher in the aorta, probably reflecting the capacity of the adrenergic nerves of the heart to take up the amines from the coronary circulation. After stimulation, there was a 3–4 fold increase in amine levels in the sinus blood with virtually no change in the aorta.

In a group of supine subjects about to undergo cardiac catheterisation, we have found that the A content of brachial vein blood is significantly lower than the A content of brachial arterial blood (Fig. 4). The NA levels

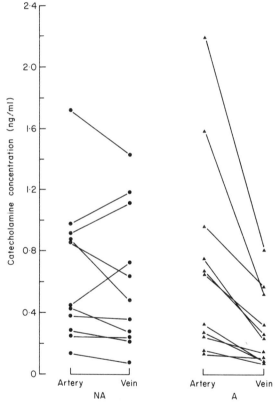

Fig. 4. Arterio–venous differences in concentrations of plasma NA and A. Blood samples withdrawn from brachial artery and vein of 11 supine patients immediately before coronary angiography. Mean concentrations ± s.e.m.: NA—artery 3·96 ± 0·76 nmol/l (0·67 ± 0·13 ng/ml), vein 3·66 ± 0·83 nmol/l (0·62 ± 0·14 ng/ml); A—artery 4·48 ± 1·09 nmol/l (0·82 ± 0·20 ng/ml), vein 1·64 ± 0·38 nmol/l (0·30 ± 0·07 ng/ml) (Barrand, Callingham and Evans, unpublished).

are more variable, which would indicate a balance between uptake and release of NA in the blood vessels of the arm, while the loss of A during passage of the blood through the arm illustrated the effects of uptake alone.

It is possible that regional shunting of blood may modify the amount of uptake capacity to which the venous blood has been subjected before sampling (Roizen, Weise, Moss and Kopin, 1975b) making interpretation difficult. Similarly, arm vein blood levels may be poor indicators of the levels of amines elsewhere in the body, and do not appear to reflect changes in local release in the heart. However, if these limitations are recognised, the catecholamine concentrations in brachial venous blood can provide valuable information when taken together with other parameters.

2. Some Factors that Influence the Plasma Levels of Catecholamines

(a) Diurnal variation

Measurements of urinary catecholamine levels indicate that there may be a diurnal rhythm in sympathetic nerve activity and adrenal medullary secretion. Such variations have been found in A (Elmadjian, Hope and Lamson, 1957) and total amine (Wertheimer, Hassen and Delman, 1972) excretion, with maxima occurring during the day. Similar results were found by Levi (1966) who showed that the rhythm was still retained in men deprived of sleep. Townshend and Smith (1973) also found diurnal variations in both NA and A excretion, which were less obvious in cases where the output of NA was high, e.g. in patients recovering from myocardial infarction and in patients with phaeochromocytoma.

Theorell and Åkerstedt (1976) found that, in shift-workers changing from day to night shifts, the pattern of NA excretion was related to activity, while the A output remained raised during the hours of sleep for at least the first week of the change in shift. There appears to be an underlying rhythm of A excretion but not of NA (Åkerstedt and Levi, 1978).

Daily fluctuations in tissue catecholamine levels have also been detected. Dunn and Lin (1974) found changes in adrenal catecholamines in adult rats which appeared to be correlated with cyclic variations in glucocorticoids. Lew (1976) also observed circadian variations in the NA content of rat adrenal glands.

Eleftheriou (1974) measured NA levels at six hourly intervals in rabbit plasma and found a significant increase coinciding with peak motor activity of the rabbit colony during dusk hours. The variation of plasma NA paralleled that of corticosteroids, suggesting that diurnal rhythms of adrenal medullary activity may be associated with rhythms of adrenal cortical activity and ACTH secretion.

In human subjects, diurnal changes in both plasma NA and A have been reported (Hartley, Mason, Hogan, Jones, Kotchen, Mougey, Wherry, Pennington and Ricketts, 1972b). However, Aronow, Harding, DeQuattro, and Isbell (1973) measured venous blood at four hourly intervals in a variety of in-patients and could detect significant fluctuations of plasma NA in only two of 10 patients and in plasma A in only one subject. Turton and Deegan (1974) withdrew blood samples via an indwelling venous catheter every two hours from a group of 12 patients confined to bed. A decrease was found during the evening initially in plasma A, and then later in NA. Lowest levels of both amines occurred during the hours of sleep, followed by an increase, immediately on waking, in A but not in NA.

(b) Age

Early evidence (Callingham, 1967a) to suggest that there is a rise in plasma catecholamines with increasing age has been confirmed by more recent investigations. Christensen (1973a) found a clear correlation between plasma NA levels and age in subjects from 21 to 77 years old. Coulombe, Dussault and Walker (1976b) found a very high degree of correlation in 41 subjects between NA and age, but not between A and age. In view of this observation, they emphasised the need to make corrections for the ages of subjects used in studies involving the assay of plasma NA, if they have not been age-matched. This correlation did not appear to be related to either pulse rate or blood pressure (Lake, Ziegler and Kopin, 1976). The absolute increase in NA which occurred in response to tilt and isometric exercise was significantly higher in older subjects due, it was suggested, to a decreased responsiveness of older men to the effects of released NA (Ziegler, Lake and Kopin, 1976a). No correlation between NA levels and age has been seen, however, in thyrotoxicosis (Christensen, 1973a), or in hypertension (Sever, Birch, Osikowska and Tunbridge, 1977).

(c) Postural change

Sundin (1958) showed that head-up tilting of human subjects resulted in a rise in the urinary output of NA. Subsequently, measurements of all three catecholamines have indicated that NA and A excretion rise, but DA excretion falls on assumption of the upright posture (Cuche, Kuchel, Barbeau, Boucher and Genest, 1972; Kuchel, Cuche, Buu, Guthrie, Unger, Nowaczynski, Boucher and Genest, 1977).

Alterations in the levels of catecholamines in the plasma have frequently been observed (Hickler, Hamlin and Wells, 1959; Molzahn, Dissmann, Halim, Lohmann and Oelkers, 1972; Christensen and Brandsborg, 1973; Fluck and Salter, 1973; Cryer et al., 1974a; Mueller, Millward and Woods, 1974; Christensen and Brandsborg, 1976; Lake et al., 1976; Moerman et al.,

1976; Johnson, Peuler and Baker, 1977; Hörtnagl et al., 1977). In all cases, significant increases in plasma NA were seen when the subjects were tilted. In the studies where A was also measured, only small, often non-significant rises in this amine were seen. There is little information concerning the effects on plasma DA. De Champlain et al. (1976) reported that there was no change in the levels of DA on assuming an upright posture, and our own studies have failed to find any consistent change in plasma DA when the subject stands up.

Christensen and Brandsborg (1973) suggest that the change in plasma NA with posture is due to the NA released from the vasomotor nerves and also from the heart following vasoconstriction and sympathetic stimulation of the heart on standing. However, it seems, from the evidence previously discussed, that venous blood samples from the arm would not detect any contribution from the NA released in the heart. Christensen (1972a) had previously estimated the cardiac contribution to be about 30 % of the plasma NA, due, he suggested to the very rich sympathetic innervation of the heart. It would seem necessary to elucidate this problem.

Since postural change elicits a consistent alteration in sympathetic activity that is reflected in the levels of plasma catecholamines, it has been used as a test in several studies where impaired or abnormal sympathetic function has been suspected. A greater than normal response to postural change has been reported for hypertensive subjects (De Champlain et al., 1976; Sever et al., 1977), while less than normal responses have been seen in patients with autonomic insufficiency (Cryer and Weiss, 1976; Bannister, Sever and Gross, 1977; Ziegler, Lake and Kopin, 1977), and in diabetics with neuropathy (Christensen, 1972a).

(d) Exercise

Häggendal, Hartley and Saltin (1970) showed that the rise in plasma NA in exercise was related to the work load, and that in untrained subjects for a given work load the rise was greater. Later studies of NA and A found similar rises in brachial vein NA that varied with the intensity of exercise (Kotchen, Hartley, Rice, Mougey, Jones and Mason, 1971; Hartley, Mason, Hogan, Jones, Kotchen, Mougey, Wherry, Pennington and Ricketts, 1972a; Banister and Griffiths, 1972; Galbo, Holst and Christensen, 1975). Rises in A were also observed but only at heavy work loads and at exhaustion (Hartley et al., 1972a; Hawkey, Britton, Wood, Peele and Irving, 1975). Banister and Griffiths (1972) considered that the effect of A was to augment cAMP levels in liver and skeletal muscle during work.

Davies, Few, Foster and Sargeant (1974) concluded that the rises in catecholamine levels were independent of the type of exercise and of the concentration of oxygen inspired, but more closely related to cardiac rate.

They suggested that this correlation of plasma catecholamines with heart rate reflected the ability of the body to maintain adequate blood pressure in the face of increased blood flow demands of the active muscles. Indeed it was found that with β-blockade, which may cause a fall in arterial blood pressure during exercise by inhibiting the normal compensatory increase in cardiac output whilst still allowing vasodilation in muscles, the rise in plasma NA in response to exercise was enhanced (Irving, Britton, Wood, Padgham and Carruthers, 1974). Since it is known that with progressive increments in exercise intensity, blood flow to spanchnic, renal and inactive muscle areas becomes progressively reduced by active vasoconstriction (Rowell, 1974), it seems probable that at least a proportion of the NA in the circulation during exercise derives from vasoconstrictor sympathetic activity.

The stimulus for increased sympathetic nerve activity is thought to be partly via reflexes from the working muscles (Kozlowski, Brzezinska, Nazar, Kowalski and Franczyk, 1973; Rowell, 1974). It has been postulated that sensory nerve fibres located in the muscles play the role of "metabolic receptors" and are stimulated by chemical substances released locally during muscular activity (Coote, Hilton and Perez-Gonzalez, 1971). Indeed it was observed that the rise in plasma NA was significantly greater in response to isometric exercise than to dynamic exercise although the energy cost of the dynamic exercise was several times greater (Kozlowski et al., 1973).

The rise in A in response to exercise is thought to be at least partly associated with the decline in availability of glucose (Galbo, Richter, Hilsted, Holst, Christensen and Henriksson, 1977). During hypoglycemia, circulating A has been observed to increase rapidly (Christensen, Alberti and Brandsborg, 1975). Also during β-blockade with propranolol, which inhibits catechola-mine-stimulated glycogenolysis, both decline in blood sugar and the increase in plasma A in response to exercise was greatly enhanced (Irving et al., 1974; Galbo, Holst, Christensen and Hilsted, 1976b). However, if blood sugar levels were maintained by glucose infusion during β-blockade the A response was reduced (Galbo, Christensen and Holst, 1976a). During prolonged sub-maximal exercise, it was found that the increase in plasma A was not so marked as during maximal short-lived exercise (Hartley et al., 1972b; Galbo et al., 1975). When exercise was performed after intake of a fat diet, glucose concentrations were seen to decline more rapidly than after a carbohydrate diet and the rises in both glucagon and A were intensified (Galbo et al., 1977). Further it was observed that the A response to exercise was much greater in untrained than in trained individuals (Hartley et al., 1972b; Bloom, Johnson, Park, Rennie and Sulaiman, 1976; Galbo et al., 1977).

(e) Temperature change

Urinary levels of NA, A and their metabolites have been measured in a wide variety of animals on exposure to heat or cold (Gale, 1973). It has been found in general that there is an increase in catecholamine excretion with cold exposure.

Early work by Keatinge, McIlroy and Goldfien (1964) in human subjects showed that the intense vasomotor response to acute cold stress with increase in heart rate and blood pressure was accompanied by a slight rise in plasma NA. Cuddy, Smulyan, Keighley, Markason and Eich (1966) noticed an increase in both NA and A in the plasma of most normal human subjects in response to immersion of the hand in ice-cold water. Recent studies (Winer and Carter, 1977) have been able to confirm that in humans subjected to the cold pressor test there is a rapid and significant rise in plasma NA levels coinciding with an increase in blood pressure.

In rats, Roizen et al. (1975b) measured plasma NA levels in blood taken from animals killed after exposure to various temperatures. When the body temperature was lowered by immersion in ice-cold water the total plasma catecholamines were elevated; when the body temperature was raised the catecholamine levels decreased. Benedict, Fillenz and Stanford (1977) used indwelling cannulae to sample blood from rats over the course of several hours at 4°. They found a gradual rise in plasma NA during the first 4 hr of exposure followed by a gradual decline.

The adrenal medulla is also known to secrete in response to changes in ambient temperature (von Euler, 1960; Leduc, 1961). A levels 10 times basal have been reported in adrenal venous blood of dogs exposed to cold (Tanche, 1976). Taggart, Parkinson and Carruthers (1972) noticed a large rise in the levels of A though not of NA in the plasma of men exposed to the heat of sauna bath. Adrenal medullary secretion is thought to play an important role at least during cold exposure thermogenesis by mobilising energy supplies (i.e. glycogenolysis and lipolysis) and by increasing the use of energy substrates by increasing glucose and FFA metabolism (Tanche, 1976; Masoro, 1976).

With long term exposure to heat or cold the catecholamine response to temperature changes and adaptation of the peripheral adrenergic system takes place. Cold acclimatised rats become more sensitive to the calorigenic effects of catecholamines (Fregly, Field, Nelson, Tyler and Dasler, 1977), and excrete less NA than do warm acclimatised animals in response to cold stress (Ostman and Sjöstrand, 1975). The available evidence suggests that acclimatisation to cold involves synergistic action between thyroid hormones and catecholamines (Gale, 1973). Though less information exists on heat acclimatised animals, there are indications that catecholamines injected into such animals have little calorigenic effect (Chaffee, 1976).

As far as is known, no conclusive studies on the effects of long term changes in temperature on plasma catecholamines levels have been done.

(f) Stress

Von Euler (1964) reviewed studies in which it was shown that urinary excretion of catecholamines increased with stress, e.g. during parachute jumps, space flights and gravitational stress. In many of these studies increases in A excretion were noticed before the actual stress. Increased excretion of A and sometimes NA was also seen during mental activity during examinations and during the viewing of various types of films. In general in those forms of stress which are associated with anger, aggression or exhilaration, NA was increased, while in emotional states characterised by apprehension, discomfort, painful and unpleasant feelings, A excretion was increased.

Similar findings have been made in studies in which plasma catecholamines were measured during stress conditions. Holmberg, Levi, Mathé, Rosén and Scott (1967) found increases in plasma NA in response to mental or noise-light stress in hypertensive patients. O'Hanlon (1970) observed increases in plasma A under alerted conditions and decreases during monotonous conditions, which he took to indicate that A levels were related to the state of vigilance. Taggart and Carruthers (1971) detected vastly raised levels of both A and NA in the blood of racing drivers just before and immediately after races, i.e. 20·9 nmol/l (3·54 ng/ml) NA and 3·00 nmol/l (0·55 ng/ml) A 1–3 min after racing, compared with 4·37 nmol/l (0·74 ng/ml) NA and 0·16 nmol/l (0·03 ng/ml) A 3 hr later. During β-blockade with oxprenolol in these subjects, increases in plasma catecholamines were still evident in response to racing stress but the concomitant increases in free fatty acid, glucose and heart rate were reduced (Taggart and Carruthers, 1972). It was felt that during stress, rises in catecholamines associated with elevations in free fatty acid predisposed subjects to atheroma (Carruthers, 1969). Friedman, Byers, Diamant and Rosenman (1975) noticed significant increases in plasma NA levels during the mental stress of problem solving in "coronary-prone" subjects but not in "coronary-resistant" subjects. It was proposed that the coronary-prone subjects in general react more aggressively to various stresses by releasing more NA than do the coronary-resistant subjects and that this adrenergic hyperactivity could well play some part in the pathogenesis of coronary heart disease.

Increases in plasma catecholamines have been detected also during surgical stress. Britton, Hawkey, Wood and Peele (1974) in a study on the role of sympatho-adrenal stimulation in the hypercoagulability which accompanies surgical trauma found significant increases in plasma A levels during abdominal surgery in 14 of the 30 patients examined. Halter, Pflug and Porte (1977) observed large rises in both NA and A during abdominal surgery in man. The concentrations reached were comparable with those seen during exercise or hypoglycaemia, and with the circulating levels achieved during infusion of catecholamines in doses sufficient to cause lipolysis, hyperglycaemia and inhibition of insulin release. Thus such metabolic changes seen during surgical stress were presumed to be mediated by adrenergic activity. A and NA are important in instigating metabolic changes during injury stress (Johnson, 1972), the metabolic effects apparently being directed at maintaining an adequate supply of glucose in the circulation.

Levels of plasma catecholamines have also been measured in patients suffering depression and anxiety (Wyatt, Portnoy, Kupfer, Snyder and Engelman, 1971) and higher than normal concentrations were found, i.e. 0·54 ng/ml total catecholamines compared with the normal value 0·26 ng/ml. During psychotherapy plasma catecholamine levels fell in association with the decrease in anxiety.

In experimental animals, raised levels of plasma catecholamines have been found in response to the stress of immobilisation and to handling (Table 5).

Table 5

Concentrations of NA and A in the plasma of rats subjected to stress (from Popper et al. 1977).

	NA (ng/ml ± S.E.M.)	A (ng/ml ± S.E.M.)
Asleep	0·46 ± 0·08	0·18 ± 0·024
Awake	0·71 ± 0·11	0·25 ± 0·03
Handled	0·83 ± 0·13	0·46 ± 0·06
Immobilised	2·80 ± 0·71	2·40 ± 0·51
Decapitated	7·60 ± 0·77	15·0 ± 0·67

NA 1 ng/ml = 5·91 nmol/l
 A 1 ng/ml = 5·46 nmol/l

In all studies great care must be used when withdrawing blood to avoid stress induced rises in catecholamines (Depocas and Behrens, 1977; Popper, Chiueh and Kopin, 1977; Bühler, Da Prada, Haefely and Picotti, 1978).

(g) Sodium intake

Both increases in dietary sodium and infusions of saline in man have been found to decrease adrenergic activity as measured by a decrease in urinary NA and plasma dopamine-β-hydroxylase (Alexander, Gill, Yamabe, Lovenberg and Keiser, 1974). It was suggested that the change in blood volume was at least partially responsible. Recently it has been found that blood volume expansion, by infusions of either saline or 25% albumin in dogs, reduces both plasma NA and A. DA levels remained unaltered in the plasma but increased significantly in the urine during the infusion of saline (Faucheux, Buu and Kuchel, 1977). The DA was considered to originate in the kidney and was implicated in the regulation of the excretion of sodium. Sodium loading in rats increases plasma NA (Reid, Zivin and Kopin, 1975).

By contrast, in 12 normal male subjects on a restricted sodium diet, Kelsh, Light, Luciano and Oliver (1971) found significant elevations in haematocrit and a decline in plasma volume, together with a rise in plasma NA. In another study (Robertson, Johnson, Brilis, Hill, Watson and Oates, 1977), 15 normal volunteers were brought into balance first on 150 mmol/day sodium and then changed to 10 mmol/day. Plasma NA concentrations rose, on reduction of sodium intake, from 1·42 to 1·83 nmol/l (0·24 to 0·31 ng/ml) at rest, and from 2·66 to 3·90 nmol/l (0·45 to 0·66 ng/ml) on standing. Similarly, in three patients with severe sodium depletion there was a higher than normal level of plasma NA, together with an exaggerated sympathetic response on standing, which were corrected by sodium repletion (Cryer, 1976).

(h) Hypoglycaemia

In early studies it was found that there was an increase in plasma A without change in NA during insulin-induced hypoglycaemia (Vendsalu, 1960; Goldfien, Moore, Zileli, Havens, Boling and Thorn, 1961; Wallace and Harlan, 1965). Later studies confirmed that plasma A levels rose during insulin-induced hypoglycaemia (Brandsborg, Brandsborg and Christensen, 1975; Christensen *et al.*, 1975; Garber, Cryer, Santiago, Haymond, Pagliara and Kipnis, 1976). The rise in plasma A was correlated with the level of hypoglycaemia produced (Brandsborg *et al.*, 1975). A smaller but still significant rise in plasma NA level was also seen in these later studies. The lowest blood glucose levels were reached 30 min after intravenous insulin and maximum A and NA levels attained at 45 min (Brandsborg *et al.*, 1975; Christensen *et al.*, 1975). Since plasma catecholamine levels rose before glucose increase it was concluded that they were responsible for the return of glucose to normal levels. Indeed Garber *et al.* (1976) who studied the rates of uptake and of production of glucose during hypoglycaemia, observed that while insulin levels were high, there was an increase in uptake and a decrease in production of glucose. When the levels of circulating catecholamines rose, production of glucose increased and tissue uptake decreased. These results they argue, are consistent with the *in vitro* observations showing that A can activate glycogenolysis and gluconeogenesis and decrease glucose utilisation. Further, A is known to mobilise lipids which may provide alternative fuels for peripheral tissues during hypoglycaemia thus sparing glucose and allowing more rapid restoration of blood glucose levels to normal

(Christensen et al., 1975). It has also been suggested that beyond these direct effects of adrenergic secretion, adrenergic recruitment of other hormones involved in glucose homeostasis may augment the hyperglycaemic response (Garber et al., 1976).

A secretion in response to hypoglycemia is thought to be mediated via central reflexes. Hansson (1976) showed that non-selective β-receptor blockade reduced A secretion while β_1-blockade enhanced secretion and from this he concluded that β_2-receptor mechanisms were involved. Himsworth (1970) identified chemoreceptors sensitive to low blood sugar within the lateral hypothalamus of rat brain. He found if both sides of the hypothalamus were anaesthetised with lignocaine that the A response to hypoglycaemia no longer occurred. Recent studies (Stricker, Rowland, Saller and Friedman, 1977) have indicated that adreno–medullary secretion during hypoglycaemia may result from decreased availability not only of glucose but also of all other usable fuels.

(i) Oestrous cycle and pregnancy

Changes in circulating levels of catecholamine have been said to occur during the oestrous cycle and in pregnancy. In rats, Green and Miller (1966) reported lower NA but higher A levels during oestrus than during dioestrus. However, the techniques for the collection of blood in this study were stressful and produced high catecholamine levels. In two human subjects Zuspan and Zuspan (1973) observed a surge in both NA and A levels, coinciding with the transient rise in LH and the drop in temperature seen at ovulation.

Studies in rats during pregnancy (Parvez, Parvez and Gripois, 1973) have shown an increase in plasma A on the 18th day of gestation and during parturition but a decline in plasma NA. At the same time catecholamine stores in the adrenal gland were seen to decline. But here again levels of circulating catecholamines appeared to be very high, probably due to the techniques of blood collection.

In human subjects, Zuspan (1970) followed the excretion of free NA and A during the latter part of pregnancy, at birth and during the four weeks after birth. He found a rise in NA and A excretion at birth but otherwise no significant change of pattern in excretion at the other times.

However, catecholamine levels in the hypothalamus fluctuate during the oestrous cycle. Ben-Jonathan, Oliver, Weiner, Mical and Porter (1977) sampled small quantities of blood from the hypophysial portal system during the oestrous cycle and during pregnancy in rats. They could not detect any NA or A either in hypophysial portal blood or in arterial blood, possibly owing to the small amount of plasma available and to the fact that the rats were under anaesthesia. They did however find in the hypophysial portal blood large concentrations of DA which changed during the course of pregnancy and showed cyclic variations during the oestrous cycle. These fluctuations in DA levels in the hypophysial portal blood were not reflected in similar changes in arterial plasma. They suggested from these findings that endogenous DA secreted into the portal blood from the hypothalamus may play an important part in regulating anterior pituitary function though the exact nature of its effects during the oestrous cycle and pregnancy is not yet clear.

3. Plasma Levels of Catecholamines in Disease

(a) Thyroid disease

Early studies on urinary and plasma catecholamine levels in thyroid disease produced conflicting data, which led to the idea that abnormal thyroid function had little effect on catecholamine levels (Stoffer, Jiang, Gorman and Pikler, 1973). However, recent evidence shows that there are abnormal levels of circulating catecholamines in hypothyroidism (Christensen, 1972b, 1973a; Stoffer et al., 1973; Ghione, Pellegrini, Buzzigoli, Carpi, Valori and Donato, 1974; Coulombe et al., 1976b). Significantly higher plasma levels of NA but not A were observed. Coulombe et al. (1976b) suggested that this increase reflected adrenergic overactivity to compensate for the marked diminution in thyroid function with consequential disturbances in energy production, thermogenesis and cardiac contractility. This is supported by the observations of Fregly, Nelson, Resch, Field and Lutherer (1975) who were able to demonstrate reduced responsiveness to the β-effects of isoprenaline in hypothyroid rats, which could be restored by administration of thyroxine.

In hyperthyroidism the information is conflicting. Stoffer et al. (1973), Ghione et al. (1974), and Christensen (1973a) observed lower than normal levels of circulating NA and indeed Stoffer et al. (1973) were able to find an inverse correlation between thyroxine levels and plasma catecholamine levels. Coulombe et al. (1976b) disagreed with the interpretation of this data and stated that if the values were corrected for the age of the patient any apparent difference in NA levels between normal and hyperthyroid patients disappeared. They were also unable to find any correlation between plasma NA and either serum thyroxine, free thyroxine or triodothyronine. They measured the secretion rates after infusion of NA (Coulombe, Dussault and Walker, 1977) and A (Coulombe, Dussault, Letarte and Simard, 1976a) and concluded that there was no difference in the rates of catecholamine secretion between euthyroid and hyperthyroid subjects but NA secretion was elevated in the hypothyroid state.

There is some evidence to suggest a supersensitivity at least to the metabolic effects of catecholamines in hyperthyroidism (see Landsberg, 1977). Williams, Lefkowitz, Watanabe, Hathaway and Besch (1977) were able to measure β-receptor site numbers in the cardiac membranes of normal rats and of rats made hyperthyroid by administration of triodothyronine or thyroxine and found a large increase in the number of receptors in the hyperthyroid state.

(b) Heart disease

It is generally believed that there is an increase in sympathetic nervous activity during acute myocardial infarction. Measurements of urinary catecholamine levels have found raised excretion of NA and A during the acute stages of infarction with the most pronounced and persistent increases being found in patients with infarction complicated by shock and cardiac arrhythmias (Januszewicz, Sznajderman, Wocial and Preibisz, 1968; Prakash, Parmley, Horvat and Swan, 1972).

Similarly in plasma, higher than normal levels of catecholamines, particularly NA, have been found in patients during the first 48 hr after the onset of infarction (McDonald, Baker, Bray, McDonald and Restieaux, 1969; Griffiths and Leung, 1971; Januszewicz, Sznajderman, Ciswicka-Sznajderman, Wocial and Rymaszewski, 1971; Siggers, Salter and Fluck, 1971; Lukomsky and Oganov, 1972; Videbaek, Christensen and Sterndorff, 1972; Christensen and Videbaek, 1974; Strange, Vetter, Rowe and Oliver, 1974; Vetter, Strange, Adams and Oliver, 1974) (see Table 6). The highest levels appeared to be associated with severe cardiogenic shock, the development of arrhythmias and the highest mortality after infarction (McDonald *et al.*, 1969; Griffiths and Leung, 1971; Videbaek *et al.*, 1972, Lukomsky and Oganov, 1972; Strange *et al.*, 1974). Indeed Griffiths and Leung (1971) suggested that the degree to which the plasma catecholamines were elevated could help to forecast the outcome.

The raised levels of plasma NA found during infarction have been said to originate from nerve endings in the heart and be released as a compensatory mechanism to increase the contractility of the heart, and that A secretion from the adrenal gland is induced reflexly from receptors at the site and boundary of ischaemic areas of the heart (Videbaek *et al.*, 1972). It would however seem more likely that the NA found in the plasma is released from other areas of the circulation as a device to compensate for the altered haemodynamics that occur following myocardial infarction.

It has been suggested that the clinical events associated with myocardial infarction may not cause but be in some cases the result of increased catecholamine release (Siggers *et al.*, 1971). Christensen and Videbaek (1974) concluded from the magnitude of the plasma catecholamine levels found in their studies that circulating NA could itself give rise to the metabolic and circulatory effects seen during myocardial infarction.

It is questionable whether the high levels of catecholamine produced during infarction are physiologically useful or in fact deleterious (Siggers

Table 6

Concentrations of catecholamines in venous blood sampled within 24 hr following myocardial infarction.

Number	Control patients (ng/ml ± S.E.M.) NA	A	Number	Patients with infarction (ng/ml ± S.E.M.) NA	A	References
50	0·24 ± 0·01	0·04 ± 0·01	9[a]	4·10 ± 0·2	0·27 ± 0·04	Griffiths and Leung (1971)
			8[b]	1·5 ± 0·15	0·12 ± 0·02	
			8[c]	0·61 ± 0·08	0·09 ± 0·01	Januszewicz et al. (1971)
			25	1·34 ± 0·04	0·30 ± 0·03	
			[d]	1·30 ± 0·16	0·88 ± 0·14	
			[e]	1·00 ± 0·09	0·55 ± 0·06	Siggers et al. (1971)
5	0·43 ± 0·04	0·05 ± 0·01	10	0·97 ± 0·17	0·55 ± 0·06	Christensen and Videbaek (1972)
8	0·23 ± 0·03[f]		10	1·00 ± 0·14[f]	0·12 ± 0·02	Videbaek et al. (1972)

[a] Patients in clinical shock.
[b] Abnormal blood pressure, central venous pressure and heart rate.
[c] Normal blood pressure and heart rate.
[d] No arrhythmias.
[e] With pulmonary oedema.
[f] Total catecholamines.
NA 1 ng/ml = 5·91 nmol/l
A 1 ng/ml = 5·46 nmol/l

et al., 1971). For instance, significant rises in both plasma NA and free fatty acid have been found in patients suffering acute myocardial infarction (Januszewicz *et al.*, 1971; Christensen and Videbaek, 1974; Vetter *et al.*, 1974). NA is known to be one of the most potent factors releasing free fatty acids into the blood. It has been suggested that the increased sympathetic activity raises free fatty acid levels promoting augmented myocardial oxygen consumption which may be particularly harmful to the ischaemic myocardium. (Januszewicz *et al.*, 1971). However, high catecholamine levels during heart failure may be beneficial in maintaining cardiac output and peripheral resistance, whereas with infarction without heart failure, raised catecholamine levels may increase the risk of arrhythmias and sympathetic blockade could then be appropriate (Siggers *et al.*, 1971).

(c) Hypertension

Both plasma and urinary catecholamines, as indicators of sympathetic activity, have been measured in a wealth of different studies of human and experimental hypertension. Increased catecholamine excretion has been reported in 5% (DeQuattro, 1971) and in 25% (Esler and Nestel, 1973) of hypertensive patients, while raised plasma levels of total catecholamines (Engelman, Portnoy, Sjoerdsma, 1970; DeQuattro and Chan, 1972) and of NA (Cuche, Kuchel, Barbeau, Langlois, Boucher and Genest, 1974) have also been observed. A close correlation between plasma NA, but not A, and the resting systolic blood pressure has also been seen (Louis, Doyle and Anavekar, 1973a; Louis, Doyle, Anavekar and Chua, 1973b). However, other studies have failed to detect any evidence of raised NA excretion in hypertensive patients (Berglund, Tibblin and Aurell, 1975; Bing, Harlow, Smith and Townshend, 1977). But evaluation of adrenergic activity by the measurement of urinary catecholamines, may be misleading since they may be influenced by changes in kidney function (De Champlain *et al.*, 1976).

Further investigations on plasma catecholamine levels (Christensen and Christensen, 1972; Pedersen and Christensen, 1975; Lake, Ziegler, Coleman and Kopin, 1977), have likewise been unable to reveal significant differences in the plasma levels of NA between hypertensive and normotensive subjects. When the subjects were age-matched, any initial differences disappeared (Lake *et al.*, (1977) However, this conclusion has been challenged (Campese, Myers and DeQuattro, 1977; De Champlain and Cousineau, 1977; Sever *et al.*, 1977). In their study, Sever *et al.* (1977) found that the plasma NA levels increased with age only in the normotensive group. In older people there was no significant difference in plasma NA levels between normotensives and hypertensives but the younger age group included hypertensives with significantly raised plasma NA levels. This they felt supported the hypothesis that in some patients autonomic overactivity is important in the early stages of development of essential hypertension but that other factors are subsequently involved in maintaining the raised pressure.

Other studies have attempted to define more closely the type of hypertension under scrutiny. De Champlain *et al.* (1976) found that 50% of the hypertensives that they studied had plasma levels of catecholamine significantly above the normotensive range. This group differed in their cardiovascular characteristics in having higher systolic pressure and faster heart rate than the remaining hypertensives. DeQuattro, Campese, Miura and Meijer (1976) investigated a series of 66 hypertensives and found only 27% of them had raised circulating catecholamine levels. However, when they divided the hypertensives into groups of low, normal and high renin activity they found that 70% of the hypertensives in the high renin group showed raised catecholamine levels. In a subsequent study, comparing 31 patients with essential hypertension and 32 age-matched normotensives, Esler, Julius, Zweifler, Randall, Harburg, Gardiner and DeQuattro (1977) were able to confirm that plasma NA levels are elevated only in the group of hypertensives with high renin activity.

By contrast in a group of hypertensives with low renin hypertension Esler, Zweifler, Randall, Julius, Bennett, Rydelek, Cohen and DeQuattro (1976) found lower than normal resting levels of circulating NA and a diminished rise in NA in response to tilting (see Table 7). Further, infusion of tyramine, which releases NA from nerve endings produced a smaller than normal rise in blood pressure in these subjects. These authors suggested that low renin hypertension although of diverse aetiology, shows a common secondary sympathetic underactivity.

However, Lowder, Hamet and Liddle (1976) noted reduced effects of hypoglycaemia in low renin hypertension and concluded that there was a decreased β-adrenergic responsiveness in this type of hypertension. Since it is A which is involved in insulin hypoglycaemia, Kuchel (1976) looked at both NA and A excretion in low renin hypertension. He found no significant increase in NA excretion but a highly significant increase in A excretion. This he considered to be a compensatory increase in A due to β-adrenergic hypo-responsiveness in this type of hypertension.

(d) Experimental hypertension

It has been suggested that, when rats are made hypertensive by treatment with deoxycorticosterone and loading with sodium, both secretion from the adrenergic nerves and adrenal medulla are involved (De Champlain and van Ameringen, 1972). De Champlain *et al.* (1976) found significantly raised circulating levels of total catecholamines in the hypertensive rats, which they suggested appeared before the onset of the hypertension. Reid *et al.* (1975) observed significant increases in NA only, which could be produced

Table 7

Concentrations of catecholamines in venous plasma of hypertensive patents.

Normotensive subjects		Hypertensive subjects		References
Number	Total catecholamines (ng/ml ± S.E.M.)	Number	Total catecholamines (ng/ml ± S.E.M.)	
32	0·24 ± 0·01	18	0·45 ± 0·04	Engelman et al. (1970)
10	0·27 ± 0·05	10	0·39 ± 0·05	DeQuattro and Chan (1972)
15	0·218 ± 0·014	22	0·37 ± 0·032	De Champlain et al. (1976)
	NA A		NA A	
26♂	0·26 0·05	9♂	0·26 0·08–0·43	Pedersen and Christensen (1975)
6♀	0·24 0·06	10♀	0·23 0·13–0·34	
84	0·30 ± 0·02	67	0·34 ± 0·02	Lake et al. (1977)
41	0·28 ± 0·02[a]	40	0·39 ± 0·03	
	Number		Number	
12	15 0·14 ± 0·01	Low renin 0·10 ± 0·02 High renin 0·25 ± 0·01	17 Normal renin 0·17 ± 0·02	Esler et al. (1976)
20	16 0·14 ± 0·01		15 Normal renin 0·18 ± 0·02	Esler et al. (1977)

[a] Values corrected for the ages of the subjects.

by sodium loading on its own without any rise in blood pressure, suggesting that the raised plasma catecholamines alone were not sufficient to cause hypertension, but required mineralocorticoid-induced sodium retention as well.

In rats made hypertensive by unilateral nephrectomy and clipping the renal artery, plasma NA levels rose above those found in sham operated normotensive animals, seven days after treatment (Dargie, Franklin and Reid, 1977). These rises in plasma NA could be prevented by intracisternal administration of 6-hydroxy-DA.

In rats with spontaneous genetic hypertension, plasma levels of NA, but not of total catecholamines, were raised at four weeks of age (Grobecker, Roizen, Weise, Saavedra and Kopin, 1975). It was proposed that, in these animals, there was an increase in sympathetic neuronal activity with a decrease in adrenal medullary secretion. Nagaoka and Lovenberg (1976) also observed raised levels of plasma NA in young hypertensive rats, but these were not maintained as the animals grew older. In spontaneously hypertensive rats studied at 8–12 weeks of age, an increase in the level of total catecholamines, but not of NA was seen (Roizen, Weise, Grobecker and Kopin, 1975a), which would indicate that it was now the adrenal medulla that was important. However, it is possible that it is the adrenal cortical activity rather than the adrenal medulla, which contributes to the maintenance of hypertension in these animals (Aoki, Takikawa and Hotta, 1973).

(e) Phaeochromocytoma

Tumours involving the chromaffin cells of the adrenal medulla and elsewhere in the body often produce large quantities of catecholamines, which are released into the circulation, to cause hypertension (Manger and Gifford, 1977). The hypertension produced is often spasmodic and combined with cardiac arrhythmias and hypermetabolic symptoms similar to those seen in hyperthyroidism and diabetes (Engelman, 1977). Tumours of the adrenal medulla secrete either NA alone or NA and A, while extramedullary tumours secrete NA (DeQuattro, Campese and Antonaccio, 1977). Sustained hypertension appears to be more often associated with NA secreting tumours, and pallor and tremor are more common when A is secreted as well (Lance and Hinterberger, 1976).

In the presence of such tumours the levels of catecholamines in peripheral blood may become raised as much as 10–50 times the normal levels, although this may vary since release into the circulation is often spasmodic. When NA and A were measured separately, Louis and Doyle (1971) found raised NA in all cases but raised A in only four of the five patients studied. The fifth patient with normal A levels was subsequently found to have an extra-adrenal tumour in the mediastinum secreting only NA (see Table 8A).

Table 8

Concentrations of catecholamines in plasma of patients with phaeochromocytoma.

A. Concentrations in peripheral venous plasma compared with those in essential hypertension

Number	Phaeochromocytoma Total catecholamines (ng/ml ± S.E.M.)	Number	Essential hypertension Total catecholamines (ng/ml ± S.E.M.)	References
7	10·4 ± 1·7	9	0·28 + 0·01	Louis and Doyle (1971)
11	5·75 ± 0·41	31	0·34 ± 0·01	Geffen et al. (1973)
	NA		NA	
5	A 6·4 ± 0·67	7	A 0·24 ± 0·15	Louis and Doyle (1971)
	1·05 ± 0·22		0·07 ± 0·04	

B. Concentrations of total catecholamines (ng/ml) in plasma taken from different points in the circulation

Location of tumour	Iliac bifurcation	IVC above renal veins	IVC at diaphragm	IVC below right atrium	SVC	References
Ectopic at level of diaphragm	1·70	1·79	4·23	5·17	0·36	Engelman et al. (1968)
Mediastinal tumour	13·0	15·0	—	16·5	30·0	Louis and Doyle (1971)
Left adrenal tumour	0·9	3·8	—	1·6	0·35	Louis and Doyle (1971)
Left adrenal tumour	4·90	right renal vein 5·57 left renal vein 12·18	6·94	6·21	—	Barrand and Callingham (unpub.)

Measurement of plasma catecholamine levels in samples from selected areas of the circulation can localise the site of the tumour to the region where the catecholamine content of the venous drainage is highest (see Table 8B). It has been suggested that the release of catecholamines from the tumours is due to continuous synthesis without parallel synthesis of storage granules, allowing the catecholamines to diffuse into the circulation (Winkler and Smith, 1968). Phaeochromocytoma tumours have been found to synthesise catecholamines at higher rates than normal adrenal medullary tissue, possibly because of a disturbance in the normal feedback inhibition by catecholamines of tyrosine hydroxylase. Indeed it has been noted that inhibition of tyrosine hydroxylase activity by α-methyl tyrosine lowers the blood pressure in phaeochromocytoma patients but not in patients with hypertension due to other causes (Winkler and Smith, 1968). The spasmodic bursts of catecholamine release are thought to be precipitated by mechanical irritation, e.g. during a sudden change in posture, causing discharge of blood rich in catecholamines which accumulates in the sinusoidal spaces present in some tumours (Winkler and Smith, 1968).

Geffen, Rush, Louis and Doyle (1973) measured the circulating levels of catecholamines and of dopamine-β-hydroxylase, and found a significant correlation between them in the plasma of patients with essential hypertension. However, they could find no correlation between plasma levels of NA and dopamine-β-hydroxylase, which would support the view that the catecholamines bypass the storage granules and release by exocytosis. Further support comes from the observation that prostaglandin E_2 will inhibit the release of catecholamines from normal adrenal medullary tissue but not from medullary tumours (Gutman and Boonyaviroj, 1976).

(f) Disorders of the autonomic nervous system

Disorders of the autonomic nervous system, of both central and peripheral origin, may reduce the efficiency with which the sympathetic neurons bring about the changes in the distribution of circulating blood and control the blood pressure in response to postural change (Moskowitz, 1977). Under these conditions, the levels of NA in particular in the circulation may be different from those in normal subjects.

(1) Idiopathic orthostatic hypotension. In one group of patients with primary autonomic dysfunction, Cryer, Weiss and Landau (1974b) found that the plasma levels of total catecholamines were lower than normal in both supine and upright positions. However, in a later study, Cryer and Weiss (1976) found that the NA levels were only reduced below normal when the subjects stood up. No significant abnormalities in A levels were seen at any time. These authors suggested that the postural hypotension was due to a

decreased release of NA from adrenergic neurons rather than any change in uptake or catabolism. Osikowska and Sever (1976) and Bannister *et al.* (1977) have found a reduction in the circulating NA of patients both standing and supine. The NA levels were lowest in those with the most severe autonomic defects. It was suggested that measurement of plasma NA could serve as a useful indicator of the extent of the sympathetic dysfunction.

Ziegler *et al.* (1977) studied the circulating NA response to standing in a group of patients with idiopathic orthostatic hypotension. They found that in the patients with signs of central neurological defects, the levels of plasma NA were normal in the supine position while in those patients with no signs of central defects the recumbent levels of plasma NA were subnormal. However, in both groups of patients NA levels failed to rise in response to tilting.

In patients with isolated autonomic dysfunction i.e. without any signs of central lesions, Kontos, Richardson and Norvell (1975a) found depletion of the NA content of blood vessels. Furthermore, the pressor response in these patients to tyramine infusion was much reduced, and they were supersensitive to infusions of NA. In contrast patients with central lesions were found to have normal responses to tyramine and were not as sensitive to NA infusion (Kontos, Richardson and Norvell, 1975b).

(2) *Familial dysautonomia.* Circulating catecholamine levels in this condition have been found to be normal at rest but they fail to rise appropriately on standing and during exercise (Ziegler, Lake and Kopin, 1976b). Though there is some debate whether sympathetic nerve endings are structurally normal in this disease, at least at rest, they appear to release normal quantities of NA.

(3) *Peripheral neuropathy of diabetes mellitus.* Peripheral neuropathies, involving the autonomic nervous system, may occur as a result of diseases such as diabetes (Christensen, 1971; Moskowitz, 1977), leading to abnormal responses to postural change and to exercise, with concomitant effects on plasma levels of catecholamines.

Christensen (1972a) measured total plasma catecholamine levels both at rest and in response to standing in three different groups of diabetics, each controlled by diet and insulin: those with neuropathy, those without such symptoms, and those with neuropathy that had been treated by hypophysectomy. He found plasma catecholamine levels to be significantly lower than normal only in the group of diabetics with neuropathy not treated by hypophysectomy both resting and on standing (see Table 9A). He suggested that his findings on diabetics with neuropathy showed that there was a normal catecholamine output from the heart but a reduced output from the periphery. Clinical and physiological studies have shown that diabetic neuropathy is most severe in the lower extremities, and it appears from studies

Table 9

Concentrations of catecholamines in venous plasma of diabetic subjects.

	No. of subjects	Plasma concentrations of total catecholamines (ng/ml ± s.D.)		
		Resting	5 min standing	10 min standing
A. Effects of postural change (from Christensen, 1972)				
Non-diabetics	7	0·26 ± 0·09	0·69 ± 0·15	0·72 ± 0·13
Diabetics without neuropathy	6	0·26 ± 0·09	0·75 ± 0·26	0·72 ± 0·17
Diabetics with neuropathy	9	0·11 ± 0·06	0·30 ± 0·09	0·37 ± 0·12
Diabetics with neuropathy treated by hypophysectomy	8	0·28 ± 0·10	0·27 ± 0·27	0·73 ± 0·23
B. Effects of ketoacidosis (from Christensen, 1974)				
			NA	A
Untreated diabetics without neuropathy	10		1·27 ± 1·13	0·51 ± 0·62
Diabetics treated with insulin	6		0·18 ± 0·06	0·05 ± 0·03

NA 1 ng/ml = 5·91 nmol/l
A 1 ng/ml = 5·46 nmol/l

comparing the tissue levels of NA and A from post-mortem material in diabetic patients with neuropathy and non-diabetic subjects (Neubauer and Christensen, 1976), that there are significantly lower than normal levels of NA in the radial artery and even lower levels in the fibial and femoral arteries of the diabetic patients.

In the diabetics with neuropathy treated by hypophysectomy, Christensen (1972a) found apparently normal catecholamine levels in the plasma. In the diabetics without neuropathy, normal blood catecholamine levels were observed during treatment with diet and insulin (Christensen, 1972a). However in untreated diabetics where ketoacidosis had developed, grossly elevated plasma levels of NA and in some cases A as well were observed (Christensen, 1970, 1974). The increases were exaggerated during exercise. The level of plasma NA appeared to be correlated to the degree of metabolic derangement expressed as total carbon dioxide in the plasma. On treatment with insulin the catecholamines fell to normal values within three days (Table 9B). Christensen (1974) suggested that the rise in plasma NA seen during ketoacidosis could be partly due to increases in heart rate and to adrenergic adjustment to circulatory volume depletion, but that the complicated circulatory and metabolic situation in a ketotic diabetic made it impossible to separate the rise in plasma NA into circulatory and metabolic components.

(4) *Spinal section.* Quadriplegic patients with complete cervical spinal cord transection no longer possess supraspinal control of their sympathetic outflow. In patients with such lesions, resting plasma levels of both NA and A have been found to be significantly lower than normal (Table 10) (Debarge, Christensen, Corbett, Eidelman, Frankel and Mathias, 1974; Mathias, Christensen, Corbett, Frankel, Goodwin and Peart, 1975; Mathias, Frankel, Christensen and Spalding, 1976b) presumably due to loss of centrally mediated stimulation of sympathetic activity. Indeed by comparison, plasma catecholamine levels were normal in a group of paraplegic patients with lesions below T12/LI i.e. with an intact sympathetic outflow (Mathias et al., 1976b). It was also found that in patients with cervical lesions, plasma NA levels failed to rise as normal in response to tilt (Mathias et al., 1975). With bladder and muscle stimulation, marked increases in both blood pressure and plasma NA occurred (Debarge et al., 1974; Mathias, Christensen, Corbett, Frankel and Spalding, 1976a). An enhanced pressor response to infused NA was also seen in these patients (Mathias et al., 1976b). Both hypersensitivity of adrenergic receptors and loss of baroceptor reflexes controlling blood pressure were thought to account for these findings.

Table 10

Concentrations of catecholamines in venous plasma of quadriplegic subjects.

Number	Normal subjects (ng/ml)		Number	Quadriplegic subjects (ng/ml)		References
	NA	A		NA	A	
16	0·22	0·05	6	0·04	0	Debarge et al. (1974)
5	0·13	0·03	4	0·07	0·02	Mathias et al. (1975)
15	0·20	0·06	16	0·05	0·005	Mathias et al. (1976a)

NA 1 ng/ml = 5·91 nmol/l
A   1 ng/ml = 5·46 nmol/l

4. Effects of Some Drugs on the Plasma Levels of Catecholamines

(a) *Nicotine and smoking*

Early studies (Woods, Richardson, Richardson and Bozeman, 1956; Watts, 1961) showed that injection of nicotine in dogs led to significant increases in the arterial concentrations of catecholamines, particularly A, together with increases in the blood pressure and heart rate. More recently, Tsujimoto, Nishikawa, Dohi and Kojima (1974) found that injections of nicotine in monkeys and dogs, caused large rises in total catecholamine concentrations within 15–30 sec in the vena cava above the outflow from the adrenal glands, and within 30–35 sec in the femoral artery. They estimated that about 70% of the increase was due to A. The increases in plasma glucose, free fatty acid and serum potassium that were seen at the same time, could also be produced by the injection of A alone.

Reserpine administration, which depletes the stores of catecholamines, was found to block the peripheral vasoconstrictor action of nicotine (Burn, 1961) and to abolish nicotine-induced inhibition of gastro-intestinal contractility (Carlson, Ruddon, Hug and Bass, 1970a). Both adrenalectomy and vagotomy with spinal anaesthesia were also found to reduce the inhibitory effects of nicotine on gastro-intestinal contractility. It was proposed that nicotine had multiple sites of action on catecholamine release, in part centrally mediated and in part via peripheral mechanisms (Carlson, Ruddon, Hug, Schmiege and Bass, 1970b).

The pharmacological effects of smoking appear to depend largely on the action of nicotine, though inhalation of carbon monoxide may also be involved (Schievelbein and Eberhardt, 1972). Changes in plasma catecholamines during smoking were investigated in man by Klensch (1965, 1966) who found a rise in NA coinciding with an increase in circulating free fatty acids. When prenylamine was administered seven days prior to smoking, the effects were attenuated. However, Hill and Wynder (1974) observed a change in A only during smoking, which was dependent on the nicotine content of the cigarettes. In subjects smoking nicotine-free cigarettes there was no significant increase, with low nicotine cigarettes A levels rose from 1·75 to 2·56 nmol/l (0·32 to 0·47 ng/ml) and with high nicotine cigarettes from 1·64 to 4·42 nmol/l (0·30 to 0·81 ng/ml). No clear cut elevations in free fatty acids were evident in this study. Cryer, Haymond, Santiago and Shah (1976) re-investigated the effects of smoking on catecholamine levels in man using a more sensitive radioenzymatic method. They found significant rises in both A and NA within 10–15 min of smoking. These were associated with cardio-vascular changes (increases in blood pressure and heart rate), and metabolic changes (increases in blood glycerol, lactate and pyruvate), all of which were prevented by adrenergic blockade with phentolamine and propranolol combined. Since the cardiovascular effects preceded any noticeable change in plasma catecholamine levels, locally released rather than circulating catecholamines were thought to be responsible. Recently Robson and Fluck (1977) were able to take simultaneous blood samples from the coronary sinus and the brachial artery during smoking in patients undergoing catheterisation for the investigation of angina pectoris. Although smoking evoked an increase in heart rate, no significant changes in total catecholamines were detectable in either area possibly due to the effective neuronal re-uptake mechanisms in the heart. However, during β-blockade with oxprenolol, catecholamine levels were noticeably raised in the coronary sinus blood after smoking.

(b) Anaesthesia

Although early work on the effects of anaesthetics on plasma catecholamine levels in human subjects failed to detect any changes with either ether or pentothal-nitrous oxide (Hammond, Aronow and Moore, 1956), in later studies, significant increases in plasma NA (Black, McArdle, McCullough and Unni, 1969), and in both NA and A (Anton, Gravenstein and Wheat, 1964) were seen with ether but not with halothane anaesthesia. In dogs, Richardson, Woods and Richardson (1957) found that ether, chloroform and vinyl ether would all raise the levels of NA and A in the plasma.

Halothane anaesthesia has been reported to decrease cardiac output and myocardial contractility at first (Eger, Smith, Stoelting, Cullen, Kadis and Whitcher, 1970), which may be followed by an increase, due possibly to activation of the β-receptors (Price, Skovsted, Pauca and Cooperman, 1970). Significantly lower levels of plasma catecholamines have also been found in rats anaesthetised with halothane (Roizen, Moss, Henry and Kopin, 1974), although differences in plasma catecholamines have also been seen between awake and sleeping rats without any anaesthesia (Popper *et al.*, 1977). Since both plasma NA and A levels in normal rats, and plasma NA in adrenalectomised animals were reduced by halothane, halothane probably affected release from neurons and from the adrenal medulla. Similar decreases in plasma catecholamines were also seen in dogs with halothane and iso-flurane (Perry, van Dyke and Theye, 1974). In human subjects, anaesthesia induced by barbiturate and maintained with halothane and nitrous oxide, may lead to a fall in the plasma level of A but not of NA (Halter *et al.*, 1977). Although halothane depresses firing in the cervical sympathetic trunk (Skovsted, Price and Price, 1970), it may, together with methoxyflurane and enflurane, also inhibit the release of catecholamines from the adrenal medulla (Göthert and Wendt, 1977a, b).

Barbiturate anaesthesia has been reported to depress sympathetic activity (Roizen *et al.*, 1974) and block the release by exocytosis of catecholamines from the adrenal medulla (Holmes and Schneider, 1973). Similarly, cyclo-propane has also been observed to inhibit NA release *in vitro* (Roizen, Thoa, Moss and Kopin, 1976). However, cyclopropane anaesthesia was shown to cause an increase in the plasma levels of A in dogs, and of NA in human subjects (Perry *et al.*, 1974). It was suggested that the depth of anaesthesia could be important in affecting the response.

Many studies of the effects of anaesthesia are beset by the difficulty of devising valid and stable controls.

(c) Caffeine and coffee ingestion

Though some effects of caffeine are mediated through inhibition of phos-phodiesterase with the consequent accumulation of cAMP (Robertson, Frölich, Carr, Watson, Hollifield, Shand and Oates, 1978), stimulation of the sympathoadrenomedullary system is also thought to be involved.

In 1959, De Schaepdryver found that intravenous injection of caffeine in dogs stimulated the secretion of NA and A into the adrenal venous blood. With human subjects, coffee is more often studied than caffeine itself, though a recent report (Kalsner, 1977) has suggested that there may be a coronary vasoconstrictor substance unrelated to caffeine which is present both in regular and decaffeinated coffee. After ingestion of coffee containing 220–225 mg of caffeine, significant increases in the excretion of both A and NA have been shown (Levi, 1967; Bellet, Roman, De Castro, Kim and Kershbaum, 1969). In a recent study, plasma levels of both NA and A were significantly raised in samples taken via an intravenous catheter after ingestion of 250 mg of caffeine itself (Robertson *et al.*, 1978).

However, in our studies (Barrand, Callingham, James, Jung and Shetty, unpublished) with both oral and intravenous caffeine, we have failed to detect any consistent effect on the levels of plasma catecholamines in either lean or obese women. This may be due to our choice of subjects, since tolerance develops to the effects of caffeine. Robertson *et al.* (1978) were able to select subjects that had never previously been exposed to caffeine.

(d) Some other drugs

In rats, the simultaneous administration of desmethylimipramine (DMI) and metanephrine produced significant increases in circulating levels of total catecholamines in venous blood (Roizen *et al.*, 1975b). Neither drug on its own was effective which was thought to indicate that both neuronal and extra neuronal uptake mechanisms are important in the inactivation of catecholamines and that if one pathway is blocked the other may compensate for the deficiency. In a recent study by Benedict, Fillenz and Stanford (1978), venous blood was collected via a catheter from the right atrium of freely moving rats. In these animals a single intraperitoneal injection of 10 mg/kg of DMI and 50 mg/kg normetanephrine raised the circulating levels of NA within 30 min from 11·1 to 31·1 nmol/l (1·88 to 5·26 ng/ml) at rest, and from 268 to 1770 nmol/l (45·28 to 299·59 ng/ml) during a swim stress. The drugs also lengthened the half life of exogenous NA in the circulation from 1·5 to 6·3 min.

Cocaine alone has been reported to increase the NA and A levels in the blood of conscious rats (Chiueh, Popper and Kopin, 1976), and previous work by Trendelenburg (1959) in cats revealed that cocaine could delay removal of exogenous NA.

Phenoxybenzamine (10 mg/kg) has been shown to raise the levels of circulating NA in rats (Reid and Kopin, 1975), while in dogs, Millar, Keener and Benfey (1959) had previously found increases in both NA and A levels after phenoxybenzamine particularly during periods of sympathetic stimulation. Recent work on catecholamine release from nerve endings appears to indicate that phenoxybenzamine may well increase transmitter release, but only during nerve stimulation (Thoa, Wooten, Axelrod and Kopin, 1972). Indeed the phenoxybenzamine induced increases in plasma A and NA seen in conscious rats were abolished by ganglion blockade (Chiueh et al., 1976). However, the effects of phenoxybenzamine are further complicated by the α-blocking capacity of the drug which may produce reflex increases in sympathetic activity as well.

Drugs which inhibit catecholamine metabolism have been reported to affect circulating catecholamine levels in rats (Chiueh et al., 1976). Tropolone, a COMT inhibitor, was found to increase NA only, while tranylcypromine, an MAO inhibitor increased both NA and A.

Ganglionic blockade with chlorisondamine (2 mg/kg) has been shown to reduce NA levels in rats from 13·6 to 2·6 nmol/l (2·30 to 0·44 ng/ml) (Reid and Kopin, 1975) and another ganglion blocker, hexamethonium was effective in preventing the increase in NA release induced by phenoxybenzamine.

Drugs which modify the storage and release of catecholamines at nerve endings have similarly been shown to affect circulating levels of catecholamines. Repeated injections of tyramine in rats were found to increase NA levels in the plasma whilst depleting the vesicle stores of this amine in the rat heart (Grobecker, Roizen and Kopin, 1977). Intravenous injections of tyramine in man have also been reported to elevate plasma NA (Grobecker et al., 1977).

In rats reserpine decreased plasma NA levels within 24 hr of drug administration (Reid and Kopin, 1975). Guanethidine displaces NA from neuronal stores and after chronic treatment may damage adrenergic nerve endings. Daily injections of this drug for five weeks in rats were found to cause a fall in circulating NA levels (Grobecker et al., 1977). Since the drug does not destroy the adrenal medulla compensatory increases in medullary amine release were thought to contribute to circulating levels remaining after drug treatment.

In dogs, the infusion of angiotensin II has been found to raise significantly the circulating concentrations of NA, even in adrenalectomised animals (Peach and Ford, 1968). Recent studies have also indicated that angiotensin may enhance the stimulation-evoked release of NA in some tissues possibly through an action on receptors for angiotensin on the presynaptic membranes, coupled with the inhibition of neuronal uptake of NA (Starke, Taube and Borowski, 1977). The competitive inhibitor of angiotensin, saralasin, may elicit pressor responses together with a rise in plasma levels of NA but not of A (McGrath, Ledingham and Benedict, 1977). These effects are thought to be mediated through an agonist effect on the vascular receptors together with an action in the central nervous system.

Several drugs which are believed to act via the central nervous system have been found to affect circulating catecholamine levels. Clonidine administered systemically or by intracerebroventricular injection in rats decreased plasma catecholamine levels (Chiueh et al., 1976). In human subjects (Wing, Reid, Hamilton, Davies and Dollery, 1976) a single oral dose of 300 µg caused a decrease in plasma NA from 2·42 to 0·06 nmol/l (0·41 to 0·01 ng/ml) 6 hr after treatment together with a significant reduction in blood pressure. Fenfluramine, which can lower the blood pressure in hypertensive patients, caused significant reductions in plasma NA levels both at rest and on standing in depressed patients (de la Vega, Slater, Ziegler, Lake and Murphy, 1977).

Acute β-receptor blockade with single doses of propranolol has been reported in some studies to raise the resting levels of plasma NA but not A (Galbo et al., 1976b; Hansen, Hesse and Christensen, 1978), though in other studies no significant changes of either catecholamine could be detected (Irving et al., 1974; Lütold, Bühler and Da Prada, 1976). During exercise however, in all these studies, β-blockade was found to enhance the normal rises in both A and NA. It was suggested that β-blockade mediated this effect at least partly by reducing the normal increase in cardiac output, thus enhancing vasoconstrictor nerve activity (Irving et al., 1974; Galbo et al., 1976b). The greater rise in plasma A induced by propranolol was said to be due to a decrease in the availability of glucose to the glucose-sensitive areas of the CNS, thus leading to increased adrenomedullary secretion (Galbo et al., 1976a).

Long term β-blockade with pindolol however, has been found to decrease plasma NA levels in patients with essential hypertension (Brecht, Banthien, Ernst and Schoeppe, 1976) both at rest and during mild exercise. In this case a centrally mediated effect of the β-receptor blocking agent on sympathetic nervous activity was proposed. However, other studies have failed to find any significant changes in plasma catecholamine levels after long-term non-selective β-blockade with either penbutolol (Hansson, 1976) or pindolol (Anavekar, Louis, Morgan, Doyle and Johnston, 1975) and also after cardioselective β_1-blockade with metoprolol (Hansson, Dymling, Hedeland and Hulthén, 1977).

E. CONCLUSION

The developments that have taken place in assay methods over the past few years, have led to the accumulation of a vast amount of information concerned with the levels of catecholamines in the plasma of man and animals. This explosion of data is the consequence of increased reliability and sensitivity of the assay methods enabling measurements to be made under conditions that previously would have been impossible.

Although there is considerable room for improvement in techniques on all counts, plasma levels of catecholamines can now be measured with a sufficient degree of precision, to provide an index of sympathetic activity. The assay of plasma levels of catecholamines is the single most reliable and convenient way of assessment, and is superior to that provided by measurements of plasma dopamine-β-hydroxylase (Reid and Kopin, 1974). Studies of NA turnover, although valuable in individual organs of experimental animals, are of limited application to the human subject (Young and Landsberg, 1977).

The significance of many of the factors that influence the actual concentrations of the catecholamines in the plasma are still not understood. Clearly the site from which blood is withdrawn for sampling is important, in view of the different sites of origins and sensitivities of the catecholamines to uptake from the circulation. Although A is present in the plasma as a true hormone released almost entirely from a single site, the NA must represent that residue of amine released throughout the cardiovascular system, which has escaped the processes of conservation and catabolism. It is unlikely that the NA released from a single organ, such as the heart, could be identified above this generalised release, unless the sample was taken from the immediate venous outflow of the organ concerned.

The status of the DA in the circulation is again unclear. The sites of origin have not been identified with any certainty, and no consistent changes in plasma levels with stimuli known to alter sympathetic activity have been found. It remains to be seen whether or not any function for the DA in the circulation will be found in addition to the possible action of DA in the hypophysial portal blood on the control of anterior pituitary function (Ben-Jonathan et al., 1977). The DA, thought to be involved in the regulation of sodium excretion that appears in the urine, is probably of renal origin and not derived from the plasma DA (Faucheux et al., 1977).

Not only is the function of plasma DA still unresolved, but there is really no clear picture of the function of NA in the circulation. It may only be on its way to elimination and excretion.

ACKNOWLEDGEMENT

Our own observations were supported by a grant from Imperial Chemical Industries Ltd., Pharmaceutical Division.

REFERENCES

Abrams, W. B. and Solomon, H. M. (1969). Clin. Pharmac. Ther. 10, 702.
Åkerstedt, T. and Levi, L. (1978). Eur. J. clin. Invest. 8, 57.
Alexander, R. W., Gill, J. R., Yamabe, H., Lovenberg, W. and Keiser, H. R. (1974). J. clin. Invest. 54, 194.
Anavekar, S. N., Louis, W. J., Morgan, T. O., Doyle, A. E. and Johnston, C. I. (1975). Clin. exp. Pharmac. Physiol. 2, 203.
Anton, A. H., Gravenstein, J. S. and Wheat, M. W. (1964). Anesthesiology. 25, 262
Anton, A. H. and Sayre, D. F. (1962). J. Pharmac. exp. Ther. 138, 360.
Anton, A. H. and Sayre, D. F. (1972). In "The Thyroid and Biogenic Amines. Methods in Investigative and Diagnostic Endocrinology" (J. E. Rall and I. J. Kopin, eds), Vol. 1, pp. 398–436. North Holland Publishing Co., Amsterdam and New York.
Antoniades, H. N., Goldfein, A., Zileli, S. and Elmadjian, F. (1958). Proc. Soc. exp. Biol. Med. 97, 11.
Aoki, K., Takikawa, K. and Hotta, K. (1973). Nature, New Biol. 241, 122.
Armstrong, J. and Barlow, R. B. (1976). Br. J. Pharmac. 57, 501.
Aronow, W. S., Harding, P. R., DeQuattro, V. and Isbell, M. (1973). Chest, 63, 722.
Atack, C. V. (1973). Br. J. Pharmac. 48, 699.
Atack, C. V. (1977). Acta physiol. scand. Suppl. 451.
Axelrod, J. (1957). Science, 126, 400.
Axelrod, J. (1962). J. biol. Chem. 237, 1657.
Axelrod, J. and Cohn, C. K. (1971). J. Pharmac. exp. Ther. 176, 650.
Axelrod, J., Weil-Malherbe, H. and Tomchick, R. (1959). J. Pharmac. exp. Ther. 127, 251.
Banister, E. W. and Griffiths, J. (1972). J. appl. Physiol. 33, 674.
Bannister, R., Sever, P. S. and Gross, M. (1977). Brain, 100, 327.
Bellet, S., Roman, L., De Castro, O., Kim, K. E. and Kershbaum, A. (1969). Metabolism, 18, 288.
Benedict, C. and Boutagy, J. (1977). Biochem. Med. 18, 455.
Benedict, C. R., Fillenz, M. and Stanford, C. (1977). J. Physiol. Lond. 269, 47P.
Benedict, C. R., Fillenz, M. and Stanford, C. (1978). Br. J. Pharmac. 64, 305.
Ben-Jonathan, N., Oliver, C., Weiner, H. J., Mical, R. S. and Porter, J. C. (1977). Endocrinology, 100, 452.

Ben-Jonathan, N. and Porter, J. C. (1976). *Endocrinology*, **98**, 1497.
Berglund, G., Tibblin, G. and Aurell, M. (1975). *Clin. Sci. mol. Med.* **49**, 485.
Berkowitz, B. A. and Spector, S. (1976). *In* "Vascular Neuroeffector Mechanisms" (J. A. Bevan, B. Johansson, R. A. Maxwell and O. A. Nedergaard, eds), pp. 102–111. S. Karger, Basel.
Bertler, Å., Carlsson, A. and Rosengren, E. (1958). *Acta physiol. scand.* **44**, 273.
Bevan, J. A., Bevan, R. D., Osher, J. V. and Su, C. (1972). *Eur. J. Pharmac.* **19**, 239.
Bevan, J. A., Hosmer, D. W., Ljung, B., Pegram, B. L. and Su, C. (1974). *Circulation Res.* **34**, 541.
Bevan, J. A. and Osher, J. V. (1970). *Eur. J. Pharmac.* **13**, 55.
Bing, R. F., Harlow, J., Smith, A. J. and Townshend, M. M. (1977). *Clin. Sci. mol. Med.* **52**, 319.
Black, G. W., McArdle, L., McCullough, H. and Unni, V. K. N. (1969). *Anaesthesia*, **24**, 168
Blaschke, E. and Hertting, G. (1971). *Biochem. Pharmac.* **20**, 1363.
Blaschko, H. (1939). *J. Physiol. Lond.* **96**, 50P.
Blaschko, H. (1974). *Rev. Physiol. Biochem. Pharmac.* **70**, 83.
Blaschko, H. and Welch, A. D. (1953). *Naunyn-Schmiedebergs Arch. Pharmak.* **219**, 17.
Bloom, S. R., Johnson, R. H., Park, D. M., Rennie, M. J. and Sulaiman, W. R. (1976). *J. Physiol. Lond.* **258**, 1.
Bönisch, H. and Trendelenburg, U. (1974). *Naunyn-Schmiedebergs Arch. Pharmac.* **283**, 191.
Bönisch, H., Uhlig, W. and Trendelenburg, U. (1974). *Naunyn-Schmiedebergs Arch. Pharmac.* **283**, 223.
Born, G. V. R., Hornykiewicz, O. and Stafford, A. (1958). *Br. J. Pharmac. Chemother.* **13**, 411.
Born, G. V. R. and Smith, J. B. (1970). *Br. J. Pharmac.* **39**, 765.
Branco, D., Fleming Torrinha, J. and Osswald, W. (1974). *Naunyn-Schmiedebergs Arch. Pharmac.* **285**, 367.
Brandsborg, O., Brandsborg, M. and Christensen, N. J. (1975). *Gastroenterology*, **68**, 455.
Brecht, H. M., Banthien, F., Ernst, W. and Schoeppe, W. (1976). *Clin. Sci. mol. Med.* **51**, 485.
Britton, B. J., Hawkey, C., Wood, W. G. and Peele, M. (1974). *Br. J. Surg.* **61**, 814.
Brownstein, M., Kizer, J. K., Palkovits, M. and Saavedra, J. M. (1974). *Brain Res.* **97**, 163.
Bühler, H. U., Da Prada, M., Haefely, W. and Picotti, G. B. (1978). *J. Physiol. Lond.* **276**, 311.
Burn, J. H. (1932). *J. Pharmac. exp. Ther.* **46**, 75.
Burn, J. H. (1961). *Ann. N.Y. Acad. Sci.* **90**, 81.
Burnstock, G., McLean, J. R. and Wright, M. (1971). *Br. J. Pharmac.* **43**, 180.
Callingham, B. A. (1967a). *In* "Hormones in Blood" (C. H. Gray and A. L. Bacharach, eds), Vol. 2, pp. 519–599 (2nd edition). Academic Press, London and New York.
Callingham, B. A. (1967b). *In* "Proceedings of the First International Symposium on Antidepressant Drugs" (S. Garattini and M. N. G. Dukes, eds), pp. 35–43. Excerpta Medica Foundation, Amsterdam.
Callingham, B. A. (1975). *In* "Handbook of Physiology, Section 7: Endocrinology, Vol. 6" (H. Blaschko, G. Sayers and A. D. Smith, eds), pp. 427–445. American Physiological Society, Washington.
Callingham, B. A. and Barrand, M. A. (1976). *J. Pharm. Pharmac.* **28**, 356.

Callingham, B. A. and Burgen, A. S. V. (1966). *Mol. Pharmac.* **2**, 37.

Callingham, B. A. and Cass, R. (1963). *In* "The Clinical Chemistry of Monoamines" (H. Varley and A. H. Gowenlock, eds), pp. 19–30. Elsevier Publishing Co., Amsterdam, London and New York.

Campese, V., Myers, M. R. and DeQuattro, V. (1977). *New Engl. J. Med.* **297**, 53.

Carlson, G. M., Ruddon, R. W., Hug, C. C., Jr. and Bass, P. (1970a). *J. Pharmac. exp. Ther.* **172**, 367.

Carlson, G. M., Ruddon, R. W., Hug, C. C., Jr., Schmiege, S. K. and Bass, P. (1970b). *J. Pharmac. exp. Ther.* **172**, 377.

Carlsson, A. and Waldeck, B. (1958). *Acta physiol. scand.* **44**, 293.

Carruthers, M. E. (1969). *Lancet*, **ii**, 1170.

Chaffee, R. R. J. (1976). *In* "Progress in Biometeorology" Division B. Progress in animal biometeorology", Vol. I, Part I, pp. 239–258. Sweitz and Zeitunger, Amsterdam.

Chiueh, C. G., Popper, C. W. and Kopin, I. J. (1976). *Pharmacologist*, **18**, 135.

Christensen, M. S. and Christensen, N. J. (1972). *Scand. J. clin. Lab. Invest.* **30**, 169.

Christensen, N. J. (1970). *Scand. J. clin. Lab. Invest.* **26**, 343.

Christensen, N. J. (1971). *Acta med. scand.* (Suppl. 541).

Christensen, N. J. (1972a). *J. clin. Invest.* **51**, 779.

Christensen, N. J. (1972b). *J. clin. Endocr. Metab.* **35**, 359.

Christensen, N. J. (1973a). *Clin. Sci. mol. Med.* **45**, 163.

Christensen, N. J. (1973b). *Scand. J. clin. Lab. Invest.* **31**, 343.

Christensen, N. J. (1974). *Diabetes*, **23**, 1.

Christensen, N. J., Alberti, K. G. M. M. and Brandsborg, O. (1975). *Eur. J. clin. Invest.* **5**, 415.

Christensen, N. J. and Brandsborg, O. (1973). *Eur. J. clin. Invest.* **3**, 299.

Christensen, N. J. and Brandsborg, O. (1976). *Scand. J. clin. Lab. Invest.* **36**, 591.

Christensen, N. J. and Videbaek, J. (1974). *J. clin. Invest.* **54**, 278.

Ciaranello, R. D. (1977). *In* "Structure and Function of Monoamine Enzymes" (E. Usdin, N. Weiner and M. B. H. Youdim, eds), pp. 497–525. Marcel Dekker, New York and Basel.

Coote, J. H., Hilton, S. M. and Perez-Gonzalez, J. F. (1971). *J. Physiol. Lond.* **215**, 789.

Cornish, E. J., Goldie, R. G. and Miller, R. C. (1978). *Br. J. Pharmac.* **63**, 445.

Costa, E., Koslow, S. H. and LeFevre, H. F. (1975). *In* "Handbook of Psychopharmacology" (L. L. Iversen, S. D. Iversen and S. H. Snyder, eds), Vol. 1, pp. 1–24. Plenum Press, New York and London.

Coulombe, P., Dussault, J. H., Letarte, J. and Simard, S. J. (1976a). *J. clin. Endocr. Metab.* **42**, 125.

Coulombe, P., Dussault, J. H. and Walker, P. (1976b). *Metabolism*, **25**, 973.

Coulombe, P., Dussault, J. H. and Walker, P. (1977). *J. clin. Endocr. Metab.* **44**, 1185.

Coupland, R. E. (1965). "The Natural History of the Chromaffin Cell." Longmans, London.

Coyle, J. T. and Henry, D. (1973). *J. Neurochem.* **21**, 61.

Cryer, P. E. (1976). *Diabetes*, **25**, 1071.

Cryer, P. E., Haymond, M. W., Santiago, J. V. and Shah, S. D. (1976). *New Engl. J. Med.* **295**, 573.

Cryer, P. E., Santiago, J. V. and Shah, S. (1974a). *J. clin. Endocr. Metab.* **39**, 1025.

Cryer, P. E. and Weiss, S. (1976). *Archs Neurol.* **33**, 275.

Cryer, P. E., Weiss, S. and Landau, W. (1974b). *Clin. Res.* **22**, 594A.

Cuche, J. L., Kuchel, O., Barbeau, A., Boucher, R. and Genest, J. (1972). *Clin. Sci.* **43**, 481.

Cuche, J. L., Kuchel, O., Barbeau, A., Langlois, Y., Boucher, R. and Genest, J. (1974). *Circulation Res.* **35**, 281.

Cuddy, R. P., Smulyan, H., Keighley, J. F., Markason, C. R. and Eich, R. H. (1966). *Am. Heart J.* **71**, 446.

Cuello, A. C., Hiley, R. and Iversen, L. L. (1973). *J. Neurochem.* **21**, 1337.

Danon, A. and Sapira, J. D. (1972a). *Clin. Pharmac. Ther.* **13**, 916.

Danon, A. and Sapira, J. D. (1972b). *J. Pharmac. exp. Ther.* **182**, 292.

Da Prada, M., Obrist, R. and Pletscher, A. (1975). *Br. J. Pharmac.* **53**, 257.

Da Prada, M. and Zürcher, G. (1976). *Life Sci.* **19**, 1161.

Dargie, H. J., Franklin, S. S. and Reid, J. L. (1977). *Clin. Sci. mol. Med.* **52**, 477.

Davies, C. T. M., Few, J., Foster, K. G. and Sargeant, A. J. (1974). *J. Physiol. Lond.* **236**, 21P.

Debarge, O., Christensen, N. J., Corbett, J. L., Eidelman, B. H., Frankel, H. L. and Mathias, C. J. (1974). *Paraplegia*, **12**, 44.

De Champlain, J. and Cousineau, D. (1977). *New Engl. J. Med.* **297**, 672.

De Champlain, J., Farley, L., Cousineau, D. and van Ameringen, M.-R. (1976). *Circulation Res.* **38**, 109.

De Champlain, J. and van Ameringen, M.-R. (1972). *Circulation Res.* **31**, 617.

De la Lande, I. S., Harvey, J. A. and Holt, S. (1974). *Blood Vessels*, **11**, 319.

de la Vega, C. E., Slater, S., Ziegler, M. G., Lake, C. R. and Murphy, D. L. (1977). *Clin. Pharmac. Ther.* **21**, 216.

Depocas, F. and Behrens, W. A. (1977). *Can. J. Physiol. Pharmac.* **55**, 212.

DeQuattro, V. (1971). *Circulation Res.* **28**, 84.

DeQuattro, V. and Chan, S. (1972). *Lancet*, i, 806.

DeQuattro, V., Campese, V. and Antonaccio, M. M. (1977). *In* "Cardiovascular Pharmacology" (M. Antonaccio, ed.), pp. 185–268. Raven Press, New York.

DeQuattro, V., Campese, V., Miura, Y. and Meijer, D. (1976). *Am. J. Cardiol.* **38**, 801.

De Schaepdryver, A. F. (1959). *Archs int. Pharmacodyn.* **119**, 517.

Diamant, J. and Byers, S. O. (1975). *J. lab. clin. Med.* **85**, 678.

Douglas, W. W. (1975). *In* "Handbook of Physiology, Section 7: Endocrinology Vol. 6" (H. Blaschko, G. Sayers and A. D. Smith, eds), pp. 367–388. American Physiological Society, Washington.

Dunn, J. D. and Lin, F.-J. (1974). *Experientia*, **30**, 348.

Eger, E. I., Smith, N. T., Stoelting, R. K., Cullen, D. J., Kadis, L. B. and Whitcher, C. E. (1970). *Anesthesiology* **32**, 396.

Eleftheriou, B. E. (1974). *Brain Res.* **75**, 145.

Elliott, T. R. (1905). *J. Physiol. Lond.* **32**, 401.

Elmadjian, F., Hope, J. M. and Lamson, E. T. (1957). *J. clin. Endocr. Metab.* **17**, 608.

Engelman, K. (1977). *Clin. Endocr. Metab.* **6**, 769.

Engelman, K. and Portnoy, B. (1970). *Circulation Res.* **26**, 53.

Engelman, K., Portnoy, B. and Lovenberg, W. (1968). *Am. J. med. Sci.* **255**, 259.

Engelman, K., Portnoy, B. and Sjoerdsma, A. (1970). *Circulation Res.* **26/27** (Suppl. 1), 1.

Eränkö, O. and Härkonen, M. (1965). *Acta physiol. scand.* **63**, 511.

Esler, M., Julius, S., Zweifler, A., Randall, O., Harburg, E., Gardiner, H. and DeQuattro, V. (1977). *New Engl. J. Med.* **296**, 405.

Esler, M. D. and Nestel, P. L. (1973). *Aust. N.Z. J. Med.* **3**, 117.

Esler, M., Zweifler, A., Randall, O., Julius, S., Bennett, J., Rydelek, P., Cohen, E. and DeQuattro, V. (1976). *Lancet*, ii, 115.

Euler, U. S. von (1956). "Noradrenaline." Charles C. Thomas, Springfield.

Euler, U. S. von (1959). *Pharmac. Rev.* **11**, 262.

Euler, U. S. von (1960). *Fed. Proc.* **19** (Suppl. 5), 79.

Euler, U. S. von (1964). *Clin. Pharmac. Ther.* **5**, 398.

Fales, H. M. and Pisano, J. J. (1962). *Analyt. Biochem.* **3**, 337.

Faucheux, B., Buu, N. T. and Kuchel, O. (1977). *Am. J. Physiol.* **232**, F123.

Fluck, D. C. and Salter, C. (1973). *Cardiovascular Res.* **7**, 823.

Franksson, G. and Änggård, E. (1970). *Acta pharmac. tox.* **28**, 209.

Fregly, M. J., Field, F. P., Nelson, E. L., Jr., Tyler, P. E. and Dasler, R. (1977). *J. appl. Physiol.* **42**, 349.

Fregly, M. J., Nelson, E. L., Jr., Resch, G. E., Field, F. P. and Lutherer, L. O. (1975). *Am. J. Physiol.* **229**, 916.

Friedman, M., Byers, S. O., Diamant, J. and Rosenman, R. H. (1975). *Metabolism,* **24**, 205.

Gaddum, J. H. (1959). *Pharmac. Rev.* **11**, 241.

Galbo, H., Christensen, N. J. and Holst, J. J. (1976a). *Acta physiol. scand.* (Suppl. 440), 179.

Galbo, H., Holst, J. J. and Christensen, N. J. (1975). *J. appl. Physiol.* **38**, 70.

Galbo, H., Holst, J. J., Christensen, N. J. and Hilsted, J. (1976b). *J. appl. Physiol.* **40**, 855.

Galbo, H., Richter, E. A., Hilsted, J., Holst, J. J., Christensen, N. J. and Henriksson, J. (1977). *Ann. N.Y. Acad. Sci.* **301**, 72.

Gale, C. C. (1973). *A. Rev. Physiol.* **35**, 391.

Ganellin, C. R. (1977). *J. med. Chem.* **20**, 579.

Garber, A. J., Cryer, P. E., Santiago, J. V., Haymond, M. W., Pagliara, A. S. and Kipnis, D. M. (1976). *J. clin. Invest.* **58**, 7.

Gauchy, C., Tassin, J. P., Glowinski, J. and Cheramy, A. (1976). *J. Neurochem.* **26**, 471.

Geffen, L. B., Rush, R. A., Louis, W. J. and Doyle, A. E. (1973). *Clin. Sci.* **44**, 421.

Ghione, S., Pellegrini, M., Buzzigoli, G., Carpi, A., Valori, C. and Donato, L. (1974). *Hormone. Metab. Res.* **6**, 93.

Gillespie, J. S. (1973). *Br. med. Bull.* **29**, 136.

Gillespie, J. S. (1974). *In* "Drugs and Transport Processes" (B. A. Callingham, ed.), pp. 287–295. Macmillan, London.

Gillespie, J. S. and Muir, T. C. (1970). *J. Physiol. Lond.* **206**, 591.

Gillis, C. N. (1976). *In* "The Mechanisms of Neuronal and Extraneuronal Transport of Catecholamines" (D. M. Paton, ed.), pp. 281–297. Raven Press, New York.

Gillis, C. N. and Roth, J. A. (1976). *Biochem. Pharmac.* **25**, 2547.

Glowinski, J. and Iversen, L. L. (1966). *J. Neurochem.* **13**, 655.

Goldfien, A., Moore, R., Zileli, S., Havens, L. L., Boling, L. and Thorn, G. W. (1961). *J. clin. Endocr. Metab.* **21**, 296.

Göthert, M. and Wendt, J. (1977a). *Anesthesiology,* **46**, 400.

Göthert, M. and Wendt, J. (1977b). *Anesthesiology,* **46**, 404.

Green, J. P., Johnson, C. L. and Kang, S. (1974). *A. Rev. Pharmac.* **14**, 319.

Green, R. D. III and Miller, J. W. (1966). *Science, N.Y.* **151**, 825.

Griffiths, J. and Leung, F. (1971). *Am. Heart J.* **82**, 171.

Grobecker, H., Roizen, M. F. and Kopin, I. J. (1977). *Life Sci.* **20**, 1009.

Grobecker, H., Roizen, M. F., Weise, V., Saavedra, J. M. and Kopin, I. J. (1975). *Nature, Lond.* **258**, 267.

Grol, C. J. and Rollema, H. (1977). *J. Pharm. Pharmac.* **29**, 153.

Guldberg, H. C. and Marsden, C. A. (1975). *Pharmac. Rev.* **27**, 135.
Gutman, Y. and Boonyaviroj, P. (1976). *Prostaglandins*, **12**, 487.
Haefely,W. Hürlimann, A. and Thoenen, H. (1965). *J. Physiol. Lond.* **181**, 48.
Häggendal, J. (1962a). *Scand. J. clin. Lab. Invest.* **14**, 537.
Häggendal, J. (1962b). *Acta physiol. scand.* **56**, 258.
Häggendal, J. (1963a). *Acta physiol. scand.* **59**, 242.
Häggendal, J. (1963b). *Acta physiol. scand.* **59**, 255.
Häggendal, J., Hartley, L. H. and Saltin, B. (1970). *Scand. J. clin. Lab. Invest.* **26**, 337.
Halter, J. B., Pflug, A. E. and Porte, D., Jr. (1977). *J. clin. Endocr. Metab.* **45**, 936.
Halter, J. B., Pflug, A. E. and Porte, D. (1977). *J. clin. Endocr. Metab.* **45**, 936.
Hammond, W. G., Aronow, L. and Moore, F. D. (1956). *Annals Surg.* **144**, 715.
Hansen, J. F., Hesse, B. and Christensen, N. J. (1978). *Eur. J. clin. Invest.* **8**, 31.
Hansson, B.-G. (1976). *Acta med. scand.* (Suppl. 598), 5.
Hansson, B.-G., Dymling, J.-F., Hedeland, H. and Hulthén, U. L. (1977). *Eur. J. clin. Pharmac.* **11**, 239.
Hartley, L. H., Mason, J. W., Hogan, R. P., Jones, L. G., Kotchen, T. A., Mougey, E. H., Wherry, F. E., Pennington, L. L. and Ricketts, P. T. (1972a). *J. appl. Physiol.* **33**, 602.
Hartley, L. H., Mason, J. W., Hogan, R. P., Jones, L. G., Kotchen, T. A., Mougey, E. H., Wherry, F. E., Pennington, L. L. and Ricketts, P. T. (1972b). *J. appl. Physiol.* **33**, 607.
Harvey, J. A. and Pennefather, J. N. (1962a). *J. Physiol. Lond.* **160**, 14P.
Harvey, J. A. and Pennefather, J. N. (1962b). *Br. J. Pharmac. Chemother.* **18**, 183.
Hawkey, C. M., Britton, B. J., Wood, W. G., Peele, M. and Irving, M. H. (1975). *Br. J. Haemat.* **29**, 377.
Hellmann, G., Hertting, G. and Peskar, B. (1971). *Br. J. Pharmac.* **41**, 256.
Henry, D. P., Starman, B. J., Johnson, D. G. and Williams, R. H. (1975). *Life Sci.* **16**, 375.
Hickler, R. B., Hamlin, J. T. III and Wells, R. E., Jr. (1959). *Circulation*, **20**, 422.
Hill, P. and Wynder, E. L. (1974). *Am. Heart J.* **87**, 491.
Hillarp, N.-Å., Lagerstedt, S. and Nilson, B. (1953). *Acta physiol. scand.* **29**, 251.
Himsworth, R. L. (1970). *J. Physiol. Lond.* **206**, 411.
Hökfelt, T., Fuxe, K., Goldstein, M. and Johansson, O. (1974). *Brain Res.* **66**, 235.
Holmberg, G., Levi, L., Mathé, A., Rosén, A. and Scott, H. (1967). *In* "Emotional Stress" (L. Levi, ed.), pp. 201–210. S. Karger, Basel and New York.
Holmes, J. C. and Schneider, F. H. (1973). *Br. J. Pharmac.* **49**, 205.
Holzbauer, M. and Sharman, D. F. (1972). *In* "Handbook of Experimental Pharmacology" (H. Blaschko and E. Muscholl, eds), Vol. 33, pp. 110–185. Springer-Verlag Berlin and New York.
Holzbauer, M. and Vogt, M. (1954). *Br. J. Pharmac. Chemother.* **9**, 249.
Holzbauer, M. and Vogt, M. (1955). *Br. J. Pharmac. Chemother.* **10**, 186.
Horn, A. S., Post, M. L. and Kennard, O. (1975). *J. Pharm. Pharmac.* **27**, 553.
Horst, W. D., Gattanell, P., Urbano, S. and Sheppard, H. (1969). *Life Sci.* **8**, 473.
Hörtnagl, H., Benedict, C. R., Grahame-Smith, D. G. and McGrath, B. (1977). *Br. J. clin. Pharmac.* **4**, 553.
Hughes, I. E. and Smith, J. A. (1978). *J. Pharm. Pharmac.* **30**, 124.
Irving, M. H., Britton, B. J., Wood, W. G., Padgham, C. and Carruthers, M. (1974). *Nature, Lond.* **248**, 531.
Iversen, L. L. (1963). *Br. J. Pharmac. Chemother.* **21**, 523.
Iversen, L. L. (1964). Ph.D. Thesis, University of Cambridge.
Iversen, L. L. (1965a). *Br. J. Pharmac. Chemother.* **24**, 387.

Iversen, L. L. (1965b). *Br. J. Pharmac. Chemother.* **25**, 18.
Iversen, L. L. (1967). "The Uptake and Storage of Noradrenaline in Sympathetic Nerves." Cambridge University Press, Cambridge, London and New York.
Iversen, L. L. (1974). *Biochem. Pharmac.* **23**, 1927.
Iversen, L. L. (1975). *In* "Handbook of Physiology, Section 7: Endocrinology, Vol. 6" (H. Blaschko, G. Sayers and A. D. Smith, eds), pp. 713–722. American Physiological Society, Washington.
Januszewicz, W., Sznajderman, M., Ciswicka-Sznajderman, M., Wocial, B. and Rymaszewski, Z. (1971). *Br. Heart J.* **33**, 716.
Januszewicz, W., Sznajderman, M., Wocial, B. and Preibisz, J. (1968). *Am. Heart J.* **76**, 345.
Jiang, N.-S., Machacek, D. and Wadel, O. P. (1976). *Mayo Clin. Proc.* **51**, 112.
Johnson, I. D. A. (1972). *Adv. clin. Chem.* **15**, 255.
Johnson, G. A., Peuler, J. D. and Baker, C. A. (1977). *Curr. ther. Res.* **21**, 898.
Kalsner, S. (1974). *Br. J. Pharmac.* **51**, 453.
Kalsner, S. (1976). *Br. J. Pharmac.* **58**, 261.
Kalsner, S. (1977). *Life Sci.* **20**, 1689.
Kalsner, S., Frew, R. D. and Smith, G. M. (1975). *Am. J. Physiol.* **228**, 1702.
Kalsner, S. and Nickerson, M. (1969a). *Br. J. Pharmac.* **35**, 428.
Kalsner, S. and Nickerson, M. (1969b). *Br. J. Pharmac.* **35**, 440.
Kalsner, S. and Nickerson, M. (1969c). *J. Pharmac. exp. Ther.* **165**, 152.
Karoum, F., Cattabeni, F., Costa, E., Ruthven, C. R. J. and Sandler, M. (1972). *Analyt. Biochem.* **47**, 550.
Keatinge, W. R., McIlroy, M. B. and Goldfien, A. (1964). *J. appl. Physiol.* **19**, 1145.
Keller, R., Oke, A., Mefford, I. and Adams, R. N. (1976). *Life Sci.* **19**, 995.
Kelsh, R. C., Light, G. S., Luciano, J. R. and Oliver, W. J. (1971). *J. Lab. clin. Med.* **77**, 267.
Kirshner, N. (1962). *J. biol. Chem.* **237**, 2311.
Kirshner, N. (1975). *In* "Handbook of Physiology, Section 7: Endocrinology, Vol. 6" (H. Blaschko, G. Sayers and A. D. Smith, eds), pp. 341–355. American Physiological Society, Washington.
Klensch, H. (1965). *Z. Kreislaufforsch.* **54**, 771.
Klensch, H. (1966). *Z. Kreislaufforsch,* **55**, 1035.
Kontos, H. A., Richardson, D. W. and Norvell, J. E. (1975a). *Ann. int. Med.* **82**, 336.
Kontos, H. A., Richardson, D. W. and Norvell, J. E. (1975b). *Trans. Am. clin. Climatol. Ass.* **87**, 26.
Kopin, I. J. (1977). *Clin. Endocr. Metab.* **6**, 525.
Koslow, S. H., Cattabeni, F. and Costa, E. (1972). *Science,* **176**, 177.
Kotchen, T. A., Hartley, L. H., Rice, T. W., Mougey, E. H., Jones, L. G. and Mason, J. W. (1971). *J. appl. Physiol.* **31**, 178.
Kozlowski, S., Brzezinska, Z., Nazar, K., Kowalski, W. and Franczyk, M. (1973). *Clin. Sci. mol. Med.* **45**, 723.
Kuchel, O. (1976). *Circulation Res.* **39**, 289.
Kuchel, O., Cuche, J. L., Buu, N. T., Guthrie, G. P., Unger, T., Nowaczynski, W., Boucher, R. and Genest, J. (1977). *J. clin. Endocr. Metab.* **44**, 639.
Lake, C. R., Ziegler, M. G., Coleman, M. D. and Kopin, I. J. (1977). *New Engl. J. Med.* **296**, 208.
Lake, C. R., Ziegler, M. G. and Kopin, I. J. (1976). *Life Sci.* **18**, 1315.
Lance, J. W. and Hinterberger, H. (1976). *Archs Neurol.* **33**, 281.
Landsberg, L. (1977). *Clin. Endocr. Metab.* **6**, 697.

Langer, S. Z. (1977). *Br. J. Pharmac.* **60**, 481.
Laverty, R. and Sharman, D. F. (1965). *Br. J. Pharmac. Chemother.* **24**. 538.
Leduc, J. (1961). *Acta physiol. scand.* **53** (Suppl. 183).
Levi, L. (1966). *Forsvarsmedicin*, **2**, 3.
Levi, L. (1967). *Acta med. scand.* **181**, 431.
Lew, G. M. (1976). *Gen. Pharmac.* **7**, 35.
Libet, B. and Tosaka, T. (1970). *Proc. natn. Acad. Sci. USA*, **67**, 667.
Lightman, S. L. and Iversen, L. L. (1969). *Br. J. Pharmac.* **37**, 638.
Louis, W. J. and Doyle, A. E. (1971). *Aust. N.Z. J. Med.* **3**, 212.
Louis, W. J., Doyle, A. E. and Anavekar, S. N. (1973a). *New Engl. J. Med.* **288**. 599.
Louis, W. J., Doyle, A. E., Anavekar, S. N. and Chua, K. G. (1973b). *Clin. Sci. mol. Med.* **45**, 119s.
Lovelady, H. G. (1976). *Biochem. Med.* **15**, 138.
Lovenberg, W., Weissbach, H. and Udenfriend, S. (1962). *J. biol. Chem.* **237**, 89.
Lowder, S. C., Hamet, P. and Liddle, G. W. (1976). *Circulation Res.* **38**, 105.
Lukomsky, P. E. and Oganov, R. G. (1972). *Am. Heart J.* **83**, 182.
Lütold, B. E., Bühler, F. R. and Da Prada, M. (1976). *Schweiz. med. Wschr.* **106**, 1735.
Maas, J. W. (1970). *J. Pharmac. exp. Ther.* **174**, 369.
McDonald, L., Baker, C., Bray, C., McDonald, A. and Restieaux, N. (1969). *Lancet*, **ii**, 1021.
McEwen, J. E. (1967). *J. Sci. Tech.* **13**, 98.
McGrath, B. P., Ledingham, J. G. G. and Benedict, C. R. (1977). *Clin. Sci. mol. Med.* **53**, 341.
Malor, R., Griffin, C. J. and Taylor, S. (1973). *Cardiovascular Res.* **7**, 95.
Manger, W. M. and Gifford, R. W. (1977). "Pheochromocytoma." Springer-Verlag, New York, Heidelberg and Berlin.
Maruyama, Y. and Takemori, A. E. (1971). *Biochem. Pharmac.* **20**, 1833.
Maruyama, Y. and Takemori, A. E. (1972). *Analyt. Biochem.* **49**, 240.
Masoro, E. J. (1976). *In* "Progress in Biometeorology" Division B. Progress in animal biometeorology, Vol. I, Part I, pp. 19–26. Sweitz and Zeitunger, Amsterdam.
Mathias, C. J., Christensen, N. J., Corbett, J. L., Frankel, H. L., Goodwin, T. J. and Peart, W. S. (1975). *Clin. Sci. mol. Med.* **49**, 291.
Mathias, C. J., Christensen, N. J., Corbett, J. L., Frankel, H. L. and Spalding, J. M. K. (1976a). *Circulation Res.* **39**, 204.
Mathias, C. J., Frankel, H. L., Christensen, N. J. and Spalding, J. M. K. (1976b). *Brain*, **99**, 757.
Maxwell, R. A., Ferris, R. M. and Burcsu, J. E. (1976). *In* "The Mechanism of Neuronal and Extraneuronal Transport of Catecholamines" (D. M. Paton, ed.), pp. 95–153. Raven Press, New York.
Millar, R. A., Keener, E. B. and Benfey, B. G. (1959). *Br. J. Pharmac. Chemother.* **14**, 9.
Miura, Y., Campese, V., DeQuattro, V. and Meijer, D. (1977). *J. Lab. clin. Med.* **89**, 421.
Miura, Y., Haneda, T., Sato, T., Miyazawa, K., Sakuma, H., Kobayashi, K., Minai, K., Shirato, K., Honna, T., Takishima, T. and Yoshinaga, K. (1976). *Jap. circ. J.* **40**, 929.
Mizuno, Y. (1977). *Clin. chim. Acta*, **74**, 11.
Moerman, E. J., Bogaert, M. G. and De Schaepdryver, A. F. (1976). *Clin. chim. Acta.* **72**, 89.

Molinoff, P. B., Orcutt, J. C., Nelson, D. L. and Harden, T. K. (1977). *In* "Structure and Function of Monoamine Enzymes" (E. Usdin, N. Weiner and M. B. H. Youdim, eds), pp. 401–421. Marcel Dekker, New York and Basel.

Molzahn, M., Dissmann, T. H., Halim, S., Lohmann, F. W. and Oelkers, W. (1972). *Clin. Sci.* **42**, 209.

Moskowitz, M. A. (1977). *Clin. Endocr. Metab.* **6**, 745.

Mueller, R. A., Millward, D. K. and Woods, J. W. (1974). *Pharmac. Biochem. Behav.* **2**, 757.

Nagaoka, A. and Lovenberg, W. (1976). *Life Sci.* **19**, 29.

Nagatsu, T. (1975). *In* "Chemical Tools in Catecholamine Research II Regulation of Catecholamine Turnover" (O. Almgren, A. Carlsson and J. Engel, eds), pp. 3–8. North-Holland, Amsterdam, London; American Elsevier, New York.

Nagatsu, T., Levitt, M. and Udenfriend, S. (1964). *J. biol. Chem.* **239**, 2910.

Neubauer, B. and Christensen, N. J. (1976). *Diabetes*, **25**, 6.

Nishioka, M. (1971). *Kobe J. med. Sci.* **17**, 129.

O'Hanlon, J. F. (1970). "Vigilance, the Plasma Catecholamines and Related Biochemical and Physiological Variables" Technical Report 787-2. Human Factors Research, Inc., Goleta, CA.

Osikowska, B. A. and Sever, P. S. (1976). *Br. J. clin. Pharmac.* **3**, 963P.

Ostman, I. and Sjöstrand, N. O. (1975). *Acta physiol. scand.* **95**, 209.

Parvez, S., Parvez, H. and Gripois, D. (1973). *Pharmac. Res. Commun.* **5**, 265.

Passon, P. G. and Peuler, J. D. (1973). *Analyt. Biochem.* **51**, 618.

Paton, D. M. (1976). *In* "The Mechanism of Neuronal and Extraneuronal Transport of Catecholamines" (D. M. Paton, ed.), pp. 155–174. Raven Press, New York.

Peach, M. J. and Ford, G. D. (1968). *J. Pharmac. exp. Ther.* **162**, 92.

Pederscn, E. B. and Christensen, N. J. (1975). *Acta med. scand.* **198**, 373.

Perlman, R. L. and Chalfie, M. (1977). *Clin. Endocr. Metab.* **6**, 551.

Perry, L. B., van Dyke, R. A. and Theye, R. A. (1974). *Anesthesiology*, **40**, 465.

Peuler, J. D. and Johnson, G. A. (1977). *Life Sci.* **21**, 625.

Philippu, A. (1976). *In* "The Mechanism of Neuronal and Extraneuronal Transport of Catecholamines" (D. M. Paton, ed.), pp. 215–246. Raven Press, New York.

Pohorecky, L. A. and Wurtman, R. J. (1971). *Pharmac. Rev.* **23**, 1.

Poole, T. R. and Watts, D. T. (1959). *Am. J. Physiol.* **196**, 145.

Popper, G. W., Chiueh, C. C. and Kopin, I. J. (1977). *J. Pharmac. exp. Ther.* **202**, 144.

Powis, G. (1973). *J. Physiol. Lond.* **234**, 145.

Powis, G. (1974). *J. Pharm. Pharmac.* **26**, 344.

Powis, G. (1975). *Biochem. Pharmac.* **24**, 707.

Prakash, R., Parmley, W. W., Horvat, M. and Swan, H. J. C. (1972). *Circulation*, **45**, 736.

Price, H. L. and Price, M. L. (1957). *J. Lab. clin. Med.* **50**, 769.

Price, H. L., Skovsted, P., Pauca, A. L. and Cooperman, L. H. (1970). *Anesthesiology*, **32**, 389.

Refshauge, C., Kissinger, P. T., Dreiling, R., Blank, L., Freeman, R. and Adams, R. N. (1974). *Life Sci.* **14**, 311.

Reid, J. L. and Kopin, I. J. (1974). *Proc. natn. Acad. Sci. USA*, **71**, 4392.

Reid, J. L. and Kopin, I. J. (1975). *J. Pharmac. exp. Ther.* **193**, 748.

Reid, J. L., Zivin, J. A. and Kopin, I. J. (1975). *Circulation Res.* **37**, 569.

Reis, D. J. and Joh, T. H. (1977). *In* "Structure and Function of Monoamine Enzymes" (E. Usdin, N. Weiner and M. B. H. Youdim, eds), pp. 169–192. Marcel Dekker, New York and Basel.

Richardson, J. A., Woods, E. F. and Richardson, A. K. (1957). *J. Pharmac. exp. Ther.* **119**, 378.

Robertson, D. H., Frölich, J. C., Carr, K., Watson, J. T., Hollifield, J. W., Shand, D. G. and Oates, J. A. (1978). *New Engl. J. Med.* **298**, 181.

Robertson, D. H., Johnson, G. A., Brilis, G. M., Hill, R. E., Watson, J. T. and Oates, J. A. (1977). *Fedn Proc. Fedn Am. Socs exp. Biol.*, **36**, 956.

Robson, R. H. and Fluck, D. C. (1977). *Eur. J. clin. Pharmac.* **12**, 81.

Roizen, M. F., Moss, J., Henry, D. P. and Kopin, I. J. (1974). *Anesthesiology*, **41**, 432.

Roizen, M. F., Thoa, N. B., Moss, J. and Kopin, I. J. (1976). *Anesthesiology*, **44**, 54.

Roizen, M. F., Weise, V., Grobecker, H. and Kopin, I. J. (1975a). *Life Sci.* **17**, 283.

Roizen, M. F., Weise, V., Moss, J. and Kopin, I. J. (1975b). *Life Sci.* **16**, 1133.

Rolewicz, T. F., Whitmore, L. and Zimmerman, B. G. (1969). *Am. J. Physiol.* **217**, 1459.

Rosendorff, C., Bloom, D. S. and Stein, M. G. (1976). *Clin. Sci. mol. Med.* **51**, 469.

Ross, S. B. (1976). *In* "The Mechanism of Neuronal and Extraneuronal Transport of Catecholamines" (D. M. Paton, ed.), pp. 67–93. Raven Press, New York.

Roston, S. (1967). *Nature, Lond* **215**, 432.

Rowell, L. B. (1974). *Physiol. Rev.* **54**, 75.

Russell, J. C. and Doty, D. M. (1973). *Physiol. Chem. Phys.* **5**, 75.

Salt, P. J. (1972). *Eur. J. Pharmac.* **20**, 329.

Salt, P. J. and Iversen, L. L. (1972). *Nature New Biol.* **238**, 19.

Schanker, L. S., Nafpliotis, P. A. and Johnson, J. M. (1961). *J. Pharmac. exp. Ther.* **133**, 325.

Schievelbein, H. and Eberhardt, R. (1972) *J. nat. Cancer Inst.* **48**, 1785.

Sever, P. S., Birch, M., Osikowska, B. and Tunbridge, R. D. G. (1977). *Lancet*, i, 1078.

Sharman, D. F. (1971). *In* "Methods in Neurochemistry" (R. Fried, ed.), Vol. 1, pp. 83–127. Marcel Dekker, New York.

Sharman, D. F. (1973). *Br. med. Bull.* **29**, 110.

Sharman, D. F. (1975). *In* "Handbook of Physiology. Section 7: Endocrinology, Vol. 6" (H. Blaschko, G. Sayers and A. D. Smith, eds), pp. 699–712. American Physiological Society, Washington.

Sharman, D. F., Vanov, S. and Vogt, M. (1962). *Br. J. Pharmac. Chemother.* **19**, 527.

Siggers, D. C., Salter, C. and Fluck, D. C. (1971). *Br. Heart J.* **33**, 878.

Siggers, D. C., Salter, C. and Toseland, P. A. (1970). *Clin. chim. Acta*, **30**, 373.

Skovsted, P., Price, M. L. and Price, H. L. (1970). *Anesthesiology*, **31**, 507.

Smith, A. D. (1972). *Pharmac. Rev.* **24**, 435.

Smith, A. D. (1973). *Br. med. Bull.* **29**, 123.

Sole, M. J. and Hussain, M. N. (1977). *Biochem. med.* **18**, 301.

Starke, K., Endo, T. and Taube, H. D. (1975). *Naunyn-Schmiedebergs Arch. Pharmac.* **291**, 55.

Starke, K., Montel, H. and Schümann, J. J. (1971). *Naunyn-Schmiedebergs Arch. Pharmac.* **270**, 210.

Starke, K., Taube, H. D. and Borowski, E. (1977). *Biochem. Pharmac.* **26**, 259.

Stjärne, L. and Brundin, J. (1975). *Acta physiol. scand.* **94**, 139.

Stjärne, L., Kaijser, L., Mathé, A. and Birke, G. (1975). *Acta physiol. scand.* **95**, 46.

Stoffer, S. S., Jiang, N.-S., Gorman, C. G. and Pikler, G. M. (1973). *J. clin. Endocr. Metab.* **36**, 587.

Strange, R. C., Vetter, N., Rowe, M. J. and Oliver, M. F. (1974). *Eur. J. clin. Invest.* **4**, 115.

H

Stricker, E. M., Rowland, N., Saller, C. and Friedman, M. I. (1977). *Science*, **196**, 79.
Su, C. and Bevan, J. A. (1970). *J. Pharmac. exp. Ther.* **172**, 62.
Sundin, T. (1958). *Acta med. scand.* **161** (Suppl. 336).
Taggart, P. and Carruthers, M. E. (1971). *Lancet*, **i**, 363.
Taggart, P. and Carruthers, M. E. (1972). *Lancet*, **ii**, 256.
Taggart, P., Parkinson, P. and Carruthers, M. (1972). *Br. med. J.* **iii**, 71.
Tanche, M. (1976). *Israel J. med. Sci.* **12**, 1019.
Theorell, T. and Åkerstedt, T. (1976). *Acta med. scand.* **200**, 47.
Thoa, N. B., Wooten, G. F., Axelrod, J. and Kopin, I. J. (1972). *Proc. natn. Acad. Sci. USA*, **69**, 520.
Tipton, K. F. (1973). *Br. med. Bull.* **29**, 116.
Townshend, M. M. and Smith, A. J. (1973). *Clin. Sci.* **44**, 253.
Trendelenburg, U. (1959). *J. Pharmac. exp. Ther.* **125**, 55.
Tsujimoto, A., Nishikawa, T., Dohi, T. and Kojima, S. (1974). *Eur. J. Pharmac.* **26**, 236.
Turton, M. B. and Deegan, T. (1973). *Clin. chim. Acta*, **48**, 347.
Turton, M. B. and Deegan, T. (1974). *Clin. chim. Acta*, **55**, 389.
Uhlig, W., Fiebig, R. and Trendelenburg, U. (1976). *Naunyn-Schmiedebergs Arch. Pharmac.* **295**, 45.
Valori, C., Brunori, C. A., Renzini, V. and Corea, L. (1970). *Analyt. Biochem.* **33**, 158.
Vane, J. R. (1969). *Br. J. Pharmac.* **35**, 209.
Vanov, S. and Vogt, M. (1963). *J. Physiol. Lond.* **168**, 939.
Vendsalu, A. (1960). *Acta physiol. scand.* **49** (Suppl. 173).
Verity, M. A. (1971). *In* "Physiology and Pharmacology of Vascular Neuroeffector Systems" (J. A. Bevan, R. F. Furchgott, R. A. Maxwell and A. P. Somlyo, eds), pp. 2–12. S. Karger, Basel.
Vetter, N. J., Strange, R. C., Adams, W. and Oliver, M. F. (1974). *Lancet*, **i**, 284.
Videbaek, J., Christensen, N. J. and Sterndorff, B. (1972). *Circulation*, **46**, 846.
Viveros, O. H. (1975). *In* "Handbook of Physiology, Section 7: Endocrinology, Vol. 6" (H. Blaschko, G. Sayers and A. D. Smith, eds), pp. 389–426. American Physiological Society, Washington.
Vogt, M. (1952). *Br. J. Pharmac. Chemother.* **7**, 325.
Wallace, J. M. and Harlan, W. R. (1965). *Am. J. Med.* **38**, 531.
Wang, M.-T., Imai, K., Yoshioka, M. and Tamura, Z. (1975). *Clin. chim. Acta*, **63**, 13.
Watts, D. T. (1961). *Ann. N.Y. Acad. Sci.* **90**, 74.
Weiner, N. (1975). *In* "Handbook of Physiology, Section 7: Endocrinology, Vol. 6" (H. Blaschko, G. Sayers and A. D. Smith, eds), pp. 357–366. American Physiological Society, Washington.
Weiner, N., Lee, F.-L., Barnes, E. and Dreyer, E. (1977). *In* "Structure and Function of Monoamine Enzymes " (E. Usdin, N. Weiner and M. B. H. Youdim, eds), pp. 109–148. Marcel Dekker, New York and Basel.
Weise, V. K. and Kopin, I. J. (1976). *Life Sci.* **19**, 1673.
Welsh, L. H. (1952). *J. Am. pharm. Ass.* **41**, 545.
Wertheimer, L., Hassen, A. Z. and Delman, A. J. (1972). *Clin. Res.* **20**, 404.
Williams, L. T., Lefkowitz, R. J., Watanabe, A. M., Hathaway, D. R. and Besch, H. R. (1977). *J. biol. Chem.* **252**, 2787.
Winer, N. and Carter, C. (1977). *Life Sci.* **20**, 887.
Wing, L. M. H., Reid, J. L., Hamilton, C. A., Davies, D. S. and Dollery, C. T. (1976). *Clin. Sci. mol. Med.* **51**, 15P.
Winkler, H. and Smith, A. D. (1968). *Lancet*, **i**, 793.

Winkler, H. and Smith, A. D. (1975). In "Handbook of Physiology, Section 7: Endocrinology, Vol. 6" (H. Blaschko, G. Sayers and A. D. Smith, eds), pp. 321–339. American Physiological Society, Washington.

Woods, E. F., Richardson, J. A., Richardson, A. K. and Bozeman, R. F. (1956). J. Pharmac. exp. Ther. 116, 351.

Wyatt, R. J., Portnoy, B., Kupfer, D. J., Snyder, F. and Engelman, K. (1971). Archs gen. Psychiat. 24, 65.

Yamaguchi, N., De Champlain, J. and Nadeau, R. (1975). Circulation Res. 36, 662.

Young, J. B. and Landsberg, L. (1977). Science, 196, 1473.

Zia, H., Cox, R. H. and Luzzi, L. A. (1971). J. pharm. Sci. 60, 89.

Ziegler, M. G., Lake, C. R. and Kopin, I. J. (1976a). Nature, Lond. 261, 333.

Ziegler, M. G., Lake, C. R. and Kopin, I. J. (1976b). New Engl. J. Med. 294, 630.

Ziegler, M. G., Lake, C. R. and Kopin, I. J. (1977). New Engl. J. Med. 296, 293.

Zimon, R. P., Sheps, S. G., Hazelrig, C. G., Schirger, A. and Owen, C. A. (1966). Mayo Clin. Proc. 41, 649.

Zuspan, F. P. (1970). J. clin. Endocr. Metab. 30, 357.

Zuspan, F. P. and Zuspan, K. J. (1973). Am. J. Obstet. Gynec. 117, 654.

V. Serotonin

G. A. SMYTHE

INTRODUCTION

In 1933 a substance capable of stimulating contractions of intestinal and uterine muscle strips was isolated from gastric mucosa and called "enteramine" (Vialli and Erspamer, 1933). Subsequently, Erspamer and Asero (1952) showed that enteramine was identical with the vasoconstrictor substance which had been isolated from plasma, structurally identified and named "serotonin" (Rapport, Green and Page, 1947; 1948a, b). Serotonin has been the subject of several books and in the foreword to one of these (Garattini and Valzelli, 1965) one of the major discoverers of serotonin, Irvine Page, was led to comment "Serotonin in walnuts and bananas and in jelly-fish and in carcinoids and in brain leaves me with a sense of bewilderment and fear that some(one) will ask me what serotonin does". This comment was provoked by the ubiquitous nature of serotonin itself as well as the wide range of proposals put forward for its biological function. Early suggestions about the biological role of serotonin were based on knowledge of its ability to contract smooth muscle. Serotonin has been proposed to play a physiological role in the regulation of peristalsis (Bulbring and Lim, 1958), in antidiuresis (Erspamer and Ottolenghi, 1953; Benditt, 1958; Page, 1958), in cardiovascular regulation (Page, 1958) and in anaphylatic and inflammatory reactions (see Garattini and Valzelli, 1965). Serotonin is released from blood platelets during the clotting process (Hardisty and Stacey, 1955; Humphrey and Jacques, 1955) and a role for the indoleamine in this process has been examined. Quite early, hypotheses concerning the role of brain serotonin in behaviour and mental health were put forward (Brodie, 1958; Wooley and Shaw, 1954). Today serotonin remains a major topic of research with main attention focused on its apparently diverse actions in the brain where it participates in neuro-endocrine control mechanisms (Smythe, 1977) and possibly in the integration of information about the metabolic state in the control of homeostasis and behaviour (Fernstrom and Wurtman, 1971). Serotonin is a putative gastro-intestinal hormone (Kellum and Jaffe, 1976) and its blood concentration has been shown to be altered in diseases not only of the gastro-intestinal tract but also of the central nervous system. Answers to questions about the precise roles of serotonin will almost certainly come from recent advances in methodology and technology which enable serotonin to be estimated in physiological fluids with high sensitivity, specificity and precision.

A. SOME CHEMICAL AND PHYSICAL PROPERTIES AND SYNTHESES OF SEROTONIN

Serotonin and 5-hydroxytryptamine are common names for the compound 5-hydroxy-3-(2-aminoethyl) indole (Fig. 1(a)). Throughout this chapter the common name "serotonin" will be used to describe this compound. As the systematic name implies, serotonin is a derivative of indole (Fig. 1(b)). Indole itself is a planar hetero-aromatic molecule having a 10 electron π-system. The heterocyclic nitrogen atom is very weakly basic because of

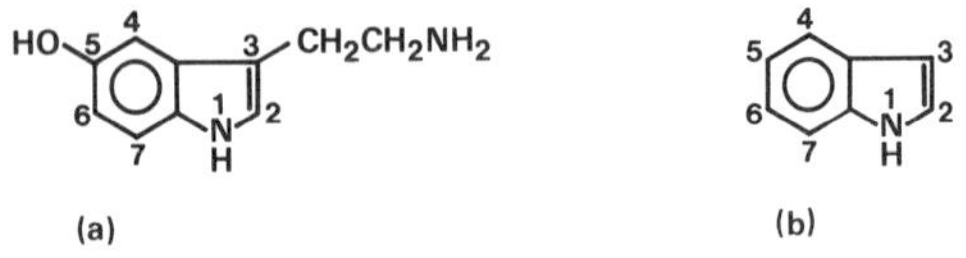

Fig. 1. Serotonin (a) and indole (b).

delocalisation of its unshared electron pair into the π-system and protonation of indole takes place at the carbon atom at position 3 in preference to the nitrogen (Hinman and Lange, 1964). The presence of the hydroxyl group at the 5-position of the indole ring in serotonin has a strong influence on electron delocalisation and proton-exchange takes place preferentially at the 4-position in 5-hydroxyindole (Daly and Witkop, 1967). The acid dissociation equilibria of serotonin in aqueous solutions have been studied by Sakurai and Ishimitsu (1975). At physiological pH serotonin exists completely in the cationic form (Fig. 2(a)) and at pH 10·5 approximately 30% each of the neutral form and the zwitterionic form (Fig. 2(b)) exists. In

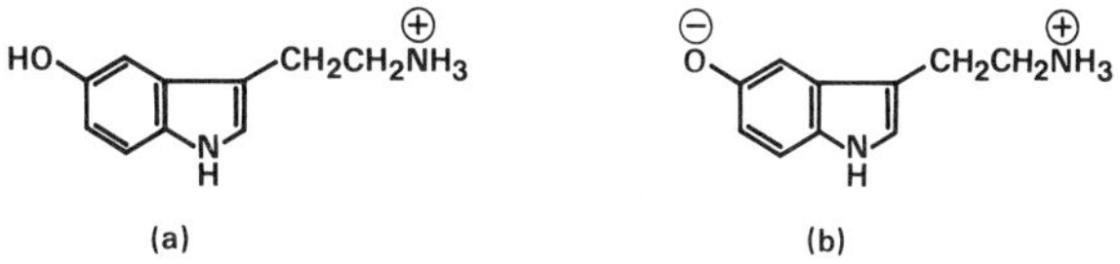

Fig. 2. Cationic (a) and zwitterionic (b) forms of serotonin.

the preferred conformation the 2-amino-ethyl side-chain of serotonin is perpendicular to the plane of the indole ring and the quaternary nitrogen is 0·19 nm above the plane of the indole ring (Courriere, Coubeils and Pullman, 1971).

Serotonin is relatively unstable, being rapidly oxidised by atmospheric oxygen, eventually to a melanin-like pigment. The oxidation of serotonin under controlled conditions has been studied by Eriksen, Martin and Benditt (1960). These workers tentatively identified one of the intermediates in this process as a dimer formed by dehydrogenative coupling of two serotonin molecules. Serotonin has good stability at acid pH even at elevated temperatures (Rapport et al., 1948b). At alkaline pH, serotonin in solution is destroyed rapidly when heated (Joyce, 1958). Because of its instability, serotonin, as the free base, is not used in practice but is mainly used in the form of its more stable creatinine sulphate complex.

The chemical synthesis of serotonin was first reported by Hamlin and Fischer (1951). In this procedure 5-benzyloxyindole (Fig. 3(a)) was used as starting material and converted to serotonin in a four-step procedure. A novel total synthesis of serotonin described by Harley-Mason and Jackson (1953) proceeded simply by the cyclisation of 2-(2,5-dihydroxyphenyl)-4-aminobutylamine (Fig. 3(b)). Of importance is the synthetic route to serotonin used by Speeter and Anthony (1954) which also started from 5-benzyloxyindole. In this procedure one of the intermediate compounds is 5-(benzyloxy) indole -3-glyoxylamide (Fig. 3(c)) which is readily reduced by lithium aluminium hydride to O-benzylserotonin (Fig. 3(d)). The substitution of lithium aluminium deuteride in this reaction leads to O-benzyl-$\alpha,\alpha,\beta,\beta,$-$d_4$-serotonin (Fig. 3(e)) which is converted to $\alpha,\alpha,\beta,\beta,$-$d_4$-serotonin (Fig. 3(f)) by catalytic hydrogenation (Shaw, Wright and Milne, 1976). This tetra-deuterated serotonin derivative is important as a readily accessible standard for serotonin in its estimation by mass fragmentography (see Section C.6).

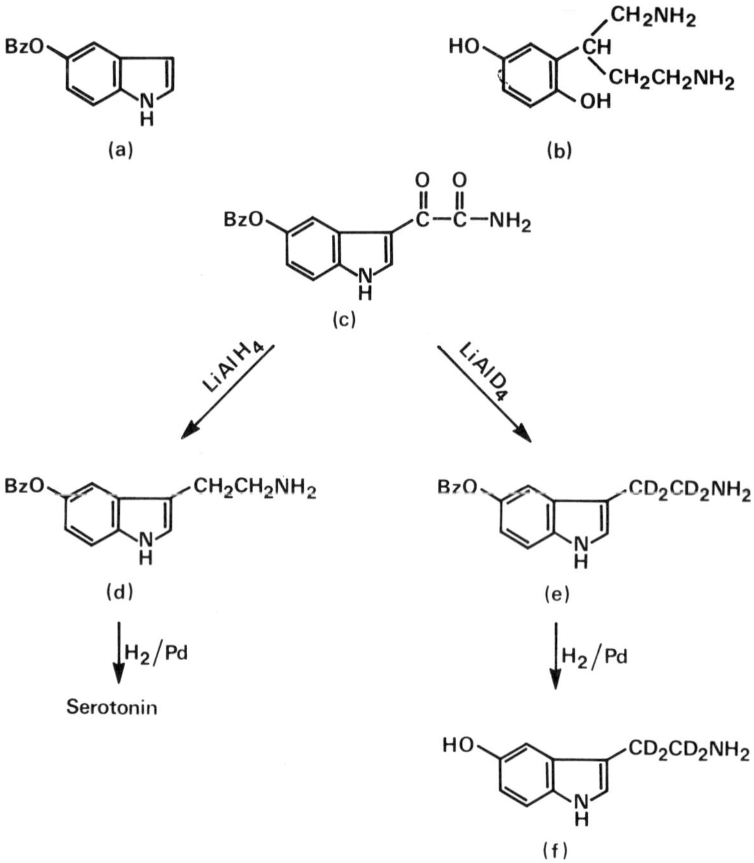

Fig. 3. Precursors and routes for the chemical synthesis of serotonin and its d_4-derivative.

B. ORIGIN, BIOSYNTHESIS AND METABOLISM

1. Biological Distribution

Serotonin is widely distributed in both plants and animal tissues (see Garattini and Valzelli, 1965). In mammals, significant concentrations of serotonin are found in the gut and central nervous system (CNS) and blood. In blood, serotonin is contained almost exclusively within the platelets. Platelets do not synthesise serotonin and are believed to build their stores by concentrating serotonin from the plasma via the intestine (Toh, 1954).

In the alimentary tract, serotonin is classically thought to be contained in and secreted by the enterochromaffin cells of the gastro-intestinal mucosa which can biosynthesise serotonin from L-tryptophan. Cells from the intestinal mucosa of rats have uptake mechanisms for serotonin and are also capable of serotonin biosynthesis from L-tryptophan (Kuhar, Roth and Aghajanian, 1972). Patients with malignant carcinoid disease (argentaffinoma tumours) show a markedly increased capacity to synthesis serotonin from dietary L-tryptophan (Sjoerdsma, Weissback and Udenfriend, 1965). The mammalian intestine has recently been shown to contain neurons, intrinsic to the gut itself, which are able both to take up and synthesise serotonin (Gershon, Dreyfus, Pickel, Joh and Reis, 1977).

Serotonin-containing nerve terminals in the CNS originate from cell bodies mainly concentrated in the different raphe nuclei of the brain stem and mesencephalon (Dahlstrom and Fuxe, 1965) and are present in most parts of the CNS. In the rat brain, serotonin concentrations are highest in the hypothalamus, mid-brain, brain stem and raphe nucleus, are relatively low in the cerebral cortex and lower in the cerebellum (Dahlstrom, Haggendal and Atack, 1973; Saavedra, Brownstein and Axelrod, 1973). The concentration of serotonin is considerably higher in the lower spinal cord than in the upper spinal cord (Anden, Fuxe and Henning, 1969). Of considerable interest is the high concentration of serotonin in the mammalian pineal gland (see Quay, 1974). Pineal serotonin is present in two locations; the cytoplasm of pinealocytes where it is synthesised, and in pineal sympathetic nerve endings which appear to have uptake and release capabilities (Owman, 1964; Owman, 1968, Quay, 1974).

The mammalian pituitary gland contains significant concentrations of a monoamine having histochemical fluorescence characteristic of serotonin (Bjorklund and Falck, 1969; Piezzi, Larin and Wurtman, 1970). Using a more specific radioenzymatic method Saavedra et al. (1973) detected serotonin in the rat pituitary in concentrations similar to those estimated by Bjorklund and Falck (1969). Histochemical fluorescence techniques have indicated the presence of serotonin in other endocrine cell systems including the thyroid and pancreas (Falck and Owman, 1968).

2. Biosynthesis

While the regulatory mechanisms of serotonin biosynthesis remain to be completely clarified (Renson, 1973; Lovenberg, Besselaar, Bensinger and

Jackson, 1973) it is clear that the biosynthetic pathway to serotonin proceeds from dietary L-tryptophan in two steps (Fig. 4). First in a rate-limiting step, L-tryptophan is 5-hydroxylated by the mono-oxygenase enzyme, tryptophan -5-hydroxylase to form 5-hydroxy-L-tryptophan which is then converted to serotonin by the enzyme 5-hydroxy-tryptophan decarboxylase. The 5-hydro-xylation of L-tryptophan has been observed in a number of biological

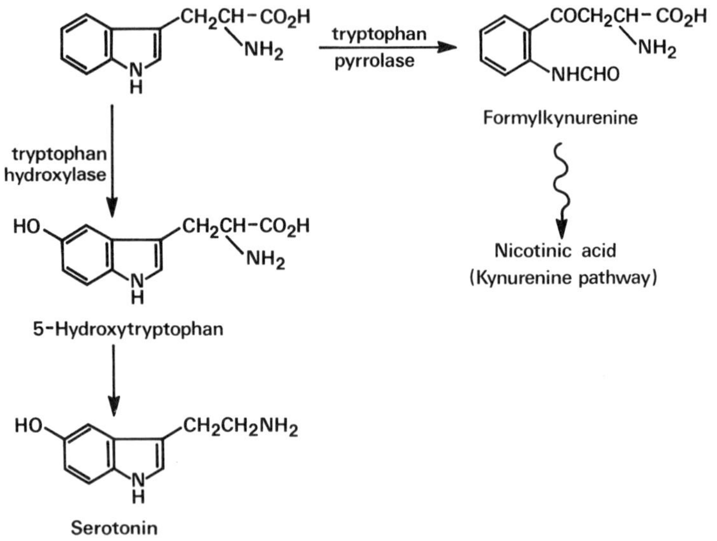

Fig. 4. Biosynthesis of serotonin from L-tryptophan.

systems (Mitoma, Weissbach and Udenfriend, 1965; Renson, Weissbach and Udenfriend, 1962; Freedland, 1963; Gal, Poczic and Marshall 1963; Graham-Smith, 1964; Lovenberg, Levine and Sjoerdsma, 1965; Lovenberg, Jequier and Sjoerdsma, 1967).

Brain tryptophan-5-hydroxylase has been the most extensively studied preparation of this enzyme (see Gal, 1974; Renson, 1973). In the brain, this enzyme is largely restricted to serotoninergic neurons and has been used as a marker for such neurons (Kuhar, Aghajanian and Roth, 1972).

The liver enzyme phenylalanine hydroxylase is also capable of 5-hydroxyl-ating L-tryptophan but this is not considered to be a significant pathway to serotonin (Renson et al., 1962). Tryptamine is not a substrate for tryptophan-5-hydroxylase (Udenfriend, Greveling, Posner, Redfield, Daly and Witkop, 1959).

There is currently some debate concerning the second enzyme system involved in serotonin biosynthesis. An enzyme preparation from guinea-pig kidney with 5-hydroxy-L-tryptophan decarboxylating activity was first isolated and proposed to be specific by Clark, Weissbach and Udenfriend (1954). Later however, workers from the same laboratory reported that the decarboxylation of all the natural aromatic L-amino acids was catalysed by the enzyme preparation from guinea-pig kidney (Lovenberg, Weissbach and Udenfriend, 1962). These workers proposed that the enzyme be referred to as "aromatic L-amino acid decarboxylase". More recent evidence suggests that the 5-hydroxy-L-tryptophan decarboxylating enzyme isolated from rat brain may be relatively specific for 5-hydroxy-L-tryptophan (Sims, Davis and Bloom, 1973).

3. Metabolism

The major pathway of metabolism of both peripheral and brain serotonin is by oxidative deamination to 5-hydroxyindole-3-acetaldehyde (Fig. 5a) by

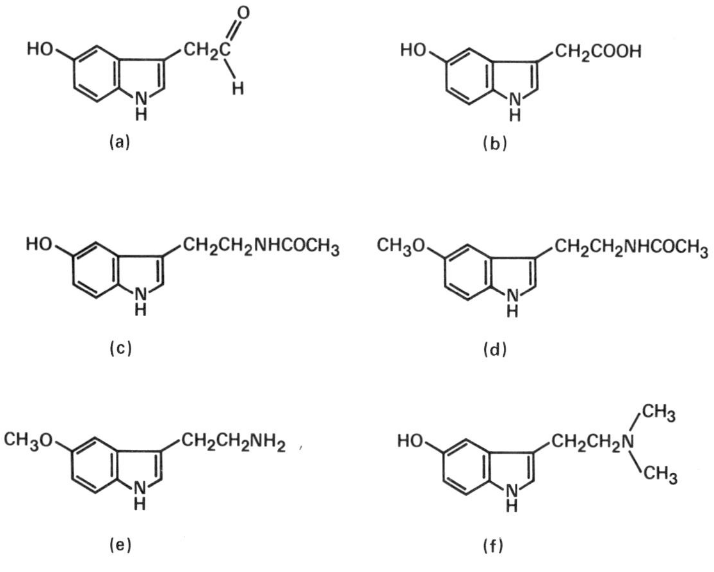

Fig. 5. Some metabolites of serotonin (a) 5-hydroxyindole-3-acetaldehyde; (b) 5-hydroxyindole-3-acetic acid; (c) N-acetylserotonin; (d) melatonin; (e) 5-methoxy-tryptamine; (f) bufotenin.

the enzyme monoamine oxidase (MAO). The action of MAO is followed by that of an aldehyde dehydrogenase to form the major urinary and CSF metabolite 5-hydroxyindole-3-acetic acid (5-HIAA; Fig. 5(b)). A significant proportion of administered serotonin is converted to N-acetylserotonin (Fig. 5(c)) in the liver and excreted in urine (McIsaac and Page, 1958).

N-acetylation of serotonin is a major step in the synthesis of melatonin (Fig. 5(d)) by the pineal gland (Weissbach, Redfield and Axelrod, 1961). Pineal N-acetyltransferase is involved in the maintenance of a circadian rhythm of pineal serotonin concentration. The activity of rat pineal N-acetyltransferase increases some 15 times in the nocturnal phase (Klein and Weller, 1970) when pineal serotonin reaches its lowest concentration (Quay, 1963). The other major pineal gland enzyme which acts on serotonin as well as N-acetylserotonin is hydroxyindole-O-methyltransferase (HIOMT) (Axelrod and Weissbach, 1961). HIOMT catalyses the conversion of serotonin to O-methylserotonin (5-methoxytryptamine; Fig. 5(e)) as well as N-acetylserotonin to melatonin and is not restricted to the pineal gland, being present in the retina (Cardinali and Rosner, 1971) and, significantly, the enterochromaffin cells of the gastrointestinal tract where melatonin is also synthesised (Raikhlin, Kvetnay and Tolkachev, 1975). The origin of hypothalamic O-methylserotonin (Koslow, 1974) has not been ascertained. This compound may come from the pineal gland or be synthesised locally from hypothalamic serotonin.

One further possible pathway of metabolism of serotonin is via N-methylation. The hallucinogen butotenin (N,N-dimethylserotonin; Fig. 5(f)) is formed in vitro by the action of a brain N-methyltransferase enzyme and S-adenosylmethionine on serotonin (Morgan and Mandell, 1969; Mandell and Morgan, 1971). The significance of this pathway of serotonin metabolism in mental disease states such as schizophrenia as suggested by Himwich (1970) remains to be determined.

4. Dietary Control of Brain Serotonin

As noted above, the regulatory mechanism of serotonin biosynthesis requires elucidation. Since the rate-limiting enzyme tryptophan hydroxylase is not normally saturated with its substrate L-tryptophan, the concentration of L-tryptophan in the brain is the most important controller of the rate of brain serotonin synthesis and both small and large changes in the concentration of brain L-tryptophan alter the rate of serotonin synthesis (Grahame-Smith, 1971; Fernstrom and Wurtman, 1971). Diet-induced changes in the plasma concentrations of L-tryptophan and of other, competing, neutral amino acids influence brain tryptophan and hence brain serotonin levels (Wurtman and Fernstrom, 1974). In the rat, injection of insulin or consumption of carbohydrate cause sequential increases in the concentration of L-tryptophan in the plasma and brain and of serotonin in the brain (Fernstrom and Wurtman, 1971). These findings led these workers to propose that serotoninergic neurons play a role in the mechanisms whereby the brain integrates information about the metabolic state and control of homeostatis and behaviour and thus, voluntary dietary habits exert control on brain serotonin and biochemistry (Wurtman and Fernstrom, 1974).

In rats, the consumption of a tryptophan-free diet leads to very rapid falls in the concentration of brain serotonin (Biggio, Fadda, Fanni, Tagliamonte and Gessa, 1974).

C. METHODS OF DETERMINATION AND EXTRACTION

Six distinct methods are used for the measurement of serotonin in blood, tissue extracts and other physiological fluids. These methods vary considerably in terms of convenience and equipment required as well as in terms of specificity, sensitivity and precision. These methods are listed in Table 1, together with their approximate lower limit of sensitivity.

Table 1
Methods for serotonin estimation

Method	Lower limit of serotonin sensitivity
Bioassay	570 fmol (100 pg)
Fluorometric	30 pmol (5 ng)
Radioenzymatic (no internal standard)	100 fmol (20 pg)
Radioimmunoassay	570 fmol (100 pg)
Gas chromatography	60 pmol (10 ng)
Mass-fragmentography, selected ion monitoring	30 fmol (5 pg)

Before serotonin can be estimated by any of these procedures it must be subjected to some degree of separation (from protein, peptides, and other indoles etc., which might interfere in the particular assay being used) and extraction into a suitable medium or solvent. The extent of the preliminary work-up required varies according to the assay type, and the general procedures used will be discussed with each of the methods.

In all the procedures in which blood serotonin concentration is being measured, scrupulous care must be taken to avoid platelet disruption during blood sampling. Platelets do not adhere to non-wettable surfaces and use is made of this fact by collecting blood using needles, syringes and tubes which have been silicone-coated.

1. Bioassay

Bioassay procedures were the methods first available for the determination of serotonin (Erspamer, 1940, 1942). Of historical importance is the rabbit ear-vein preparation (Page, 1942) used by Page and his coworkers in the isolation and identification of serotonin (Rapport, Green and Page, 1947; 1948a, b). Bioassays for serotonin rely on its ability to contract mammalian smooth muscle. Various muscle preparations have been devised (see Garattini and Valzelli, 1965) but the most widely used have been the rat uterus preparation first proposed by Erspamer (1940), the rat colon (Feldberg and Toh, 1953; Dalgliesh, Toh and Work, 1953) and rat stomach (fundus) (Vane, 1957).

The bioassay procedures are relatively sensitive but are of questionable specificity and precision. Many physiological substances such as the catecholamines, histamine, acetylcholine and substance P interfere with the activity of serotonin in these systems. For these reasons and in view of the greater precision and specificity of the physicochemical methods for the determination of serotonin, bioassays are now rarely used. Significant studies in which the blood concentration of serotonin has been estimated by bioassay are referred to in Section D below.

2. Fluorimetric Methods

Fluorimetric assays for serotonin take advantage of its natural fluorescence and have become the most widely used methods for the determination of serotonin in blood and tissue extracts. The fluorimetric determination of serotonin in blood platelets was first described by Udenfriend, Weissbach and Clark (1955b) making use of a colorimetric reaction between serotonin and 1-nitroso-2-naphthol. The finding that serotonin fluoresces at about 550 nm in 3M HCl (Udenfriend, Weissbach and Bogdanski, 1955a) simplified the fluorimetric estimation of serotonin and this method was used by Bogdanski, Pletscher, Brodie and Udenfriend (1956) to measure brain serotonin concentrations. The method used by these workers to extract and concentrate serotonin may be applied to both tissue and blood extracts of serotonin and is currently widely used.

In the method of Bogdanski et al. (1956) serotonin is isolated from tissue (or blood, following platelet lysis and de-proteinisation) by extraction into n-butanol at pH 10. After washing and heptane addition the serotonin is extracted into 0·1 M HCl. This aqueous phase may then be appropriately treated for use in any of the physico-chemical methods for serotonin determination. In the case of fluorimetry, using the methods of Udenfriend et al. (1955a) or Bogdanski et al. (1956) the dilute HCl solution is brought to 3M with

HCl and the fluorescence measured directly at 540–550nm, using an excitation wavelength of 290nm.

For measurement of serotonin in blood, Davis (1959), Crawford and Rudd (1962) and, more recently, Rao, White, Jachimowicz and Witkop (1976) modified the methods of Udenfriend et al. (1955a, b) and Bogdanski et al. (1956) mainly by incorporating protein precipitation steps into the extraction procedures.

In the method of Davis (1959) serum from clotted blood, previously treated with ascorbic acid, is deproteinised by treatment with $NaOH/ZnSO_4$ and, after centrifugation, the supernatant is treated similarly to brain tissue extracts in the procedure of Bogdanski et al. (1956) and the fluorescence measured in 3M HCl. The most widely used method for the extraction of serotonin from blood is that of Crawford and Rudd (1962) in which the analysis is performed on platelet rich plasma (PRP) separated under carefully standardised conditions from EDTA-treated blood. If PRP serotonin is to be determined, PRP is transferred to an unsiliconised tube for freezing and thawing before analysis. For the determination of serotonin in platelet suspension a platelet button is prepared by centrifugation and the platelet-poor plasma is removed by careful decantation. The platelet button is resuspended in aqueous EDTA. Partial disruption of the platelets in both the PRP and platelet suspension is achieved by freezing the samples rapidly below $-40°$ and thawing to room temperature. After freezing-thawing, trichloracetic acid is used to precipitate protein. The serotonin is then extracted and estimated essentially according to Bogdanski et al. (1956).

For the determination of free-serotonin in plasma, Crawford (1963) carries the platelet-poor plasma obtained as described above through the same trichloracetic acid precipitation and extraction steps as used for PRP.

In the method of Rao et al. (1976) PRP is treated with aqueous 1M perchloric acid and homogenised by sonication. This method was found by Rao et al. (1976) to give recoveries of added serotonin comparable to those obtained using trichloracetic acid but much superior to those obtained using alkaline $ZnSO_4$ precipitation.

Assays for serotonin utilising its natural fluorescence in 3M HCl have a sensitivity of about 30ng. In a search for increased sensitivity enhanced fluorescence is obtained when serotonin is derivatised with ninhydrin (Snyder, Axelrod and Zweig, 1965) or with O-phthalaldehyde (OPT) (Maickel and Miller, 1966). The procedure of Maickel and Miller (1966) using OPT has become a widely used method of fluorimetric estimation of serotonin and optimal conditions for the OPT-serotonin reaction have been studied (Thompson, Spezia and Angulo, 1969).

A method for the fluorimetric determination of serotonin developed by Anton and Sayre (1972) is based on their observation that serotonin gives an enhanced fluorescence when heated in the presence of potassium ortho-phosphate buffer. Anton and Sayre (1972) have made a comparison of the sensitivity and specificity obtained by this method with those obtained using the fluorometric methods using 3M HCl (Bogdanski et al., 1965), ninhydrin (Snyder et al., 1965) and OPT (Maickel and Miller, 1966). The method using 3M HCl was the least sensitive while the other three methods were similar but all methods differed considerably in their specificity (Table 2).

Table 2

Comparison of the specificities toward various indoles of fluorometric methods used to measure serotonin.

		Method of fluorophore formation	
Indole	3 MHCl	O-phthalaldehyde	K_3PO_4
Serotonin	100	100	100
5-Hydroxyindoleacetic acid	72	94	217
N-Acetylserotonin	27	228	148
5-Hydroxytryptophan	66	142	9
Tryptophan	<0·005	<1	<0·005
5-Methoxytryptamine	72	550	<0·005
Melatonin	25	574	<0·005
5-Methoxyindole acetic acid	56	240	<0·005
Tryptamine	<0·005	<1	<0·005
N,N-dimethyltryptamine	<0·005	3	<0·005

3. Radioenzymatic

A radioenzymatic method for the determination of serotonin was first described by Saavedra et al. (1973). The method is based on the ability of the pineal gland enzyme, hydroxyindole-O-methyl transferase to transfer the ^{3}H-methyl group of ^{3}H-methyl-S-adenosyl-1-methionine (^{3}H-SAM) to N-acetylserotonin to form ^{3}H-melatonin. The N-acetylserotonin is also formed enzymatically by the action of N-acetyltransferase and acetyl coenzyme A. Advantage is taken of the ease with which ^{3}H-melatonin can be separated from serotonin and N-acetylserotonin by extraction into toluene. The method of Saavedra et al. (1973) has been modified by Boireau, Ternaux, Bourgoin, Hery, Glowinski and Hamon (1976) in an attempt to produce an assay sufficiently sensitive to measure serotonin in cerebrospinal fluid (CSF). In an artificial simulated CSF (1–3 ml) these workers claimed to be able to measure serotonin levels as low as 10 pg. The method incorporates a gel filtration step to remove CSF salts and thin layer chromatography to purify the radiolabelled melatonin product.

These radioenzymatic procedures apart from high sensitivity also have excellent specificity since ^{3}H-melatonin can only be derived from either serotonin or N-acetylserotonin. The problem of interference due to endogenous N-acetylserotonin is overcome by running blanks without acetylcoenzyme A, thus also providing a concurrent determination of N-acetylserotonin (Saavedra et al., 1973). Precautions must be taken in the storage of the enzymes and acetylcoenzyme A used in these procedures (Saavedra et al., 1973). The precision and recoveries of serotonin in radioenzymatic methods require further investigation but any problem in this regard could be overcome by using ^{14}C-labelled serotonin as an internal standard, although such a double isotope system would necessarily reduce the absolute sensitivity of the method.

4. Radioimmunoassay

The formation of antibodies to serotonin suitable for use in a radioimmunoassay was reported by Peskar and Spector (1973). The antibodies to serotonin were produced in rabbits immunised with antigen prepared by reacting serotonin with a diazotized p-aminophenylalanyl derivative of bovine serum albumin. This antigen was also used in the recent development and validation of a radioimmunoassay for serotonin (Kellum and Jaffe, 1976). The antibodies against serotonin (Peskar and Spector, 1973) cross-react significantly only with 5-methoxytryptamine and tryptamine.

The radioimmunoassay for serotonin described by Kellum and Jaffe (1976) was used by these workers to measure blood serotonin levels following an alkaline $ZnSO_4$ precipitation and the results compare favourably with those obtained by fluorimetry. The radioimmunoassay was found to have high sensitivity (100 pg of serotonin).

5. Gas Chromatography

A gas chromatographic method for the concurrent estimation of serotonin, noradrenaline and dopamine has been described by Martin and Ansell (1973). This method was designed principally for the estimation of brain tissue levels of these amines and utilises homogenisation of the tissue in butanol, alumina absorption and subsequent ion-pair extraction using di-(2-ethylhexyl) phosphate. The amines were derivatized using trifluoroacetic anhydride and the trifluoroacetyl derivative chromatographed on a column of 5% s.e.52 on 100–120 mesh gas chrom Q. While this method is very specific, it is not highly sensitive having a lower limit of detection of about (10 ng) serotonin (Martin and Ansell, 1973).

6. Mass Fragmentography

The latest technique to lend itself to the increasing need for highly sensitive, specific, and precise methods for determining serotonin (and other biogenic amines) is that of mass fragmentography. Mass fragmentography is the technique of selected multiple ion monitoring using a mass spectrometer interfaced to a gas chromatograph (Cattabeni, Koslow and Costa. 1972; Koslow and Green, 1973; Beck, Wiesel and Sedvall, 1977; Vol. 3, Ch. 3).

This method has the disadvantage of the high cost incurred in setting it up but no other method currently can estimate serotonin with such a high degree of sensitivity (low pg range), precision and with virtually absolute specificity. If serotonin is to be measured in blood this method requires the preliminary deproteinisation and extraction procedures such as used for the fluorimetric methods above but there is no necessity to separate other mono-amines and indoles as these are adequately separated by the gas chromato-graph. Before injection of the sample containing serotonin into the gas chromatography–mass spectrometer (GC/MS) it is necessary to convert serotonin (and other amines) to trifluoroacetyl (Martin and Ansell. 1973) or pentafluorpropionyl (Cattabeni et al., 1972) derivatives.

The method used at the Garvan Institute for the mass fragmentographic determination of serotonin is briefly as follows:

(a) Instrumentation

A Hewlett-Packard 5992A bench-top GC/MS system controlled by a Hewlett-Packard 21MX-E computer is used. For the determination of low pg levels of serotonin this system is operated in the selected ion monitor (SIM) mode which measures the intensity at the most intense 0·1 amu point for the mass peaks chosen during each scan. The gas chromatograph utilises all-glass columns (870 × 2 mm i.d.) packed with 2–3% OV-101 on Chromo-sorb W. Runs are usually isothermal at 180° using an injection port tempera-ture of 220°. Helium carrier gas flow is 30 ml/min using a membrane separator.

(b) Derivatisation

After extraction of serotonin into n-butanol and then dilute formic acid the samples are dried in vacuo under nitrogen in 1 ml reaction vials and the residue, dissolved in dry acetonitrile (50 µl) is treated with 100 µl pentafluoro-propionic anhydride. The vials are capped (Teflon) and either heated at 60° for 15 min or advantageously left overnight at 0–4°. Solvent and excess reagents are removed under a stream of dry nitrogen and the residue dis-solved in a suitable volume of ethyl acetate for injection into the GC/MS.

A typical mass spectrum of the pentafluoropropionyl derivative of serotonin is shown in Fig. 6. The molecular ion (m/e 614) and the base peak (m/e 451) are eminently suitable ions for estimation of serotonin in the SIM

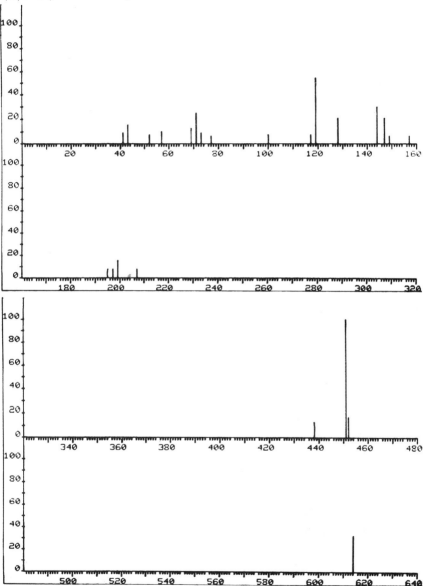

Fig. 6. The mass spectrum of the pentafluoropropionic anhydride derivative of serotonin.

mode. The structure of the molecular ion of the pentafluorpropionyl derivative of serotonin and its fragmentation pattern is shown in Fig. 7.

(c) Standards

For the quantitative assay of serotonin by mass fragmentography it is
necessary to have as an internal standard a compound which can be carried
through the whole procedure with endogenous serotonin and which will

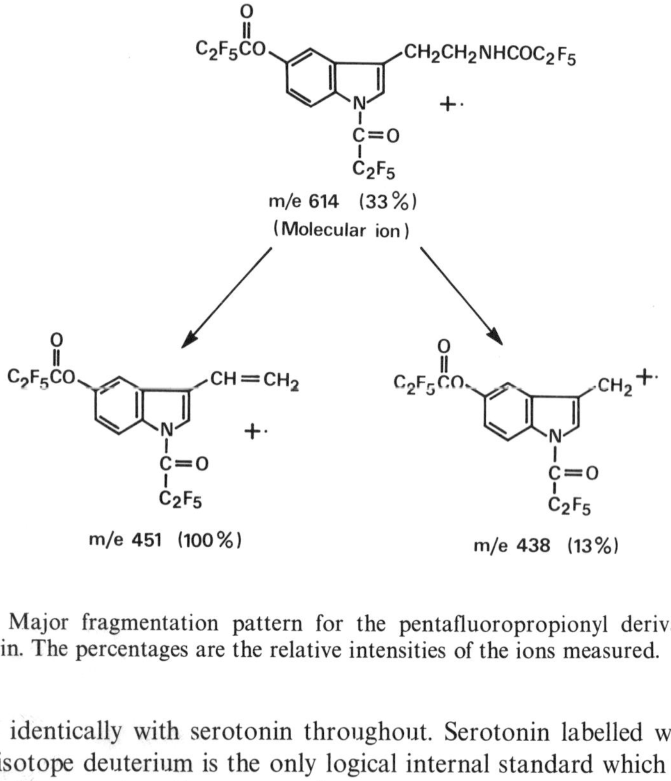

m/e 614 (33%)
(Molecular ion)

m/e 451 (100%)

m/e 438 (13%)

Fig. 7. Major fragmentation pattern for the pentafluoropropionyl derivative of
serotonin. The percentages are the relative intensities of the ions measured.

behave identically with serotonin throughout. Serotonin labelled with the
stable isotope deuterium is the only logical internal standard which can be
used in this procedure. In our procedure $\alpha,\alpha,\beta,\beta$,-tetradeuteroserotonin (Fig.
3(e)) is synthesised by the method of Shaw et al. (1976), and added in appropriate quantities to tissue or blood before homogenisation and/or extraction.
In this way, the absolute level of endogenous serotonin in the sample is
obtained by comparison of the GC/MS signal (peak areas) from the d_4-sero-
tonin standard with that due to non-deuterated (endogenous) serotonin.
The ions selected for detection of d_4-serotonin in the SIM mode correspond
to those selected for serotonin (see above) and are the molecular ion (m/e

618) and the base peak fragment (m/e 454). Using this technique (SIM), as little as 5 pg serotonin can be measured.

Mass fragmentography is considerably more sensitive than any other method of estimating serotonin. Other biogenic monoamines and indoles of interest may be estimated simultaneously. Also, the problem of specificity or cross-contamination which occurs with other methods is avoided. Provided a suitably deuterated serotonin internal standard is used, the estimation can be carried out with a high degree of precision.

D. BLOOD LEVELS OF SEROTONIN

1. Normal Blood Concentrations

Since most of the serotonin circulating in blood is concentrated, or stored, in dense granules of platelets (Rand and Reid, 1951; Humphrey and Jaques, 1954; Udenfriend and Weissbach, 1954; Davis and White, 1968) its estimation has, in general, been made after isolation of platelets by differential centrifugation and disruption/lysis of platelets to release serotonin (see methods above). Concentrations of serotonin have thus been expressed in terms of 10^9 platelets, mg of platelet protein, ml of platelet rich plasma and ml of whole blood. The estimation of serotonin in serum has also been performed but it has been suggested that when blood clots, only part of the serotonin in the platelets reaches the serum and this fraction may not be constant (Hardisty and Stacey, 1955). However, Davis (1959) reported constant recoveries of serotonin from serum if the blood was allowed to clot in the presence of ascorbic acid. In addition to estimating platelet serotonin some attention has been paid to the level in plasma of "free" serotonin (Crawford, 1963) as distinct from that transported in close association with the platelets.

(a) Platelet-bound serotonin

The levels of serotonin in the blood of normal subjects have been estimated by bioassay, fluorimetric methods and radioimmunoassay and, in general, good agreement exists between the values obtained using these different methods.

Table 3 lists the levels of serotonin in normal subjects in a number of relatively large studies. No evidence of any sex difference has been noted. Few investigations have reported any significant effect of age on blood serotonin concentration but this aspect may warrant further investigation. Erspamer (1954) reported higher levels (mean 680 pmol (120 ng)/ml; range 400–1140 pmol (70–200 ng)/ml) of serum serotonin in young adults than in elderly people (mean 500 pmol (90 ng)/ml; range 170–850 pmol (30–150

Table 3

Concentrations of serotonin in normal blood obtained by different methods.

Method	No. of subjects	Source of serotonin	Mean level ± S.D. (range) (1 ng = 5·7 pmol)	References
Bioassay	25	serum	70 ± 20 ng/ml	Snow, Lennard-Jones, Curzon and Stacey (1955)
	31	serum	98 ng/ml (44-247)	Barkhan (1955)
	35	platelet suspension	570 ± 180 ng/10^9 platelets (160 ± 60 ng/ml blood)	Hardisty and Stacey (1955)
Fluorimetric	50	serum	210 ± 53 (100-320)	Davis (1959)
	27	platelet-rich plasma	336 ng/10^9 platelets (127-501)	Crawford (1965)
	20	blood	186 ± 12 (S.E.M.) ng/ml	Garelis, Gillam, Wyatt and Neff (1975)
Radioimmunoassay	55	blood	168 ± 13·4 (S.E.M.) ng/ml	
	15	platelet-rich plasma	341 ± 27 (S.E.M.) ng/10^9 platelets	
		blood	337 ± 40 ng/10^9 platelets	Kellum and Jaffe (1976)

ng)/ml). Pare, Sandler and Stacey (1957) reported blood serotonin levels of 700 ± 80 pmol (124 ± 14 ng)/ml in 15 hospitalised children awaiting tonsillectomy compared with a quoted normal adult level of 570 ± 90 pmol (99 ± 16 ng)/ml. In 16 children aged 1–11 years (mean 5·8 years) awaiting elective surgery the mean plasma serotonin concentration was 1240 ± 900 pmol (218 ± 156 ng)/ml (Campbell, Friedman, Green, Collins, Small and Breuer, 1975).

Children are reported to have higher levels of serotonin in CSF than adults (Akcasu, Akcasu, Turnay, 1960). The reports indicate that the level of serotonin in biological fluids may fall with increasing age.

(b) *Plasma free serotonin levels*

In 27 young adult subjects, Crawford (1965) reported a mean plasma free serotonin level of 74 pmol (13 ng)/ml (range 0–165 pmol (0–29 ng)/ml). Similar levels have been reported by other groups (Genefke and Mandel 1967; Kellum and Jaffe, 1976; Somerville and Hinterberger, 1975). No sex difference was observed in the level of free serotonin but levels were reported to be at a minimum—34 pmol (6 ng)/ml in fasted, early morning samples (Genefke and Mandel, 1967). Kellum and Jaffe (1976) observed that if blood was treated with prostaglandin E1, to inhibit platelet aggregation before separating platelet-poor plasma there was a significant reduction in the amount of free serotonin appearing in the plasma. Whether plasma free serotonin is of physiological significance or whether it is an artifact of platelet lysis during sample collection and preparation remains to be settled.

(c) *Diurnal variation*

Evidence for a significant circadian rhythm of serotonin levels in whole blood has been reported by Sauerbier and Von Mayersback (1976). Studying 64 military personnel, those workers found that high levels of blood serotonin (approximately 1000 pmoles (175 ng)/ml) were maintained from 6.00 p.m. until 6.00 a.m. After 6.00 a.m. there was a fall in blood serotonin concentration reaching a nadir of approximately 540 ± 46 pmol (95 ± 8 ng)/ml at 2.00 p.m. The amplitude of the deviation was found to exceed 50% of the 24 hr mean 920 pmol (161 ng)/ml.

In a more limited study Genefke and Mandel (1967) reported lower platelet concentrations of serotonin in the mid-morning than early evening and early morning.

(d) *Effect of meals*

The study of Kellum and Jaffe (1976) using radioimmunoassay clearly demonstrated that blood serotonin concentrations increase after feeding.

228 G. A. SMYTHE

Seventeen subjects showed a significant elevation of blood serotonin from 1130 ± 210 pmol (198 ± 37 ng)/ml to 2060 ± 97 pmol (362 ± 16·9 ng)/ml within 60 min following a standard test meal, while fasting control subjects exhibited no change in blood serotonin levels (Kellum and Jaffe, 1976).

2. Serotonin Levels in Disease

The concentration of serotonin in blood has been found to be altered in a number of diseases and for the most part, these diseases involve the gastro-intestinal tract, blood platelets or the CNS—sites already noted to be of significance in storage and concentration of serotonin. The use of blood serotonin estimations in the clinical diagnoses of these diseases has not been generally recognised (Gitlow, Warner and Bertani, 1972) but with the development of more specific and convenient assay methods this situation is likely to improve.

(a) Carcinoid disease

This syndrome is associated with malignant carcinoid of the small intestine with metastases to the liver from primary argentaffinoma tumours. That elevated serotonin secretion might be responsible for the symptoms of this disease was first suggested by Thorson, Biorck, Bjorkman and Waldenstrom (1954). Sjoerdsma, Weissbach and Udenfriend (1956) subsequently demonstrated that patients with malignant carcinoid disease had blood levels of serotonin 5–10 times the normal levels (up to 15·4 nmol (2700 ng)/ml) and that urinary 5-hydroxyindole acetic acid (5-HIAA) excretion was some 40–60 times normal. In addition tryptophan metabolism was altered in these patients with as much as 60% of dietary L-tryptophan being converted to serotonin compared to 1% in normal subjects (Sjoerdsma et al., 1956). Alterations of blood serotonin or urinary 5-HIAA may not be as high in some patients with carcinoid syndrome as in those studied by Sjoerdsma et al. (1956) but an elevated blood serotonin or urinary 5-HIAA concentration is necessary to establish diagnosis of this condition (Gitlow et al., 1972). It has been suggested that Peyronie's disease, which is manifested by plastic induration of the penis, can be a presenting complaint in male patients with carcinoid syndrome and that all patients with Peyronie's disease should be screened for carcinoid disease (Bivens, Merecek and Feldman, 1973).

(b) Other gastro-intestinal diseases

In a study of patients with gastro-intestinal disease, and presenting severe symptoms (nausea, vomiting and diarrhoea), nine out of 65 were found to have elevated blood serotonin concentrations (Warner, 1963). These were, generally, untreated malabsorption diseases. To date, there have been no studies investigating possible interrelationships between serotonin levels and polypeptide hormones of the gastro-intestinal tract.

(c) Hermansky–Pudlak syndrome (albinism)

Blood platelet abnormalities have been shown in patients with this syndrome (White, Edson, Desmick and Witkop, 1971) and these workers reported finding platelet serotonin concentrations at 10% of normal levels. More recently Rao et al. (1976) reported similar findings. In platelets from patients with Hermansky–Pudlak syndrome serotonin concentrations were 284 ± 114 pmol (50 ± 20 ng)/10^9 platelets compared with normal levels of 5334 ± 340 pmol (940 ± 60 ng)/10^9 platelets (Rao et al., 1976).

(d) Down's syndrome

Children with Down's syndrome have significantly lower blood serotonin concentrations than healthy controls (Rosner, Ong, Paine and Mahanand, 1965) although the values quoted for both patients and controls in that report are an order of magnitude higher than other studies have indicated. The quoted ranges of serotonin concentrations are: for patients with trisomic mongolism 2·6–5·7 nmol (450–1000 ng)/ml (M. 4·0 nmol (700 ng)/ml); for patients with translocation mongolism 7·1–10·0 nmol (1250–1750 ng)/ml (M. 8·4 nmol (1470 ng)/ml) and for healthy controls 6·8–13·1 nmol (1200–2300) ng/ml (M. 10.3 nmol (1810 ng)/ml). Platelet serotonin concentration has also been estimated in Down's syndrome. Serotonin content was found to be reduced from 2·54 ± 0·38 nmol (446 ± 66 ng)/mg platelet protein in sibling controls and 2·80 ± 0·42 nmol (492 ± 74 ng)/mg in non-sibling controls to 0·90 ± 0·09 nmol/mg (158 ± 16 ng)/mg, in 14 patients with Down's syndrome (Lott, Chase and Murphy, 1972).

(e) Migraine

During migraine attacks blood serotonin concentration shows a marked fall to about 50% of the basal level (Anthony, Hinterberger and Lance, 1967). These workers suggested that relief from the migraine attack required repletion of released platelet serotonin and a return to normal plasma levels.

(f) Phenylketonuria

Blood serotonin levels were shown to be reduced from 705 ± 80 pmol (124 ± 14 ng)/ml in 15 control children to 324 ± 63 pmol (57 ± 11 ng)/ml in nine children with untreated phenylketonuria (Pare et al., 1957).

(g) Central nervous system (CNS) disturbances

Changes from normal blood levels of serotonin have been suggested and are being investigated for a number of CNS disorders. Kreigner, Kolodney and Warner (1964) observed lower than normal blood serotonin concentrations in patients with CNS lesions involving the hypothalamus and limbic systems. Low platelet serotonin levels were shown in 22 of 25 children with symptoms of hyperactivity (Coleman, 1971). It was also observed in this study that in hyperactive children kept in hospital, there was a slow return of serotonin concentrations toward normal with a corresponding lessening of hyperactive symptoms. Gadelis et al. (1975) observed higher serotonin concentrations in the blood of unmedicated patients with schizophrenia 1700 $\pm$ 160 pmol (298 $\pm$ 28 ng)/mg than in that of medicated schizophrenic patients 1130 $\pm$ 95 pmol (199 $\pm$ 17 ng)/ml or normal controls 1060 $\pm$ 68 pmol (186 $\pm$ 12 ng)/ml. Corresponding changes were noted in serotonin concentration expressed in terms of platelet number (Garelis et al., 1975). There have been consistent findings of elevated blood serotonin levels in autistic and mentally retarded children (with the exceptions of Down's syndrome and phenylketonuria noted above) from several research groups (Pare, Sandler and Stacey, 1960; Schain and Freedman, 1961, Ritvo, Yuwiler, Geller, Ornitz, Saeger and Plotkin, 1970; Tu and Partington, 1972; Campbell et al., 1975; Hanley, Stahl and Freedman, 1977).

It has been proposed that serotonin activity is reduced in spinal cord injury (Bular, Lackovic, Jakupsevic and Damjanor, 1974) and depression (Ashcroft, Crawford, Eccleston, Sharman, MacDougall, Stanton and Binns, 1966; Tuomisto and Tukiainen, 1976). Recent developments in serotonin assay methods will enable these proposals to be investigated by estimating the level of serotonin in cerebrospinal fluid.

3. Drug Effects

Many drugs are known to alter the activity and metabolism of serotonin and to interfere with its uptake into blood platelets (see Garattini and Valgelli, 1965) but there is a paucity of studies demonstrating the effect of these drugs on blood serotonin concentrations. Reserpine administration has been shown to result in marked elevations in serum serotonin concentrations in human subjects (Warner, 1963). Cyproheptadine therapy causes elevated serum serotonin levels to fall to normal levels in some patients with gastrointestinal disease (Warner, 1963). Most of the drugs known to interfere with adrenergic activity also interfere with serotonin activity (Smythe, 1977).

Other drugs which have significant effects on serotonin activity and metabolism include p-chorophenylalanine, which blocks serotonin biosynthesis (Koe and Weissman, 1966) and fluoxetine (Lilly 110140), which is a specific inhibitor of serotonin uptake (Wong, Horng, Bymaster, Hauser and Molloy, 1974).

Aspirin inhibits uptake of serotonin into blood platelets *in vitro* and also causes release of platelet serotonin (Rendu, 1976).

E. SEROTONIN–ENDOCRINE HORMONE INTERACTIONS

There is increasing evidence that serotonin plays an important role in the neuro-endocrine control of pituitary hormone release and it has been concluded that hypothalamic serotoninergic pathways predominantly stimulate pituitary hormone release (Smythe, 1977). The role of serotonin in growth hormone release is controversial (Smythe, 1977) but recent evidence indicates that serotonin stimulates human growth hormone release (Smythe, Compton and Lazarus, 1976; Lancranjan, Wirz-Justice, Puhringer and Delpozo, 1977). Alterations of brain serotonin metabolism have been demonstrated in growth hormone-deficient animals (Cocchi, Di Giulio, Groppetti, Mantegazza, Muller and Spano, 1975). Further, serotonin-growth hormone interactions have been noted in the periphery and *in vitro*. In dogs, the administration of growth hormone causes the release of serotonin into the pancreatico-duodenal venous blood (Sirek, Geerling and Sirek, 1966). After resection of pituitary tumours in acromegalic subjects, previously elevated serum serotonin levels fall to normal in parallel with the fall in serum growth hormone (Essman *et al.*, 1973).

The activity of the growth-promoting substance, somatomedin was shown to be stimulated *in vitro* by serotonin—an effect which could be blocked by its derivative melatonin (Smythe, Stuart and Lazarus, 1974).

A possible role of serotonin in the release of insulin from the pancreas is controversial, as it has been suggested that serotonin stimulates (Telib, Raptis, Schroder and Pfeiffer, 1968; Gagliardino, Ziecher, Iturriza, Hernandez and Rodriguez, 1971) as well as inhibits (Feldman and Lebovitz, 1972, Feldman, Quickel and Lebovitz, 1972) insulin release. In the rat, insulin administration results in increased synthesis of brain serotonin (Fernstrom and Wurtman, 1971). Marco, Hedo and Villaneuva (1977) have shown that serotonin inhibits the release of glucagon, as well as insulin, from mouse pancreatic islets *in vitro* and, in support of such an action *in vivo*, it was shown that serotonin antagonists cause increased glucagon release in normal human subjects (Campbell, Smythe, Lazarus and Kraegen, 1977).

Much evidence suggests that serotonin has a role in the neuro-endocrine mechanisms leading to release of adrenocorticotrophin (ACTH) from the pituitary (see Smythe, 1977).

Serotonin is an important mediator in the circadian periodicity of plasma glucocorticoid hormones (Kreiger and Rizzo, 1969). The serotonin antagonist cyproheptadine has been shown to inhibit the rise in cortisol secretion normally following insulin-induced hypoglycaemia (Plonk, Bivens and Feldman, 1974) and also to induce clinical remission in Cushing's disease (Krieger, Amorosa and Linick, 1975). Further support for a serotoninergic neural pathway stimulating ACTH release was obtained using the serotonin uptake inhibitor fluoxetine which was shown to elevate plasma corticosterone levels in rats (Fuller, Snoddy and Molloy, 1976). Administration of the serotonin precursor 5-HTP causes significant elevation of plasma corticosterone levels in the rat (Okada, Saito, Fujieda and Yammashita, 1972) and of plasma cortisol levels in both man (Imura, Nakai and Yoshimir, 1973) and the monkey (Chambers and Brown, 1976). There is evidence of a feedback effect of glucocorticoids on rat brain serotonin activity and synthesis (Telegdy and Vermes, 1975; Neckers and Sze, 1975).

Much of the data used to implicate serotonin and other biogenic amines in hormone interactions has been obtained using monoamine receptor-blocking drugs and we have suggested that these data must be interpreted with great caution because of the structural similarity between dopamine and serotonin and the consequent similarity of requirements for binding at their respective receptor sites (Smythe et al., 1976; Smythe, 1977). The current availability of highly sensitive and specific methods for measuring serotonin could play an important role in settling some of the controversial issues concerning serotonin–endocrine hormone interactions.

REFERENCES

Akcasu, A., Akcasu, M. and Tumay, S. B. (1960) *Nature, Lond.* **187**, 324.

Anden, N. E., Fuxe, K. and Henning, M. (1969). *Eur. J. Pharmacol.* **8**, 302.

Anthony, M., Hinterberger, H. and Lance, J. (1967). *Arch. Neurol.* **16**, 544.

Anton, A. H. and Sayre, D. F. (1972). "The Thyroid and Biogenic Amines" (J. E. Rall and I. J. Kopin, eds), p. 398. North Holland Publishing Co., Amsterdam and London.

Ashcroft, G. W., Crawford, T. B. B., Eccleston, D., Sharman, D. F., MacDougall, E. J., Stanton, J. B. and Binns, J. K. (1966). *Lancet*, ii, 1049.

Axelrod, J. and Weissbach, H. (1961). *J. biol. Chem.* **236**, 211.

Barkhan, P. (1955). *S. Afr. J. med. Sci.* **20**, 49.

Beck, O., Wiesel, F-A. and Sedvall, G. (1977). *J. Chromat.* **134**, 407.

Benditt, E. P. (1958) "5-Hydroxytryptamine" (G. P. Lewis, ed.), p. 127. Pergamon, London.

Biggio, G., Fadda, F., Fanni, P., Tagliamonte, A. and Gessa, G. L. (1974). *Life Sci.* **14**, 1321.

Bivens, C. H., Marecek, R. L. and Feldman, J. M. (1973). *New Engl. J. Med.* **289**, 844.

Bjorklund, A. and Falck, B. (1969). *Z. Zellforsch.* **93**, 254.

Bogdanski, D. F., Pletscher, A., Brodie, B. R. and Udenfriend, S. (1956). *J. Pharmac. exp. Ther.* **117**, 82.

Boireau, A., Ternaux, J. P., Bourgoin, S., Hery, F., Glowinski, J. and Hamon, M. (1976). *J. Neurochem.* **26**, 201.

Brodie, B. B. (1958). " 5-Hydroxytryptamine" (G. P. Lewis, ed.), p. 93. Pergamon, Oxford and London.

Bulat, M., Lackovic, Z., Jakupcevic, M. and Damjanov, I. (1974). *Science*, **185**, 527.

Bulbring, E. and Lin, R. C. Y. (1958). *J. Physiol.* **140**, 381.

Campbell, M., Friedman, E., Green, W. H., Collins, P. J., Small, A. M. and Breuer, H. (1975). *Int. Pharmacopsychiat.* **10**, 213.

Campbell, L. V., Smythe, G., Lazarus, L. and Kraegen, E. W. (1977). *Aust. N.Z. J. Med.* **7**, 686.

Cardinali, D. P. and Rosner, J. M. (1971). *J. Neurochem.* **18**, 1769.

Cattabeni, F., Koslow, S. H. and Costa, E. (1972). *Science*, **178**, 176.

Chambers, J. W. and Brown, G. M. (1976). *Endocrinology*, **98**, 420.

Clark, C. T. Weissbach, H. and Udenfriend, S. (1954). *J. biol. Chem.* **210**, 139.

Cocchi, D., Di Giulio, A., Groppetti, A., Mantegazza, P., Muller, E. E. and Spano, P. F. (1975). *Acta vit. enzymol.* **29**, 90.

Coleman, M. (1971). *J. Pediat.* **78**, 985.

Courriere, P., Coubeils, J. L. and Pullman, B. (1971). *C.r. Acad. Sci.* (Ser. D.) **272**, 1697.

Crawford, N. (1963). *Clin. chim. Acta*, **8**, 39.

Crawford, N. (1965). *Clin. chim. Acta*, **12**, 274.

Crawford, N. and Rudd, B. T. (1962). *Clin. chim. Acta*, **7**, 114.

Dahlstrom, A. and Fuxe, K. (1965). *Acta physiol. scand.* (Suppl. 62), **232**, 1.

Dahlstrom, A., Haggendal, J. and Atack, C. (1973). "Serotonin and Behaviour" (J. Barchas and E. Usdin, eds), p. 87. Academic Press, New York and London.

Dalgliesh, C. E., Toh, C. C. and Work, T. S. (1953). *J. Physiol.* **120**, 298.

Daly, J. W. and Witkop, B. (1967). *J. Am. chem. Soc.* **89**, 1032.

Davis, R. B. (1959). *J. Lab. clin. Med.* **54**, 344.

Davis, R. B. and White, J. G. (1968). *Br. J. Haemat.* **15**, 93.

Eriksen, N., Martin, G. M. and Benditt, E. P. (1960). *J. biol. Chem.* **235**, 1662.

Erspamer, V. (1940). *Arch. exp. Pathol. Pharmacol., Naunyn-Schmiedeberg's*, **196**, 343.

Erspamer, V. (1954). "Ciba Foundation Symposium on Hypertension" (G. E. W. Wolstenholme and M. P. Cameron, eds), p. 78. Little, Brown and Co., Boston.

Erspamer, V. and Asero (1952). *Nature, Lond.* **169**, 800.

Essman, W. B. Sherman, S. and Kolodny, L. (1973). *New Engl. J. Med.* **289**, 870.

Falck, B. and Owman, C. (1968). *Adv. Pharmacol.* **6A**, 211.

Feldberg, W. and Toh, C. C. (1953). *J. Physiol.* **119**, 352.

Feldman, J. M. and Lebovitz, H. E. (1972). *Endocrinology*, **91**, 809.

Feldman, J. M., Quickel, K. E. and Lebovitz, H. E. (1972). *Diabetes*, **21**, 779.

Fernstom, J. D. and Wurtman, R. J. (1971). *Science*, **174**, 1023.

Freedland, R. A. (1963). *Biochim. biophys. Acta*, **73**, 71.

Fuller, R. W., Snoddy, H. D. and Molloy, B. B. (1976). *Life Sci.* **19**, 337.

Gagliardino, J. J. Zieher, L. M., Iturriza, F. C. Hernandez, R. E. and Rodriguez, R. R. (1971). *Horm. metab. Res.* **3**, 145.

Gal, E. M. (1974). "Serotonin—New Vistas" (E. Costa, G. L. Gessa and M. Sandler, eds), p. 1. Raven Press, New York.

Gal, E. M., Poczik, M. and Marshall, F. D. (1963). *Biochem. biophys. Res. Commun.* **12**, 39.

Garattini, S. and Valzelli, L. (1965). "Serotonin." Elsevier Publishing Co., Amsterdam, London and New York

Garelis, E., Gillan, J. C., Wyatt, R. J. and Neff, N. (1975). *Am. J. Psychiat.* **132**, 184.

Genefke, I. K. and Mandel, P. (1967). *Clin. chim. Acta*, **19**, 131.

Gershon, M. D., Dreyfus, C. F., Pickel, V. M. Joh, T. H. and Reis, D. J. (1977). *Proc. natn. Acad. Sci., USA*, **74**, 3086.

Gitlow, S. E., Warner, R. R. P. and Bertani, L. M. (1972). "The Thyroid and Biogenic Amines" (J. E. Rall and I. J. Kopin, eds), p. 641. North-Holland Publishing Co., Amsterdam and London.

Grahame-Smith, D. G. (1964). *Biochem. biophys. Res. Commun.* **16**, 586.

Grahame-Smith, D. G. (1971). *J. Neurochem.* **18**, 1053.

Hamlin, K. E. and Fischer, F. E. (1951). *J. Am. Chem. Soc.* **73**, 5007.

Hanley, H. G., Stahl, S. M. and Freedman, D. X. (1977). *Arch. gen. Psychiat.* **34**, 521.

Hardisty, R. M. and Stacey, R. S. (1955). *J. Physiol.* **130**, 711.

Harley-Mason, J. and Jackson, A. H. (1953). *J. chem. Soc.* p. 200.

Himwich, H. E. (1970). "Biochemistry, Schizophrenias and Affective Illnesses" (H. E. Himwich, ed.), p. 79. Williams and Wilkins, Baltimore.

Hinman, R. L. and Lang, J. (1964). *J. Am. chem. Soc.* **86**, 3796.

Humphrey, J. H. and Jaques, R. (1954). *J. Physiol.* **124**, 305.

Imura, H., Nakai, Y. and Yoshimi, T. (1973). *J. clin. Endocr. Metab.* **36**, 204.

Joyce, D. (1958). *Nature, Lond.* **182**, 463.

Kellum, J. M. and Jaffe, B. M. (1976). *Gastroenterology*, **70**, 516.

Klein, D. C. and Weller, J. L. (1970). *Science*, **167**, 1093.

Koe, B. K. and Weissman, A. (1966). *J. Pharmacol. exp. Ther.* **154**, 499.

Koslow, S. H. (1974). "Serotonin–New Vistas" (E. Costa, G. L. Gessa and M. Sandler, eds), p. 95. Raven Press, New York.

Koslow, S. H. and Green, A. R. (1973). *Adv. biochem. Psychopharmacol.* **7**, 33.

Koslow, S. H., Cattabeni, F. and Costa, E. (1972). *Science*, **176**, 177.

Krieger, D. T. and Rizzo, F. (1969). *Am. J. Physiol.* **217**, 1703.

Krieger, D. T., Kolodny, H. D. and Warner, R. R. P. (1964). *Neurology*, **14**, 578.

Krieger, D. T., Amorosa, L. and Linick, F. (1975). *New Engl. J. Med.* **298**, 893.

Kuhar, M. J., Roth, R. H. and Aghajanian, G. K. (1972). *J. Pharmacol. exp. Ther.* **181**, 36.

Kuhar, M. J., Aghajanian, G. K. and Roth, R. H. (1972). *Brain Res.* **44**, 165.

Lancranjan, I., Wirz-Justice, A., Puhringer, W. and Del Pozo, E. (1977). *J. clin. Endocr. Metab.* **45**, 588.

Lott, I. T., Chase, T. N. and Murphy, D. L. (1972). *Pediat. Res.* **6**, 730.

Lovenberg, W., Weissbach, H. and Udenfriend, S. (1962). *J. biol. Chem.* **237**, 89.

Lovenberg, W., Levine, R. and Sjoerdsma, A. (1965). *Biochem. Pharmacol.* **14**, 887.

Lovenberg, W., Jequier, E. and Sjoerdsma, A. (1967). *Science*, **155**, 217.

Lovenberg, W., Besselaar, G. H., Bensinger, R. E. and Jackson, R. L. (1973). "Serotonin and Behaviour" (J. Barchas and E. Usdin, eds), p. 49. Academic Press, New York and London.

Maickel, R. P. and Miller, F. P. (1966). *Anal. Chem.* **38**, 1937.

Mandell, A. and Morgan, M. (1971). *Nature, New Biol.* **230**, 85.

Marco, J., Hedo, J. A. and Villanueva, M. L. (1977). *Diabetologia*, **13**, 585.

Martin, I. L. and Ansell, G. B. (1973). *Biochem. Pharmacol.* **22**, 521.

McIsaac, W. M. and Page, I. H. (1959). *J. biol. Chem.* **234**, 858.

Mitoma, C., Weissbach, H. and Udenfriend, S. (1956). *Archs. biochem. Biophys.* **63**, 122.

Morgan, M. and Mandell, A. (1969). *Science*, **165**, 492.

Neckers, L. and Sze, P. Y. (1975). *Brain Res.* **93**, 123.

Okada, F., Saito, Y., Fujieda, T. and Yamashita, I. (1972). *Nature, Lond.* **238**, 355.

Owman, C. (1964). *Int. J. Neuropharmacol.* **3**, 105.

Owman, C. (1968). "Advances in Pharmacology" (S. Garrattini and P. A. Shore, eds), Vol. 6A, p. 21. Academic Press, New York and London.
Page, I. H. (1942). *Am. Heart J.* 23, 336.
Page, I. H. (1958). "5-Hydroxytryptamine" (G. P. Lewis, ed.), p. 93. Pergamon, Oxford and London.
Pare, C. M. B., Sandler, M. and Stacey, R. S. (1957). *Lancet*, i, 551.
Pare, C. M. B., Sandler, M. and Stacey, R. S. (1960). *J. Neurol. Neurosurg. Psychiat.* 23, 341.
Peskar, B. and Spector, S. (1973). *Science*, 179, 1340.
Piezzi, R. S., Larin, F. and Wurtman, R. J. (1970). *Endocrinology*, 86, 1460.
Plonk, J. W., Bivens, C. H. and Feldman. J. M. (1974). *J. clin. Endocr. Metab.* 38, 836.
Quay, W. B. (1963). *Gen. comp. Endocr.* 3, 473.
Quay, W. B. (1974). "Pineal Chemistry." Charles C. Thomas, Springfield, Illinois.
Raikhlin, N. T., Kvetnoy, I. M. and Tolkachev, V. N. (1975). *Nature, Lond.* 255, 344.
Rand, M. and Reid, G. (1951). *Nature, Lond.* 168, 385.
Rao, G. H. R., White, J. G., Jachimowicz, A. A. and Witkop, C. J. (1976). *J. lab. clin. Med.* 87, 129.
Rapport, M. M., Green, A. A. and Page, I. H. (1947). *Fed. Proc.* 6, 184.
Rapport, M. M., Green, A. A. and Page, I. H. (1948a). *Science*, 108, 329.
Rapport, M. M., Green, A. A. and Page, I. H. (1948b). *J. biol. Chem.* 176, 1243.
Rendu, F. (1976). *Br. J. Pharmac.* 57, 149.
Renson, J., Weissbach, H. and Udenfriend, S. (1962). *J. biol. Chem.* 237, 2261.
Renson, J. (1973). "Serotonin and Behaviour" (J. Barchas and E. Usdin, eds), p. 19. Academic Press, New York and London.
Ritvo, E., Yuviler, A., Geller, E., Ornitz, E. M., Saeger, K. and Plotkin, S. (1970). *Arch. gen. Psychiat.* 23, 566.
Rosner, F., Ong, B. H., Paine, R. S. and Mahanand, D. (1965). *Lancet*, i, 1191.
Saavedra, J. M. Brownstein, M. and Axelrod, J. (1973). *J. Pharm. exp. Ther.* 186, 508.
Sakurai, H. and Ishimitsu, T. (1975). *Yakugaku Zasshi*, 95, 1384.
Sauerbier, I. and von Mayersbach, (1976). *Horm. Metab. Res.* 8, 159.
Schain, R. J. and Freedman, D. X. (1961). *J. Pediat.* 58, 315.
Shaw, G. J., Wright, G. J. and Milne, G. W. A. (1976). *Biomed. mass Spec.* 3, 146.
Sims, K. L. Davis, G. A. and Bloom, F. E. (1973). *J. Neurochem.* 20, 449.
Sirek, A., Geerling, E. and Sirek, O. V. (1966). *Am. J. Physiol.* 211, 1018.
Sjoerdsma, A., Weissbach, H. and Udenfriend, S. (1956). *Am. J. Med.* 20, 520.
Somerville, B. and Hinterberger, H. (1975). *Clin. chim. Acta*, 65, 399.
Smythe, G. A. (1977). *Clin. Endocr.* 7, 325.
Smythe, G. A., Stuart, M. C. and Lazarus, L. (1974). *Experientia*, 30, 1356.
Smythe, G. A., Compton, P. J. and Lazarus, L. (1976). "Growth Hormone and Related Peptides" (A. Pecile and E. E. Muller, eds), p. 222. Excerpta Medica, Amsterdam.
Snow, P. J. D., Lennard-Jones, J. E., Curzon, G. and Stacey, R. S. (1955). *Lancet*, 269, 1004.
Snyder, S. H., Axelrod, J. and Zweig, M. (1965). *Biochem. Pharmacol.* 14, 831.
Speeter, M. E. and Anthony, W. C. (1954). *J. Am. chem. Soc.* 76, 6208.
Telegdy, G. and Vermes, I. (1975). *Neuroendocrinology*, 18, 16.
Telib, M., Raptis, S., Schroder, K. E. and Pfeiffer, E. F. (1968). *Diabetologia*, 4, 253.
Thompson, J. H., Spezia, C. A. and Angulo, M. (1969). *Experientia*, 25, 927.
Thorson, A., Biorck, G., Bjorkman, G. and Waldenstrom, J. (1954). *Am. Heart J.* 47, 795.
Toh, C. C. (1954). *J. Physiol.* 126, 248.

Tu, J. and Partington, M. W. (1972). *Dev. Med. Child Neurol.* **14**, 457.

Tuomisto, J. and Tukiainen, E. (1976). *Nature, Lond.* **262**, 596.

Udenfriend, S., Greveling, C. R., Posner, H., Redfield, B. G., Daly, J. and Witkop, B. (1959). *Arch. biochem. Biophys.* **83**, 501.

Udenfriend, S. and Weissbach, H. (1954). *Fed. Proc.* **13**, 412.

Udenfriend, S., Weissbach, H. and Bogdanski, D. F. (1955). *Science,* **122**, 972.

Udenfriend, S., Weissbach, H. and Clark, C. T. (1955). *J. biol. Chem.* **215**, 337.

Vane, J. R. (1957). *Br. J. Pharmacol.* **12**, 344.

Vialli, M. and Erspamer, V. (1933). *Zschr. Zellforsch. microsk. Anat.* **19**, 743.

Warner, R. R. P. (1963). *Annals int. Med.* **59**, 464.

Weissbach, H. Redfield, B. G. and Axelrod, J. (1961). *Biochim. biophys. Acta,* **54**, 190.

White, J. G., Edson, R., Desnick, S. J. and Witkop, C. J. (1971). *Am. J. Pathol.* **63**, 319.

Wong, D. T., Horng, J. S., Bymaster, F. P., Hauser, K. L. Molloy, B. B. (1974). *Life Sci.* **15**, 471.

Wooley, D. W. and Shaw, E. (1954). *Proc. natn. Acad. Sci., USA.* **40**, 228.

Wurtman, R. J. and Fernstrom, J. D. (1974). *Nutr. Rev.* **32**, 193.

VI. Prostaglandins and Related Compounds

J. A. SALMON and R. J. FLOWER

INTRODUCTION

In 1974 most people considered that there were really only two important prostaglandins—PGE_2 and $PGF_{2\alpha}$*—but we now realise that the intermediates in prostaglandin biosynthesis (see Section A.2) may be metabolised to products of very high biological activity which are not strictly "prostaglandins", but in this chapter will be treated as members of the prostaglandin family. The type of product obtained from the prostaglandin bio-

* PG is the abbreviation for prostaglandin and TX is the abbreviation for thromboxane.

1

synthetic system varies from tissue to tissue. E and F type prostaglandins are relatively minor products, and most work on prostaglandin analysis has been done on these, not on the more interesting prostaglandin derivatives, thromboxane or prostacyclin. We have therefore included as much as possible on the analysis of the latter compounds, although because they are fairly recent discoveries these data are necessarily incomplete.

One definition of a hormone is "a chemical substance produced in an organ, which carried to an associated organ by the blood stream, influences its activity". Defined in this way it would be rather difficult to include prostaglandins in the hormone family because there is no single "organ" which produces prostaglandins—they are produced by practically every cell type in the body. Furthermore, with the possible exception of prostacylin, prostaglandins do not "circulate" in the bloodstream as does (say) thyroxine. This is because prostaglandins are rapidly metabolised *in vivo*, especially by the lungs, which means that prostaglandins liberated into the venous circulation seldom pass into the arterial side. In some cells (platelets for example) prostaglandins exert their effect on the cells that generate them. To retain the concept that prostaglandins are hormones we have to think of the original Greek meaning of the word hormone "to urge on". Unlike many classical hormones the physiological significance of prostaglandins cannot be assessed by extirpating any one particular organ, although this effect can be approximated by treatment of the patient/animal/cell with certain drugs, notably those of the "aspirin-like anti-inflammatory type" which are powerful inhibitors of prostaglandin biosynthesis.

A problem arises because of the recent discovery that prostaglandin endoperoxides can be metabolised by different cells to different products, e.g. the distinction between platelets and vascular walls. The chief product formed by the former is TXA_2, and by the latter PGI_2. It would obviously not make sense to approach the problem of measuring prostaglandin biosynthesis in these tissues with an immunoassay system designed to quantitate $PGF_{2\alpha}$. Several investigators have examined different tissues to discover which endoperoxide isomerases they contain, and the information given (see Section A.2) should be considered before deciding which prostaglandins were appropriate to assay.

There are several problems which are associated with (although not unique to) prostaglandin analysis. The first of these concerns the fact that most parent prostaglandins are rapidly metabolised *in vivo*, thus the concentrations of the parent prostaglandins in most animal tissues are < 3 pmol/g (< 1.0 ng/g) (although there are exceptions—seminal plasma for example). A consequence of this is that very sensitive assays are required. The chosen method also needs to be very selective because there are many closely related prostaglandins or prostaglandin metabolites (see Section A.1).

Other potentially serious pitfalls are associated with the collection of samples for prostaglandin analysis. Prostaglandin biosynthesis is greatly stimulated by mechanical trauma such as that caused by excision of tissue for analysis. Blood samples are especially susceptible to artefacts because platelets (which are very sensitive to foreign surfaces) can produce large concentrations of thromboxane and other prostaglandins when stimulated. Biosynthesis within the sample itself is not the only hazard: prostaglandins may be metabolised in tissue samples, or be chemically altered during the extraction process. An example of this is the facile dehydration of E prostaglandins which occurs in acid or basic solutions giving rise to A or B prostaglandins: an effect which for years convinced many scientists that A prostaglandins were formed endogenously; they are now known to be extraction artefacts.

The selection of a suitable analytical strategy is of the utmost importance; the following questions should therefore be asked:

(i) Which prostaglandin(s) should be measured? This may depend upon the tissue type under study; in studying prostaglandin biosynthesis by the heart for example, it is essential to know which is the major prostaglandin produced.

(ii) Should the prostaglandin, degradation product or metabolite be measured? Because of the short half lives of TXA_2 and PGI_2 it is usually easier (except with bioassay) to measure the degradation products TXB_2 and 6-keto-$PGF_{1\alpha}$. The possibility that the prostaglandin is partially or wholly metabolised by the generating tissue should be considered. If this is so then measurements of the metabolite are more important than the parent prostaglandin.

When studying prostaglandin biosynthesis by the "whole body" one has to consider the relative merits of measuring metabolites in blood and urine. Urinary data are probably more representative of the day to day production, whereas the blood levels give a more dynamic picture of the minute-by-minute changes which can occur. A second rule is to measure only prostaglandin metabolites in blood, and not the parent compounds. This is because prostaglandins can be synthesised by the blood sample (and thus give rise to falsely high results) unless stringent precautions are taken. However, prostaglandins are not further metabolised in blood and therefore concentrations of metabolites are not altered and should reflect the circulating levels.

It is essential to use the most suitable technique and money would be wasted buying a gas liquid chromatograph-mass spectrometer (GLC-MS) to measure the concentrations of E prostaglandins in semen because concentrations are generally high and can easily be quantitated with a simple UV-spectrophotometer. At least as important as the choice of assay is the choice of purification technique. For example combination of thin layer chromatography (TLC) with radioimmunoassay (RIA) can overcome most of the problems associated with cross-reactivity.

A. PROSTAGLANDIN BIOCHEMISTRY

The smooth muscle-stimulating activity of compounds in male accessory genital glands and human semen were described independently by vor Euler (1935, 1936) and Goldblatt (1933, 1935). However, there was a long interval before the active components (prostaglandins) were isolated in crystalline form (Bergström and Sjövall, 1960a,b) thereby enabling the elucidation of their structures (Bergström, Rhyage, Samuelsson and Sjövall 1962b, 1963).

Early investigators had to biosynthesise prostaglandins from fatty acic precursors (see Section A.2) but the surprising discovery of a prostaglandir in a coral, *Plexaura homomalla* (Weinheimer and Spraggins, 1969) anc advances in total organic synthesis of prostaglandins enabled a more facile and economic production of the compounds.

1. Prostaglandin Chemistry

The prostaglandins are a group of oxygenated, polyunsaturated C_{20} fatty acids containing a cyclopentane ring, and may be considered chemically as derivatives of prostanoic acid (Fig. 1). The compounds are divided into groups (A, B, C, D, E, F, G, H) according to the substituent groups of the cyclopentane ring and are further divided into subgroups according to the number of double bonds in the side chains (for example E_1, E_2 and E_3) Greek subscripts are sometimes added to clarify the stereochemistry (e.g. $PGF_{2\alpha}$). This nomenclature system is well reviewed by Nelson (1974).

Recently, the structure of a new prostaglandin, prostacyclin, has beer established and it differs from the other prostaglandins in that it has a second ring (Fig. 1). Prostacyclin will be referred to in this chapter as PGI_2 (original papers had used the abbreviation PGX). A second group of fatty acid derivatives which will be considered are the thromboxanes. Although these compounds contain a six-membered ring (Fig. 1), they are derived from prostaglandin precursors (see Section A.2).

Before complete characterisation, various authors had referred to some of the prostaglandins by a different nomenclature; Table 1 lists the presently accepted designations and their earlier equivalents.

Several of the most potent prostaglandins are very unstable. For example the half lives of TXA_2, PGG_2, PGH_2 and PGI_2 in aqueous solution (pH 7·5) at $37°$ are approximately 32 sec, 4 min, 3·5 min and 4 min respectively

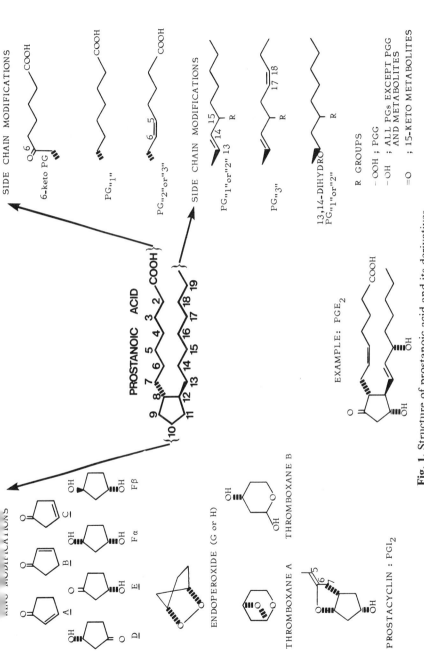

Fig. 1. Structure of prostanoic acid and its derivatives.

These compounds break down to the more stable (but biologically less active) derivatives TXB_2, PGE_2, PGD_2, $PGF_{2\alpha}$ and 6-keto-$PGF_{1\alpha}$. Even these compounds may be relatively unstable: for example, the β-hydroxyketone group of the PGE compounds is labile, and loss of protons at C-8 and C-10 occurs readily in both acid and alkaline media (Shaw and Ramwell, 1969). The loss of a proton at C-10 from PGE compounds results in the formation of the corresponding PGA which, under base treatment, undergoes an internal rearrangement to form PGB.

Table 1

Old and new prostaglandin nomenclature.

Old or original nomenclature	Current designation
PGE_{217}	PGA
PGE_{278}	PGB
RCS (rabbit aorta contracting substance)	mixture of TXA_2 and PG endoperoxides
PHD (8-(1-hydroxy-3-oxopropyl)-9.12L-dihydroxy-5,10-heptadecadienoic acid)	TXB_2
PGX	PGI_2 (Prostacyclin)
LASS (labile aggregation stimulating substance)	TXA_2 and/or endoperoxides
PGR_2	PGH_2
15-Hydroxyperoxy R_2	PGG_2

Prostaglandins are partially ionsied at physiological pH; the ionised form is generally lipid-soluble although the presence of several polar groups may reduce solubility. For example, PGE and PGF compounds partition differently between ether and phosphate buffer at neutral pH and this is in fact the origin of the nomenclature: thus, PGE passes readily into ether whilst prostaglandins of the F series remain in the phosphate ("fosfat" in Swedish) buffer.

2. Prostaglandin Biosynthesis

Prostaglandins are not stored in tissues (Jouvenaz, Nugteren, Beerthuis and van Dorp, 1970; Piper and Vane, 1971) and consequently, biosynthesis must immediately precede release and so the capacity of a tissue to release prostaglandins primarily reflects its biosynthetic ability. The prostaglandins are only formed from free i.e. nonesterified fatty acids (Lands and Samuelsson, 1968; Vonkmann and van Dorp, 1968) but the concentration of such acids is low in most tissues. The most common substrates dihomo-γ-linolenic

(20:3, ω6) and arachidonic acid (20:4, ω6) are present in relatively high concentration in the cell as esters, mainly in the 2'-position of phospholipids (e.g. phosphatidylcholine and ethanolamine). The acids can also occur in triacylglycerols (e.g. in adipose tissue), and as cholesterol esters (e.g. in adrenal and ovary). Dihomo-γ-linolenic acid is the precursor of prostaglandins of the "1" series whilst arachidonic acid is converted to prostaglandins of the "2" series.

The initial step in the biosynthesis of the prostaglandin is, therefore, the release of the free acid substrate from an "ester-reservoir" which, in the case of the phospholipid pool, occurs under the influence of the hydrolytic enzyme, phospholipase A_2. These free fatty acids are then converted to prostaglandin endoperoxides by a multi-enzyme complex located in the high-speed particulate fraction of cells (Fig. 2). This enzyme which has been referred to as the

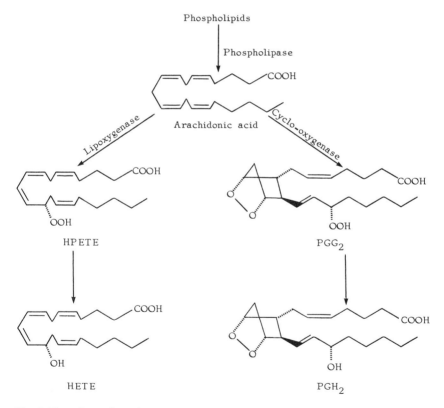

Fig. 2. Transformation of arachidonic acid by the cyclo-oxygenase and lipoxygenase enzymes. (HPETE = hydroperoxy intermediate; HETE = 12 L-hydroxy-5,8,10,14, isosatetraineoic acid.)

"prostaglandin synthetase" system, but is now more correctly termed "fatty acid cyclo-oxygenase", has recently been solubilised and purified (Miyamoto, Yamamoto and Hayaishi, 1974; Miyamoto, Ogino, Yamamoto and Hayaishi, 1976). One component is a dioxygenase enzyme which converts the fatty acid to a cyclic endoperoxide with a hydroperoxy radical at C-15; this intermediate, now universally known as PGG has been isolated by Hamberg and Samuelsson, (1973), Hamberg, Svensson, Wakabayashi and Samuelsson (1974b) and Nugteren and Hazelhof (1973). A second cyclic endoperoxide (PGH) is formed from PGG by reduction of the C-15 hydroperoxy group to the corresponding hydroxy compound under the influence of another enzyme in the cyclo-oxygenase complex (Miyamoto et al., 1976). The latter endoperoxide has also been isolated (Hamberg and Samuelsson, 1973; Hamberg et al., 1974b; Nugteren and Hazelhof, 1973). In aqueous solution the endoperoxides spontaneously decompose (to malondialdehyde, HHT (see below), PGE_2, PGD_2 and traces of $PGF_{2\alpha}$) with half lives (in aqueous solution, pH 7·5 at 37°) of approximately 5 min (Hamberg et al.,1974b) but, they may be kept for several months in dry acetone at −20°. The endoperoxides play a pivotal role in prostaglandin synthesis, since they can be converted enzymatically (or in some cases non-enzymatically) into TXA_2, PGE_2, PGD_2, $PGF_{2\alpha}$ or PGI_2 depending on the cell type (see Fig. 3 and Table 2; Pace-Asciak and Rangaraj, 1977; Sun, Chapman and McGuire, 1977).

Thromboxane A_2 (TXA_2) is formed by an enzyme located in the high-speed particulate fraction of blood platelets (Hamberg, Svensson and Samuelsson, 1975; Needleman, Moncada, Bunting, Vane, Hamberg and Samuelsson, 1976) and other tissues (see Table 2). The enzyme has recently been solubilised (Yoshimoto, Yamamoto, Okuma and Hayaishi, 1977; Hammarström and Falardeau, 1977). TXA_2 decomposes rapidly (half life, 32 sec at 37°) in aqueous media to TXB_2. TXA_2 has potent vascular smooth muscle contractile, and platelet aggregating activities. TXA_1 and TXA_3 are formed from the corresponding endoperoxide but they have different pharmacological properties (Needleman, Minkes and Raz, 1976; Raz, Minkes and Needleman, 1977).

Another terminal pathway of prostaglandin endoperoxide metabolism has recently been described. Prostacyclin (PGI_2), was initially demonstrated to be a biosynthetic product of prostaglandin endoperoxides in vascular walls (Moncada, Gryglewski, Bunting and Vane, 1976a; Moncada, Higgs and Vane, 1977b). Prostacyclin has potent vascular smooth muscle relaxing and anti-aggregatory properties and is thus opposite in nature to those of TXA_2; it is unstable in aqueous solution (having a half life of 10·8 min at 20° and pH 7·5; Johnson, Morton, Kinner, Gorman, McGuire, Sun, Whittaker, Bunting, Salmon, Moncada and Vane, 1976) but can be stabilised

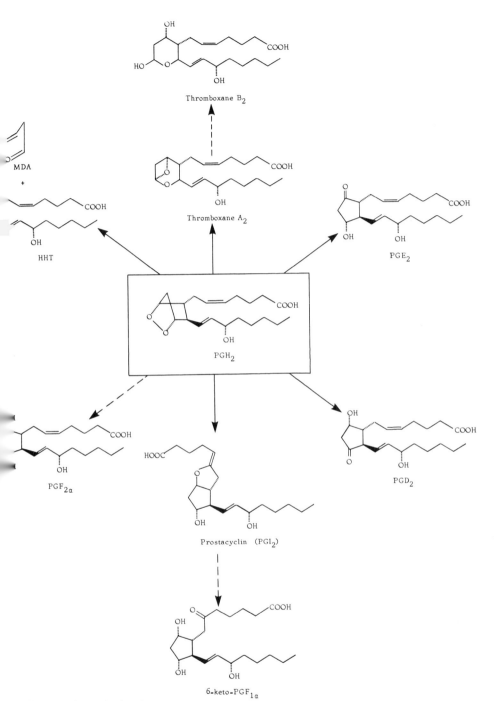

Fig. 3. Biosynthesis of prostaglandins, prostacyclin and thromboxane from the prostaglandin endoperoxide, **PGH₂**. The continuous arrows indicate confirmed enzymatic conversions whereas the dashed arrows represent transformations which do not appear to be enzymatic. (HHT = 12L-hydroxy-5,8,10-heptadecatrienoic acid; MDA = malonyl dialdehyde.)

Table 2

Major prostaglandins formed in various tissues.

Tissue/organ	Prostaglandin formed[a]	Comments
Lung	6-keto-PGF$_{1\alpha}$ > TXB$_2$ > PGE$_2$ > PGF$_{2\alpha}$	TXB$_2$ formed in rat, guinea-pig and rabbit tissue but not in human or monkey
Liver	PGE$_2$ > PGF$_{2\alpha}$	data from rat only
Spleen	TXB$_2$ > 6-keto-PGF$_{1\alpha}$ > PGE$_2$ > PGF$_{2\alpha}$	
Platelets	TXB$_2$	TXB$_2$ not formed in rat
Heart	6-keto-PGF$_{1\alpha}$ > PGE$_2$	
Blood vessels	6-keto-PGF$_{1\alpha}$	
Stomach	6-keto-PGF$_{1\alpha}$ ≫ PGE$_2$ > PGF$_{2\alpha}$ = PGD$_2$	
Stomach fundus (forestomach)	6-keto-PGF$_{1\alpha}$	data from rat tissue only
Kidney	low conversion to a mixture of prostaglandins	
Uterus	6-keto-PGF$_{1\alpha}$ > PGE > PGF$_{2\alpha}$	
Corpus luteum	6-keto-PGF$_{1\alpha}$ > PGE$_2$	

[a] The data are derived from transformation of arachidonic acid (Pace-Asciak and Rangaraj, 1977) or PGH$_2$ (Sun, Chapman and McGuire, 1977). Usually the information has been obtained in two or more of the following species: rat, guinea-pig, rabbit, cow, horse, monkey and human. The complete profile of prostaglandin production for other tissues has not been published but it has been reported that 6-keto-PGF$_{1\alpha}$ is formed in low yield from prostaglandin endoperoxides if there is a low substrate/enzyme ratio in the following organs: adrenal, thyroid, pituitary, testis and small intestine (Sun et al., 1977). Also, TXB$_2$ is biosynthesised in placenta, bone marrow, thyroid and brain (Sun et al., 1977). PGD$_2$ is the major prostaglandin in rat brain (Abdel-Halim, Hamberg, Sjöqvist and Änggård, 1977).

by raising the pH and thus forming the salt (half life at pH 8·4 and 20° is 79·6 min). The end product of the PGI$_2$ decay in a mildly acidic environment is 6-keto-PGF$_{1\alpha}$ (Johnson et al., 1976); 6-keto-PGF$_{1\alpha}$ was previously detected in rat stomach fundus (Pace-Asciak, 1976a, 1976b) and has subsequently been found to occur in uterus (Fenwick, Jones, Naylor, Poyser and Wilson, 1977) lung (Dawson, Boot, Cockerill, Mallen and Osborne, 1976) and seminal vesicles (Chang and Murota, 1977; Cottee, Flower, Moncada, Salmon and Vane, 1977).

The PGI$_2$ synthesising enzyme is also located in the high speed particulate fraction of cells (Moncada et al., 1976a; Salmon, Smith, Flower, Moncada and Vane, 1978) and has been partially characterised (Salmon et al., 1978). It is powerfully inhibited by low concentrations of the hydroperoxides of several fatty acids (Moncada, Gryglewski, Bunting and Vane, 1976b; Salmon *et al.*, 1978).

Prostaglandin E is formed from prostaglandin endoperoxides enzymatically under the influence of prostaglandin E isomerase, an enzyme which has a specific requirement for reduced glutathione (Samuelsson, 1965; Nugteren, Beerthuis and van Dorp, 1966; van Dorp, 1967). This isomerase has been solubilised and purified from the high speed particulate fraction of bovine seminal vesicles (Miyamoto *et al.*, 1974; Ogino, Miyamoto, Yamamoto and Hayaishi, 1977) and it was found that glutathione was specifically involved as a coenzyme in the reaction.

PGD can be produced under the influence of prostaglandin D isomerase, an enzyme which also requires glutathione for maximal activity. This enzyme (or at least one such enzyme) is not particulate but is apparently a soluble protein (Nugteren and Hazelhof, 1973). PGD can also be formed by interaction of endoperoxides with protein, particularly albumin although there is a marked species variation (Hamberg and Fredholm, 1976; Christ-Hazelhof, Nugteren and van Dorp, 1976).

It is known that the presence of reducing agents rapidly causes decomposition of endoperoxides to PGF, but at present there is no evidence to suggest that this conversion can occur under the influence of an "endoperoxide-reductase" enzyme. Thus, PGF may be formed in those tissues in which there is (i) high cyclo-oxygenase activity but low isomerase, thromboxane or prostacyclin synthesising activity and/or (ii) high concentration of reducing agents (e.g. SH-compounds, ferri-haem compounds etc).

The 17-C monohydroxy fatty acid, HHT (12L-hydroxy-5,8,10-heptadecatrienoic acid), was separated from incubation mixtures of arachidonic acid and sheep seminal vesicle homogenates by Wlodawer and Samuelsson (1973), and is also found as a by-product of the chemical reduction of the endoperoxides PGG_2 and PGH_2 by $SnCl_2$ (Hamberg *et al.*, 1974a, 1974b). It is also produced during incubation of prostaglandin endoperoxides with blood platelets (Hamberg and Samuelsson, 1974a; Hamberg *et al.*, 1974b; Yoshimoto *et al.*, 1977). In the latter case, it is not certain whether breakdown of TXA_2 results in formation of TXB_2 and HHT, whether HHT is enzymatically synthesised independently from the endoperoxide or whether it is simply a non-enzymatic breakdown of the endoperoxide. Yoshimoto *et al.* (1977) suggest that TXA_2 probably decomposes to TXB_2 and HHT but Diczfalusy, Falardeau and Hammarström (1977) provided evidence that the formation of HHT does not involve TXA_2 as an intermediate.

Once it has been released from the ester pools, arachidonic acid can also be converted to non-cyclooxygenase products. Several authors (Hamberg and Samuelsson, 1974a; Hamberg *et al.*, 1974b and Nugteren, 1975b) demonstrated that 12L-hydroxy-5,8,10,14-eicosatetraenoic acid (HETE) was a major product of arachidonate oxidation in platelets. The enzyme which controls this formation is present in the high speed supernatant and the reaction proceeds via a hydroperoxy intermediate (HPETE) (see Fig. 2). The mechanism of reaction is reminiscent of the soyabean lipoxygenase described by Hamberg and Samuelsson (1967). A different lipoxygenase enzyme is present in leucocytes where arachidonic acid is converted to 5-hydroxy-6,8,-11,14-eicosatetraenoic acid (Borgeat, Hamberg and Samuelsson, 1976).

Hamberg and Samuelsson (1974b) have also isolated (albeit in low yield) two other C-20 fatty acids from guinea-pig lung homogenates. These were 15-hydroxy-5,8,11,13-eicosatetraenoic acid and 11-hydroxy-5,8,11,14-eico-satetraenoic acid. These latter acids were probably formed by reduction of the parent fatty acid hydroperoxides believed to be intermediates in endo-peroxide formation.

3. Prostaglandin Catabolism

Prostaglandins of the E and F series are readily metabolised *in vivo*. For example, Hamberg and Samuelsson (1971) demonstrated that only 3% of a bolus intravenous injection of tritiated PGE_2 remained unchanged in the plasma after 90 sec. Several different metabolic reactions have been documented (see Fig. 4). The initial step is the oxidation of the 15-hydroxyl group to the corresponding ketone, a reaction which occurs under the influence of the enzyme 15-hydroxy-prostaglandin dehydrogenase (PGDH) (Änggård and Samuelsson, 1964, 1966; Hamberg and Samuelsson, 1971). PGDH is distributed in many tissues, the highest concentrations being present in the lung, spleen, kidney and adipose tissues (Änggård, Larsson and Samuelsson, 1971). That the lung contained high concentration of metabolising enzymes was also shown by Ferreira and Vane (1967) who found that more than 95% of infused PGE_2 was biologically inactivated during one circulation through the lung.

The second reaction of the metabolic sequence is catalysed by prosta-glandin Δ^{13}-reductase and results in saturation of the 13,14 double bond. The highest reductase activity is in the spleen, liver, kidney, adrenals and small intestine (Änggård *et al.*, 1971). Both PGDH and PG-Δ^{13} reductase are soluble enzymes, present in the 100,000 g supernatant of cell free homogenates. These two metabolic transformations occur rapidly (i.e. probably during one pass through the lung) but subsequent metabolism occurs more slowly; thus, the biological half-life of 13,14-dihydro-15-keto-PGE_2 is approximately 8 min (Hamberg and Samuelsson, 1971) compared with less than 1 min for PGE_2.

The secondary, slower, metabolic reactions consist of β and ω oxidation giving rise to a dicarboxylic acid, which (probably because of its high polarity)

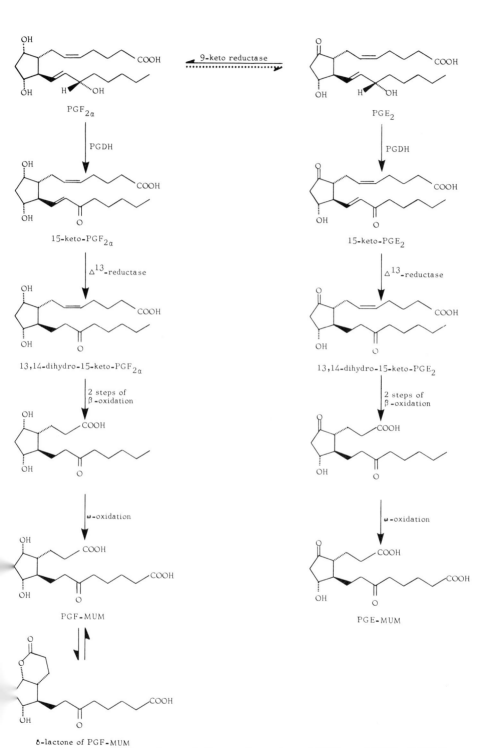

Fig. 4. Summary of the main metabolic transformations of $PGF_{2\alpha}$ and PGE_2, (MUM) = major urinary metabolite.)

is readily excreted in urine. The enzyme controlling these oxidations are not specific to the prostaglandins, but are common to many fatty acids. The liver is the major site of β- and ω-oxidation (Samuelsson, Granström, Gréen and Hamberg, 1971) but the reactions also occur in lung, kidney (Nakano and Morsy, 1971) and intestine (Parkinson and Schneider, 1969). Thus, in man the major plasma metabolites of $PGF_{2\alpha}$ and PGE are the corresponding 13,14-dihydro-15-keto compounds whilst $5\alpha,7\alpha$-dihydroxy-11-keto-tetranor-prostane-1,16-dioic acid (PGF-MUM) and 7α-hydroxy-5,11-diketo-prostane-1,16-dioic acid (PGE-MUM) are the main urinary metabolites (MUM) of PGF and PGE respectively. The di-acid metabolite of PGF may also exist as a δ-lactone. Several other products of metabolism of prostaglandins in primates have been identified (Granström and Samuelsson, 1971a, b; 1972b; Granström, 1972; Hamberg and Wilson, 1973; Sun and Stafford, 1974).

The presence of a specific enzyme, 9-keto reductase, which causes the 9-keto of PGE to be reduced to the corresponding hydroxyl compound (i.e. to PGF), has been demonstrated in kidney of monkey (Lee and Levine, 1974), pig (Lee, Pong, Katzen, Wu and Levine, 1975) and rabbit (Stone and Hart, 1975).

Enzymes in plasma have also been described which cause dehydration of PGE to PGA (Levine, Gutierrez-Cernosek and Van Vunakis, 1973) isomerisation of PGA to PGC (Jones, 1970) and isomerisation of PGC to PGB (Polet and Levine, 1971). However, these enzymatic conversions appear to be of minor importance. In fact, the observation of dehydrase activity may be suspect and the formation of PGA could arise as an artifact of the extraction techniques employed (see Section B.2).

Prostaglandin D is not a substrate for PGDH (Sun, Armour, Bockstanz and McGuire, 1976) and consequently this prostaglandin has longer biological half life than PGE or PGF. PGA is a substrate for PGDH in vitro (Nakano, Änggård and Samuelsson, 1969) but it appears to traverse the lungs without deactivation presumably because it is not a substrate for the uptake mechanism (McGiff, Terragno, Strand, Lee, Lonigro and Ng, 1969).

PGI_2, itself, is a relatively good substrate for PGDH but the breakdown product, 6-keto-$PGF_{1\alpha}$ was metabolised at only 10% the rate of PGE_2 (Sun, McGuire and Taylor, 1978; Pace-Asciak, Domazet and Carrara, 1977b). 6-Keto-$PGF_{1\alpha}$ is also a poor substrate for prostaglandin Δ^{13}-reductase (Pace-Asciak et al., 1977b), thus 6,15-diketo-$PGF_{1\alpha}$ may be expected to be the major circulating metabolite. Pace-Asciak, Carrara and Domazet (1977a) demonstrated that a considerable amount (ca 30%) 6-keto-$PGF_{1\alpha}$ administered to rats was excreted unchanged; these investigators also identified dinor-6-keto-$PGF_{1\alpha}$ and dinor-ω-1-hydroxy-6-keto-$PGF_{1\alpha}$ as urinary metabolites. Sun et al. (1978) reported that the urinary metabolites of PGI_2 have a 15-keto group (whereas metabolites of 6-keto-$PGF_{1\alpha}$ have a 15-hydroxy group) thus implying that PGI_2 is metabolised under the influence of 15-PGDH although 6-keto-$PGF_{1\alpha}$ is not. However, prostacyclin and 6-keto-$PGF_{1\alpha}$ appear to be metabolised at approximately the same rate *in vivo*, since plasma levels obtained during infusion of both compounds at the same rate were very similar but were approximately ten times higher than the plasma level of $PGF_{2\alpha}$ obtained after a comparable infusion into dogs (Dusting, Moncada, Mullane, Salmon and Vane, 1978).

A novel compound believed to be a metabolite of TXB_2, was identified as 13,14-dihydro-15-keto-TXB_2 by Dawson *et al.* (1976). The compound was obtained during infusion of arachidonic acid through antigen-challenged guinea-pig lungs. The major urinary metabolite of TXB_2 in man was identified as 2,3-dinor-TXB_2 (Roberts, Sweetman, Payne and Oates, 1977).

The duration and intensity of the activity of prostaglandins is dependent, not only on the synthesis of the compounds, but also on the metabolism. Therefore, it is interesting to note that the levels of the specific metabolising enzymes are dependent on the age of the animal (Pace-Asciak and Miller, 1973) and may also alter during pregnancy or treatment with steroids (Sun and Armour, 1974; Bedwani and Marley, 1974; Blackwell and Flower, 1976).

4. Drugs and the Prostaglandin System

Although it is not the primary purpose of this chapter to discuss the pharmacology of the prostaglandin system, one or two aspects are important since they may have a profound effect on the validity of the prostaglandin assays.

In general all non-steroidal anti-inflammatory drugs such as aspirin, indomethacin, salicylates, etc. either completely prevent, or seriously impair the ability of the cyclo-oxygenase enzyme to generate prostaglandin endoperoxides. This fact, first noted by Vane (1971), is the basis of an exciting theory about the mechanism of action of these drugs, but its relevance here is that prostaglandin levels will obviously be lower than normal if these drugs have been taken. Aspirin is particularly important because it is the active ingredient in many over-the-counter medicines. Most people do not regard aspirin as a "drug". Volunteer blood donors are frequently required for studies on platelet aggregation but on enquiring which drugs they may have taken, they usually forget to mention aspirin. Figure 5 shows what a difference this can make; 7–10 days should elapse between taking the last dose of aspirin or other inhibitors and the taking of samples for prostaglandin determination reviewed (see Flower, 1974).

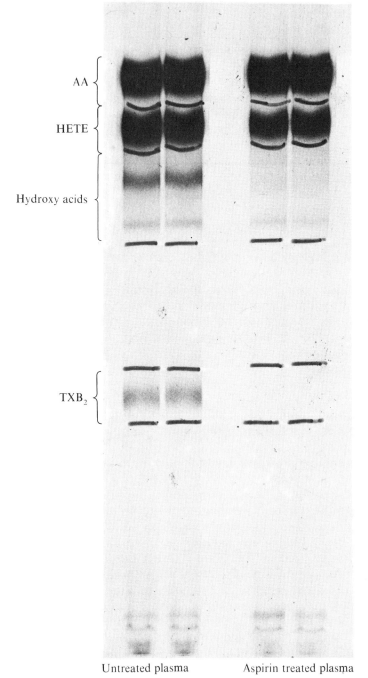

AA

HETE

Hydroxy acids

TXB₂

Untreated plasma   Aspirin treated plasma

Fig. 5. Effect of aspirin on the products formed from arachidonic acid in platelet-rich plasma (PRP). ^{14}C-arachidonic acid (AA) was incubated with PRP before and two days after ingestion of aspirin (5·5 mmol; 1 g) by a normal, healthy volunteer. After extraction and thin-layer chromatography (developing solvent: chloroform, methanol, acetic acid, water, 90:8:1:0·8 (by vol) the products were detected by auto-radiography. Note the absence of TXB_2 and a hy roxy acid (probably HHT) in the sample taken after aspirin treatment; TXB_2 and HHT are the major products of arachidonic acid metabolism via the cyclo-oxygenase pathway in PRP. However, HETE, the product of lipoxygenase activity, is unaffected by the administration of aspirin.

B. COLLECTION AND PURIFICATION OF SAMPLES FOR PROSTAGLANDIN DETERMINATION

1. Collection and Storage of Samples

The procedures used for the collection and handling of blood and tissue samples are critical. Surgical trauma and inflammation cause a marked elevation of prostaglandin content (Piper and Vane, 1971; Änggård and Jonsson, 1972; Caldwell, Burstein, Brock and Speroff, 1971) and consequently any acute experiment involving surgery requires a period of stabilisation. Even the collection of blood from a peripheral blood vessel may cause sufficient trauma to stimulate local aggregation of platelets (Silver, Smith, Ingerman and Kocsis, 1973b) thus causing the generation of products by the cyclo-oxygenase system (Smith and Willis, 1970; Silver, Smith, Ingerman and Kocsis, 1972; 1973a, b; Schoene and Iacono, 1974; Hamberg and Samuelsson, 1974; Hamberg et al., 1974a; Hamberg et al., 1975). However, Dray, Charbonnel and Maclouf (1975) demonstrated that the trauma of venipuncture did not influence the PGF_α ($PGF_{1\alpha} + PGF_{2\alpha}$) concentration in plasma; the concentration in the first 20 ml withdrawn was identical with that in the following 20 ml of blood. Obviously, an imperfect venipuncture will increase the likelihood of elevated prostaglandin levels.

There have been many conflicting reports as to the most suitable blood fraction for prostaglandin analysis. Some investigators have reported serum levels of $PGF_{2\alpha}$ and/or metabolites (Gutierrez-Cernosek, Morill and Levine, 1972a; Gutierrez-Cernosek, Zuckerman and Levine, 1972b; Levine and Gutierrez-Cernosek, 1973; Brummer, 1972, 1973) but the majority of workers have measured the concentration of prostaglandins in plasma. There is a significant difference between plasma and serum levels from the same subject, as measured by radioimmunoassay (see Fig. 6; Kirton, Cornette and Barr, 1972; Orczyk and Behrman, 1972; Dray et al., 1975). Therefore, it appears that an immunoreactive compound is synthesised and released during coagulation, probably by platelets. An elegant experiment reported by Axen, Baczynskyj, Duchamp, Kirton and Zieserl (1973) proved that $PGF_{2\alpha}$ was actually synthesised by platelets and not stored and released.

Prostaglandins are generated during storage of platelet-rich plasma and there is a good correlation between the amount of PGE_2 formed during a three week storage and the platelet count (see Fig. 7; Jubiz and Frailey, 1974). The latter authors concluded that prostaglandins should be assayed in serum (i.e. platelet-free) rather than plasma. However, since prostaglandins are released during coagulation we consider that the collection of platelet-free plasma is preferable. Plasma should be centrifuged at 2500 g for 15 min soon after collection in order to separate the platelets and white cells. The

addition of a cyclo-oxygenase inhibitor (e.g. indomethacin) to the plasma
is also recommended to limit the synthesis of prostaglandins although some
workers found that the inhibitor was not essential (Dray et al., 1975). Centrifugation of the blood should be performed within the first hour after collection because an increase in $PGF_{2\alpha}$ concentration has been observed with
a longer delay (Dray et al., 1975). However, storage at 4° and the addition of
a cyclo-oxygenase inhibitor can extend this interval to over an hour.

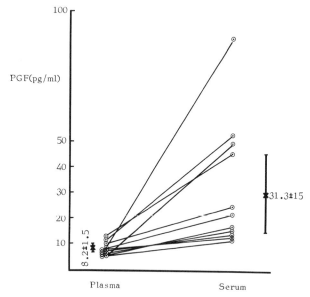

Fig. 6. Comparison between the concentration of PGF_{α} in plasma and serum in 11
healthy adult subjects (From Dray, Charbonnel and Maclouf, 1975. Reproduced with
permission.)

    The choice of anticoagulant also appears to be important. Dray et al. (1975)
showed in two cases, that the levels of $PGF_{2\alpha}$ were higher in plasma collected
in tubes containing heparin than in tubes containing EDTA. As the concentration of $PGF_{2\alpha}$ in the EDTA-treated plasma was identical to that in blood
which had been immediately centrifuged to remove all blood cells including
platelets Dray et al. (1975) concluded that EDTA was the preferred anti-
coagulant.
    The standard method we have adopted for collection of blood samples
for prostaglandin analysis is outlined in Fig. 8. Even though some investigators (Jaffe, Behrman and Parker, 1973; Auletta, Zusman and Caldwell,
1974; Zusman, Caldwell, Speroff and Behrman, 1972) failed to detect a

significant difference between plasma and serum levels of prostaglandins, we strongly recommend that prostaglandins are assayed in platelet-free plasma.

Despite the precautions taken to prevent false increases of the concentrations of prostaglandins in plasma, elevations of immunoreactive material are detected when plasma is stored at 4°. This increase in levels is greatly diminished during storage at − 20° (Dray et al., 1975; Sharma, Hibbard,

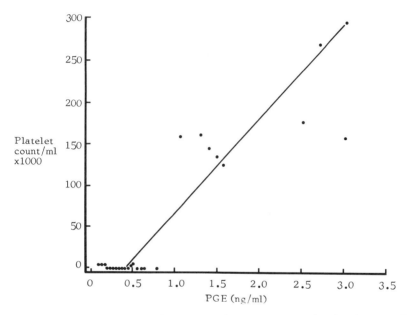

Fig. 7. Correlation between platelet count and PGE concentration in plasma and serum samples from normal subjects. Samples were assayed three weeks after collection. The correlation coefficient is 0·88, $p < 0·01$. (From Jubiz and Frailey, 1974. Reproduced with permission.)

Hamlett and Fitzpatrick, 1973); storage of up to two months at − 20° failed to produce increased levels of $PGF_{2\alpha}$ (Sharma et al., 1973). PGE deteriorates more rapidly in plasma than in aqueous solution (see Section A.1) and it is therefore recommended that the storage time for the plasma samples is kept to a minimum. If a complete analysis cannot be performed immediately then it is suggested that the prostaglandins are extracted (see Section B.2), and stored at − 20° in organic solvents, after any trace of acid has been removed by back-washing with water.

The same precautions about collection and handling of blood samples also apply to other tissues. Most cells contain prostaglandin-synthesising and metabolising enzymes so the prostaglandins should be extracted immediately or, if this is not feasible, samples should be snap-frozen and stored at − 20° until analysis is possible.

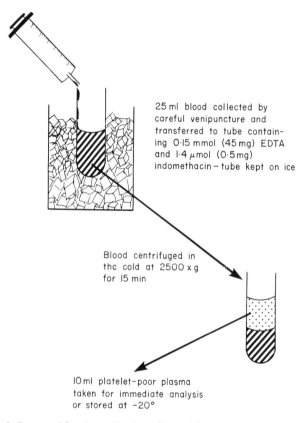

25 ml blood collected by careful venipuncture and transferred to tube containing 0·15 mmol (45 mg) EDTA and 1·4 μmol (0·5 mg) indomethacin – tube kept on ice

Blood centrifuged in the cold at 2500 x g for 15 min

10 ml platelet-poor plasma taken for immediate analysis or stored at −20°

Fig. 8. Protocol for the collection of blood for prostaglandin analysis.

2. Extraction of Samples

Although not essential for some methods of analysis, extraction of prostaglandins into organic solvents is a highly desirable step. It removes protein, imparts some specificity to the analysis and improves sensitivity by concentration of the prostaglandins. There have been reports of direct radioimmunoassays (RIA) for prostaglandins in plasma or serum (Kirton et al., 1972; Brummer, 1972, 1973; Youssefnejadian, Walker, Sommerville and Craft, 1974) but the levels obtained were unacceptably high. Plasma proteins, particularly albumin, bind prostaglandins (Unger, 1972; Raz, 1972) and results obtained by direct RIA should be regarded with some scepticism unless the anti-prostaglandin serum has a very high affinity and specificity. We recommend that prostaglandins should always be extracted from plasma before RIA is performed.

Unfortunately, extraction does make analyses more time-consuming and can itself be a source of error. It is usually necessary to include a tracer of radioactive prostaglandin (or deuterated prostaglandin if GLC-MS is used) in the sample in order to calculate the efficiency of extraction and correct the assay result for procedural losses. The tracer should be mixed with the sample for a time sufficient for equilibrium of the radioactive prostaglandin with the endogenous compound; probably 10–15 min at room temperature is sufficient.

Using the urinary excretion data and knowing the rate of metabolism of prostaglandins, Samuelsson (1973a) calculated that the theoretical levels of prostaglandins in plasma were extremely low (*ca* 5·6 pmol/l (2 pg/ml) $PGF_{2\alpha}$ and 28·4–56·8 pmol/l (10–20 pg/ml) PGE_2) and consequently large volumes of plasma must be analysed even when the most sensitive assays are available. For example, Dray *et al.* (1975) have demonstrated that at least 10 ml plasma was required for accurate RIA of $PGF_{2\alpha}$ and 5 ml was required for analysis of PGE_2. Analysis of large volumes of plasma may also reduce the contribution of collection artifacts.

The choice of extraction technique is governed by its efficiency, specificity, reproducibility and practicality. As weakly acidic lipids, prostaglandins are readily extracted into organic solvents in their protonated form. However, acidification must be done cautiously since decomposition of some prostaglandins (e.g. PGE) occurs at low pH. A pH of 3 is satisfactory if only PGF is to be measured but the pH should not be lower than 4·5 when PGE is extracted. It is more practical to use an acid with a relatively high pK_a to adjust the pH of the sample. Although hydrochloric acid has been used in some studies (Bygdeman and Samuelsson, 1966) it is probably preferable to use organic acids. Formic acid (1–3 % v/v) (Unger, Stamford and Bennett, 1971) and citric acid (0·5–2M) (Jouvenaz, Nugteren, Beerthuis and Van Dorp, 1970) have frequently been used, and some investigators have used acetate buffers (Saksena, Watson, Lau and Shaikh, 1974). Jaffe and Parker (1972) described a method for extracting plasma with a mixture of ethyl acetate, *iso*-propanol and 0·1 M hydrochloric acid (pH about 6).

Chloroform, diethyl ether and ethyl acetate are the extracting solvents most frequently used, although the use of butanol has also been described (Caldwell *et al.*, 1971). After suitable acidification plasma may be extracted directly with solvent. Auletta *et al.* (1974) extracted 1 ml plasma twice with five volumes of ethyl acetate and Dray *et al.* (1975) extracted 10 ml plasma twice with two volumes of a mixture of cyclohexane:ethyl acetate (1:1). Using these direct methods, emulsions are occasionally formed making extraction difficult and inefficient (the addition of saturated sodium chloride or sodium sulphate followed by centrifugation usually eliminates this difficulty). A further problem is that the organic extract itself may still be unsuitable for subsequent analysis.

Frölich (1976) has described a method which produces an extract suitable for direct injection into a high pressure liquid chromatograph. Protein in aqueous samples was precipitated with acetone at −20° and the acetone layer extracted with light petroleum ether which not only removed contaminating neutral lipids but also reduced the volume of the aqueous-acetone layer. The remaining aqueous-acetone solution was acidified with formic acid and extracted twice with chloroform. The combined chloroform layers were evaporated *in vacuo*, the residue repeatedly washed with ethanol and dried to remove all traces of formic acid. We have confirmed the usefulness of this procedure (see Fig. 9).

Unger *et al.* (1971) added non-precipitating amounts of ethanol (40–50%) to plasma before acidification whilst other investigators (Gutierrez-Cernosek *et al.*, 1972a) used methylal-ethanol mixtures and subjected the extracts to dialysis; the dialysates could be analysed directly by RIA.

Another method of extracting prostaglandins from aqueous solutions is the use of non-ionic resins such as Amberlite XAD-2. This particular resin can be used for the removal of many water soluble organic molecules. When used to extract prostaglandins, a column of the resin (e.g. 1 g per 100 ml aqueous solution to be extracted) is washed with water and methanol and equilibrated with distilled water. The solution to be extracted is then percolated slowly through the resin bed. This is followed by a wash with distilled water (2–3 bed volumes) to remove salts and the prostaglandins are recovered by elution with methanol or ethanol (2–5 bed volumes). This method can be very useful—for example an Amberlite column can be placed under the outflow of a perfused organ and to trap the prostaglandins directly they are released.

Organic molecules bind most effectively to Amberlite when non-ionised (i.e. most lipophilic) and the binding of the prostaglandins may be increased by lowering the pH of the aqueous solution. In the authors experience this is not usually necessary. An alternative method for recovery of the prostaglandins from the resin bed is by elution with 1M NaOH: this elutes the compounds as the sodium salts. This would obviously not be suitable for use if PGE was to be measured. Gréen (1971) and Samuelsson, Granström, Gréen and Hamberg (1971) have utilised Amberlite extensively for the extraction of prostaglandin metabolites from urine, and Keirse and Turnbull (1973) used the resin to remove prostaglandins efficiently from amniotic

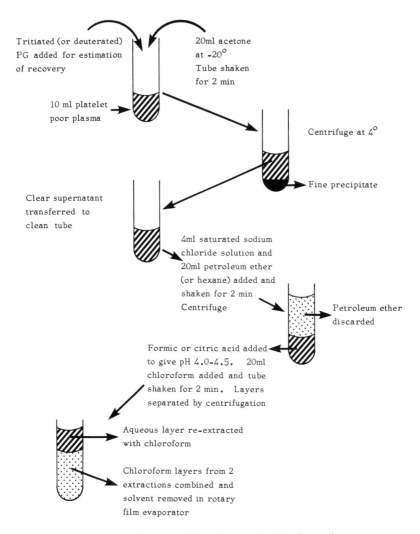

Fig. 9. Methods for extraction of prostaglandins from plasma.

fluid. Other resins (IRP-64M and CG-50) have also been employed to concentrate prostaglandins and metabolites from urine (Fretland, 1974).

3. Chromatographic Separation

The extraction procedures, described above, efficiently remove all groups of prostaglandins and thromboxanes from the sample, but if specific analysis of an individual prostaglandin is required a further purification is necessary. Chromatographic procedures, particularly column chromatography, have proved to be ideally suited to separation of prostaglandins.

(a) *Simple column chromatography*

Silicic acid column chromatography (Samuelsson, 1963; Bygdeman and Samuelsson, 1966) has been most widely used since it permits good resolution of all groups of prostaglandins, it is rapid, and it gives low "blanks" in most assay systems. A micro-scale method, which is ideal for practical analyses of prostaglandins in blood, was developed by Caldwell et al. (1971). These authors utilised mixtures of benzene and ethyl acetate with increasing concentrations of methanol. The prostaglandins were eluted in order of increasing polarity, i.e. PGA + PGB, then PGE and finally PGF. This method has been successfully employed by other investigators (Jaffe, Behrman and Parker, 1973; Dray et al., 1975). Chloroform with increasing amounts of methanol provides a similar resolution of the groups of prostaglandins (Fig. 10; see Salmon and Karim, 1976) and avoids the use of toxic solvents. Both these chromatographic procedures were developed before the discovery of thromboxanes and prostacyclin and unfortunately both TXB_2 and 6-keto-$PGF_{1\alpha}$ cochromatograph with PGE. Thus, if measurement of 6-keto-$PGF_{1\alpha}$, TXB_2 and PGE_2 is required in the same sample, a different chromatographic procedure is probably necessary.

Analytical columns of celite (Meldrum and Abraham, 1976), silica gel (Hillier and Dilley, 1974) and Sephadex LH-20 (Änggård and Bergkvist, 1970; Zia and Horton, 1973) have also been used. Other workers (Nyström and Sjövall, 1973; Brash and Jones, 1974) investigated the application of a range of lipophilic gels bonded to long chain hydrocarbons for chromatography of prostaglandins.

Reversed phase chromatography has found several applications in prostaglandin analyses especially in the purification of urinary metabolites (see Shaw and Ramwell, 1969; Granström and Samuelsson, 1971b; Hamberg, Israelsson and Samuelsson, 1971).

(b) *High pressure liquid chromatography*

Early applications of high pressure liquid chromatography (HPLC) to analysis of prostaglandins were to separate $PGF_{2\alpha}$ and 15-epi-$PGF_{2\alpha}$ (Weinshenker and Longwell, 1972) PGC_2 (Corey and Sachdev, 1973), $PGF_{2\alpha}$ and $PGF_{2\beta}$ (Mikes, Schurig and Gil-Av, 1973), PGB and PGE (Dunham and Anders, 1973), PGE_2, PGE_1, $PGF_{1\alpha}$ and $PGF_{2\alpha}$ (Andersen and Leovey, 1974). Carr, Sweetman and Frölich (1976), Hubbard and Watson (1976), and Frölich (1976) have described systems which resolve many prostaglandins and metabolites: these systems were ideal for subsequent analysis by gas chromatography-mass spectrometry (GLC-MS). Carr *et al.* (1976) preferred a stainless steel column (4 × 300 mm) pre-packed with 10 μm particles of silica (μ-Porasil) rather than Carbowax 400. Two solvents, chloroform and a mixture of chloroform, methanol and acetic acid (500:50:11 v/v) were pumped through the μ-Porasil column at a flow rate of 1 ml/min under the

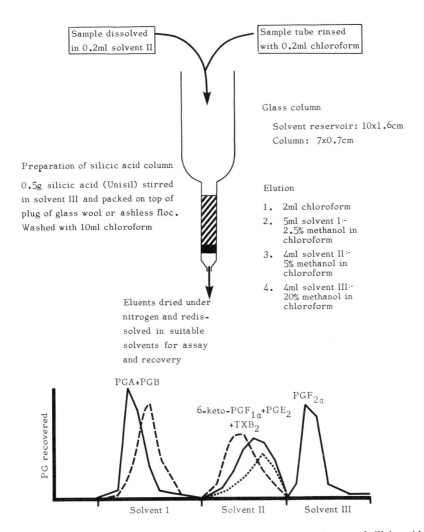

Fig. 10. Scheme for separating groups of prostaglandins on columns of silicic acid using mixtures of chloroform and methanol as eluting solvents.

control of a gradient control device. The system enables excellent resolution of PGA, PGE and PGF (see Fig. 11); the peak shape is symmetrical and so sharp that each prostaglandin is eluted in only 2–3 ml solvent (in contrast to 10 ml with the column of Carbowax 400). Recoveries from the column exceeded 90 % and the retention volumes were reproducible. The same solvent system as above has been utilised to separate plasma metabolites (Hubbard and Watson, 1976). Urinary metabolites, usually after derivatisation (see Section C.1.b.1) were resolved during isocratic elution with chloroform (Frölich, 1976). However, the high resolution obtained with HPLC is not without its hazards; for example, Frölich (1976) has pointed out that octa-tritiated PGE_2 can be partially resolved from unlabelled PGE_2 and this could lead to misleading assessments of recovery.

Despite the excellent separating power of HPLC, the system described by Carr et al. (1976) does not clearly resolve either TXB_2 or 6-keto-$PGF_{1\alpha}$

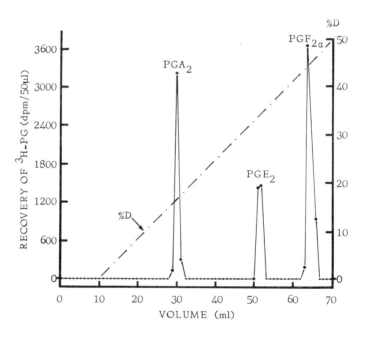

Fig. 11. High-pressure liquid chromatography of an extract of blood containing a mixture of PGA_2, PGE_2 and $PGF_{2\alpha}$. Chromatography was performed on a column of μ-Porasil using chloroform and an increasing concentration of chloroform. methanol and acetic acid (500:50:11; by vol—solvent D) at a flow rate of 1ml/min. (From Carr, Sweetman and Fröhlich, 1976; Reproduced with permission.)

from PGE_2. However, it is confidently predicted that reversed-phase systems will resolve these prostaglandins.

The most frequently used detectors for identifying compounds eluted during HPLC are based on UV absorption and refractive index (RI). Unfortunately, neither detector is sensitive to sub-μg amounts of prostaglandins (with the exception of A and B groups which absorb at 217 and 278 nm, respectively). However, the UV absorption of prostaglandins can be enhanced by reacting the compounds with chromophore reagents. p-Nitrobenzyl and p-nitrophenacyl derivatives of prostaglandins have been used to increase UV absorption; Morozowich and Douglas (1975) preferred the use of p-nitrophenacyl esters because of their rapid formation. Fitzpatrick (1976) converted PGE_1 and its metabolites to their p-bromophenacyl esters which were separated by reverse phase chromatography on a μ-Bondapak C18 column. However, neither of these techniques is applicable to quantitation of prostaglandins in blood since the sensitivity is not sufficient (at least 1 ng of the derivative must be injected on the column) and at low concentrations (i.e. high sensitivity of the detector) there is a likelihood that excess reagent will overwhelm the detector.

(c) Thin-layer chromatography

Many developing systems have been devised to separate groups of prostaglandins by thin layer chromatography (TLC), either as the free acids or methyl esters (Gréen and Samuelsson, 1964; Hamberg and Samuelsson, 1966; Andersen, 1969a; Willis, 1970). Most investigators have used silica gel G as the adsorbent. Prostaglandins may be separated on the basis of their unsaturation (i.e. PGE_1 from PGE_2) on plates coated with a thin layer of silica gel G impregnated with either silver nitrate (Gréen and Samuelsson, 1964; Hamberg and Samuelsson, 1966) or ferric chloride (Wickramasinghe and Shaw, 1974a). The R_f's of various prostaglandins in a selection of particularly useful TLC developing solvents are listed in Table 3.

TLC can often achieve clearer resolution of the components than column chromatography, but inconsistent and low recoveries are common. Location of prostaglandins after TLC is accomplished by exposure to iodine vapour or spraying with a visualising reagent (see Gréen and Samuelsson, 1964; Shaw and Ramwell, 1969); quantitation is also possible provided that several μg of the prostaglandin is present. However, when lower amounts of prostaglandins are encountered the prostaglandin "zones" must be scraped from the plate, extracted and assayed by other means. TLC has been employed to effect the separation of $PGF_{2\alpha}$, PGD_2, PGE_2 and TXB_2 from 6-keto-$PGF_{1\alpha}$ required for a specific radioimmunoassay for 6-keto-$PGF_{1\alpha}$ (Salmon, 1978).

Table 3

Thin-layer separation of prostaglandins: some useful solvent systems.

Code	Solvent system	Comments	Approximate $R_F \times 100^a$							
			E_1	E_2	$F_{1\alpha}$	$F_{2\alpha}$	TXB_2	6-keto-$PGF_{1\alpha}$	PGD_2	PGA_2
1	Ethyl acetate, acetic acid (98:2)	6-keto-$PGF_{1\alpha}$ chromatographs as two spots, one of which tails	40	40	21	21	53	76 and 2–43	73	84
2	Ethyl acetate, acetone, acetic acid (90:10:1)	6-keto-$PGF_{1\alpha}$ "streaks"	46	46	25	25	55	16–55	73	83
3	Ethyl acetate, acetic acid, iso-octane, water (11:2:5:10); organic phase only		36	36	25	25	30	18	48	61
4	Ethyl acetate, acetic acid, iso-octane, water (11:2:5:10); organic phase only	+5% $AgNO_3$	36	18	12	6	18	13	18	70
5	Ethyl acetate, acetic acid, methanol, iso-octane, water (110:30:35:10:100); organic phase only	+5% $AgNO_3$	74	46	42	26	40	50	45	90
6	Benzene, dioxan, acetic acid (66:33:1)	carcinogenic solvent, 6-keto-$PGF_{1\alpha}$ tails	31	31	16	16	38	10–45	54	72
7	Benzene, ethyl acetate, acetic acid (50:50:2)	carcinogenic solvent, 6-keto-$PGF_{1\alpha}$ streaks	10	10	4	4	13	53	27	56
8	Hexane, ethyl acetate, methanol, acetic acid (40:40:10:2)	6-keto-$PGF_{1\alpha}$ streaks	62	62	44	44	59	46–63	63	83
9	Chloroform, methanol, acetic acid (80:10:10)		73	73	56	56	61	70	75	90
10	Chloroform, methanol, acetic acid (80:10:10)	+5% $AgNO_3$	85	74	57	41	57	83	68	88

	Solvent system								
11	Chloroform, methanol, acetic acid, water (90:9:1:0·65)		60	60	42	42	47	58	ND	ND
12	Chloroform, tetrahydrofuran, acetic acid (10:2:1)		20	20	10	10	22	13	36	77
13	Benzene, dioxan (40:60)	as methyl esters, carcinogenic solvent	68	68	56	56	72	74	78	83
14	Ethyl acetate, methanol, water (8:2:5); organic phase only	as methyl esters	69	55	32	23	47	70	62	84

[a] All these results were obtained using Anachem "Uniplates" (250 μm) Silica gel G thin layer plates without further activation. For impregnation with 5% $AgNO_3$ the following technique was used: 5 g $AgNO_3$ was dissolved in 5 ml distilled water, added to 95 ml methanol and mixed rapidly. The methanolic solution was tipped into a flat dish and the plate submerged in the solution for 1 min. The plate was then removed, air-dried and used immediately.

The R_f values are obviously not definitive for all conditions and should only be used as guides. Generally speaking the R_f values of all compounds in any one system may be increased by reducing the ratio of non-polar solvent in the mixture. The acetic acid should be kept constant since this is necessary to keep the prostaglandins in a non-ionised form. In solvent systems which form two phases (3, 4, 5, 14), the mixture should be thoroughly shaken and allowed to stand in a cool place for 30 min. The water saturated organic phase can then be carefully removed from the top.

ND = Not determined.

C. QUANTITATION OF PROSTAGLANDINS

1. Physico-chemical Techniques

(a) *Spectrophotometry*

Spectrophotometry has only a limited application in the field of prostaglandin analysis. Treatment of PGE and PGA with alkali results in the formation of the corresponding PGB which can be measured by UV spectrophotometry (Samuelsson, 1964; Andersen, 1969b; Zusman, 1972). The dienone structure present in PGB has a characteristic absorbance $\lambda_{max}^{ethanol}$ at 278 nm, and an extinction coefficient of about 28,600. A UV spectrophotometric assay was used for a quantitative estimation of PGE_1, PGE_2 and PGE_3 in human seminal fluid and tissues after separation of the individual prostaglandins by TLC (Änggård and Samuelsson, 1964, 1966; Bygdeman and Samuelsson, 1964, 1966). The procedure is simple and relatively inexpensive but the sensitivity (minimum detectable amount is not less than approximately 1·5 nmol (0·5 µg) for each prostaglandin) precludes it from being used for determination of prostaglandins in blood. 15-Keto-PGE_2 was determined by measurement of the strong but transient absorption at 500 nm which appeared after treatment with base (Änggård and Samuelsson, 1970; see Section C.2.d). The sensitivity of spectrophotometric methods for analysis of prostaglandins can be increased several fold by coupling the prostaglandins to a suitable chromophore. *p*-Nitrobenzyl, *p*-nitrophenacyl and *p*-bromophenacyl esters of prostaglandins and their metabolites have been used for this purpose (Morozowich and Douglas, 1975; Fitzpatrick, 1976) but there are limitations to the procedure as discussed previously (see Section B.2.b).

Direct spectrofluorimetry is also too insensitive to be of use in the estimation of prostaglandins in biological samples. Gantt, Kizlaitis, Thomas and Greslin (1968) described a fluorimetric assay of PGE_1 which was only sensitive in the 0·6–1·5 nmol (0·2–0·5 µg) range. In this assay, the prostaglandin was reacted with sulphuric acid and the fluorescence was measured at 402 nm after activation at 366 nm; PGE_2, PGE_3, PGA_1 and PGB produced similar fluorescence but $PGF_{1\alpha}$ emitted light at a longer wavelength.

(b) *Gas–liquid chromatography*

Gas–liquid chromatography (GLC) has proved to be of immense value in the separation and analysis of prostaglandins. When used with conventional detectors it provides a reliable and fairly cheap—if somewhat insensitive—assay method for most of the prostaglandins, and when used in conjunction with a mass spectrometer (MS) it provides the ultimate method of identification and structural analysis. Before proceeding with the discussion of the use of different detectors we will consider two important preliminaries—the choice of derivatising reagent and columns.

(1) *Derivatisation procedures.* The presence of polar groups in prostaglandins and thromboxane render the compounds susceptible to thermal decomposition and irreversible adsorption on active sites of the GLC columns. It is therefore essential to react the functional groups with suitable reagents to reduce that polarity and improve the chromatography. The ideal derivative should be volatile but thermally stable, should exhibit little or no adsorption on the column, and it should be produced by a quantitative and simple chemical reaction.

Esterification of the carboxyl group by treatment with diazomethane is employed almost universally. However, some compounds (e.g. 15-keto-metabolites; Cockerill, Gutteridge, Mallen, Osborne and Rackham, 1977) are further modified by prolonged exposure to diazomethane. In addition, it is sometimes possible to methylate some of the hydroxyl groups in prostaglandins with diazomethane, although this hazard is eliminated if a small quantity of methanol is added to the reaction mixture to provide "sacrificial alcohol" groups. A methyl ester of a prostaglandin could also be produced by reaction with methanolic boron trifluoride but this procedure caused dehydration of PGE (Albro and Fishbein, 1969). Alternatively, the acid can be trimethylsilylated using *bis*-trimethylsilylacetamide (BSA) (Vane and Horning, 1969), however, this product is susceptible to hydrolysis.

Hydroxyl groups are readily silylated by reaction with any one of several silylating reagents, e.g. *N,O-bis*-trimethylsilylacetamide (BSA); *bis*-trimethylsilyltrifluoroacetamide (BSTFA). Probably the most commonly used method employs BSTFA containing 1 % trimethylchlorosilane (TMCS) as a catalyst; derivatisation is usually complete within 30 min at room temperature although many analysts perform the reaction at 60°. BSTFA is very volatile and the derivative can be injected directly into the GLC in the reagent, since the latter will be rapidly eluted. However, such an excess of reagent may overwhelm electron capture detectors (ECD) and it also leaves residues on other detectors, it is therefore advisable to remove excess reagent before injection into the GLC. Since the derivatives are readily hydrolysed in the presence of moisture, the removal of BSTFA is most successfully accomplished in a vacuum desiccator.

Brash, Baillie, Clare and Draffan (1976) formed the *t*-butyldimethylsilyl ether derivative of the methyl ester of PGF$_\alpha$-MUM by reaction with a mixture of *t*-butyldimethylchlorosilane (*t*-BDMCS), imidazole and dimethylformamide. This derivative offers significant advantages, namely it is more resistant to hydrolysis, it can be subjected to TLC without decomposition and it gives a simple mass spectrum.

The reaction of prostaglandins with halogenated silyl reagents enabled the sensitive detection of the derivatives by ECD (Jouvenaz, Nugteren, Beerthuis and Van Dorp, 1970; Van Dorp, 1971; Jouvenaz, Nugteren and Van Dorp, 1973; see Section C.1.b.4).

Alternatively, hydroxyl groups may be transformed to acetates by reaction with acetic anhydride in pyridine (Gréen, 1969). Similar halogenated derivatives have been prepared by reaction with trifluoroacetic anhydride (TFA) (Thompson, Los and Horton, 1970; Änggård, 1971) or heptafluorobutyric anhydride (Levitt, Josimovich and Broskin, 1972) but these compounds, especially those formed with the latter reagent, produce thermally unstable compounds which give rise to multiple GLC peaks.

The β-dihydroxy system present in the PGF series may be converted to the 9,11-n-butane boronate derivatives by reaction with n-butaneboronic acid in dimethoxypropane (Pace-Asciak and Wolfe, 1971; Kelly, 1972; Kelly, 1973; Hensby, 1974; Smith and Brooks, 1977). The C-15 hydroxy group remains underivatised and must be silylated before GLC. Methane-, cyclohexane- and benzene-boronates have also been evaluated (Kelly, 1974; Smith and Brooks, 1977). Since the same 9,11-diol system is present in 6-keto-PGF$_{1\alpha}$, the above boronate derivatives can also be prepared for this prostaglandin: Pace-Asciak (1976a) have described the n-butaneboronate derivative.

The ketone groups present in some prostaglandins have been converted to an oxime derivative by reaction with methoxylamine (Gréen, 1969; Albro and Fishbein, 1969; Pace-Asciak, 1976a; Johnson et al., 1976), benzoxylamine (Axen, Baczynskyj, Duchamp, Kirton and Zieserl, 1973) and ethoxylamine (Middleditch and Desiderio, 1972, 1973). The oxime derivatives of PGE usually produce comparable amounts of the syn- and anti-isomers which are resolved during GLC (Gréen, 1969); only one major GLC peak is observed for the methoxime of 6-keto-PGF$_{1\alpha}$ (Pace-Asciak, 1976a; Johnson et al., 1976). The formation of these oximes is necessary because the trimethylsilyl ether, methyl ester derivatives of PGE are unstable to GLC (Gréen, 1969) whilst two peaks are observed for the trimethylsilyl ether, methyl ester of 6-keto-PGF$_{1\alpha}$ (one peak is due to the derivative of 6-keto-PGF$_{1\alpha}$ whilst the other peak is attributable to loss of trimethylsilanol from the hemi-ketal form; Johnson et al., 1976).

It is possible to convert PGE to PGB by treatment with base and the resulting PGB can be successfully chromatographed as the trimethylsilyl ether, methyl ester. The analysis of PGE as PGB has the added advantage that the latter compound can be sensitively detected by ECD (Albro and Fishbein, 1969; Jouvenaz, Nugteren, Beerthuis and Van Dorp, 1970; Keirse and Turnbull, 1973; Salmon and Karim, 1976). Trimethylsilyl ether, methyl ester derivatives of PGA do not chromatograph well (Thompson et al., 1970).

PGE could also be converted to the corresponding PGF by treatment with sodium borohydride but this reaction yields both the PGF_α and PGF_β isomers in variable ratios. These isomers may be resolved by GLC, thus making quantitative estimations more difficult.

The procedures available for derivatisation of prostaglandins are summarised in Table 4. The sequence for derivatisation is usually esterification of the carboxyl followed by oxime formation of ketone groups and finally silylation of hydroxy groups. However, several authors (Cory, Lascelles, Millard, Sneddon and Wilson, 1976; Pace-Asciak, Domazet and Carrara, 1977a; Cockerill et al., 1977) have observed that initial reaction of 15-keto metabolites of prostaglandins with diazomethane produced variable amounts of pyrazoline derivatives which were resolved by GLC and which produced different mass spectra. These authors advised that oxime formation should precede esterification.

(2) *Columns for gas–liquid chromatography.* The choice of column for GLC is governed by several considerations:

(i) that the individual components in the sample should be clearly resolved;

(ii) that the column should be inert and should not adsorb components;

(iii) the column should produce a low background detector response ("bleed").

The siloxane polymers are most frequently employed for GLC of prostaglandins although a variety of other stationary phases have also been used. Two dimethyl siloxane polymers, SE-30 and OV-1 have been used extensively (Änggård and Samuelsson, 1965; Gréen, 1969; Vane and Horning, 1969; Thompson, Los and Horton, 1970; Hamberg, Israelsson and Samuelsson, 1971; Pace-Asciak and Wolfe, 1971; Wolfe and Pace-Asciak, 1972; Wickramsinghe, Morozowich, Hamlin and Shaw, 1973). OV-1 is now preferred since it produces a lower "bleed" at higher temperatures—a distinct advantage when the ECD or mass spectrometer (MS) are utilised. Methyl-phenyl siloxane polymers containing 50% phenyl groups (OV-17; Gréen, 1969; Vane and Horning, 1969) or 65% phenyl groups (OV-22; Vane and Horning, 1969) have also been used successfully. The above siloxane polymers do not resolve prostaglandins of the same group with different degrees of unsaturation as their trimethylsilyl ether-methyl ester derivatives although individual PGE's may be separated as their methoxime-trimethylsilyl ether-methyl ester derivative, and $PGF_{1\alpha}$ may be distinguished from $PGF_{2\alpha}$ as the *n*-butaneboronate-trimethylsilyl ether-methyl ester derivatives on a column containing 3% SE-30 (Pace-Asciak and Wolfe, 1971). Separation of the individual prostaglandins is also partially achieved on more selective stationary phases such as Apiezon L grease (Bergström, Dressler, Ryhage, Samuelsson and Sjövall, 1962a; a methyl-trifluoropropyl siloxane polymer, QF-1 Struijk, Beerthuis, Pabon and Van Dorp, 1966;

K

Table 4
Procedures available for synthesis of suitable derivatives for GLC.

Group	Reagent	Derivative	Comments
—COOH	Diazomethane	Methyl ester	15-Keto derivatives should be converted to oxime derivatives prior to treatment with diazomethane
	Methanolic boron trifluoride	Methyl ester	Not suitable for PGE or other unstable PGs
	BSA, BSTFA-TMCS	Trimethylsilyl ester	Derivatives readily hydrolysed
	Pentafluorobenzyl bromide	Pentafluorobenzyl ester	Permits sensitive detection by ECD
—OH	BSA, BSTFA-TMCS	Trimethylsilyl ether	Hydrolyses in presence of moisture
	Chloromethyl, dimethylsilyl chloride	Chloromethyl, dimethylsilyl ether	Readily hydrolyse in presence of moisture, long retention times, can be detected by ECD
	Bromomethyl, dimethylsilyl chloride	Bromomethyl, dimethylsilyl ether	
	t-Butyldimethylchlorosilane	t-Butyldimethylsilyl ether	Resistant to hydrolysis; may be subjected to TLC without decomposition and it gives a simple mass-spectrum
	Acetic anhydride	Acetate	
	Trifluoroacetic anhydride, Heptafluorobutyric anhydride	Trifluoroacetate, Heptafluorobutyrate	May produce multiple GLC peaks, can permit sensitive detection by ECD
	Heptafluorobutyl imidazole	Heptafluorobutyrate	Appears to produce single GLC peak, permits sensitive detection by ECD
(β-dihydroxy cyclopentane) OH ... OH	n-Butane boronic acid	n-Butane boronate	Formation of these derivatives confirms the presence of a β-dihydroxy system (e.g. $PGF_{2\alpha}$, 6-keto-$PGF_{1\alpha}$)
	Methane boronic acid	Methane boronate	
	Cyclohexane boronic acid	Cyclohexane boronate	
	Benzene boronic acid	Benzene boronate	
O=C—	Methoxylamine HCl	Methoxime	Syn and anti-isomers are formed and these may be resolved by GLC
	Ethoxylamine HCl	Ethoxime	
	Benzoxylamine HCl	Benzoxime	

Jouvenaz et al., 1970), cyclohexane dimethanol succinate, CHDMS or Hi-Eff 8B (Albro and Fishbein, 1969; Bygdeman and Samuelsson, 1966).

The stationary phase is usually coated (1–5 %) on any of the commercially available supports (e.g. Gas chrom Q, Gas chrom P, Diatoport S, Supersorb AW, Chromosorb W) and packed into glass columns. However, Maclouf, Rigaud, Durand and Chebroux (1976) recently described the use of stationary phases coated directly onto glass capillary columns for chromatography of prostaglandins. The resolution of individual prostaglandins was excellent, and the technique also offers more sensitive analysis due to shorter retention times and minimal adsorption.

(3) *Flame ionisation detector.* There are several detectors available for detecting compounds in the effluent from GLC. The flame ionisation detector (FID) has been used to analyse prostaglandins in body fluids and tissues (Bygdeman and Samuelsson, 1966; Ramwell, Shaw, Clarke, Grostic, Kaiser and Pike, 1968; Shaw and Ramwell, 1969; Albro and Fishbein, 1969; Pace-Asciak and Wolfe, 1971) but it is not sufficiently sensitive for a practical assay of prostaglandins in blood. Only the electron capture detector and the mass spectrometer possess the necessary sensitivity. The latter two detectors will now be considered separately.

(4) *Electron capture detector.* The electron capture detector (ECD) can provide a very sensitive and selective measurement of electron capturing components in the GLC effluent. PGB compounds are inherently good electron captors. Jouvenaz et al. (1970) developed an assay for PGE_1 and PGE_2 in tissue by initial treatment with strong alkali and measurement of the resulting PGB compound by GLC-ECD. These authors used ω-nor-PGE_2 and ω-homo-PGE_1 as internal standards to monitor extraction, chromatography, and derivatisation of the natural prostaglandins. The lower limit of detection was less than 1 ng. This method has been applied to measurement of PGE in tissue homogenates of various species (Christ and Van Dorp, 1972) and in amniotic fluid before and during labour (Jouvenaz, Nugteren and Van Dorp, 1973; Keirse and Turnbull, 1973).

Prostaglandins and thromboxanes can be reacted with electron-capturing reagents to produce derivatives which can be detected in the sub-ng range by GLC-ECD, but two basic problems with this coupling have been noted; (i) excess reagent must be removed before GLC since its presence will swamp the ECD (unfortunately, the reagents are usually difficult to eliminate completely), (ii) impurities may also react with the electron capturing reagents and these derivatives themselves can also swamp the detector. These difficulties are formidable and therefore GLC-ECD assays have been confined to the assay of samples containing relatively high amounts of prostaglandin but low levels of impurities.

Jouvenaz et al. (1973) reported that the bromomethyl-dimethylsilyl ether, methyl ester derivatives of PGF could be detected in the ng range by GLC-ECD but these authors also noted that these derivatives were readily hydrolysed. Sub-ng amounts (0·09–2·38 pmol; 0·03–0·84 ng) of $PGF_{2\alpha}$ were detected as the pentafluorobenzyl ester derivative (Wickramasinghe et al., 1973) and this method was applied to the determination of $PGF_{2\alpha}$ in plasma after administration of the drug to rhesus monkeys (9·84 μmol/kg; 3·49 mg/kg) (Wickramasinghe and Shaw, 1974b). The pentafluorobenzyl ester of TXB_2 has also been studied (Fitzpatrick, Gorman and Wynalda, 1977) but it exhibited multiple chromatographic peaks with excessive tailing. After an investigation of other electron capturing derivatives of TXB_2, Fitzpatrick et al. (1977) concluded that the pentafluorobenzyl oxime, trimethylsilyl ether, methyl ester was the most suitable although the reproducibility of the derivatisation was poor and the method was only considered to be semi-quantitative.

Trifluoroacetate and heptafluorobutyrate derivatives of PGF are good electron captors but produce multiple GLC peaks when prepared by reaction with the corresponding anhydride (Levitt and Josimovich, 1971; Levitt, Josimovich and Broskin, 1972; Middleditch and Desiderio, 1972). However, Sugiura and Hirano (1974) claimed that only one GLC peak was obtained when either $PGF_{1\alpha}$ or $PGF_{2\alpha}$ was reacted with heptafluorobutyryl imidazole.

(5) *Mass spectrometer*. Gas chromatography coupled with mass spectrometry (GLC-MS) has become probably the most powerful analytical tool for the qualitative and quantitative analysis of prostaglandins. The technique was employed for the original identification of PGE and PGF (Bergström, Rhyage, Samuelsson and Sjövall, 1962b, 1963) and has since played a major role in the elucidation of the structure of, and mechanism of formation of prostaglandin metabolites (see Samuelsson et al., 1971, 1975; Sun, 1974; Sun and Stafford, 1974), the prostaglandin endoperoxides (PGG and PGH; Hamberg and Samuelsson, 1973, 1974), thromboxane A_2 and B_2 (Hamberg, Svensson and Samuelsson, 1974a, 1975), 6-keto-$PGF_{1\alpha}$ and prostacyclin (Pace-Asciak, 1976a; Johnson et al., 1976). Most investigators consider that GLC-MS provides the most reliable quantitative data for these compounds if suitable internal standards are employed and therefore, it has been proposed that GLC-MS should be the reference method for analysis of prostaglandins. The principal advantages of the technique are its high specificity, and sensitivity (sub-ng amounts of prostaglandins may be measured with confidence). However, the lengthy derivatization steps which are mandatory for good chromatography prolong the analysis time and adds to the difficulty of the procedure. Also the sophisticated instrumentation required is expensive (£20,000–100,000 in 1977) thereby limiting the availability to few establishments. The use of a computer to control the GLC-MS and to calculate the results is highly desirable if not essential. The theoretical

concepts of the technique as well as the variety of GLC-MS instrumentation available for analysis of prostaglandins have been throughly reviewed by Frölich (1976).

(i) *Internal standards for GLC-MS*. Since so many steps have to be performed before the injection of the prostaglandin into the GLC-MS (i.e. extraction, preliminary purification and derivatisation), the overall efficiency of the procedure is variable. It is therefore essential to include an internal standard which enables precise quantification of the prostaglandin in the original sample. Such an internal standard should not occur naturally in the biological sample but it should behave in an identical manner to the prostaglandin under test on extraction, purification and derivatisation; it should only be separated during the final step of GLC or by MS. The use of derivatives containing deuterium or other stable isotopes (such as ^{13}C and ^{18}O) are ideal since they can only be distinguished from the native prostaglandin in the MS. These compounds can also be used to prevent the small mass of prostaglandins encountered in biological samples from being adsorbed to chromatography columns, etc., during analysis. Thus, Samuelsson, Hamberg and Sweeley (1970) used a large excess of the deuterated O-methyl oxime ($=NOCD_3$) derivative of PGE_1 as both a standard and a "carrier" in an assay of PGE_1. It is essential for absolute quantification and high sensitivity that the deuterated compound is very pure, both chemically and isotopically (i.e. it should not contain any of the protium form) although this difficulty may be overcome by measuring the increase in the protium ion above the background (thus the standard curve will not pass through the origin). The deuterium ions should not be exchangeable and should not be eliminated during fragmentation in the MS (Gréen, 1973b). Cory *et al.* (1976) observed that proton exchange occurred during a four week storage of their dilute deuterated standard $(3,3,4,4\text{-}d_4\text{-}PGF_{2\alpha})$ in methanol and that this resulted in high assay "blank". These authors demonstrated that no such exchange occurred in a concentrated methanolic solution of the standard when stored at $-20°$. Elimination of deuterium from $d_8\text{-}PGF_{2\alpha}$ in the MS itself has been reported (McCracken, Carlson, Glew, Goding, Baird, Gréen and Samuelsson, 1972; Hamberg and Samuelsson, 1972) thereby limiting the sensitivity of the method. The purity of deuterated prostaglandin is especially critical when it is also being used as a carrier since it is added in 125–1000 fold excess.

Fragmentation blanks can also occur as a result of elution of high boiling point impurities from earlier runs and "bleeding" from the column (Gréen, 1973b); also, the mass spectrum of the deuterated standard may actually include an ion at the same m/e as the selected ion in the protium form. It is important to monitor ions which have low blanks and to check the blank frequently during the course of an analysis.

The deuterated standards used in early assays were formed by reacting the prostaglandin in the sample with a deuterated reagent. For instance, Samuelsson *et al.* (1970) and Hamberg (1972) formed the deuterated O-methyl oxime ($=NOCD_3$) of PGE_1 and the main urinary metabolite of PGE_1 and PGE_2 (PGE-MUM) whereas Wolfe and Pace-Asciak (1972) and Gillett, Kinch, Wolfe and Pace-Asciak (1972) formed the deuterated methyl ester of $PGF_{2\alpha}$ ($-COOCD_3$). However, these deuterated derivatives could not be considered as true internal standards since they did not compensate for losses of the prostaglandin encountered during extraction, purification and derivatisation. A significant advance was made when PGE_2 and $PGF_{2\alpha}$ were synthesised with deuterium incorporated into the 3,3,4,4-positions (Axen, Gréen, Horling and Samuelsson, 1971; see Section C.1.b.5.ii).

Owing to the problems which may occur in assays using deuterated standards, Middleditch and Desiderio (1973) investigated the use of non-deuterated prostaglandins as internal standards for quantitative analysis of PGE. These internal standards have different GLC retention times from the prostaglandin under test but Cory *et al.* (1976) claimed that if the same m/e ion was monitored in both the prostaglandin and the standard spectrum, then the method is more sensitive and precise than procedures which require monitoring of two or more ions. The reason for the reduced sensitivity when several ions are monitored is that there must always be a finite "dead time" while the MS switches from one ion to another. The method described by Cory *et al.* (1976) used deuterated $PGF_{2\alpha}$ as a carrier in the assay of $PGF_{2\alpha}$ whilst ω-trinor-16-cyclohexyl-$PGF_{2\alpha}$ was used as standard; thus the comments made about the purity of the deuterated compounds also apply to this method.

(ii) *Assays.* For analysis of PGE_2, Axen *et al.* (1971) added 3,3,4,4-d_4-PGE_2 standard in excess (1:1000 to 1:16000) to the sample. The O-methyl oxime, acetyl, methyl ester derivatives were analysed in a LKB 9000 GLC-MS which was designed to focus alternately the protium and deuterium ions on the electron multiplier with the aid of an accelerating voltage alternator (AVA) unit. The selected ions which were monitored were the base ions of the protium (m/e 419) and deuterium (m/e 423) forms in the second GLC peak. The standard curve obtained after injecting 710 pmol (250 ng) of the mixtures was linear over the range 1–15 pmol PGE_2/nmol d_4 carrier (1–15 ng PGE_2/μg d_4 carrier).

A similar method was described for analysis of $PGF_{2\alpha}$ (Axen *et al.*, 1971). $PGF_{2\alpha}$ and 3,3,4,4-d_4-$PGF_{2\alpha}$ were injected into the GLC-MS as their triacetyl, methyl ester derivatives and the ions at m/e 314 and m/e 318 were monitored. The trimethylsilyl ether, methyl ester derivatives were also evaluated and in this case the ions at m/e 423 and m/e 427 were followed.

Also, using 3,3,4,4-d_4-$PGF_{2\alpha}$, Axen, Baczynskyj, Duchamp and Zierserl (1972) and Axen, Baczynskyj, Duchamp, Kirton and Zierserl (1973) developed a method based on repetitive magnetic scanning of the GLC peak over a narrow mass range rather than using the AVA technique. The advantages of this technique were that it avoided focusing problems and it permitted the monitoring of several ions simultaneously. It is however, less sensitive than measuring pre-selected ions (multiple ion detection; MID).

Deuterated internal standards (usually $3,3,4,4$-d_4) have also been synthesised and utilised for analysis of the major circulating metabolites of PGE_2 and $PGF_{2\alpha}$, namely 13,14-dihydro-15-keto-PGE_2 and 13,14-dihydro-15-keto-$PGF_{2\alpha}$ (Gréen, Granström and Samuelsson, 1972; Gréen, Béguin, Bygdeman, Toppozada and Wiqvist, 1972; Béguin, Bygdeman, Gréen, Samuelsson, Toppozada and Wiqvist, 1972; Granström and Samuelsson, 1972a; Gréen, 1973a; Gréen, Granström, Samuelsson and Axen, 1973; Gréen, Bygdeman, Toppozada and Wiqvist, 1974a). The method has also been extended to the measurement of the main urinary metabolites of PGE (Hamberg, 1972) and PGF (Hamberg, 1973). As with analysis of the parent prostaglandins, there are large discrepancies between the measurement of metabolites by GLC-MS and by radioimmunoassay (RIA). For example, the results of the GLC-MS assay of 13,14-dihydro-15-keto-$PGF_{2\alpha}$ in blood (Samuelsson and Gréen. 1974) were approximately 100 times lower than the RIA data of Levine and Gutierrez-Cernosek (1972; 1973).

The quantitative analysis of TXB_2, HETE and HHT in blood have been achieved by GLC-MS using octadeuterated derivatives as internal standards (Hamberg, Svensson and Samuelsson, 1974a). GLC-MS has also been applied to the detection of 6-keto-$PGF_{1\alpha}$ (Pace-Asciak, 1976a; Johnson et al., 1976; Dawson et al., 1976; Cottee et al., 1977). Only the method of Pace-Asciak and Rangaraj (1977) incorporated an internal standard (the methyl ester of 8,11,12,14,15-d_5-6-keto $PGF_{1\alpha}$) but it was not applied to measurement of the prostaglandin in blood.

Although it would be impractical to measure the concentration of prostaglandin endoperoxides in circulating blood by physico-chemical means, it is perhaps, pertinent to describe briefly a method which was used to measure these compounds in experimental conditions. Both endoperoxides (PGG_2 and PGH_2) were reduced to $PGF_{2\alpha}$ by treatment with stannous chloride or triphenyl phosphine and consequently the difference between the concentration of $PGF_{2\alpha}$ (measured by GLC-MS) in a sample before and after treatment with reducing agent was a measure of the concentration of the endoperoxides (Hamberg and Samuelsson, 1973; Hamberg, Svensson, Wakabayshi and Samuelsson 1974b; Hamberg, Svensson and Samuelsson, 1974a; Svensson, Hamberg and Samuelsson, 1975).

The GLC-MS methods which have been referred to so far in this section have involved the fragmentation of compounds by electron impact (EI). However, an alternative approach is to use chemical ionisation (CI); the latter technique usually results in less fragmentation compared to EI and therefore the spectrum is characterised by a few ions of high mass. Since there are relatively few ions, the relative abundance of each will be high which may result in increased sensitivity. Despite the advantage of CI-MS there have been only a few brief reports on the use of this source in prostaglandin research (Desiderio and Hagele, 1971; Desiderio, 1972; Oswald, Parks, Eling and Corbett, 1974; Finnegan, Knight, Fies and DaGragnano, 1974; Cottee et al., 1977; Smith and Brooks, 1977) but none have, as yet, applied the technique to quantitative analysis of prostaglandins in blood; this is probably due to the inherently high background present when hydrocarbon reagent gases are employed.

(c) Isotope derivative methods

Bojesen and Buchave (1972) described an isotope dilution method for the determination of PGE_1 and PGE_2 in serum using 2-amino-^{35}S-thiazole as the reagent. The assay was sensitive in the pg range but the procedure was lengthy and complicated. A simplified and more rapid method was developed by Flower and McClure (1975); the basis of this procedure was the reaction of PGE with sodium ^3H-borohydride to form 9-^3H-$PGF_{2\alpha+\beta}$. The amount of PGE in the sample was assessed using PGE-methyl ester as an internal standard. Provided that the PGE had been purified the assay could detect amounts as low as 2·84 pmol (1 ng) but the authors recommended that it should not be used for samples of biological origin containing less than 28·4 pmol (10 ng). The assay can be adapted to analysis of other prostaglandins and metabolites containing a keto function (e.g. PGD, PGA, PGB and 15-keto metabolites). Aizawa and Yamada (1974, 1976) measured PGE_2 and $PGF_{2\alpha}$ in samples of human cerebrospinal fluid by another isotope dilution method. The prostaglandin in the sample was converted to the ^{14}C-methyl ester by treatment with ^{14}C-methanol and concentrated sulphuric acid. ^3H-prostaglandin was added as internal standard. After TLC, the $^3H/^{14}C$ ratio was measured in zones corresponding to the methyl esters of PGE_2 and $PGF_{2\alpha}$; thus the prostaglandin concentration could be estimated.

2. Biological Techniques

(a) Bioassay

Prostaglandins were originally discovered by bioassay and even in recent years when many sophisticated physico-chemical assay techniques are available, bioassay has been of fundamental importance in several major advances in our knowledge of the biosynthesis of prostaglandins and related compounds. Possibly, the single most important advantage of bioassay, especially that of the continuous superfusion system of Vane (1964, 1969) is its dynamic quality and its ability to detect short-lived compounds in circulating blood or in effluent from perfused isolated organs. In the superfusion assay, it is unnecessary to process the sample; the blood from an anaesthetised animal or perfusate from an isolated organ is passed directly over a cascade of several isolated smooth muscle preparations in series (Vane, 1964, 1969). Specificity is achieved by careful selection of the tissues used in the cascade and by the addition of antagonists to other biologically active compounds which may be present in the sample and which would otherwise compromise the assay. A variety of combinations of tissues in the cascade is possible, and since tissues respond differently to the various prostaglandins (see Bergström, Carlson and Weeks, 1968; Bennett, 1972; Main, 1973; Salmon and Karim, 1976; Moncada, Ferreira and Vane, 1978) it is possible to cautiously identify the prostaglandin in the sample.

A combination of superfused rat stomach strip, rat colon and chick rectum has frequently been used for analysis of classical prostaglandins (PGE_2 and $PGF_{2\alpha}$) since these tissues respond relatively selectively to prostaglandins even in the absence of antagonists (Vane, 1969). Other tissues should now be included to permit detection of the recently identified, short-lived compounds. Piper and Vane (1969) demonstrated that strips of rabbit aorta were contracted by "RCS" (Rabbit aorta Contracting Substance) which was subsequently found to be a mixture of both TXA_2 and prostaglandin endoperoxides both of which contracted this preparation, TXA_2 being more potent (Needleman, Moncada, Bunting, Vane, Hamberg and Samuelsson, 1976). Bunting, Gryglewski, Moncada and Vane (1976) differentiated TXA_2 and PGI_2 by their different responses on rabbit aorta and, additionally, their opposite activities on rabbit coeliac or mesenteric arteries. The response of bovine coronary arteries distinguishes PGI_2 from PGE_2 (Dusting, Moncada and Vane, 1977). Thus, an ideal cascade would consist of rabbit aorta, rabbit coeliac (or mesenteric) artery, bovine coronary artery, rat stomach strip and rat colon (see Table 5 for activities of prostaglandins on these tissues).

Further confirmation of the prostaglandin present in the sample may be obtained by determining the stability of the biologically active component; TXA_2, PGI_2 and prostaglandin endoperoxides readily decompose to less active compounds whereas PGE_2, $PGF_{2\alpha}$, PGD_2 and 6-keto-$PGF_{1\alpha}$ are relatively stable. Thus, the inclusion of a delay coil of varying length between the animal or perfused organ will eliminate responses due to TXA_2, PGI_2 and prostaglandin endoperoxides. Also, the fact that PGI_2 is unstable in acidic media may be utilised to further substantiate its presence.

Other biologically active compounds which may be present in the sample

Table 5

Response of isolated superfused tissues to various prostaglandins and related compounds. The stability of these compounds and their effect on platelet aggregation are also summarised.

	6-keto-PGF$_{1\alpha}$	PGF$_{2\alpha}$	PGE$_2$	PGD$_2$	PGG$_2$ PGH$_2$	TXA$_2$	Prostacyclin (PGI$_2$)
Half life, H$_2$O 37° pH 7·6	>6 hr	>6 hr	>6 hr	>6 hr	≃5 min	≃30 sec	≃5 min
Rabbit aorta							
Rabbit coeliac artery							
Bovine coronary artery							
Rat stomach strip							
Rat colon							
Platelet aggregation	0	0	0	−	+	+ + +	− −

(e.g. acetylcholine, 5-hydroxytryptamine, histamine and catecholamines) can be blocked by specific inhibitors (e.g. atropine, methysergide, mepyramine, phenoxybenzamine and propanolol, respectively). Also, the addition of indomethacin to inhibit intramural generation of prostaglandins by the isolated tissues may benefit the assay.

In the blood-bathed organ superfusion technique (Vane, 1969), heparinised blood is continuously withdrawn from an artery or vein of an anaesthetised animal, passed over a cascade of tissues and then returned under gravity to the animal through a large vein (Fig. 12). The technique cannot be used

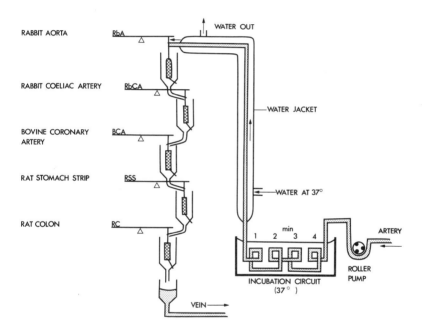

Fig. 12. Diagram of the blood-bathed superfusion bioassay.

under sterile conditions and this precludes the application of this technique *per se* to human subjects. A variation of this procedure was developed by Collier (1972); the blood was dialysed against a counter current of a balanced salt solution, antagonists were added to the buffer (to gain assay specificity) which was then passed over the tissues.

Other ingenious modifications of the superfusion technique have also been reported. Korbut (1975) and Gryglewski and Korbut (1976) used columns of aluminium hydroxide or Amberlite XAD-2 to remove mediators from the stream of Krebs' solution before it passed over the assay tissues. For example, the release of mediators (histamine and prostaglandins) from immunologically challenged perfused lung was studied using an Amberlite XAD-2 column placed in the middle of a cascade of tissues (Gryglewski and Korbut, 1976). Thus, the top tissues were superfused with a mixture of prostaglandins and histamine but the tissues beneath the column of Amberlite only received histamine since the resin effectively removes the prostaglandins. Columns of aluminium hydroxide were similarly used to remove catecholamines (Korbut, 1975).

Gryglewski, Korbut, Ocetkiewicz and Stachura (1978b) superfused Achilles tendons from healthy rabbits with blood from anaesthetised and heparinised cats. The tendons gained in weight due to deposition of platelet thrombi on their surface and this increase in weight was continuously monitored. Gryglewski, Korbut and Ocetkiewicz (1978a) demonstrated that administration of prostacyclin to the cat inhibited this deposition of platelet thrombi and this could serve as a useful bioassay for prostacyclin.

Additional evidence for the presence of some prostaglandins may be achieved by studying the effect of the sample on platelet aggregation. For example, TXA_2 and prostaglandin endoperoxides are potent inducers of platelet aggregation (Hamberg et al., 1974a, b, 1975; Willis, Vane, Kuhn, Scott and Petrin, 1974) whereas PGE_1, PGD_2 (Kloeze, 1967; Smith, Silver, Ingerman and Kocsis, 1974) and PGI_2 (Moncada et al., 1976a; Gryglewski et al., 1976) inhibit aggregation.

Strips of various smooth muscles have been used in individual organ baths (see Bergström et al., 1968; Bennett, 1972; Main, 1973; Salmon and Karim, 1976; Moncada et al., 1978). As already mentioned some tissues may respond specifically to a particular prostaglandin but partial purification (e.g. by extraction and chromatography) of a sample containing a mixture of compounds before assay is desirable, if not essential. Tissues in organ baths are usually more sensitive than similar tissues in a cascade and even greater sensitivity may be achieved by superfusing the sample in Krebs' buffer over a tissue bathed in mineral oil (Ferreira and Souza Costa, 1976).

In vivo bioassays for prostaglandins are rarely used; the exception being the blood pressure assay for PGA. Smooth muscle preparations are relatively insensitive to PGA but the threshold dose for PGA_2 on the lowering of arterial blood pressure in the cat (spinal or anaesthetised) is ca 10 ng (Horton and Jones, 1969).

One of the major strengths of bioassay—that it depends upon specific biological activity—is also a weakness for it means that the prostaglandin metabolites cannot be measured since these are relatively inactive.

(b) *Immunological techniques*

(*1*) *Antibodies.* All prostaglandins can be readily conjugated via the carboxyl function to the free amino groups of lysine residues present in proteins. Serum albumin, of either human or bovine origin, is the most common protein employed but thyroglobin (Stylos, Howard, Ritzi and Skarnes, 1974), keyhole limpet haemocyanin (Jaffe, Smith, Newton and Parker, 1971), polylysine (Levine and Van Vunakis, 1970) and porcine γ-globulin (Jubiz, Frailey and Bartholomew, 1972a) have also been used successfully. Water soluble carbodiimides have been utilised in conjugating relatively stable prostaglandins (e.g. PGF, PGA and PGB) to protein (Fig. 13; Caldwell *et al.*, 1971):

1-Ethyl-3-(3-dimethyl aminopropyl) carbodiimide (104 μmol; 20 mg) is added to an aqueous solution of BSA (40 mg in 2 ml): pH of the mixture is maintained at 5·0–5·2. Prostaglandin (28·4 μmol; 10 mg) plus *ca* 5000 cpm ^{3}H-PG in dimethyl formamide is added dropwise, pH is kept at 5·0–5·2 by addition of 0·01 M HCl or NaOH. Mixture then left at room temperature for 24 hr.

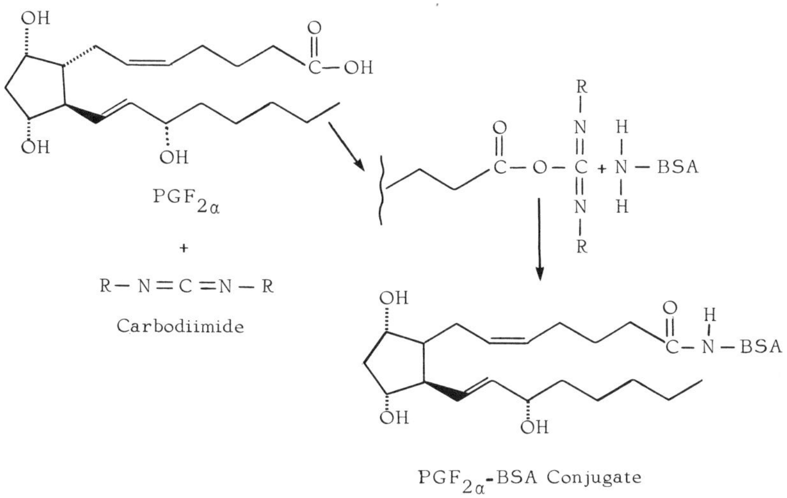

Fig. 13. Formation of the PGF$_{2\alpha}$–BSA conjugate using the carbodiimide method.

This method does cause significant decomposition of PGE to PGA and PGB. Consequently, when PGE-protein conjugates prepared by the above method have been injected into animals, the sera obtained often had a high anti-PGA and anti-PGB as well as anti-PGE activity (Levine, Gutierrez-Cernosek and Van Vunakis, 1971; Zusman, Caldwell and Speroff, 1972; Jobke, Peskar and Peskar, 1973; Pletka and Hickler, 1974). Therefore Jaffe and Behrman (1974) recommended a milder reaction for conjugation of PGE to protein:

Prostaglandin (28·4 μmol; 10 mg) plus ^{3}H-PG is dissolved in 1 ml 1,4-dioxan. Solution is kept on an ice bath. Isobutyl chloroformate (31·5 μmol; 5 μl) and tri-n-butylamine (36·5 μmol; 7·5 μl) is then added, followed by BSA (30 mg) in 0·1 M sodium bicarbonate (2·5 ml). Mixture is kept at 4° and stirred for 1 hr. In both methods the reaction mixture is dialysed twice against phosphate buffered saline (pH 7·4). Solution is diluted to the equivalent of 1 mg BSA/ml and stored frozen in 1 ml aliquots. The radioactivity in the solution is determined by liquid scintillation counting of an aliquot and thereby the number of mol of PG conjugated to 1 mol of BSA can be estimated.

The advantage of this method is that the reaction is performed at 4° for only 1 hr and the presence of excess base reduces the effect of the acid which is produced during the reaction. Jaffe and Behrman (1974) and others (Salmon and Karim, 1976) have confirmed that a more specific anti-PGE sera can be generated using Method 2.

Both methods of conjugation are equally efficient; approximately 15–25 mol prostaglandin are conjugated to each mol BSA. The degree of conjugation is most readily assessed by including a trace of tritiated homologous prostaglandin in the reaction mixture and measuring the radioactivity associated with the purified conjugate.

A third conjugation reaction using N,N-carbonyldiimidazole has been described (Axen, 1974).

Conjugates of prostaglandin metabolites and protein can be prepared by the methods described above. However, PGF-MUM and PGE-MUM are dioic acids and therefore, there are two possible sites for conjugation. In order to produce highly specific antisera it is desirable to couple selectively the protein to only one of the carboxyl groups. Cornette, Kirton, Schneider, Sun, Johnson and Nidy (1975) and Granström and Kindahl (1976) took advantage of the facile formation of PGF$_\alpha$-MUM δ-lactone at low pH. This metabolite was kept in glacial acetic acid prior to coupling with BSA and it was therefore coupled to the ω-carboxyl group. At pH 7·4 the compound exists primarily as the dioic acid and consequently the antisera were directed against this form rather than the δ-lactone.

In order to prepare an antiserum the prostaglandin protein conjugates have to be injected into animals. Rabbits are usually the species of choice since they are simple and relatively inexpensive to maintain, and they produce sufficient antiserum of high titre and specificity. However, goats (Kirton et al., 1972) and monkeys (Levine, Gutierrez-Cernosek and Van Vunakis, 1973) have also been used.

Regimes for injecting the conjugate into animals vary greatly between laboratories. We have found the following protocol consistently satisfactory. The prostaglandin conjugate (1 mg) is dissolved in 0·9 % NaCl buffered to pH 7·4. The solution is emulsified with an equal volume of Freund's complete adjuvant and this emulsion is injected at 20–30 subcutaneous sites on the dorsal surface of New Zealand White rabbits. The injections are repeated once a week for four weeks. Thereafter, the emulsion is produced with Freund's incomplete adjuvant and booster injections are given once a month.

The concurrent administration of *Bordatella pertussis* vaccine stimulates the production of antibodies against human chorionic gonadotrophin (Vaitukaitis, Robbins, Nieschlag and Ross, 1971) and recently some authors (Dray *et al.*, 1975) have found a similar procedure to be of value in the development of anti-prostaglandin sera.

Blood is collected 7–10 days after booster injections from the marginal ear vein of the rabbit. The blood is allowed to clot and the serum is harvested and stored frozen in small aliquots. Since thromboxane is synthesised during aggregation of platelets (Hamberg and Samuelsson, 1974; Hamberg, Svensson and Samuelsson, 1975), Granström, Kindahl and Samuelsson, (1976a) utilised plasma instead of serum as a source of an antibody raised against TXB_2. However, prostaglandins are known to bind to plasma proteins (Unger, 1972; Raz, 1972) and this may affect the specificity and titre of the anti-plasma. Fitzpatrick, Gorman, McGuire, Kelly, Wynalda and Sun (1977) and Salmon (1978) have reported that anti-TXB_2 sera had a higher specificity than the anti-plasma described by Granström *et al.* (1976a). The titre of the antibody in all three reports were comparable.

(2) *Labelled prostaglandins.* Several prostaglandins and metabolites are available commercially in the tritiated form at high specific activity and these have proved highly satisfactory in RIA. It is perhaps, advisable to remind readers of the instability of certain prostaglandins (e.g. PGE) are unstable and the purity should be constantly monitored (e.g. by TLC) and the compounds repurified when necessary; the use of impure tracer will limit both the specificity and sensitivity of the RIA.

Some prostaglandins and thromboxanes are not commercially available in radioactive form and consequently must be biosynthesised. Tritiated 6-keto-$PGF_{1\alpha}$ has been prepared by incubation of ^{3}H-arachidonic acid with ram seminal vesicle microsomes (Salmon, 1978) and ^{3}H-TXB_2 has been prepared using blood platelets as an enzyme source (Granström *et al.*, 1976a; Fitzpatrick *et al.*, 1977; Salmon, 1978).

High specific activity plasma metabolites (i.e. 13,14-dihy ro-15-keto-PGE_2 and 13,14-dihydro-15-keto-$PGF_{2\alpha}$) can be prepared by incubating the parent ^{3}H-prostaglandin with isolated enzyme preparations, but care should be taken to reduce the synthesis of endogenous metabolites which would dilute the label (Granström and Samuelsson, 1972a; Levine and Gutierrez-Cernosek, 1973; Cornette, Harrison and Kirton, 1974). Alternatively, ^{3}H-15-keto-$PGF_{2\alpha}$ can be prepared from ^{3}H-$PGF_{2\alpha}$ by a simple chemical reaction (Levine and Gutierrez-Cernosek, 1972) and this labelled compound was also satisfactory for a RIA of 13,14-dihydro-15-keto-$PGF_{2\alpha}$ (Levine and Gutierrez-Cernosek, 1973). These plasma metabolites are now available commercially.

The labelled urinary metabolites must be biosynthesised by administration of the parent ^{3}H-prostaglandin or ^{3}H-plasma metabolite into indomethacin-treated rats (Cornette et al., 1975) or human subjects (Granström and Kindahl, 1976). Indomethacin decreases endogenous production of prostaglandin metabolites thus enabling the formation of relatively high specific activity compounds. However, the use of iodinated derivatives (see below) may be preferred since these need not be biosynthesised and they can, therefore, be produced at high specific activities thereby permitting more sensitive RIA.

There have been several reports (Levine and Van Vunakis, 1970; Ohki, Hanyu, Imaki, Nakazawa and Hirata, 1974; Ohki, Imaki, Hirata, Hanyu and Nakazawa, 1975; Ohki, Nishigaki, Imaki, Kurono, Hirata, Hanyu and Nakazawa, 1976; Maclouf, Pradel, Pradelles and Dray, 1976; Sors, Maclouf, Pradelles and Dray, 1977) of employing iodinated compounds as the radioactive antigen in assays of prostaglandins and their metabolites. This method necessitates the synthesis of a derivative of the prostaglandin which can be iodinated; for example Maclouf et al., (1976) and Sors et al. (1977) conjugated $PGF_{2\alpha}$ and its metabolites, 13,14-dihydro-15-keto-$PGF_{2\alpha}$ and 15-keto-$PGF_{2\alpha}$, to tyrosine methyl ester, tyramine or histamine, using a procedure similar to that described for conjugating prostaglandins to protein (see Section C.2.b.1). The resulting derivative can be iodinated by methods perfected for iodinating polypeptides (Greenwood, Hunter and Glover, 1963). There is a possiblity that the use of these tracers could lead to decreased immunoreactivity which would reduce both the specificity and sensitivity of the RIA. However, since the antibody has itself been raised against a similar conjugate, the iodinated derivatives have usually enjoyed at least equal immunoreactivity compared with that of the prostaglandins. A disadvantage of the technique is the relatively short half life of ^{125}I (60 days); ^{131}I has an even shorter half life (8 days). Consequently the radioactive prostaglandin has to be prepared frequently.

(3) Radioimmunoassay procedure. The RIA of different prostaglandins and thromboxanes are basically the same; the reagents are dissolved in assay buffer which is usually tris-HCl or phosphate buffered saline at pH 7·4–8·0 containing either 0·1 % gelatin or serum albumin. The radioactivity added should be approximately 10,000 dpm to permit accurate counting in relatively short times and to prevent the tracer added to assess recovery from influencing the RIA. The antibody is diluted so that *ca* 50 % of added radioactive prostaglandin is bound when no unlabelled antigen has been added; the final dilution of anti-prostaglandin serum in the RIA incubation is usually between 1:2000 and 1:50,000.

The immunoreaction between antibody and both radioactive and un-labelled antigen usually reaches equilibrium within 30 min at 4° but longer incubations (e.g. overnight at 4°) often permit greater reproducibility. Hennam, Johnson, Newton and Collins (1974) and Hillier and Dilley (1974) have demonstrated that a disequilibrium RIA for $PGF_{2\alpha}$ permits greater sensitivity, i.e. antibody and unlabelled antigen are preincubated before the addition of ^{3}H-prostaglandin. In assays which are continued to equilibrium the order of addition of reagents is not critical but should be consistent within each assay set.

The basis of RIA is to measure the degree of radioactive antigen bound to the antibody. Unfortunately, the antibody–antigen complex, as well as the unbound prostaglandin is soluble in the assay buffer and therefore, a separation technique must be devised. A variety of procedures have been adopted for separating the two forms. Probably the most widely used method is the addition of dextran coated charcoal (DCC); 0·2 ml buffer containing 4 mg Norit A charcoal and 0·4 mg T70 dextran is added to each assay tube and this adsorbs the free antigen (whether radioactive or unlabelled) but the complex remains in solution. The DCC method is efficient, quick and cheap but there is a danger of "stripping" antigen from the complex thereby reducing the apparent binding. Coating the charcoal with dextran reduces the danger of "stripping" and provided that other precautions are taken (e.g. performing the separation as quickly as possible and keeping all the solutions at 4°) the method is reliable for RIA of 60–80 assay tubes. Centrifugation is required for complete precipitation of the charcoal, then the total supernatant (or an aliquot) is decanted into scintillation vials to which is added a suitable scintillation fluid. Any scintillation fluid which permits high efficiency counting (greater than 35%) of tritium in 0·5–1 ml aqueous buffers can be used (e.g. Brays fluid, Insta-gel, Bio-Fluor and toluene-based solutions containing Triton X-100 or NCS or Bio-Solve).

If it is desirable to assay a large number of samples (greater than 80 tubes) a double antibody method may be more satisfactory than the DCC method. The double antibody technique involves the addition of a second antibody which complexes with the first immunocomplex, resulting in precipitation. The second antibody can be raised against the first antibody itself but it is more usually produced by injecting the γ-globulin of the animal species in which the first antibody was raised into a second species (i.e. if the anti-prostaglandin serum was produced in a rabbit, then sheep anti-rabbit γ-globulin would be suitable). Relatively high concentrations of second antibody are required for complete precipitation and this will add to the expense of the assay; also, the second antiserum could contain high concentrations of prostaglandins which may lead to spurious results. Other disadvantages of the second antibody technique are that:

(i) a second period of incubation is required (usually 18–24 hr);
(ii) immunoprecipitation can change as the plasma sample ages (Burr, Grant, Sizonenko, Kaplan and Grumbach, 1969);
(iii) salt and protein concentrations in each assay tube may modify precipitation (Buckler, 1971; Court and Hurn, 1971).

Ammonium sulphate (Jaffe *et al.*, 1971), polyethylene glycol (Van Orden and Farley, 1973) and filtration through nitrocellulose membranes (Gersham, Powers, Levine and Van Vunakis, 1972) have also been used to separate the antibody–antigen complex from the free antigen. Solid phase RIA has been utilised for assay of prostaglandins and their metabolites (McCosh, Meyer and Dupont, 1976; Fitzpatrick and Wynalda, 1976). McCosh *et al.* (1976) pre-precipitated the specific anti-prostaglandin sera with anti-rabbit γ-globulin whilst Fitzpatrick and Wynalda (1976) insolubilised the antisera by reaction with ethylchloroformate.

Although RIA for some compounds (e.g. glycoproteins) can be performed directly in plasma, we believe that data obtained by direct RIA of prostaglandins in plasma or sera must be regarded with some circumspection. Some investigators (Kirton *et al.*, 1972; Cornette *et al.*, 1972; Feldman, Plonk and Cornette, 1972; Youssefnejadian *et al.*, 1974; Jubiz *et al.*, 1972a) have measured prostaglandins or their metabolites directly in plasma or serum, but the concentrations reported were much higher than the theoretical values calculated by Samuelsson (1973a) and were invariably greater than values obtained by RIA of extracted plasma or by GLC-MS.

The sensitivity of RIA is primarily dependent on the specific activity of the radioactive antigen but other conditions, such as the concentration of antibody, should also be optimised. The minimum detectable amount of prostaglandin by RIA is frequently less than 10 pg.

Although extraction and column separation of prostaglandins is usually performed prior to RIA it is still necessary to prepare specific antisera since purification by chromatography is not perfect (e.g. prostaglandins of the same group but with different degrees of saturation are not usually separated; some prostaglandins and metabolites may co-chromatograph with other prostaglandins—see Section B.3.a). The specificity of an antiserum varies from animal to animal and even between different bleedings from the same animal; therefore, each batch of serum must be carefully characterised. The effects of other prostaglandins in a RIA for a specific prostaglandin are conveniently assessed by measuring the mass of each prostaglandin required to cause a 50% reduction of the inhibition of binding of the specific ^{3}H-prostaglandin. Most investigators have reported the development of relatively specific anti-$PGF_{2\alpha}$ sera but there is usually a cross-reaction with $PGF_{1\alpha}$, and since the latter prostaglandin may also occur in blood the results of these RIA should be expressed as $PGF_{2\alpha}$ equivalents. It is possible to obtain a more specific estimation of an individual prostaglandin by subjecting the plasma extract to argentation TLC. Ritzi and Stylos (1974) described another method which permitted estimation of an individual prostaglandin; these authors utilised two antisera raised against two prostaglandins (PGE_1 and PGE_2) which co-chromatograph. The cross-reaction of the heterologous prostaglandins in each RIA was known thus performing two simultaneous RIAs on a sample enabled the concentration of each prostaglandin to be calculated.

The production of specific anti-PGE_2 sera has been more problematic probably because of the risk of dehydration of PGE during its conjugation to protein. However, the use of milder reaction conditions (see Section C.2.b.1) has now enabled the production of more specific sera (Jaffe and Behrman, 1974; Bauminger, Zor and Lindner, 1973; Dray et al., 1975; Salmon and Karim, 1976). Specific anti-PGE_1 sera were raised with less difficulty (Jaffe et al., 1973; Jubiz et al., 1972b; Stylos et al., 1974; Yu and Burke, 1972; Dray and Charbonnel, 1973). In vivo metabolism of PGE-protein conjugates by plasma dehydrases and isomerases (see Section A.3) is apparently decreased if the carrier is a large protein such as thyroglobulin (Stylos et al., 1974) or porcine γ-globulin (Jubiz et al., 1972b), thus aiding the development of specific sera.

Antisera to 6-keto-$PGF_{1\alpha}$ cross-reacted with PGE and PGF 5–10% (Salmon, 1978) thus a specific RIA for 6-keto-$PGF_{1\alpha}$ required the inclusion of, for example, a TLC procedure to eliminate the interference by other prostglandins. Antibodies raised against thromboxane B_2 were highly specific (Granström et al., 1976a; Fitzpatrick et al., 1977; Salmon, 1978); PGD_2 cross-reacted 11% in the RIA for TXB_2 when anti-plasma was employed (Granström et al., 1976a) but this may be due to binding to non-specific protein since serum did not exhibit such a high cross-reaction with PGD_2 (Fitzpatrick et al., 1977; Salmon, 1978).

Typical cross-reactivities of prostaglandins and related compounds in RIA for $PGF_{2\alpha}$, PGE_2, 6-keto-$PGF_{1\alpha}$ and TXB_2 are recorded in Table 6.

Granström, Kindahl and Samuelsson (1976b) described an elegant RIA for the unstable TXA_2. The antiserum was generated against mono-O-methyl TXB_2 which is rapidly formed when a large excess of methanol is added to TXA_2. In the RIA, the sample was similarly quenched with methanol and the concentration of the resulting derivative was determined. The method was employed to measure the production of TXA_2 in samples of plasma containing aggregating platelets. However, it is probably not applicable to circulating plasma since the difficulties in collecting samples containing such an unstable compound would seem to be insurmountable, so most investigators will probably have to content themselves with the measurement of the more stable TXB_2.

Table 6

Cross-reactions of various prostaglandins with anti-PGE$_2$, anti-PGF$_{2\alpha}$, anti-6-keto-PGF$_{1\alpha}$ and anti-TXB$_2$ sera.

Compound	Anti-PGE$_2$[a]	Relative cross reaction (%) Anti-PGF$_{2\alpha}$[b]	Anti-6-keto-PGF$_{1\alpha}$[b]	Anti-TXB$_2$[b]
PGE$_1$	33·3	<0·01	11·4	<0·01
PGE$_2$	100·0	<0·01	4·8	<0·01
PGF$_{1\alpha}$	<0·01	12·1	2·8	<0·01
PGF$_{2\alpha}$	<0·01	100·0	1·9	0·07
6-Keto-PGF$_{1\alpha}$	0·05	1·7	100·0	<0·01
TXB$_2$	<0·01	<0·01	<0·04	100·0
PGA$_1$	0·3	<0·01	<0·04	<0·01
PGA$_2$	0·3	<0·01	<0·04	<0·01
PGB$_1$	0·04	<0·01	<0·04	<0·01
PGB$_2$	0·04	<0·01	<0·04	<0·01
PGD$_2$	0·09	<0·01	<0·04	0·12
13,14-Dihydro-15-keto-PGE$_2$	<0·01	<0·01	<0·04	<0·01
15-Keto-PGE$_2$	<0·01	<0·01	<0·04	<0·01
13,14-Dihydro-15-keto-PGF$_{2\alpha}$	<0·01	<0·01	<0·04	<0·01
15-Keto-PGF$_{2\alpha}$	<0·01	<0·01	<0·04	<0·01
13,14-Dihydro-6-keto-PGF$_{1\alpha}$	<0·01	<0·01	13·2	<0·01
6,15-Diketo-PGF$_{1\alpha}$	<0·01	<0·01	0·5	<0·01
HETE	<0·01	<0·01	<0·04	<0·01
Arachidonic acid	<0·01	<0·01	<0·04	<0·01

[a] The antigen (PGE$_2$-BSA) was synthesised by the mixed anhydride method (method 2)
[b] The antigen (PG-BSA) was synthesised using the carbodiimide procedure (method 1)

Radioimmunoassays using relatively specific anti-PGA (Jaffe *et al.*, 1971; Stylos and Rivetz, 1972; Yu and Burke, 1972; Raz and Stylos, 1973; Pletka and Hickler, 1974) and anti-PGB (Levine *et al.*, 1971; Raz and Stylos, 1973) sera have also been described.

The specificity of antisera developed against plasma metabolites of prostaglandins have been relatively good although the C-15 keto group is immunodominant in many cases (Levine, Gutierrez-Cernosek and Van Vunakis, 1973) so that it was often impossible to distinguish 15-keto-$PGF_{2\alpha}$ from 15-keto-PGE_2. However, these authors demonstrated that dehydration of 15-keto-PGE_2 by treatment with base resulted in loss of immunological activity thus permitting a selective RIA for 15-keto-$PGF_{2\alpha}$. Specific RIA for urinary metabolites of PGE_2 and $PGF_{2\alpha}$ have been described (Ohki *et al.*, 1974, 1975, 1976; Cornette *et al.*, 1975; Granström and Kindahl, 1976).

Although most workers usually evaluate the reactivity of their antisera with all available prostaglandins and other compounds which are likely to cross-react, it is possible that as yet unknown prostaglandins may cross-react. For example, the contributions of TXB_2 and 6-keto-$PGF_{1\alpha}$ in most RIA have not been assessed since these two compounds have only recently been identified. TXB_2 does not cross-react with anti-PGE_2 nor anti-$PGF_{2\alpha}$ sera (Salmon, 1978) but 6-keto-$PGF_{1\alpha}$ does exhibit low activity in both these RIA (Salmon, 1978). It should also be emphasised that a low cross-reaction of any compound in a RIA for a given prostaglandin does not necessarily mean that the compound will not contribute to the measured amount of prostaglandins; for example if the concentration of PGE_2, which cross-reacts approximately 5% in a RIA for 6-keto-$PGF_{1\alpha}$ (see Table 6), is present in the sample at 20 times the concentration of 6-keto-$PGF_{1\alpha}$ then half of the amount of 6-keto-$PGF_{1\alpha}$ detected is in fact due to the contribution of PGE_2.

(4) *Other immunological techniques.* Although RIA has been the most widely used technique of its type, other approaches using the basic immunological concept have been explored. Dray and colleagues (Dray, Maron, Tillson and Sela, 1972; Andrieu, Mamas and Dray, 1974) described an assay which was similar to radioimmunoassay except that a $PGF_{2\alpha}$-bacteriophage T_4 ($PGF_{2\alpha}$-T_4) conjugate replaced radioactive $PGF_{2\alpha}$. The proportion of $PGF_{2\alpha}$-T_4 remaining after incubation with antiserum and sample was assessed by adding *Escherichia coli* B and counting the number of plaque-forming units which developed. Andrieu *et al.*, (1974) claimed that this viroimmunoassay was five times more sensitive than RIA. Mitani and Shoji (1974) reported that a similar assay could be used to measure PGF in extracts of human plasma.

(*c*) *Receptor displacement assays*

Specific binding or radio-receptor assays are similar in concept to RIA. In this technique the natural prostaglandins and the homologous radioactive prostaglandin compete for a specific binding site other than an antibody. For example, Miller and Magee (1973) described a binding site on rat fore-stomach tissue which could detect PGE in the 14·2–284 pmol (5–100 ng) range and Frölich and colleagues (Frölich, Wilson, Smigel and Oates, 1974; Frölich, Williams, Sweetman, Smigel, Carr, Hollifield, Fleisher, Nies, Frisk-Holmberg and Oates, 1976) used a receptor in rat liver. Other high affinity binding sites for a variety of prostaglandins have been described (Wakeling, Kirton and Wyngarden, 1973; Rao, 1974; Attallah and Lee, 1973) which could be used for similar assays. The binding site is frequently specific for a particular prostaglandin and therefore selective assays are possible.

(d) Enzyme assays

The high specificity of enzymes for their substrates has often been used as a basis for assay methods. Änggård (1971) developed methods for the analysis of prostaglandins using a specific enzymatic reaction. Prostaglandins are metabolised by a specific enzyme, PGDH (see Section A.3) in the presence of NAD^+ to form stoichiometric amounts of 15-keto-prostaglandin, NADH and H^+. Änggård (1971) determined that prostaglandin in a sample by measuring either the 15-keto-prostaglandin or NADH produced after reaction of the sample with a purified PGDH from swine lung or kidney (Änggård and Samuelsson, 1970). 15-Keto-PGE was determined by measurement of the strong but transient absorption at 500 nm which appeared after base treatment. The NADH generated was either estimated by direct spectro-fluorimetry (Änggård, Matschinsky and Samuelsson, 1969; Änggård and Samuelsson, 1970) or by incubation with a luciferase from a photobacterium (*Bacterium fischeri*) and measurement of the resultant photoflash. These enzymatic analyses are specific for prostaglandins but not entirely satisfactory for measurement of prostaglandins in biological samples because of insufficient sensitivity and a variable background response (Änggård, 1971).

3. Comparison of Techniques

There are three basic procedures which have sufficient sensitivity and specificity for analysis of prostaglandins in blood—namely, bioassay, radioimmunoassay and GLC-MS. Other techniques such as viroimmunoassay and radio receptor assay also offer high sensitivity but as yet few investigators have applied these to analysis of prostaglandins; GLC-ECD may also enjoy high sensitivity but there are difficulties associated with the analysis (see Section C.1.b.4).

Bioassay can detect labile, biologically active compounds but it suffers from lack of high specificity and cannot be used to measure metabolites since these compounds have only weak biological activity.

Radioimmunoassay is perhaps the most widely used procedure since it satisfies the requirements of high sensitivity and good specificity. However, the reliability of RIA is often poor when they are applied directly to biological material. Granström (1978) noted that RIA methods usually fulfill the common criteria of reliability fairly well and that no obvious sources of error seem to exist which could explain the sometimes unphysiologically high prostaglandin levels which are sometimes obtained (see Section D.1; Table 7) and the difference between data obtained by RIA and GLC-MS (see Samuelsson, 1973b). RIA are specific and cross-reactions with related prostaglandins can probably only account for a negligible part of the discrepancies. Granström (1978) concluded that the most likely explanation for the inaccurate data is the common misinterpretation of RIA results; RIA only measure the inhibition of binding of labelled antigen to antibody, and this inhibition can be caused not only by antigen in the sample but by a multitude of completely unrelated factors such as variations in pH, ionic strength, protein concentration, presence of low molecular weight impurities etc. Non-immunological inhibition of binding will be interpreted as being caused by the presence of antigen (prostaglandin) in the sample. It is, therefore, essential to include several quality control samples (i.e. blanks and standards) in every RIA and these data must be examined critically. It is recommended that blanks are identical with samples but obtained after indomethacin treatment (in the presence of sufficient cyclo-oxygenase inhibitor, the concentrations of prostaglandins should decline to almost zero); standards should be added to the "blanks" and processed as for the normal samples. Granström (1978) suggested that the analysis of single samples should be avoided and instead changes in prostaglandin levels in a series of samples should be measured. Although this approach can be included in some experimental designs it would obviously be desirable in a clinical situation, for example, to be able to measure the absolute concentration in a single sample.

These cautionary comments about RIA should not preclude its general acceptance as an analytical procedure since it has distinct advantages over both bioassay and GLC-MS, namely its high sensitivity and specificity, its applicability to most prostaglandins and metabolites, its simplicity enabling the processing of many samples in each assay and its relatively low running costs. A comparison of the relative merits of RIA, bioassay and GLC-MS was reported by Lands, Hammarström and Parker (1976) (see Fig. 14) based on data from several laboratories. Provided that adequate safeguards (e.g. purification of samples; proper quality controls) are undertaken, RIA can be recommended for routine prostaglandin analyses.

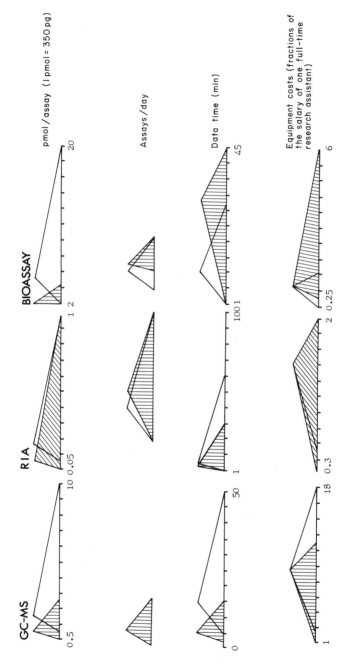

Fig. 14. Comparison of the sensitivity, analysis time and cost for GLC-MS, RIA and bioassays. The corners of the triangles indicate the lower, middle and upper quartiles of response for the whole group of participants in the study (open triangles) or for the subset who were experienced with the method (hatched triangles). (From Lands, Hammarström and Parker, 1976. Reproduced with permission.)

GLC-MS is a highly specific technique with sufficient sensitivity to enable measurement of prostaglandin in blood (although large volumes of blood may be required). However, the necessary purification and derivatisation steps are very time consuming and the equipment is expensive (see Fig. 14). The technique cannot be highly recommended for routine assays but it should be used, whenever possible, to confirm data obtained by bioassay and RIA. It also has one particular application, which is confirmation of structure or elucidation of unknown compounds.

D. PROSTAGLANDIN LEVELS

1. Prostaglandin Levels in Healthy Subjects

It must be apparent from the foregoing sections that determinations of prostaglandin levels in tissues are extremely difficult. Sample collection and storage as well as the actual assay method itself can greatly influence the result. This is particularly true for estimations of prostaglandins in blood and it is not surprising, therefore, that investigators using different techniques and conditions have reported varied levels for circulating prostaglandins. Throughout this chapter "preferred methods" have been emphasised and the data discussed in the following sections are mainly derived by such assays. However, techniques which are not completely reliable but which provide useful indications will not be ignored.

Studies on the kinetics of PGE_2 and $PGF_{2\alpha}$ metabolism (Hamberg and Samuelsson, 1971; Granström, 1972) and on the total daily production rate of the prostaglandins (Samuelsson, 1973a; Hamberg, 1972, 1973) in human subjects indicated that circulating levels of $PGF_{2\alpha}$ should be about 5·6 pmol/l (2 pg/ml) and that the level of PGE_2 should be slightly higher (Samuelsson, 1973a). However, only a few of the many investigators have reported similar levels. GLC-MS assays developed at the Karolinska Institutet, confirmed that the endogenous level of $PGF_{2\alpha}$ in blood was lower than 423 pmol/l (150 pg/ml) and of PGE_2 lower than 284 pmol/l (100 pg/ml) (Gréen et al., 1973). Data from several laboratories (by no means exhaustive) utilising RIA are summarised in Table 7. The procedure described by Dray et al. (1975) appears to be the most reliable. The latter authors measured the prostglandin content in 5–10 ml plasma by a sensitive RIA after extraction and purification by silicic acid chromatography. The circulating venous levels of PGF_α ($PGF_{2\alpha}$ and $PGF_{1\alpha}$) and PGE_2 in normal men were slightly higher than the values in normal women (Table 8). There was no significant difference in the concentration of PGF_α during the follicular (22·6 ± 6·5 pmol/l; 8·0 ± 2·3 pg/ml) and the luteal phase (19·7 ± 3·9 pmol/l; 7·0 ± 1·4 pg/ml) of the menstrual cycle. Also, there was no significant diurnal or daily variation

Table 7

Normal concentrations of $PGF_{2\alpha}$ and PGE_2 in venous serum or plasma reported by different investigators (1 pg/ml = 2·82 pmol/l).

Serum or plasma	Volume (ml)	Purification	Sex	Concentrations of Prostaglandin (pg/ml)		References
				$PGF_{2\alpha}$	PGE_2	
Serum	5	Extraction	F	300–1150 (M. = 700 ± 37)		Brummer (1972)
Plasma	1	Extraction and silicic acid chromatography	F	200–300		Caldwell et al. (1971)
Plasma	0·1	Direct RIA	F	130 ± 60		Cornette et al. (1971)
Plasma	5–10	Extraction and silicic acid chromatography	M	9·3 ± 3·5	4·5 ± 1·0	Dray and Charbonnel (1973), Dray et al. (1975)
			F	6·0 ± 2·3	4·5 ± 1·0	
Serum	3	Extraction and dialysis	M	790 } range 0–2000		Drewes (1974)
			F	740		
Serum	5	Extraction and dialysis	M	250–1000		Gutierrez-Cernosek et al. (1972)
			F	10–740		
Plasma	1	Extraction and silicic acid chromatography	M	84 ± 15	378 ± 13	Jaffe et al. (1973)
			F	154 ± 35	316 ± 36	Jubiz et al. (1972)
Plasma	0·05	Direct RIA	M	} 250–1300		
			F			
Serum	0·1	Direct RIA	F	50–2000		Kirton et al. (1972)
Plasma	1	Extraction and silicic acid chromatography	M	} 40–130		Van Orden and Farley (1973)
			F			
Plasma	1	Extraction and silicic acid chromatography	M		$E_1 + E_2$: 60–102	Van Orden et al. (1977)

Table 8

Plasma concentrations of prostaglandins and metabolites.

	Men		Women		References
	pmol/l	pg/ml	pmol/l	pg/ml	
PGF_α ($PGF_{2\alpha}$ + $PGF_{1\alpha}$)	34 ± 8·2 (4·2–82)	12·0 ± 2·9 (1·5–29)	20·6 ± 3·7 (6·8–56)	7·3 ± 1·3 (2·4–20)	Dray et al. (1975)
PGE_2	12·8 ± 2·8 (8·5–34)	4·5 ± 1·0 (3–12)	13 ± 2·8 (8·5–34)	4·5 ± 1·0 (3–12)	
PGA	4844	1620	4156	1390	Zusman et al. (1972, 1973)
	3062	1024	2655	888	Jaffe et al. (1973)
13,14-Dihydro-15-keto-$PGF_{2\alpha}$	133 ± 82	47 ± 29	68 ± 20	24 ± 7	Gréen and Samuelson (1974)
13,14-Dihydro-15-keto-PGE_2	80 ± 40	28 ± 14	60 ± 40	21 ± 14	

of PGF_α and PGE_1 in male subjects. Initially, Dray et al. (1975) detected high levels of PGE_1 in men and women (25–248 pmol/l: 9–88 pg/ml)). However, these authors reported in a footnote to their paper that with the aid of a higher affinity anti-PGE_1 serum, the plasma concentration of PGE_1 was in fact very low (7·3 $\pm$ 5·4 pmol/l; 2·6 $\pm$ 1·9 pg/ml). The discrepancy was considered to be attributable to the low affinity and poor specificity of the first antiserum which presumably measured other related substances. This variation highlights the problems of RIA; the assays are sensitive but do not necessarily give absolute data.

Zusman et al. (1972, 1973) and Jaffe et al. (1973) have reported levels of PGA by RIA which are higher than PGE or PGF_α; Table 8. Zusman et al. (1972, 1973) demonstrated that indomethacin, a potent inhibitor of cyclo-oxygenase activity (see Section A.4) reduced the circulating concentration of PGA_2 by more than 80 %. However, the elegant GLC-MS experiments by Frölich and colleagues (Frölich, Sweetman, Carr, Hollifield and Oates, 1975a, b; Frölich, Williams, Sweetman, Smigel, Carr, Hollifield, Fleisher, Nies, Frisk-Holmberg and Oates, 1976) have clearly demonstrated that PGA_2 is not present in circulating blood but may be produced by dehydration of PGE during sample purification. Gréen and Steffenrud (1976) confirmed that the concentration of PGA_2 in plasma was less than 29·9 pmol/l (10 pg/ml) by GLC-MS. Thus, the results of GLC-MS analysis contradict the theory (Lee, 1972; Zusman et al., 1972) that PGA_2 functions as a circulating hormone.

The question of whether there is a circadian rhythm in the output of prostaglandins is debatable. Jubiz et al. (1972a) observed striking circadian variations of $PGF_{2\alpha}$ titres with highest levels between midnight and 4 a.m. These results were partially confirmed by Jaffe et al. (1973) who demonstrated in two patients that PGE levels varied considerably during the day but were higher in the morning than in the late afternoon (samples were taken at 9.00 a.m., 11.00 a.m., 2.00 p.m. and 5.00 p.m.). However, Dray et al. (1975) found that in three male subjects plasma levels of PGF_α and PGE_1 were not significantly different at 10 a.m. and 5.00 p.m. on four consecutive days.

It has been proposed that PGF may cause the degeneration of the corpus luteum (i.e. that it is the luteolytic agent) (Pharris, 1970; Kirton, 1975) and therefore several studies have been undertaken to establish whether or not there is a variation in the levels of prostaglandins during the menstrual cycle. A preliminary study (Kirton et al., 1972) did not demonstrate variation of PGF during the cycle and this was later confirmed more reliably by Dray et al. (1975). But, Jubiz et al. (1972a) stated that the highest levels of PGF were found at mid-cycle; these authors also reported that levels in women on oral contraceptives were low. Harrison, Walker, Youssefnejadian and Craft (1975) analysed $PGF_{2\alpha}$ in unextracted plasma and showed that the prostaglandin reached a peak on day 13 of the menstrual cycle. However, this study also revealed that $PGF_{2\alpha}$ levels were generally higher in women receiving oral contraceptives, although there was a large variation between women and the levels fluctuated considerably during each cycle. In sheep, it has been clearly demonstrated that the concentration of PGF in utero–ovarian veins rises at oestrus and this is followed by a decline in progesterone secretion, thus implying that PGF has a luteolytic role (McCracken, Barcikowski, Carlson, Gréen and Samuelsson, 1973; Barcikowski, Carlson, Wilson and McCracken, 1974). The data in humans are probably confused by the necessity of sampling peripheral blood with all its associated complications.

There is a more consistent consensus that prostaglandin levels rise during pregnancy, especially during labour. Using bioassay after extraction and chromatography of blood samples, Karim (1968) reported that $PGF_{2\alpha}$ was present in maternal venous blood immediately before, and during, uterine contractions, but $PGF_{2\alpha}$ could not be detected in the blood of non-pregnant women. Karim (1968) found wide variations between patients but the mean concentration of $PGF_{2\alpha}$ in samples taken in the minute preceding uterine contractions (14·5 nmol/l; 5·15 ng/ml) was almost as high as during contraction (17·8 nmol/l; 6·3 ng/ml). In the minute after contraction the $PGF_{2\alpha}$ concentration fell (M. 3·2 nmol/l; 1·15 ng/ml) and could not be detected in the second minute after contraction in eight out of 10 patients. These observations led Karim (1968) to hypothesise that the $PGF_{2\alpha}$ is not released into peripheral blood as a result of contraction but that it probably initiates uterine activity. Prostaglandins are indeed potent stimulators of uterine motility and have been widely used to induce labour and abortion (see Thiery and Amy, 1975; Karim and Amy, 1975).

A preliminary study using RIA by Caldwell et al. (1971) reported levels of $PGF_{2\alpha}$ during the first trimester to be 1692–2538 pmol/l (600–900 pg/ml) (cf. 584–846 pmol/l (200–300 pg/ml) during the luteal phase of the menstrual cycle) and this level rose in labour to 3·4–8·5 nmol/l (1·2–3·0 ng/ml) during the peak of uterine contraction and to 8·5–14·1 nmol/l (3·0–5·0 ng/ml) at delivery. Brummer (1972) demonstrated that $PGF_{2\alpha}$ levels were not significantly higher in pregnant women until the onset of labour. During labour, Brummer (1972) reported that the increase of $PGF_{2\alpha}$ in blood correlated with cervical dilatation.

One exception to the general finding that PGF is increased in late pregnancy and labour was the report by Gutierrez-Cernosek et al. (1972b). These authors found that the concentration of $PGF_{2\alpha}$ in sera reached a peak during the second trimester (17–24 weeks) and declined thereafter. Brummer (1973) subsequently demonstrated that the lowest values of PGF were, in fact, found at this period of pregnancy.

Sharma et al. (1973) attempted to repeat the earlier work of Karim (1968) using RIA instead of bioassay. The simpler, more specific and sensitive RIA facilitated a more detailed study of patients in labour. Sharma et al. (1973) reported that concentrations of $PGF_{2\alpha}$ in plasma from an antecubital vein usually reached a peak in samples obtained 15–45 sec after the peak of uterine contraction. This implied that the elevation of PGF levels was the result, rather than the cause of uterine contractions. Poyser, Horton, Thompson and Los (1971) have demonstrated that stretching uterine muscle releases prostaglandins.

Other studies, in which $PGF_{2\alpha}$ was measured in unextracted plasma by RIA (Johnson, Manning, Hennam, Newton and Collins, 1975) or by RIA after extraction and dialysis of serum (Zuckerman, Reiss, Atad, Lampert, Ben Ezra and Sklan, 1977) revealed no definite correlation between contraction of the uterus and the level of $PGF_{2\alpha}$ in peripheral blood. Zuckerman et al. (1977) demonstrated that the serum level of $PGF_{2\alpha}$ during labour was markedly lowered by administration of indomethacin. Zuckerman, Reiss and Rubinstein (1974) had previously reported that administration of indomethacin could prevent premature labour and therefore it was hypothesised that $PGF_{2\alpha}$ was important in the initiation of labour.

Analysis of amniotic fluid from patients during mid-trimester, third trimester and during labour consistently revealed that $PGF_{2\alpha}$ rises significantly from about 36 weeks of pregnancy (Karim and Devlin, 1967; Salmon and Amy, 1973; Keirse, Flint and Turnbull, 1974; Hibbard, Sharma, Fitzpatrick and Hamlett, 1974; Johnson et al., 1975; Keirse, Mitchell and Turnbull, 1977; Kinoshita, Satoh and Sakamoto, 1977). The level during labour was closely correlated to cervical dilatation (Salmon and Amy, 1973). $PGF_{2\alpha}$ levels in amniotic fluid from patients in premature labour (28–37 weeks) were not significantly different from normal labour (Tambyraja, Salmon, Karim and Ratnam, 1977b) whilst low levels were detected in post-mature patients (more than 40 weeks) who were not in labour (Tambyraja, Karim, Salmon and Ratnam, 1977a).

The data discussed above clearly illustrate the discrepancies in levels of prostaglandins reported by different investigators. The reasons for these differences have been considered previously (see Sections B.1 and B.2). It has been proposed that the measurement of the plasma or urinary metabolites of prostaglandins may afford more reliable data. Using GLC-MS assays Gréen and Samuelsson (1974) found the endogenous peripheral plasma levels of 13,14-dihydro-15-keto-$PGF_{2\alpha}$ and 13,14-dihydro-15-keto-PGE_2 shown in Table 8. Hubbard and Watson (1976) have reported comparable data. These levels agree well with the levels calculated from rates of metabolism and urinary excretion data (Samuelsson, 1973a). The level of 13,14-dihydro-15-keto-$PGF_{2\alpha}$ increased from 87 ± 51 pmol/l (31 ± 18 pg/ml) 6 weeks before onset of labour to 753–2656 pmol/l (267–942 pg/ml) at delivery (Gréen et al., 1974a). This elevation correlated with cervical dilatation and there was an immediate sharp fall after delivery (Gréen et al., 1974a).

The plasma metabolites of $PGF_{2\alpha}$ and PGE_2 have also been measured by RIA. An early RIA for 13,14-dihydro-15-keto-$PGF_{2\alpha}$ produced values of 5·6–28·2 nmol/l (2–10 ng/ml) in extracted and dialysed human sera (Levine and Gutierrez-Cernosek, 1973) but subsequent investigations have shown that these values were grossly high. These authors recorded much lower levels (ca 1410 pmol/l (500 pg/ml)) of 15-keto-$PGF_{2\alpha}$ in human sera. Granström and Samuelsson (1972a) evaluated a RIA for 13,14-dihydro-15-keto-$PGF_{2\alpha}$ by comparing data obtained with this assay with that obtained by GLC-MS; there was excellent agreement between the two sets of data for normal subjects 141–338 pmol/l (50–120 pg/ml). Keirse et al. (1977) reported that 13,14-dihydro-15-keto-$PGF_{2\alpha}$ was elevated in amniotic fluid during labour.

Sors et al. (1977) reported a RIA for 13,14-dihydro-15-keto-$PGF_{2\alpha}$ using iodinated, rather than tritium labelled tracers and this permitted more sensitive determinations. These authors detected levels of 71 ± 17 pmol/l (25 ± 6 pg/ml) and 73 ± 17 pmol/l (26 ± 6 pg/ml) in normal men and women, respectively.

^3H-13,14-dihydro-15-keto-PGE_2 is unstable (Mitchell, Sors and Flint, 1977) thus limiting the development of a specific RIA for this metabolite. So far, only Powles, Coombes, Munro Neville, Ford, Gazet and Levine (1977) have published a RIA for 13,14-dihydro-15-keto-PGE_2 in blood; the mean concentration in plasma of healthy volunteers was 80 pmol/l (28 pg/ml) which is in good agreement with data from GLC-MS assays (Gréen and Samuelsson, 1974; Hubbard and Watson, 1976).

The main urinary metabolites of $PGF_{2\alpha}$ and $PGF_{1\alpha}$ (PGF_α-MUM) and PGE_2 and PGE_1 (PGE-MUM) in humans have been estimated by GLC-MS (Hamberg, 1972, 1973). The amounts of PGF_α-MUM excreted in 24-hr samples of urine were higher than the amounts of PGE-MUM (Table 9). Decreases in excretion of PGE-MUM of 77–98% were observed after administration of indomethacin (200 mg/day) or aspirin (3 g/day) Hamberg, 1972). Similar data for excretion of PGE-MUM were obtained by Seyberth, Sweetman, Frölich and Oates (1976); these authors also reported that values in younger males (3–6 years) were much lower (3–12 nmol; 1–4 µg) than in adults. Analysis of samples of urine during pregnancy revealed a continuous increase in the excretion of PGF_α-MUM to 2–5 times normal values just before the onset of labour; an additional abrupt increase occurs on the day of parturition (Hamberg, 1974). However, these studies did not help elucidate a key physiological question of whether prostaglandins are released as a cause or a consequence of uterine contractions.

Several RIA for PGF_α-MUM have been described (Ohki et al., 1974,

Table 9

Excretion of main urinary metabolites of prostaglandins.

	Men		Women		Reference
	nmol/d	µg/d	nmol/d	µg/d	
PGF_{α} – MUM ($PGF_{2\alpha}$ – MUM + $PGF_{1\alpha}$ – MUM)	32·7–177	10·8–59	23·0–41·2	7·6–13·6	Hamberg (1972, 1973)
PGE – MUM (PGE_2-MUM + PGE_1 – MUM)	19·6–141	6·5–46·7	7·5–16·0	2·5– 5·3	

1975, 1976; Cornette *et al.,* 1975; Granström and Kindahl, 1976; Kitamura, Ishihara and Kosaka, 1977) and using these assays urinary excretion of PGF_α-MUM in human subjects is comparable to data obtained by GLC-MS (i.e. daily excretion 45–197 nmol (15–65 µg) in males and 15–91 nmol (5–30 µg) in females). Also, Granström and Kindahl (1976) confirmed the rise in excretion of PGF_α-MUM during pregnancy. Although data were not obtained during a complete menstrual cycle in humans, Granström and Kindahl (1976) observed definite peaks of excretion of PGF_α-MUM during the oestrus cycle of guinea-pigs. The excretion was maximal during the last two days of the cycle and the first day of the next cycle which coincided with luteolysis. As expected, the excretion of PGF_α-MUM was decreased by administration of aspirin, indomethacin and some other non-steroidal anti-inflammatory drugs (Ohki *et al.,* 1975; Kitamura *et al.,* 1977). Ohki *et al.* (1974) originally developed the RIA based on an antiserum directed against the δ-lactone form of PGF_α-MUM but later found that the assay was more reliable if the antiserum was raised against the dioic acid (Ohki *et al.,* 1976). Using both antisera, Ohki *et al.* (1976) postulated that PGF_α-MUM exists in the urine mostly in the dioic acid form.

Frölich and colleagues (Frölich, Sweetman, Carr, Splawinski, Watson, Änggård and Oates, 1973; Sweetman, Watson, Carr, Oates and Frölich, 1973; Frölich, Wilson, Sweetman, Smigel, Nies, Carr, Watson and Oates, 1975) have also demonstrated that unmetabolised PGE_2 and $PGF_{2\alpha}$ are present in female human urine. Since prostaglandins are not recovered unchanged in urine after i.v. infusion (Granström, 1967; Granström and Samuelsson, 1969), Frölich and colleagues proposed that prostaglandins were synthesised in the kidney and these may diffuse into the tubules and thus be excreted in the urine. Measurement of unchanged prostaglandins may therefore be a useful tool to delineate renal prostaglandin physiology and pathology.

7α-11α-Dihydroxy-5-keto-tetranorprost-9-enoic acid (tetranor-PGE_1) has also been quantitatively measured in human urine but the levels were less than 1680 pmol/24 hr (500 ng/24 hr) (Oates, Sweetman, Gréen and Samuelsson, 1976).

Nugteren (1975a) converted all 16 carbon prostaglandin urinary meta-bolites to dimethyl tetranorprostanedioate which was determined by GLC; the total excretion of these metabolites in healthy subjects was 1000 ± 330 nmol (300 ± 100 µg) per 24 hr. Since this quantity is substantially higher than can be explained by urinary excretion of PGF-MUM and PGE-MUM and other minor metabolites which have been measured, Nugteren (1975a) concluded that other tetranorprostanedioic acid derivatives are present in human urine. These additional components could be metabolites of pro-stacyclin, 6-keto-$PGF_{1\alpha}$ or PGD_2 or some hitherto unrecognised product of the cyclo-oxygenase.

L

2. Prostaglandin Levels in Disease

Diseases associated with underproduction of "true" hormones can easily be investigated experimentally by removal of the particular endocrine gland, but prostaglandins can be synthesised in all tissues of the body and consequently the classical extirpation experiments of endocrinology are impossible. Nor is it easy to prove relationships between increased production of prostaglandins and symptoms of disease. The problem is not only one of analysis; prostaglandins are formed during the inflammatory response and tissue damage which accompany many pathological conditions, making it difficult to state with confidence whether prostaglandins are a causative factor in a particular disease or whether they derive from the secondary inflammatory reaction. For a comprehensive review of the role of the "classical" prostaglandins in inflammation, readers are referred to Ferreira and Vane (1974a, b) and Vane (1976). More recently, Chang, Murota, Matsuo and Tsurufuji (1976) and Chang and Murota (1978) have demonstrated that TXB_2 and 6-keto-$PGF_{1\alpha}$ were the main products of arachidonate metabolism in carrageenin-induced granuloma. Trang, Granström and Lövgren (1977) detected TXB_2 as well as the "classical" prostaglandins (PGE_2 and $PGF_{2\alpha}$) in joint fluid in rheumatoid arthritis. However, the thromboxane pathway represented only a minor component of arachidonate oxidation in rheumatoid joint inflammation. Treatment with indomethacin reduced the levels of TXB_2, PGE_2 and $PGF_{2\alpha}$ in the joint fluid but symptoms of arthritis often persisted.

Several investigators have attempted to deduce the role of prostaglandins in disease by observing the effects of administration of inhibitors of prostaglandin synthesis. Undoubtedly a positive effect would be a strong argument for the involvement of prostaglandins but it is not a substitute for comparison of concentrations of prostaglandins in the normal and pathological states. Indeed, results from using inhibitors of prostaglandin synthesis could be misleading since the disease state could conceivably be due to an altered ratio of one prostaglandin to another (e.g. $PGF_{2\alpha}$ to PGE_2; PGI_2 to TXB_2) and therefore, indomethacin or aspirin will not benefit the condition. Also, although these compounds are relatively specific inhibitors of cyclooxygenase activity it most certainly cannot be assumed that any response observed after their administration is solely due to decreased production of prostaglandin (e.g. at high doses, indomethacin also blocks prostaglandin metabolism; Pace-Asciak and Cole, 1975).

Prostaglandins have been implicated in the pathogenesis of several tumours (see Stein-Werblowsky, 1974; Karim and Rao, 1976; Easty and Easty, 1976; Jaffe and Santoro, 1977). Several types of cancer (breast, renal, oesophageal, parotid, lung and cervical) are often accompanied by hypercalcaemia.

Since prostaglandins of the E series are known to cause bone resorption it has been proposed that the hypercalcaemia associated with cancer could be due to overproduction of PGE. Bennett, McDonald, Simpson and Stamford (1975), Bennett, Charlier, McDonald, Simpson and Stamford (1976) and Bennett, Charlier, McDonald, Simpson, Stamford and Zebro (1977) have shown that more "prostaglandin-like" material can be synthesised in tissue from malignant breast tumours compared with tissue from benign tumours or normal tissue. These authors reported that the highest prostaglandin activity was correlated with the highest frequency of bone metastases. Elevated plasma levels of PGE have been detected in patients suffering from cancer with accompanying hypercalcaemia (Robertson, Baylink, Marini and Adkinson, 1975; Robertson, Baylink, Metz and Cummings, 1976; Demers, Allegra, Harvey, Lipton, Luderer, Mortel and Brenner, 1977). Powles et al. (1977) reported that levels of 13,14-dihydro-15-keto-PGE$_2$ measured by RIA, were higher than normal in the serum of patients with breast cancer. The mean values of this prostaglandin metabolite in healthy controls was 79 ± 28 pmol/l (28 ± 10 pg/ml) whilst in patients with breast cancer it was 176 ± 51 pmol/l (62 ± 18 pg/ml). Higher levels were detected in patients with malignant tumours localised in the breast and even higher concentrations were found in patients with overt metastatic disease. The concentration in patients with bone metastases were the same as in patients with metastases at other sites, suggesting that excessive prostaglandin synthesis is not a special feature of overt osteolytic metastases. Brereton, Halushka, Alexander, Mason, Keiser and DeVita (1974) and Seyberth, Morgan, Sweetman and Oates (1975) also demonstrated that excretion of PGE-MUM was elevated in patients with tumours and associated hypercalcaemia, and this elevation correlated with the severity of the cancer. Administration of indomethacin or aspirin decreased the excretion of PGE-MUM and this correlated with a reduced calcium value. However, Bockman, Myers, Kempin and Bajorunas (1977) were unable to detect PGE in the plasma of many cancer patients and that changes in serum PGE and calcium were not correlated. Benvenisti and Goldberg (1975) reported the case of a patient with squamous-cell carcinoma of the lung who had both a high parathyroid hormone level and high levels of "prostaglandin-like" material in liver metastases. The serum calcium level was not modified by treatment with indomethacin and it was, therefore, concluded that the elevated serum calcium in this patient was unrelated to the high concentrations of prostaglandins but due to the increased parathyroid hormone secretion.

Some symptoms of other cancers have been correlated with elevated prostaglandin levels. For example, Williams, Karim and Sandler (1968) and Sandler, Williams and Karim (1969) suggested that the diarrhoea associated with medullary carcinoma of the thyroid was due to elevated prostaglandin secretion. Jaffe *et al.* (1973) also reported elevated PGE plasma concentrations in medullary carcinoma of the thyroid and associated malignancies. Other authors failed to detect a consistent increase of serum $PGF_{2\alpha}$ or 13,14-dihydro-15-keto-$PGF_{2\alpha}$ in patients with carcinoid symptoms (Feldman, Plonk and Cornette, 1974). Mortel, Allegra, Demers, Harvey, Trantlein, Nahhas, White, Gillin and Lipton (1977) found that PGE levels were not increased in the local environment of gynaecological tumours and therefore concluded that PGE is unlikely to be playing a significant role in modifying host–tumour interaction.

Gould (1976) reported the virtual absence of prostaglandin-like substances in faeces from normal subjects but higher levels were detected in stools from patients with active ulcerative colitis. Later, a more reliable GLC-MS assay for PGF_{α}-MUM showed that urinary excretion of the metabolite was slightly raised in patients with ulcerative colitis (Gould, Brash and Conolly, 1977). These findings suggest that prostaglandins may cause the diarrhoea which is a characteristic of this disease but it remains to be proven whether the prostaglandins are active mediators of the inflammation or merely an epiphenomenc.

Hinsdale, Engle and Wilson (1974) reported that patients with peptic ulcer had lower concentrations of PGE in plasma and gastric juice than in normal subjects. These data suggest that PGE may play a role in pathogenesis of peptic ulcer.

Low concentrations of prostaglandins in ser inal fluid are associated with infertility (Bygdeman, 1969; Bygdeman, Fredricsson, Svanborg and Samuelsson, 1970; Collier, Flower and Stanton, 1975). Brummer and Gillespie (1972) also observed a difference between mean seminal fluid levels of prostaglandins in fertile and infertile men but these authors also noted that low levels of prostaglandins were sometimes detected in men of proven fertility. Perry and Desiderio (1977) determined PGE_1, PGE_2, 19-hydroxy-PGE_1 and 19-hydroxy-PGE_2 in seminal fluid by GLC-MS and found that each prostaglandin was lower than normal in azospermic and oligospermic conditions.

Early studies using bioassay, suggested that prostaglandins may be involved in the pathogenesis of dysmenorrhoea (Pickles, Hall, Best and Smith, 1965). Recently, Lundström, Wiqvist and Gréen (1976) have found that the concentration of 13,14-dihydro-15-keto-$PGF_{2\alpha}$ in plasma is high in women with dysmenorrhoea and is lowered by indomethacin treatment.

Gréen, Hedqvist and Svanborg (1974b) demonstrated that in five patients with type-I allergic asthma, provocation of an attack by inhalation of the specific allergen was associated with a significant increase in plasma levels of 13,14-dihydro-15-keto-$PGF_{2\alpha}$. The rise in the concentration of the metabolite was correlated with the severity of the attack. Increased synthesis of $PGF_{2\alpha}$ in asthmatic attacks was also indicated from the finding that urinary excretion of PGF_{α}-MUM was elevated during an attack (Svanborg, Hamberg and Hedqvist, 1973). However, Smith (1975) reported a clinical trial of the effects of indomethacin in asthma which failed to show objective evidence of improvement in the six patients studied. Smith (1975) concluded that this was evidence against the hypothesis that $PGF_{2\alpha}$ is a chemical mediator in the pathogenesis of asthma. However, as Green et al. (1974b) pointed out, although indomethacin markedly reduces the total body production of of $PGF_{2\alpha}$, a remaining limited synthesis of $PGF_{2\alpha}$ in the lungs may still be sufficient to cause bronchoconstriction in patients who hyperreact to this prostaglandin. Mathé, Hedqvist, Holmgren and Svanborg (1973), demonstrated that asthmatics were about 8000 times more sensitive to inhalation $PGF_{2\alpha}$ than healthy subjects. Also, if the $PGF_{2\alpha}/PGE_2$ ratio is important ($PGF_{2\alpha}$ causes bronchoconstriction whereas PGE_2 usually relaxes the muscle), then indomethacin will not modify the response since the concentrations of both prostaglandins will be similarly reduced. But since mechanical manipulation of bronchial tissue also releases prostaglandins (Änggård, 1965) it is not entirely clear whether prostaglandins are involved in the pathogenesis of asthma at a primary level or whether they are released as a result of bronchial constriction modulated by other processes. Recently, Allegra, Trantlein, Demers, Field and Gillin (1976) demonstrated a statistically significant difference in baseline plasma PGE levels between asthmatics (1505 ± 230 pmol/l; 432 ± 81 pg/ml) and control subjects (253 ± 26 pmol/l; 89 ± 9 pg/ml). It was speculated that this increase in peripheral PGE may maintain the asthmatic in a compensated state by persistent brochodilation.

Abnormal prostaglandin concentrations are associated with several skin disorders. Greaves and colleagues (Greaves and Søndergaard, 1970; Greaves, Søndergaard and McDonald-Gibson, 1971) have studied various inflammatory responses in the skin. Forström, Haapalahti and Suramo (1976), demonstrated that PGE was elevated in blistering skin diseases and administration of prednisolone appeared to reduce the prostaglandin synthesis. Hammarström, Hamberg, Samuelsson, Duell, Stawiski and Voorhees (1975) determined the concentrations of free arachidonic acid, HETE, PGE_2 and $PGF_{2\alpha}$ in involved and uninvolved epidermis of psoriasis. The concentration of each compound was elevated in the involved tissue but the largest increases were noted for arachidonic acid and HETE.

The prostaglandins and thromboxanes may exert important control over peripheral vascular resistance and blood pressure via their reactions as vasodilators, vasoconstrictors and activators or inhibitors of the renin–angiotensin system of the kidney. Dunn and Hood (1977) have reviewed the controversial subject of the involvement of prostaglandins in hypotension and concluded that their role would only be clarified when more reliable assays were employed. At present there are no data available on the blood levels of PGI_2 and TXA_2 or their stable breakdown products (6-keto-$PGF_{1\alpha}$ and TXB_2, respectively) in thrombo-embolic disorders. However, it has been speculated that synthesis of PGI_2 may be decreased in these disorders (e.g. atherosclerosis) which leads to clumping of platelets on the affected vascular walls.

Bartter, Gill, Frölich, Bowden, Hollifield, Radfar, Keiser, Oates, Seyberth and Taylor (1976) demonstrated that urinary excretion of PGE_2 was increased whilst excretion of $PGF_{2\alpha}$ was normal in Bartter's syndrome. These authors concluded that these results suggest that over-production of PGE by kidneys is a cardinal feature, but not necessarily the primary one, in the pathogenesis of this syndrome. However, Dray (1978) failed to detect a difference in urinary output of PGE_2 or $PGF_{2\alpha}$ in post-pubertal patients with Bartter's syndrome compared with age-matched normal individuals. In contrast, Dray (1978) demonstrated that the urinary excretion rates of PGE_2 and $PGF_{2\alpha}$ were markedly increased in pre-pubertal patients with Bartter's syndrome. The involvement of prostaglandins in other kidney diseases has recently been reviewed by Dunn and Hood (1977).

E. CONCLUDING REMARKS

The eminent French bacteriologist Charles Nicolle once observed—"Error is all around us and creeps in at the least opportunity. Every method is imperfect." His remarks apply with more than their usual force to the task of analysing and quantitating blood-borne prostaglandins. Throughout this chapter we have tried to stress the best approaches to prostaglandin analysis and to indicate the points at which, as Nicolle says, "Error . . . creeps in".

There is no single method currently available which satisfies all the criteria of a satisfactory prostaglandin assay and we must look to the future for an ideal technique. One highly desirable innovation would be the development of a method suitable for measuring all prostanoic acid metabolites in one step—a technique akin to that described by Nugteren (see Section D.1). Although this procedure would not permit the analysis of individual prostaglandins, it would greatly simplify many of the problems associated with the measurement of total prostaglandin levels in blood and urine. Thus, this technique would be useful for monitoring total cyclo-oxygenase activity (e.g. to test the effects of potential anti-inflammatory drugs) but it would not be a substitute for methods which measure individual prostaglandins when study of a particular pathway of prostaglandin endoperoxide metabolism is desirable (e.g. study of the significance of prostaglandins in thromboembolic disorders).

To conclude on a cautionary note: it is by no means certain that all the metabolic transformations of the prostaglandins have been described and it would therefore be prudent to keep abreast of the developments in this field.

F. APPARATUS AND
DIRECTOR OF MANUFACTURERS

The companies listed below have supplied the authors with certain items of equipment and chemicals which have proved to be highly satisfactory for analysis of prostaglandins.

Authentic prostaglandins

Many investigators have obtained prostaglandins through the generosity of The Upjohn Co., Kalamazoo, MI, USA. Some prostaglandins are now commercially available (e.g. from Cambrian Chemical Co., Suffolk House, George Street, Croydon, England).

Radioactive prostaglandins

Several prostaglandins and their metabolites are available labelled with ^{14}C or ^{3}H from either The Radiochemical Centre, Amersham, Buckinghamshire, England or New England Nuclear, 549 Albany Street, Boston, MA, USA. Both companies produce some multi-tritiated prostaglandins of high specific activity (> 100 Ci/mmol) which are ideal for radioimmunoassay.

Silicic acid

Unisil activated silicic acid (100–200 mesh from Clarkson Chemical Co. Inc., Williamsport, PA, USA).

TLC plates

Uniplate TLC plates (250 μm, silica gel G) from Anachem, 20A North Street, Luton, Bedfordshire, England or Quantum LQD TLC plates from Pierce Chemical Co., Rockford, IL, USA.

GLC columns

A complete range of stationary phases and support materials from Applied Science Laboratories Inc., PO Box 440, State College, PA, USA.

Derivatising reagents for GLC

A complete range of silylating reagents for formation of suitable derivatives for GLC are available from Pierce Chemical Co. Inc., Rockford, IL, USA. Methoxylamine hydrochloride and other GLC reagents are also obtainable from Pierce Chemical Co.

HPLC columns

A range of HPLC equipment and columns is available from Waters Associates, Maple Street, Milford, MA, USA.

Reagents for coupling prostaglandins to protein

1-Ethyl-3(dimethylaminopropyl)carbodiimide HCl was purchased from Calbiochem, SanDiego, CA, USA. N,N'-dicyclohexyl-carbodiimide from Sigma Chemical Co., PO Box 14508, St. Louis, MS. USA, and isobutyl chloroformate from Aldrich Chemical Co., Inc., Milwaukee, WI, USA.

Emulsification syringe

A syringe which produces an emulsion ideal for injecting into rabbits in order to raise antisera was purchased from Mulsijet, PO Box 269, Elmhurst, IL, USA.

REFERENCES

Abdel-Halim, M. S., Hamberg, M., Sjöqvist, B. and Änggård, E. (1977). *Prostaglandins*, **14**, 633.
Aizawa, Y. and Yamada, K. (1974). *Jap. J. Pharmac.* **24**, 647.
Aizawa, Y. and Yamada, K. (1976). *Prostaglandins*, **11**, 43.
Albro, P. W. and Fishbein, L. (1969). *J. Chromat.* **44**, 443.
Allegra, J., Trantlein, J., Demers, L., Field, J. and Gillin, M. (1976). *J. Allergy clin. Immunol.* **58**, 546.
Andersen, N. H. (1969a). *J. Lipid Res.* **10**, 316.
Andersen, N. H. (1969b). *J. Lipid Res.* **10**, 320.
Andersen, N. H. and Leovey, E. M. K. (1974). *Prostaglandins*, **6**, 361.
Andrieu, J. M., Mamas, S. and Dray, F. (1974). *Prostaglandins*, **6**, 15.
Änggård, E. (1965). *Biochem. Pharmac.* **14**, 1507.
Änggård, E. (1971). *Ann. N.Y. Acad. Sci.* **180**, 200.
Änggård, E. and Bergkvist, H. (1970). *J. Chromat.* **48**, 542.

Änggård, E. and Jonsson, C. E. (1972). "Prostaglandins in Cellular Biology" (P. W. Ramwell and B. B. Phariss, eds), p. 269. Plenum Press, New York.

Änggård, E., Larsson, C. and Samuelsson, B. (1971). *Acta physiol. scand.* **81**, 396.

Änggård, E., Matschinsky, F. and Samuelsson, B. (1969). *Science,* **163**, 479.

Änggård, E. and Samuelsson, B. (1964). *J. biol. Chem.* **239**, 4097.

Änggård, E. and Samuelsson, B. (1965). *J. biol. Chem.* **240**, 3518.

Änggård, E. and Samuelsson, B. (1966). *Ark. Kemi.* **25**, 293.

Änggård, E. and Samuelsson, B. (1970). "Methods of Enzymatic Analysis" (U. Bergmeyer, ed.), p. 1049. Verlag Chemie, Berlin.

Attallah, A. A. and Lee, J. B. (19   ). *Prostaglandins,* **4**, 703.

Auletta, F. J., Zusman, R. M. and Caldwell, B. V. (1974). *Clin. Chem.* **20**, 1580.

Axen, U. (1974). *Prostaglandins,* **5**, 45.

Axen, U., Baczynskyj, L., Duchamp, D. J., Kirton, K. T. and Zieserl, J. F., Jr. (1973). "Advances in the Biosciences" (S. Bergström, ed.), Vol. 9, p. 109. Pergamon Press, Oxford.

Axen, U., Baczynskyj, L., Duchamp, D. J. and Zieserl, J. F., Jr. (1972). "The Prostaglandins: Clinical Applications in Human Reproduction" (E. M. Southern, ed.), p. 279. Futura Publishing Co., Mount Kisco.

Axen, U., Gréen, K., Horling, D. and Samuelsson, B. (1971). *Biochem. biophys. Res. Commun.* **45**, 519.

Barcikowski, B., Carlson, J. C., Wilson, L. and McCracken, J. A. (1974). *Endocrinology,* **95**, 1340.

Bartter, F. C., Gill, J. R., Jr., Frölich, J. C., Bowden, R. E., Hollifield, J. W., Radfar, N., Keiser, H. R., Oates, J. A., Seyberth, H. and Taylor, A. A. (1976). *Trans. Assoc. Am. Phys.* **89**, 77.

Bauminger, S., Zor, U. and Lindner, H. R. (1973). *Prostaglandins,* **4**, 313.

Bedwani, J. R. and Marley, P. B. (1974). *Br. J. Pharmac.* **50**, 459P.

Béguin, F., Bygdeman, M., Gréen, K., Samuelsson, B., Toppozada, M. and Wiqvist, N. (1972). *Acta physiol. scand.* **86**, 430.

Bennett, A. (1972). "Prostaglandins; Progress in Research" (S. M. M. Karim, ed.), p. 205. Medical and Technical Publishing, Lancaster.

Bennett, A., Charlier, E. M., McDonald, A. M., Simpson, J. S. and Stamford, I. F. (1976). *Prostaglandins,* **11**, 461.

Bennett, A., Charlier, E. M., McDonald, A. M., Simpson, J. S., Stamford, I. F. and Zebro, T. (1977). *Lancet,* i, 624.

Bennett, A., McDonald, A. M., Simpson, J. S. and Stamford, I. F. (1975). *Lancet,* i, 1218.

Benvenisti, D. and Goldberg, H. (1975). *New Engl. J. Med.* **292**, 1189.

Bergström, S., Carlson, L. A. and Weeks, J. R. (1968). *Pharmac. Rev.* **20**, 1.

Bergström, S., Dressler, F., Ryhage, R., Samuelsson, B. and Sjövall, J. (1962a). *Ark. Kemi.* **19**, 563.

Bergström, S., Rhyage, R., Samuelsson, B. and Sjövall, J. (1962b). *Acta chem. scand.* **16**, 501.

Bergström, S., Rhyage, R., Samuelsson, B. and Sjövall, J. (1963). *J. biol. Chem.* **238**, 3555.

Bergström, S. and Sjövall, J. (1960a). *Acta chem. scand.* **14**, 1693.

Bergström, S. and Sjövall, J. (1960b). *Acta chem. scand.* **14**, 1701.

Blackwell, G. J. and Flower, R. J. (1976). *Br. J. Pharmac.* **56**. 343P.

Bockman, R. S., Myers, W. P. L., Kempin, S. and Bajorunas, D., (1977). *Clin. Res.* **25**, 387A.

Bojeson, E. and Buchave, K. (1972). *Biochim. biophys. Acta*, **280**, 614.
Borgeat, P., Hamberg, M. and Samuelsson, B. (1976). *J. biol. Chem.* **251**, 7816.
Brash, A. R., Baillie, T. A., Clare, R. A. and Draffan, G. H. (1976). *Biochem. Med.* **16**, 77.
Brash, A. R. and Jones, R. L. (1974). *Prostaglandins*, **5**, 441.
Brereton, H. D., Halushka, P. V., Alexander, R. W., Mason, D. M., Keiser, H. R. and DeVita, V. T., Jr. (1974). *New Engl. J. Med.* **291**, 83.
Brummer, H. C. (1972). *Prostaglandins*, **2**, 185.
Brummer, H. C. (1973). *Prostaglandins*, **3**, 3.
Brummer, H. C. and Gillespie, A. (1972). *Clin. Endocr.* **1**, 363.
Buckler, J. M. H. (1971). "Radioimmunoassay Methods" (K. E. Kirkham and W. M. Hunter, eds), p. 273. Churchill, Livingstone, London.
Bunting, S., Gryglewski, R., Moncada, S. and Vane, J. R. (1976). *Prostaglandins*, **12**, 897.
Burr, I. M., Grant, D. B., Sizonenko, P. C., Kaplan, S. C. and Grumbach, M. M. (1969). *J. clin. Endocr.* **29**, 948.
Bygdeman, M. (1969). *Int. J. Fert.* **14**, 228.
Bygdeman, M., Fredricsson, B., Svanberg, K. and Samuelsson, B. (1970). *Fert. Steril.* **21**, 622.
Bygdeman, M. and Samuelsson, B. (1964). *Clin. chim. Acta*, **10**, 566.
Bygdeman, M. and Samuelsson, B. (1966). *Clin. chim. Acta*, **13**, 465.
Caldwell, B. V., Burstein, S., Brock, W. A. and Speroff, L. (1971). *J. clin. Endocr.* **33**, 171.
Carr, K., Sweetman, B. J. and Frölich, J. C. (1976). *Prostaglandins*, **11**, 3.
Chang, W-C. and Murota, S-I. (1977). *Biochim. biophys. Acta*, **486**, 136.
Chang, W-C. and Murota, S-I. (1978). *Biochem. Pharmac.* **27**, 109.
Chang, W-C., Murota, S-I., Matsuo, M. and Tsurufuji, S. (1976). *Biochem. biophys. Res. Commun.* **72**, 1259.
Christ, E. J. and Van Dorp, D. A. (1972). *Biochim. biophys. Acta*, **270**, 537.
Christ-Hazlehof, E., Nugteren, D. H. and Van Dorp, D. A. (1976). *Biochim. biophys. Acta*, **450**, 450.
Cockerill, A. F., Gutteridge, N. J. A., Mallen, D. N. B., Osborne, D. J. and Rackham, D. M. (1977). *Biomed. Mass. Spectrom.* **4**, 187.
Collier, J. G. (1972). *Br. J. Pharmac.* **44**, 383.
Collier, J. G., Flower, R. J. and Stanton, S. L. (1975). *Fert. Steril.* **26**, 868.
Corey, E. J. and Sachdev, H. S. (1973). *J. Am. chem. Soc.* **95**, 8483.
Cornette, J. C., Harrison, K. L. and Kirton, K. T. (1974). *Prostaglandins*, **5**, 155.
Cornette, J. C., Kirton, K. T., Barr, K. C. and Forbes, A. D. (1972). *J. reprod. Med.* **9**, 355.
Cornette, J. C., Kirton, K. T., Schneider, W. P., Sun, F. F., Johnson, R. A. and Nidy, E. G. (1975). *Prostaglandins*, **9**, 323.
Cory, H. T., Lascelles, P. T., Millard, B. J., Sneddon, W. and Wilson, B. W. (1976). *Biomed. Mass Spectrom.* **3**, 117.
Cottee, F., Flower, R. J., Moncada, S., Salmon, J. A. and Vane, J. R. (1977). *Prostaglandins*, **14**, 413.
Court, G. and Hurn, B. A. L. (1971). "Radioimmunoassay Methods" (K. E. Kirkham and W. M. Hunter, eds), p. 283. Churchill, Livingstone, London.
Dawson, W., Boot, J. R., Cockerill, A. F., Mallen, D. N. B. and Osborne, D. J. (1976). *Nature, Lond.* **262**, 699.
Demers, L. M., Allegra, J. C., Harvey, H. A., Lipton, A., Luderer, J. R., Mortel, R. and Brenner, D. E. (1977). *Cancer*, **39**, 1559.

Desiderio, D. M. and Hägele, K. (1971). *J. chem. Soc. chem. Commun.* 1074.

Diczfalusy, U., Falardeau, P. and Hammarström, S. (1977). *FEBS Lett.* **84**, 271.

Dorp, D. A. van (1967). *Prog. biochem. Pharmac.* **3**, 71.

Dorp, D. A. van (1971). *Ann. N.Y. Acad. Sci.* **180**, 181.

Dray, F. (1978). *Clin. Sci. mol. Med.* **54**, 115.

Dray, F. and Charbonnel, B. (1973). "Les Prostaglandins", p. 133. Inserm, Paris.

Dray, F., Charbonnel, B. and Maclouf, J. (1975). *Eur. J. clin. Invest.* **5**, 311.

Dray, F., Maron, E., Tillson, S. A. and Sela, M. (1972). *Anal. Biochem.* **50**, 399.

Drewes, P. A. (1974). *Clin. Biochem.* **7**, 378.

Dunham, E. W. and Anders, M. W. (1973). *Prostaglandins*, **4**, 85.

Dunn, M. J. and Hood, V. L. (1977). *Am. J. Physiol.* **233**, F169.

Dusting, G. J., Moncada, S. and Vane, J. R. (1977). *Prostaglandins*, **13**, 3.

Dusting, G. J., Moncada, S., Mullane, K., Salmon, J. A. and Vane, J. R. (1978). (Unpublished).

Easty, G. C. and Easty, D. M. (1976). *Cancer Treat. Rev.* **3**, 217.

Euler, U. S. von (1935). *J. Physiol. Lond.* **81**, 102.

Euler, U. S. von (1936). *J. Physiol. Lond.* **88**, 213.

Feldman, J. M., Plonk, J. W. and Cornette, J. C. (1974). *Prostaglandins*, **7**, 501.

Fenwick, L., Jones, R. C., Naylor, B., Poyser, N. L. and Wilson, N. H. (1977). *Br. J. Pharmac.* **59**, 191.

Ferreira, S. H. and Souza Costa, F. S. (1976). *Eur. J. Pharmac.* **39**, 379.

Ferreira, S. H. and Vane, J. R. (1967). *Nature, Lond.* **216**, 868.

Ferreira, S. H. and Vane, J. R. (1974a). *Ann. Rev. Pharm.* **14**, 57.

Ferreira, S. H. and Vane, J. R. (1974b). "The Prostaglandins" (P. W. Ramwell, ed.), Vol. 2, p. 1. Plenum Press, New York.

Fitzpatrick, F. A. (1976). *J. pharm. Sci.* **65**, 1609.

Fitzpatrick, F. A., Gorman, R. R., McGuire, J. C., Kelly, R. C., Wynalda, M. A. and Sun, F. F. (1977a). *Anal. Biochem.* **82**, 1.

Fitzpatrick, F. A., Gorman, R. R. and Wynalda, M. A. (1977b). *Prostaglandins*, **13**, 201.

Fitzpatrick, F. A. and Wynalda, M. A. (1976). *Anal. Biochem.* **73**, 198.

Finnegan, R. E., Knight, J. B., Fies, W. F. and DaGragnano, V. L. (1974). "Mass Spectrometry in Biochemistry and Medicine" (A. Frigerio and N. Castagnoli, Jr., eds), p. 313. Raven Press, New York.

Flower, R. J. (1974). *Pharmac. Rev.* **26**, 33.

Flower, R. J. and McClure, W. O. (1975). *Anal. Biochem.* **68**, 436.

Forström, L., Haapalahti, J. and Suramo, M. L. (1976). *Acta. derm.-vener. Stockh.* **56**, 495.

Fretland, D. J. (1974). *Prostaglandins*, **6**, 421.

Frölich, J. C. (1976). "The Prostaglandins" (P. W. Ramwell, ed.), Vol. 3, p. 1. Plenum Press, New York.

Frölich, J. C., Sweetman, B. J., Carr, K., Hollifield, J. W. and Oates, J. A. (1975a). *Prostaglandins*, **10**, 185.

Frölich, J. C., Sweetman, B. J., Carr, K., Hollifield, J. W. and Oates, J. A. (1975b). *Clin. Res.* **23**, 236A.

Frölich, J. C., Williams, W. M., Sweetman, B. J., Smigel, M., Carr, K., Hollifield, J. W., Fleischer, W., Nies, A. S., Fris-Holmberg, M. and Oates, J. A. (1976). "Advances in Prostaglandin and Thromboxane Research" (B. Samuelsson and R. Paoletti, eds), Vol. 1, p. 65. Raven Press, New York.

Frölich, J. C., Sweetman, B. J., Carr, K., Splawinski, J., Watson, J. T., Änggård, E. and Oates, J. A. (1973). "Advances in the Biosciences" (S. Bergström, ed.), Vol. 9, p. 321. Pergamon Press, Oxford.

Frölich, J. C., Wilson, T. W., Smigel, M. and Oates, J. A. (1974). *Biochim. biophys. Acta.* **348**, 241.

Frölich, J. C., Wilson, T. W., Sweetman, B. J., Smigel, M., Nies, A. S., Carr, K., Watson, J. T. and Oates, J. A. (1975c). *J. clin. Invest.* **55**, 763.

Gantt, C. L., Kizlaitis, L. R., Thomas, D. R. and Greslin, J. G. (1968). *Anal. Chem.* **40**, 2190.

Gersham, H., Powers, E., Levine, L. and Van Vunakis, H. (1972). *Prostaglandins*, **1**, 407.

Gillet, P. G., Kinch, R. A. H., Wolfe, L. S. and Pace-Asciak, C. (1972). *Am. J. Obstet. Gynec.* **112**, 330.

Goldblatt, M. W. (1933). *J. Soc. Chem. Ind. (Lond.)* **52**, 1056.

Goldblatt, M. W. (1935). *J. Physiol. Lond.* **84**, 208.

Gould, S. (1976). *Prostaglandins*, **11**, 489.

Gould, S. R., Brash, A. R. and Conolly, M. E. (1977). *Lancet*, **ii**, 98.

Granström, E. (1967). *Prog. biochem. Pharmac.* **3**, 89.

Granström, E. (1972). *Eur. J. Biochem.* **25**, 581.

Granström, E. (1978). *Prostaglandins*, **15**, 3.

Granström, E., Gréen, K., Bygdeman, M., Toppozada, M. and Wiqvist, N. (1973). *Life Sci.* **12**, 219.

Granström, E. and Kindahl, H. (1976). *Prostaglandins*, **12**, 759.

Granström, E., Kindahl, H. and Samuelsson, B. (1976a). *Anal. Lett.* **9**, 611.

Granström, E., Kindahl, H. and Samuelsson, B. (1976b). *Prostaglandins*, **12**, 929.

Granström, E. and Samuelsson, B. (1969). *J. Am. chem. Soc.* **91**, 3398.

Granström, E. and Samuelsson, B. (1971a). *J. biol. Chem.* **246**, 5254.

Granström, E. and Samuelsson, B. (1971b). *J. biol. Chem.* **246**, 7470.

Granström, E. and Samuelsson, B. (1972a). *FEBS Lett.* **26**, 211.

Granström, E. and Samuelsson, B. (1972b). *J. Am. chem. Soc.* **94**, 4380.

Greaves, M. W. and Søndergaad, J. (1970). *J. invest. Derm.* **54**, 365.

Greaves, M. W., Søndergaad, J. and McDonald-Gibson, W. (1971). *Br. med. J.* **2**, 258.

Gréen, K. (1969). *Chem. Phys. Lipids*, **3**, 254.

Gréen, K. (1971). *Biochim. biophys. Acta*, **231**, 419.

Gréen, K. (1973a). "Advances in the Biosciences" (S. Bergström, ed.), Vol. 9, p. 91. Pergamon Press, Oxford.

Gréen, K. (1973b). "Les Prostaglandines", p. 113. Inserm, Paris.

Gréen, K., Béguin, F., Bygdeman, M., Toppozada, M. and Wiqvist, N. (1972). "Third Conference on Prostaglandins in Fertility Control" (S. Bergström, K. Gréen and B. Samuelsson, eds), Vol. 2, p. 189. WHO, Karolinska Institutet, Stockholm.

Gréen, K., Bygdeman, M., Toppozada, M. and Wiqvist, N. (1974a). *Am. J. Obstet. Gynec.* **120**, 25.

Gréen, K., Granström, E. and Samuelsson, B. (1972). "Third Conference on Prostaglandins in Fertility Control" (S. Bergström, K. Gréen and B. Samuelsson, eds), Vol. 2, p. 92. WHO, Karolinska Institutet, Stockholm.

Gréen, K., Granström, E., Samuelsson, B. and Axen, U. (1973). *Anal. Biochem.* **54**, 434.

Gréen, K., Hedqvist, P. and Svanborg, N. (1974b). *Lancet*, **ii**, 1419.

Gréen, K. and Samuelsson, B. (1964). *J. Lipid Res.* **5**, 117.

Gréen, K. and Samuelsson, B. (1974). *Biochem. Med.* **11**, 298.

Gréen, K. and Steffenrud, S. (1976). *Anal. Biochem.* **76**, 606.

Greenwood, F. C., Hunter, W. M. and Glover, J. S. (1963). *Biochem. J.* **89**, 114.

Gryglewski, R. J., Bunting, S., Moncada, S., Flower, R. J. and Vane, J. R. (1976). *Prostaglandins*, 12, 715.
Gryglewski, R. J. and Korbut, R. (1976). *Br. J. Pharmac.* 56, 39.
Gryglewski, R. J., Korbut, R. and Ocetkiewicz, A. (1978a). *Prostaglandins*, 15, 637.
Gryglewski, R. J., Korbut, R. Ocetkiewicz, A. and Stachura, J. (1978b). *Naunyn-Schmiedebergs Arch. Pharmac.* 302, 25.
Gutierrrez-Cernosek, R. M., Morill, L. M. and Levine. L. (1972a). *Prostaglandins*, 1, 71.
Gutierrez-Cernosek, R. M., Zuckerman, J. and Levine, L. (1972b). *Prostaglandins*, 1, 331.
Hamberg, M. (1972). *Biochem. biophys. Res. Commun.* 49, 720.
Hamberg, M. (1973). *Anal. Biochem.* 55, 368.
Hamberg, M. (1974). *Life Sci.* 4, 247.
Hamberg, M. and Fredholm, B. B. (1976). *Biochim. biophys. Acta*, 431, 189.
Hamberg, M., Israelsson, U. and Samuelsson, B. (1971). *Ann. N.Y. Acad. Sci.* 180, 164.
Hamberg, M. and Samuelsson, B. (1966). *J. biol. Chem.* 241, 257.
Hamberg, M. and Samuelsson, B. (1967). *J. biol. Chem.* 242, 5329.
Hamberg, M. and Samuelsson, B. (1971). *J. biol. Chem.* 246, 6713.
Hamberg, M. and Samuelsson, B. (1972). *J. biol. Chem.* 247, 3495.
Hamberg, M. and Samuelsson, B. (1973). *Proc. natn. Acad. Sci., USA*, 70, 899.
Hamberg, M. and Samelsson, B. (1974a). *Proc. natn. Acad. Sci., USA*, 71, 3400.
Hamberg, M. and Samuelsson, B. (1974b). *Biochem. biophys. Res. Commun.* 61, 942.
Hamberg, M., Svensson, J. and Samuelsson, B. (1974a). *Proc. natn. Acad. Sci., USA*, 71, 3824.
Hamberg, M., Svensson, J. and Samuelsson. B. (1975). *Proc. natn. Acad. Sci., USA*, 72, 2994.
Hamberg, M., Svensson, J., Wakabayashi, T. and Samuelsson, B. (1974b). *Proc. natn. Acad. Sci., USA*, 71, 345.
Hamberg, M. and Wilson, M. (1973). "Advances in the Biosciences" (S. Bergström, ed.), Vol. 9, p. 39. Pergamon Press, Oxford.
Hammarström, S. and Falardeau, P. (1977). *Proc. natn. Acad. Sci., USA*, 74, 3691.
Hammarström, S., Hamberg, M., Samuelsson, B., Duell, E. A., Stawiski, M. and Voorhees, J. J. (1975). *Proc. natn. Acad. Sci., USA*, 72, 5130.
Harrison, R. F., Walker, E., Youssefnejadian, E. and Craft, I. (1975). *Prostaglandins*, 10, 729.
Hennam, J. F., Johnson, D. A., Newton, J. R. and Collins, W. P. (1974). *Prostaglandins*, 5, 531.
Hensby, C. N. (1974). *Prostaglandins*, 8, 369.
Hibbard, B. M., Sharma, S. C., Fitzpatrick, R. J. and Hamlett, J. D. (1974). *J. Obstet. Gynaec. Br. Commonw.* 81, 35.
Hillier, K. and Dilley, S. R. (1974). *Prostaglandins*, 5, 137.
Hindsdale, J., Engle, J. and Wilson, D. (1974). *Clin. Res.* 22, 664A.
Horton, E. W. (1969). *Physiol. Rev.* 49, 122.
Horton, E. W. and Jones, R. L. (1969). *Br. J. Pharmac.* 37, 705.
Hubbard, W. C. and Watson, J. T. (1976). *Prostaglandins*, 12, 21.
Jaffe, B. M. and Behrman, H. R. (1974). "Methods of Hormone Radioimmunoassay" (B. M. Jaffe and H. R. Behrman, eds), p. 19. Academic Press, New York and London.
Jaffe, B. M., Behrman, H. R. and Parker, C. W. (1973). *J. clin. Invest.* 52, 398.
Jaffe, B. M. and Parker, C. W. (1972). "Third Conference on Prostaglandins in Fertility Control" (S. Bergström, K. Gréen and B. Samuelsson, eds), Vol. 2, p. 69. WHO, Karolinska Institutet, Stockholm.

Jaffe, B. M. and Santoro, M. G. (1977). "The Prostaglandins" (P. W. Ramwell, ed.) Vol. 3, p. 329. Plenum Press, New York.

Jaffe, B. W., Smith, J. W., Newton, W. T. and Parker, C. W. (1971). *Science*, **171**, 494.

Jobke, A., Peskar, B. A. and Peskar, B. M. (1973). *FEBS Lett.* **37**, 192.

Johnson, D. A., Manning, P. A., Hennam, J. F., Newton, J. R. and Collins, W. P. (1975). *Acta endocr. Copenh.* **79**, 589.

Johnson, R. A., Morton, D. R., Kinner, J. H., Gorman, R. R., McGuire, J. C., Sun, F. F., Whittaker, N., Bunting, S., Salmon, J., Moncada, S. and Vane, J. R. (1976). *Prostaglandins*, **12**, 915.

Jones, R. L. (1970). *Biochem. J.* **119**, 64P.

Jouvenaz, G. H., Nugteren, D. H., Beerthuis, R. K. and Van Dorp, D. A. (1970). *Biochim. biophys. Acta*, **202**, 231.

Jouvenaz, G. H., Nugteren, D. H. and Van Dorp, D. A. (1973). *Prostaglandins*, **3**, 175.

Jubiz, W. and Frailey, J. (1971). *Clin. Res.* **19**, 127.

Jubiz, W. and Frailey, J. (1974). *Prostaglandins*, **7**, 339.

Jubiz, W., Frailey, J. and Bartholomew, K. (1972a). *Clin. Res.* **20**, 178.

Jubiz, W., Frailey, J., Child, C. and Bartholomew, K. (1972b). *Prostaglandins*, **2**, 471.

Karim, S. M. M. (1968). *Br. med. J.* **4**, 618.

Karim, S. M. M. and Amy, J.-J. (1975). "Recent Advances in Prostaglandin Research; Prostaglandins and Reproduction" (S. M. M. Karim, ed.), p. 77. MTP Press, Lancaster.

Karim, S. M. M. and Devlin, J. (1967). *J. Obstet. Gynaec. Br. Commonw.* **74**, 230.

Karim, S. M. M. and Rao, B. (1976). "Prostaglandins: Physiological, Pharmacological and Pathological Aspects" (S. M. M. Karim, ed.), p. 303. MTP Press, Lancaster.

Keirse, M. J. N. C., Flint, A. P. F. and Turnbull, A. C. (1974). *J. Obstet. Gynaec. Br. Commonw.* **81**, 131.

Keirse, K. J. N. C., Mitchell, M. D. and Turnbull, A. C. (1977). *Br. J. Obstet. Gynaec.* **84**, 743.

Keirse, M. J. N. C. and Turnbull, A. C. (1973). *J. Obstet. Gynaec. Br. Commonw.* **80**, 970.

Kelly, R. W. (1972). *J. Chromat.* **71**, 337.

Kelly, R. W. (1973). *Anal. Chem.* **45**, 2079.

Kelly, R. W. (1974). *Adv. Mass Spectrom.* **6**, 193.

Kinoshita, K., Satoh, K. and Sakamoto, S. (1977). *Endocr. jap.* **24**, 155.

Kirton, K. T. (1975). "Advances in Prostaglandin Research; Prostaglandins and Reproduction" (S. M. M. Karim, ed.), p. 229. MTP Press, Lancaster.

Kirton, K. T., Cornette, J. C. and Barr, K. C. (1972). *Biochem. biophys. Res. Commun.* **47**, 903.

Kitamura, S., Ishihara, Y. and Kosaka, K. (1977). *Prostaglandins*, **14**, 961.

Kloeze, J. (1967). "Proceedings of 2nd Nobel Symposium, Stockholm, June 1966" (S. Bergström and B. Samuelsson, eds), p. 241. Interscience, New York.

Korbut, R. (1975). *Pol. J. Pharmac. Pharm.* **27**, 631.

Lands, W. E. M., Hammarström, S. and Parker, C. W. (1976). *J. invest. Derm.* **67**, 658.

Lands, W. E. M. and Samuelsson, B. (1968). *Biochim. biophys. Acta.* **164**, 426.

Lee, J. B. (1972). *Prostaglandins*, **1**, 55.

Lee, S-C. and Levine, L. (1974). *J. biol. Chem.* **249**, 1369.

Lee, S-C., Pong, S-S., Katzen, D., Wu, K-Y. and Levine, L. (1975). *Biochemistry*, **14**, 142.

Levine, L. and Gutierrez-Cernosek, R. M. (1972). *Prostaglandins*, **2**, 281.

Levine, L. and Gutierrez-Cernosek, R. M. (1973). *Prostaglandins*, 3, 785.
Levine, L., Gutierrez-Cernosek, R. M. and Van Vunakis, H. (1971). *J. biol. Chem.* 246, 6782.
Levine, L., Gutierrez-Cernosek, R. M. and Van Vunakis, H. (1973). "Advances in the Biosciences" (S. Bergström, ed.), Vol. 9, p. 71. Pergamon Press, Oxford.
Levine, L. and Van Vunakis, H. (1970). *Biochem. biophys. Res. Commun.* 41, 1171.
Levitt, M. J. and Josimovich, J. B. (1971). *Fed. Proc.* 30, 1081.
Levitt, M. J., Josimovich, J. B. and Broskin, K. D. (1972). *Prostaglandins*, 1, 121.
Lundström, V., Wiqvist, N. and Gréen, K. (1976). "Advances in Prostaglandin and Thromboxane Research" (B. Samuelsson and R. Paoletti, eds), Vol. 2, p. 996. Raven Press, New York.
Maclouf, J., Pradel, M., Pradelles, P. and Dray, F. (1976). *Biochim. biophys. Acta*, 431, 139.
Maclouf, J., Rigaud, M., Durand, J. and Chebroux, P. (1976). *Prostaglandins*, 11, 999.
Main, I. H. M. (1973). "Prostaglandins: Pharmacological and Therapeutic Advances" (M. F. Cuthbert, ed.), p. 287. Heinemann, London.
Mathé, A. A., Hedqvist, P., Holmgren, A. and Svanborg, N. (1973). *Br. med. J.* i, 193.
McCosh, E. J., Meyer, D. L. and Dupont, J. (1976). *Prostaglandins*, 12, 471.
McCracken, J. A., Barcikowski, B., Carlsson, J. C., Gréen, K. and Samuelsson, B. (1973). "Advances in the Biosciences" (S. Bergström, ed.), Vol. 9, p. 559. Pergamon Press, Oxford.
McCracken, J. A., Carlsson, J. C., Glew, M. E., Goding, J. R., Baird, D. T., Gréen, K. and Samuelsson, B. (1972). *Nature, Lond.* 238, 129.
McGiff, J. C., Terragno, N. A., Strand, J. C., Lee, J. B., Lonigro, A. J. and Ng, K. K. F. (1969). *Nature, Lond.* 223, 742.
Meldrum, D. R. and Abraham, G. E. (1976). *Clin. Biochem.* 9, 42.
Middleditch, B. S. and Desiderio, D. M. (1972). *Prostaglandins*, 2, 195.
Middleditch, B. S. and Desiderio, D. M. (1973). *Prostaglandins*, 4, 459.
Mikes, F., Schurig, V. and Gil-Av, E. (1973). *J. Chromat.* 83, 91.
Miller, O. V. and Magee, W. E. (1973). "Advances in the Biosciences" (S. Bergström, ed.), Vol. 9, p. 83. Pergamon Press, Oxford.
Mitani, M. and Shoji, S. (1974). *Prostaglandins*, 8, 67.
Mitchell, M. D., Sors, H. and Flint, A. P. F. (1977). *Lancet*, ii, 558.
Miyamoto, T., Ogino, N., Yamamoto, S. and Hayaishi, O. (1976). *J. biol. Chem.* 251, 2629.
Miyamoto, T., Yamamoto, S. and Hayaishi, O. (1974). *Proc. natn. Acad. Sci., USA*, 71, 3645.
Moncada, S., Ferreira, S. H. and Vane, J. R. (1978). "Advances in Prostaglandin and Thromboxane Research" (B. Samuelsson and R. Paoletti, eds), Vol. 3, p. 211. Raven Press, New York.
Moncada, S., Gryglewski, R. J., Bunting, S. and Vane, J. R. (1976a). *Nature, Lond.* 263, 663.
Moncada, S., Gryglewski, R. J., Bunting, S. and Vane, J. R. (1976b). *Prostaglandins*, 12, 715.
Moncada, S., Higgs, E. A. and Vane, J. R. (1977). *Lancet*, i, 18.
Morozowich, W. and Douglas, S. L. (1975). *Prostaglandins*, 10, 19.
Mortel, R., Allegra, J. C., Demers, L. M., Harvey, H. A., Trautlein, J., Nahhas, W., White, D., Gillin, M. A. and Lipton, A. (1977). *Cancer*, 39, 2201.
Nakano, J., Änggård, E. Samuelsson, B. (1969). *Eur. J. Biochem.* 11, 386.
Nakano, J. and Morsy, N. H. (1971). *Clin. Res.* 19, 142.

Needleman, P., Minkes, M. and Raz, A. (1976). *Science*, **193**, 163.

Needleman, P., Moncada, S., Bunting, S., Vane, J. R., Hamberg, M. and Samuelsson, B. (1976). *Nature, Lond.* **261**, 558.

Nelson, N. A. (1974). *J. med. Chem.* **17**, 911.

Nugteren, D. H. (1975a). *J. biol. Chem.* **250**, 2808.

Nugteren, D. H. (1975b). *Biochim. biophys. Acta*, **380**, 299.

Nugteren, D. H., Beerthuis, R. K. and Van Dorp, D. A. (1966). *Rec. Trav. Chim. Pays-Bas*, **85**, 405.

Nugteren, D. H. and Hazelhof, E. (1973). *Biochim. biophys. Acta*, **326**, 448.

Nyström, E. and Sjövall, J. (1973). *Anal. Lett.* **6**, 155.

Oates, J. A., Sweetman, B. J., Gréen, K. and Samuelsson, B. (1976). *Anal. Biochem.* **74**, 546.

Ogino, N., Miyamoto, T., Yamamoto, S. and Hayaishi, O. (1977). *J. biol. Chem.* **252**, 890.

Ohki, S., Hanyu, T., Imaki, K., Nakazawa, N. and Hirata, F. (1974). *Prostaglandins*, **6**, 137.

Ohki, S., Imaki, K., Hirata, F., Hanyu, T. and Nakazawa, N. (1975). *Prostaglandins*, **10**, 549.

Ohki, S., Nishigaki, Y., Imaki, K., Kurono, M., Hirata, F., Hanyu, T. and Nakazawa, N. (1976). *Prostaglandins*, **12**, 181.

Orczyk, G. P. and Behrman, H. R. (1972). *Prostaglandins*, **1**, 3.

Oswald, E. O., Parks, D., Eling, T. and Corbett, B. J. (1974). *J. Chromat.* **93**, 47.

Pace-Asciak, C. R. (1976a). *J. Am. chem. Soc.* **98**, 2348.

Pace-Asciak, C. R. (1976b). *Biochim. biophys. Acta*, **486**, 583.

Pace-Asciak, C. R., Carrara, M. C. and Domazet, Z. (1977a). *Biochem. biophys. Res. Commun.* **78**, 115.

Pace-Asciak, C. R. and Cole, S. (1975). *Experimentia*, **31**, 143.

Pace-Asciak, C. R., Domazet, Z. and Carrara, M. (1977b). *Biochim. biophys. Acta*, **487**, 400.

Pace-Asciak, C. R. and Miller, D. (1973). *Prostaglandins*, **4**, 351.

Pace-Asciak, C. R. and Rangaraj, G. (1977). *Biochim. biophys. Acta*, **486**. 579.

Pace-Asciak, C. and Wolfe, L. S. (1971). *J. Chromat.* **56**, 1290.

Parkinson, T. M. and Schneider, J. C. (1969). *Biochim. biophys. Acta*, **176**, 78.

Perry, D. L. and Desiderio, D. M. (1977). *Prostaglandins*, **14**, 745.

Pharris, B. B. (1970). *Perspect. Biol. Med.* **13**, 434.

Pickles, V. R., Hall, W. J., Best, F. A. and Smith, G. N. (1965). *J. Obstet. Gynaec. Br. Commonw.* **72**, 185.

Piper, P. J. and Vane, J. R. (1969). *Nature, Lond.* **223**, 29.

Piper, P. J. and Vane, J. R. (1971). *Ann. N.Y. Acad. Sci., USA*, **180**, 363.

Pletka, P. and Hickler, R. B. (1974). *Prostaglandins*, **7**, 107.

Polet, H. and Levine, L. (1971). *Biochem. biophys. Res. Commun.* **45**, 1169.

Powles, T. J., Coombes, R. C., Munro Neville, A., Ford, H. T., Gazet, J. C. and Levine, L. (1977). *Lancet*, **ii**, 138.

Poyser, N. L., Horton, E. W., Thompson, C. J. and Los, M. (1971). *Nature, Lond.* **230**, 526.

Ramwell, P. W., Shaw, J. E., Clarke, G. B., Grostic, M. F., Kaiser, D. G. and Pike, J. E. (1968). "Progress in the Chemistry of Fats and other Lipids" (R. T. Holman, ed.),Vol. 9, p. 231. Pergamon Press, Oxford.

Rao, C. V. (1974). *Prostaglandins*, **6**, 533.

Raz, A. (1972). *Biochem. J.* **130**, 631.

Raz, A., Minkes, M. S. and Needleman, P. (1977). *Biochim. biophys. Acta*, **488**, 305.
Raz, A. and Stylos, W. A. (1973). *FEBS Lett.* **30**, 21.
Roberts, L. J., Sweetman, B. J., Payne, N. A. and Oates, J. A. (1977). *J. biol. Chem.* **252**, 7415.
Robertson, R. P., Baylink, D. J., Marini, J. J. and Adkison, H. W. (1975). *J. clin. Endocr. Metab.* **41**, 164.
Robertson, R. P., Baylink, D. J., Metz, S. A. and Cummings, K. B. (1976). *J. clin. Endocr. Metab.* **43**, 1330.
Ritzi, E. M. and Stylos, W. A. (1974). *Prostaglandins*, **8**, 55.
Saksena, S. K., Watson, D. T., Lau, I. I., Shaikh, A. A. (1974). *Prostaglandins*, **5**, 557.
Salmon, J. A. (1978). *Prostaglandins*, **15**, 383.
Salmon, J. A. and Amy, J-J. (1973). *Prostaglandins*, **4**, 523.
Salmon, J. A. and Karim, S. M. M. (1976). "Prostaglandins: Chemical and Biochemical Aspects" (S. M. M. Karim, ed.), p. 25. MTP, Lancaster.
Salmon, J. A., Smith, D. R., Flower, R. J., Moncada, S. and Vane, J. R. (1978). *Biochim. biophys. Acta*, **523**, 250.
Samuelsson, B. (1963). *J. biol. Chem.* **238**, 3229.
Samuelsson, B. (1964). *J. biol. Chem.* **239**, 4091.
Samuelsson, B. (1965). *J. Am. chem. Soc.* **87**, 3011.
Samuelsson, B. (1973a). "Advances in the Biosciences" (S. Bergström, ed.), Vol. 9, p. 7. Pergamon Press, Oxford.
Samuelsson, B. (1973b). "Advances in the Biosciences" (S. Bergström, ed.), Vol. 9, p. 121. Pergamon Press, Oxford.
Samuelsson, B., Granström, E., Gréen, K. and Hamberg, M. (1971). *Ann. N.Y. Acad. Sci., USA*, **180**, 138.
Samuelsson, B., Granström, E., Gréen, K., Hamberg, M. and Hammarström, S. (1975). *Ann. Rev. Biochem.* **44**, 669.
Samuelsson, B. and Gréen, K. (1974). *Biochem. Med.* **11**, 298.
Samuelsson, B., Hamberg, M. and Sweeley, C. C. (1970). *Anal. Biochem.* **38**, 301.
Sandler, M., Williams, E. D. and Karim, S. M. M. (1969). "Prostaglandins, Peptides and Amines" (P. Montegazza and E. W. Horton, eds), p. 3. Academic Press, London and New York.
Schoene, N. W. and Iacono, J. M. (1974). *Prostaglandins*, **5**, 387.
Seyberth, H. W., Morgan, J. L., Sweetman, B. J. and Oates, J. A. (1975). *Clin. Res.* **23**, 423A.
Seyberth, H. W., Sweetman, B. J., Frölich, J. C. and Oates, J. A. (1976). *Prostaglandins*, **11**, 381.
Sharma, S. C., Hibbard, B. M., Hamlett, J. D. and Fitzpatrick, R. J. (1973). *Br. med. J.* **1**, 709.
Shaw, J. E. and Ramwell, P. W. (1969). *Meth. biochem. Anal.* **17**, 325.
Silver, M. J., Smith, J. B., Ingerman, C. and Kocsis, J. J. (1972) *Prostaglandins*, **1**, 429.
Silver, M. J., Smith, J. B., Ingerman, C. and Kocsis, J. J. (1973a). *Prostaglandins*, **4**, 863.
Silver, M. J., Smith, J. B., Ingerman, C. and Kocsis, J. J. (1973b) *Prog. Hemat.* **8**, 235.
Smith, A. G. and Brooks, C. J. W. (1977). *Biomed. Mass Spectrom.* **4**, 258.
Smith, A. P. (1975). *Br. J. clin. Pharmac.* **2**, 307.
Smith, J. B., Silver, M. J., Ingerman, C. M. and Kocsis, J. J. (1974). *Thromb. Res.* **5**, 291.
Smith, J. B. and Willis, A. L. (1970). *Br. J. Pharmac.* **40**, 545P.
Sors, H., Maclouf, J., Pradelles, P. and Dray, F. (1977). *Biochim. biophys. Acta*, **486**, 553.

Stein-Werblowsky, R. (1974). *Oncology*, **30**, 169.

Stone, K. J. and Hart, M. (1975). *Prostaglandins*, **10**, 273.

Struijk, C. B., Beerthuis, R. K., Pabon, H. J. J. and Van Dorp, D. A. (1966). *Rec. Trav. Chim.* **85**, 1233.

Stylos, W. A., Howard, L., Ritzi, E. and Skarnes, R. (1974). *Prostaglandins*, **6**, 1.

Stylos, W. A. and Rivetz, B. (1972). *Prostaglandins*, **2**, 103.

Suguira, M. and Hirano, K. (1974). *J. Chromat.* **90**, 169.

Sun, F. F. (1974). *Biochim. biophys. Acta*, **348**, 249.

Sun, F. F. (1977). *Biochem. biophys. Res. Commun.* **74**, 1432.

Sun, F. F. and Armour, S. B. (1974). *Prostaglandins*, **7**, 327.

Sun, F. F., Armour, S. B., Bockstanz, V. R. and McGuire, J. C. (1976). "Advances in Prostaglandin and Thromboxane Research" (B. Samuelsson and R. Paoletti, eds), Vol. 1, p. 163. Raven Press, New York.

Sun, F. F., Chapman, J. P. and McGuire, J. C. (1977). *Prostaglandins*, **14**, 1055.

Sun, F. F., McGuire, J. C. and Taylor, B. M. (1978). Presentation at the Winter Meeting on Prostaglandins at Sarasota, Florida, USA, January, 1978.

Sun, F. F. and Stafford, J. E. (1974). *Biochim. biophys. Acta*, **369**, 95.

Svanborg, N., Hamberg, M. and Hedqvist, P. (1973). *Acta, physiol. scand.* **89** (Suppl. 396), 101.

Svensson, J., Hamberg, M. and Samuelsson, B. (1975). *Acta physiol. scand.* **94**, 222.

Sweetman, B. J., Watson, J. T., Carr, K., Oates, J. A. and Frölich, J. C. (1973). *Prostaglandins*, **3**, 385.

Tambyraja, R. L., Karim, S. M. M., Salmon, J. A. and Ratnam, S. S. (1977a). *Aust. N.Z. J. Obstet. Gynaec.* **17**, 89.

Tambyraja, R. L., Salmon, J. A., Karim, S. M. M. and Ratnam, S. S. (1977b). *Prostaglandins*, **13**, 339.

Thiery, M. and Amy, J-J. (1975). "Advances in Prostaglandin Research: Prostaglandins and Reproduction" (S. M. M. Karim, ed.), p. 149. MTP, Lancaster.

Thompson, C. J., Los, M. and Horton, E. W. (1970). *Life Sci.* **9**, 983.

Trang, L. E., Granström, E. and Lövgren, O. (1977). *Scand. J. Rheum.* **6**, 151.

Unger, W. G. (1972). *J. Pharm. Pharmac.* **24**, 470.

Unger, W. G., Stamford, I. and Bennett, A. (1971). *Nature, Lond.* **233**, 336.

Vaitukaitis, J., Robbins, J. B., Nieschlag, E. and Ross, G. T. (1971). *J. clin. Endocr.* **33**, 988.

Van Orden, D. E. and Farley, D. B. (1973). *Prostaglandins*, **4**, 215.

Vane, F. and Horning, M. G. (1969). *Anal. Lett.* **2**, 357.

Vane, J. R. (1964). *Br. J. Pharmac.* **23**, 360.

Vane, J. R. (1969). *Br. J. Pharmac.* **35**, 209.

Vane, J. R. (1971). *Nature, Lond.* **231**, 232.

Vane, J. R. (1976). *J. Allergy clin. Immun.* **58**, 691.

Vonkeman, H. and Van Dorp, D. A. (1968). *Biochim. biophys. Acta*, **164**, 430.

Wakeling, A. E., Kirton, K. T. and Wyngarden, L. J. (1973). *Prostaglandins*, **4**, 1.

Weinheimer, A. J. and Spraggins, R. L. (1969). *Tet. Lett.* **59**, 5185.

Weinshenker, N. M. and Longwell, A. (1972). *Prostaglandins*, **2**, 207.

Wickramasinghe, J. A. F., Morozowich, W., Hamlin, W. E. and Shaw, S. R. (1973). *J. pharm. Sci.* **62**, 1428.

Wickramasinghe, J. A. F. and Shaw, S. R. (1974a). *Prostaglandins*, **4**, 903.

Wickramasinghe, J. A. F. and Shaw, S. R. (1974b). *Biochem. J.* **141**, 179.

Williams, E. D., Karim, S. M. M. and Sandler, M. (1968). *Lancet*, **i**, 22.

Willis, A. L. (1970). *Br. J. Pharmac.* **40**, 583P.

Willis, A. L., Vane, F. M., Kuhn, D. C., Scott, C. G. and Petrin, M. (1974). *Prostaglandins*, **8**, 453.

Wlodawer, P. and Samuelsson, B. (1973). *J. biol. Chem.* **248**, 5673.

Wolfe, L. S. and Pace-Asciak, C. R. (1972). "Third Conference on Prostaglandins, in Fertility Control" (S. Bergström, K. Gréen and B. Samuelsson, eds), p. 201. WHO, Karolinska Institute, Stockholm.

Yoshimoto, T., Yamamoto, S., Okuma, M. and Hayaishi, O. (1977). *J. biol. Chem.* **252**, 5871.

Youssefnejadian, E., Walker, E., Sommerville, I. F. and Craft, I. (1974). *Prostaglandins*, **6**, 23.

Yu, S. C. and Burke, G. (1972). *Prostaglandins*, **2**, 11.

Zia, P. and Horton, R. (1973). *Prostaglandins*, **4**, 453.

Zuckerman, H., Reiss, U., Atad, J., Lampert, I., Ben Ezra, S. and Sklan, D. (1977). *Br. J. Obstet. Gynaec.* **84**, 339.

Zuckerman, H., Reiss, U. and Rubinstein, I. (1974). *Obstet. Gynec.* **44**, 787.

Zusman, R. M. (1972). *Prostaglandins*, **1**, 167.

Zusman, R. M., Caldwell, B. V., Speroff, L. and Behrman, H. R. (1972). *Prostaglandins*, **2**, 41.

Zusman, R. M., Spector, D., Caldwell, B. V., Speroff, L., Schneider, G. and Mulrow, P. J. (1973). *J. clin. Invest.* **52**, 1093.

VII. Gastro-intestinal Hormones I: Pancreatic Polypeptide, Motilin, Gastric Inhibitory Peptide, Neurotensin, Enteroglucagon and Others

S. R. BLOOM

INTRODUCTION

Our knowledge of gut hormones has increased very rapidly in the last decade. There are now eight peptide hormones which are generally agreed to be released into the blood stream from the alimentary tract (Table 1). Three are described in the following chapter, e.g. gastrin, secretin and cholecysto-kinin-pancreozymin, while the remaining five are described in this chapter, viz. pancreatic polypeptide (PP), motilin, gastric inhibitory peptide (GIP), neurotensin and enteroglucagon. Other gut substances may also sometimes act in a hormonal capacity, for example somatostatin and vaso active intestinal peptide, but their status as true hormones is less certain. Gut hormones were among the first to be described in the new subject of endocrinology (Bayliss and Starling, 1902; Edkins, 1905) but, until recently, progress was slow. The main reason was that they belong to a diffuse endo-crine system, investigation of which poses many problems. By contrast, when endocrine cells are gathered together to form an endocrine gland, isolation of the pure hormone is quite easy. The physiological relevance can be rapidly ascertained by extirpation of the gland, to produce deficiency, and by chronic injections of active gland extracts, to produce excess. No such straightforward approach is available with the diffuse endocrine system as the endocrine cells are widely scattered through many tissues. Progress has had to await advances in peptide chemistry so that the pure hormones could be isolated from the very low concentrations present in bulk tissue extracts. Fortunately the low molecular weight of the alimentary hormones allowed their amino acid sequencing, and subsequent synthesis, to be undertaken rapidly (see Table 2). Thus once the initial hurdle of hormone isolation was overcome, large quantities of synthetic peptide quickly became available for pharmacological studies and antibody raising. The latter in turn allowed both accurate hormone measurement by radioimmunoassay and precise tissue localisation by immunocytochemistry.

Table 1
Main site of origin and action of gut hormones.

Tissue	Hormone	Action
Stomach	Gastrin	Stimulation of gastric acid, gastric mucosal growth
Pancreas	Pancreatic polypeptide	Inhibition of gall bladder contraction, inhibition of pancreatic exocrine secretion
Upper small intestine	Secretin	Stimulation of pancreatic bicarbonate
	Cholecystokinin	Gall bladder contraction, stimulation of pancreatic enzyme secretion, stimulation of pancreatic growth
	Motilin	Stimulation of upper GI motor activity
	GIP	Enhancement of insulin release
Lower small intestine	Enteroglucagon	Inhibition of intestinal transit, enhancement of muscle growth
	Neurotensin	?
Colon	Enteroglucagon	Inhibition of intestinal transit, enhancement of mucosal growth

Table 2
Size and molecular weight of gut hormones.

Hormone	No. of amino acids	mw	Successful synthesis
BPP	36	4226	No
Motilin (porc)	22	2700	Yes
GIP (porc)	43	5105	?
Neurotensin (bovine)	13	1673	Yes
VIP (porc)	28	3326	Yes
Somatostatin (ovine)	14	1640	Yes
Bombesin (amphibian)	14	1620	Yes
Substance P (bovine)	11	1348	Yes

Pavlov proposed that alimentary control was by the innervation (Babkin, 1949), while Bayliss and Starling (1902) suggested that the most important mechanism was the circulating hormones. Many hormonal peptides were subsequently found to be normal constituents of both the brain and the gut (Pearse, 1976) (Table 3). In the brain they were found to be stored in the

Table 3

Established brain–gut peptides.

Peptide	Gut localisation	Possible role
Cholecystokinin	Endocrine cells	Circulating hormone (see Chapter 8)
Substance P	Nerves and endocrine cells	?Secreto-motor, ?muscle contraction
Enkephalin	Mainly nerves	?As morphia
Bombesin	Mainly nerves	?Gastric and pancreatic secretion
Neurotensin	Endocrine cells	Circulating hormone (see below)
Vasoactive intestinal peptide	Mainly nerves	Secreto-motor, vaso-dilation, smooth muscle relaxation, inhibition of gastric acid
Somatostatin	Mainly endocrine cells	Local inhibition of hormone release, secretion and motor activity

synaptosomes and could be released by axonal depolarisation, thus strongly suggesting a role as neuro-transmitters. In contrast the same peptides were found in storage granules in conventional endocrine cells of the mucosa of the alimentary tract. Thus the old rigid division between neuro-transmitter and hormone seems to be artificial. Cholecystokinin, for example, appears able to act both as a cerebral-neuro-transmitter and as a circulating hormone (Dockray, 1976; Rehfeld, 1978). Indeed even in the gut many of the brain–gut peptides are located both in endocrine cells and in nerves. The importance of a purely local release of hormonal peptides from endocrine type cells, having an effect only on the neighbouring structures without intervention of the circulation, has recently been emphasised, and the term paracrine suggested (Pearse 1976). In the pituitary circulation it is well recognised that peptides released from nerves act via the circulation, e.g. as hormones, while, as mentioned, in the paracrine system hormonal peptides released from endocrine cells act only locally, in a manner comparable to classical neuro-transmitters. This reversal of a traditional division of roles helps to emphasise the unity of the body's control systems. It also fits well with Pearse's concept of the neuro-ectodermal embryological origin of the cells of the endocrine system (Pearse, 1969).

PANCREATIC POLYPEPTIDE

1. Properties

Pancreatic polypeptide (PP) was first discovered as a contaminant of chicken insulin (Kimmel, Pollock and Hazelwood, 1968) and subsequently a very similar peptide was found to contaminate mammalian insulins (Lin and Chance, 1972). Both contained 36 amino acids arranged in a linear sequence (see Fig. 1) (Kimmel, Pollock and Hazelwood, 1971; Lin, Evans and Chance,

```
 1    2    3    4    5    6    7    8    9   10   11   12   13   14   15   16   17   18
Ala–Pro–Leu–Glu–Pro–Gln–Tyr–Pro–Gly–Asp–Asp–Ala–Thr–Pro–Glu–Gln–Met–Ala–

19   20   21   22   23   24   25   26   27  28   29   30   31   32   33   34   35   36
Gln–Tyr–Ala–Ala–Glu–Leu–Arg–Arg–Tyr–Ile–Asn–Met–Leu–Thr–Arg–Pro–Arg–Tyr–NH₂
```

Fig. 1. Sequence of bovine pancreatic polypeptide (possible sequence changes in HPP underlined).

1974). The molecular weight of bovine PP (BPP) is 4226 and shows only four amino acid differences from human PP (HPP). It has been reported that the entire biological activity is displayed by the last six amino acids (Lin and Chance, 1978) which do not differ between pig, bovine and human PP. PP is fairly freely available as a by-product of insulin manufacture and appears to be quite stable both in plasma and on the shelf. Pharmacological studies have shown that its most sensitive action is to oppose the effects of cholecystokinin (Lin and Chance, 1978). Thus it inhibits the pancreatic output of enzymes and gall bladder contraction. At somewhat higher doses it has a biphasic effect, initially stimulating and later inhibiting pancreatic bicarbonate output. Gastric acid output is stimulated while motor activity of the upper small intestine is inhibited. Although a pancreatic hormone, PP appears to have no effect on circulating metabolites or on the release of insulin and glucagon in the mammal (Adrian, Greenberg, Besterman, McCloy, Chadwick, Barnes, Mallinson, Baron, Alberti and Bloom, 1978).

2. Distribution

As can be seen in Fig. 2, the majority of human PP arises in the pancreas. A small amount has been found in the human duodenum but insignificant quantities elsewhere in the body. It is localised in the pancreas to well described endocrine cells containing small granules (Heitz, Polak, Bloom and Pearse, 1976; Solcia, Polak, Pearse, Forssman, Larsson, Sundler, Lechago, Grimelius, Fujita, Creutzfeldt, Gepts, Faulkmer, Lefranc, Heitz. Hage, Bloom and Grossman, 1978) which are found both in the islets of Langerhans, scattered throughout the acinar cells of the exocrine pancreas and also occasionally in the walls of pancreatic ducts. In many species, for example the dog, there is a considerable concentration of PP cells in the head of the pancreas.

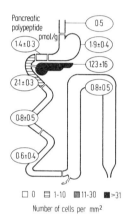

Fig. 2. The distribution of human pancreatic polypeptide in the human gastro-intestinal tract. The figures in circles depict the concentration in pmol/g wet weight whole bowel while the shading indicates the number of cells/mm² of mucosa. Each section is the mean of at least four fresh surgical specimens with no apparent abnormality.

3. Assay

The only reported method for measurement of PP is by radioimmunoassay. PP is highly antigenic and antibodies are easy to develop. As there is no known similar hormone, there are no problems with cross-reactivity, but antibodies to BPP may not fully measure HPP. Ron Chance (The Eli Lilly Co.) has purified a small amount of HPP and raised an antibody to it which he has generously distributed to the main assay centres throughout the world. Interestingly it has proven difficult to find antibodies to BPP which cross-react with rodent PP, suggesting a considerable sequence difference between these species. PP presents no problem with oxidative iodination by any of the recognised techniques as it has four tyrosines but only one methionine and no tryptophan residues. Once, prepared, radioactive PP is stable for several months. Assay sensitivity down to 4 pmol/l plasma is not difficult to achieve and is more than adequate for all plasma measurements. Interference by plasma proteins and other non-specific effects seems to have caused problems with many of the published assays (Schwartz, Stadil, Chance, Rehfeld, Larsson and Moon, 1976; Adrian, Bloom, Besterman, Barnes, Cooke, Russell and Faber, 1977; Floyd, Fajans, Pek and Chance, 1977).

4. Plasma Concentrations

Fasting human PP concentrations have been variously reported between 20 and 80 pmol/l (Schwartz *et al.*, 1976; Adrian *et al.*, 1977; Floyd *et al.*, 1977). A highly significant 10-fold rise occurs after a meal, with peak values being achieved at about 30 min. The main constituents of the meal that are responsible for the PP release appear to be fat and protein (Fig. 3) (Floyd *et al.*, 1977; Adrian, Bloom, Bestermann and Bryant, 1978). PP levels are undetectably low in patients after pancreatectomy. The postprandial rise, therefore, reflects some signals from the gut to the pancreas, an entero-PP axis

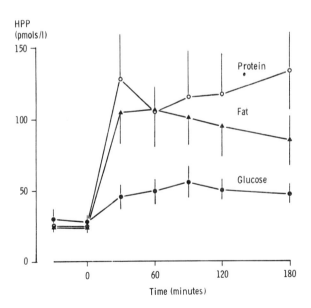

Fig. 3. The effect of individual meal components on plasma PP concentrations in six healthy subjects.

(Adrian *et al.*, 1977). Changes in the plasma concentration of amino acids, fat or glucose do not affect PP release directly. During insulin hypoglycaemia a large rise in PP concentration is seen and this is abolished by vagotomy (Fig. 4) suggesting an important vagal influence. In the isolated perfused pancreas, PP is efficiently released by acetylcholine (Schwartz, Holst,

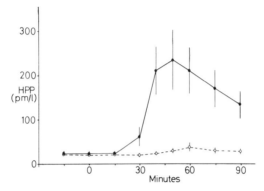

Fig. 4. Plasma PP concentrations following 0·2 units/kg insulin at times zero. Eight healthy controls (solid line) had an identical degree of hypoglycaemia to the 17 subjects who had previously had a successful truncal vagotomy (dotted line).

Fahrenkrug, Jensen, Nielsen, Rehfeld, Schaffalitzky de Muckadell and Stadil, 1978), though release is also seen with several gut hormones including GIP, cholecystokinin and VIP (Adrian, Bloom, Hermansen and Iversen, 1978). Patients who have fully recovered from a successful truncal vagotomy, however, show a normal postprandial PP rise (Fig. 5) suggesting that it is the local vagal reflexes and circulating gut hormones that are probably of major importance in the control of PP release. In order to investigate the physiological role of PP, infusions have been administered to human volunteers (1 pmol/kg/min) producing levels which closely mimic the post-prandial rise (250 pmol/l) (Greenberg, McCloy, Adrian, Chadwick, Baron and Bloom, 1978). A considerable inhibition of pancreatic enzyme and juice production and also of bile output into the duodenum was observed suggesting that PP indeed has a physiological role in the modulation of the digestive process.

A failure of PP release is seen not only in patients without a pancreas but also in those with destructive pancreatitis of sufficient severity to cause pancreatic exocrine failure (e.g. steatorrhoea) (Adrian, Bloom, Besterman and Bryant, 1978). Somewhat elevated PP levels have been reported in diabetics (Floyd *et al.*, 1977), though normal values have been found when patients were well controlled. Extremely high circulating PP levels are found in about half the patients with pancreatic endocrine tumours (Bloom, Adrian, Bryant and Polak, 1978), being more frequent in those with VIPomas and glucagonomas than in those with gastrinomas (Taylor, Walsh, Rotter and Passaro, 1978) and insulinomas. It may be that in the last two groups

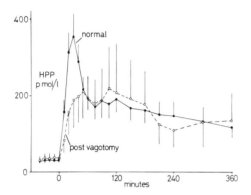

Fig. 5. Plasma PP concentrations in 10 normal subjects (solid line) and six patients who had had a successful truncal vagotomy more than six months earlier (dotted line) following a standard lunch taken at times zero.

only those patients with multiple endocrine adenopathy (MEA type 1) have a significant incidence of raised plasma PP. The PP cells appear to be an intrinsic part of the endocrine tumours and are found in equal profusion in metastases in the liver and lymph nodes. PP measurement may be clinically useful, for example, in distinguishing VIPomas of pancreatic from those of extra pancreatic origin (ganglioneuromas) as the latter never have elevated PP levels. It is interesting to note that chromatography of tumour produced-PP shows additional large molecular weight forms not usually detected in normal plasma (Fig. 6).

B. MOTILIN

1. Properties

Motilin was first discovered by Brown (1973) as a result of the observation that duodenal stimulation caused gastric contraction independently of the innervation. Motilin is a 22 amino acid straight chain peptide (see Fig. 7)

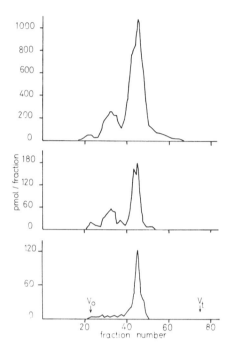

Fig. 6. Pancreatic polypeptide elution profile of plasmas from three patients with PP-producing pancreatic apudomas. Plasma was run on a 90 cm Sephadex G50 superfine column. The major peak elutes in the same position as pure bovine PP.

(Brown, Cook and Dryburgh, 1973) which appears stable in plasma. Only the porcine form has been sequenced so far (mw 2700) but from immunological studies it is clear that canine motilin has significant sequence differences. Synthetic motilin, with or without a norleucine substituted for methionine at the 13 position, is available in small quantities and has all the actions of the natural peptide (Strunz, Domschke, Domschke, Mitznegg, Wünsch, Jaeger and Demling, 1976). Porcine motilin causes powerful contractions of isolated muscle strips from the upper small intestine of many species (Strunz, Domschke, Mitznegg, Domschke, Schubert, Wünsch, Jaeger and Demling, 1975). In the dog it causes contraction of the lower oesophageal

```
   1    2    3    4    5    6    7    8    9   10   11   12   13   14   15   16   17
 Phe–Val–Pro–Ile–Phe–Thr–Tyr–Gly–Glu–Leu–Gln–Arg–Met–Gln–Glu–Lys–Glu–

  18   19   20   21   22
 Arg–Asn–Lys–Gly–Gln
```

Fig. 7. Sequence of motilin.

sphincter (Jennewein, Hummelt, Siewert and Waldeck, 1975), speeds gastric emptying (Debas, Yamagishi and Dryburgh, 1977) and can induce formation of the interdigestive myoelectric complex (Wingate, Ruppin, Thompson, Green, Domschke, Wünsch, Demling and Ritchie, 1977). It is not thought to have any effects on pancreatic or gastric secretion (Domschke, Domschke, Schmak, Tympner, Junge, Wünsch, Jaeger and Demling, 1976).

2. Distribution

Motilin is mainly found in the upper small intestine (Fig. 8) where it has been reported to be localised to a particular type of 5-hydroxytryptophan storing endocrine cell (enterochromaffin cell) (Pearse, Polak, Bloom, Adams, Dryburgh and Brown, 1974; Solcia et al., 1978).

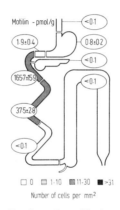

Fig. 8. The distribution of motilin in man (as Fig. 2).

3. Assay

The only reported method of motilin measurement is by radioimmunoassay Motilin is highly antigenic and almost all innoculated animals produce antibodies. Those antibodies which react with the C-terminal portion of the molecule appear able to recognise canine motilin (Dryburgh and Brown, 1975). The antibody the author routinely employs does not react with canine motilin or any of the currently available synthetic motilin fragments. Motilin iodination is extremely straightforward by any of the standard procedures and the product is usually stable for many months. Assays sensitive to less than 5 pmol/l are easy to achieve by conventional techniques and are more than adequate for the measurement of even basal plasma motilin concentrations. No problems have been reported with plasma interference effects. Chromatography of human plasma motilin shows a major peak eluting in the position of synthetic porcine motilin, but many individuals have an additional larger molecular weight peak of motilin immunoreactivity. The nature of this second peak is at present not defined.

4. Plasma Concentrations

Fasting plasma motilin concentrations in man show a skew distribution (Fig. 9) and the upper limit of normal can be put at about 300 pmol/l (Bloom,

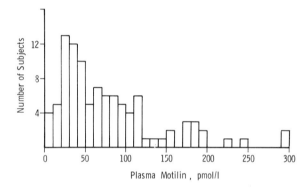

Fig. 9. The fasting plasma motilin concentration in 100 fasting healthy subjects.

Mitznegg and Bryant, 1976). Motilin has been reported to be released by large quantities of acid infused intraduodenally (Figs 10 and 11) (Modlin, Mitznegg and Bloom, 1978) and also by more physiological stimuli such as a meal and oral fat loads (Christofides and Bloom, 1978). An intravenous infusion of fat is also able to stimulate motilin release. Glucose, either orally or intravenously causes a fall in plasma motilin, but a fall is also seen following an insulin-induced hypoglycaemia (Christofides and Bloom 1978) (Fig. 12). Infusions of motilin in man have been reported to induce interdigestive myoelectric complex formation (Vantrappen, Janssens, Peeters, Bloom, Van Tongeren and Hellemans, 1978) but it is uncertain whether this effect is physiological. A motilin infusion of 0·34 pmol/kg/min, which produces a 60 pmol/l rise in plasma motilin concentrations, significantly delays the emptying of the solid component of a breakfast meal (Bloom, Christofides, Modlin and Fitzpatrick, 1978) suggesting a possible physiological role for motilin in the control of gastric emptying.

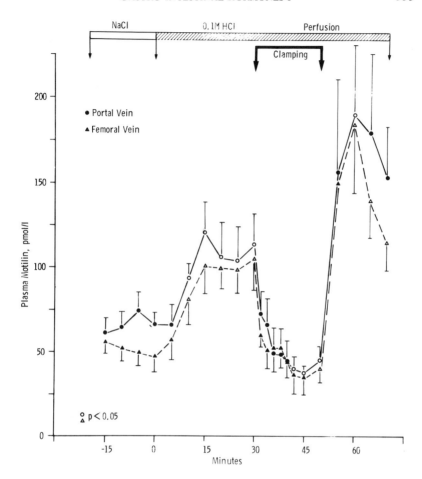

Fig. 10. Motilin concentrations in portal and peripheral plasma following 0·1 molar HCl perfusion of the duodenum at 1 ml/min in six anaesthetised pigs. After complete vascular occlusion of the perfused segment (clamping) motilin concentrations fall below the baseline indicating that the release of motilin in response to acid is a local phenomenon.

C. GASTRIC INHIBITORY PEPTIDE

1. Properties

Gastric inhibitory peptide (GIP) was first isolated as an intestinal factor capable of inhibiting histamine-stimulated gastric acid. The N-terminal portion of the straight chain 43 amino acid polypeptide (mw 5105) (Brown and Dryburgh, 1971) showed considerable sequence homologies with the

M

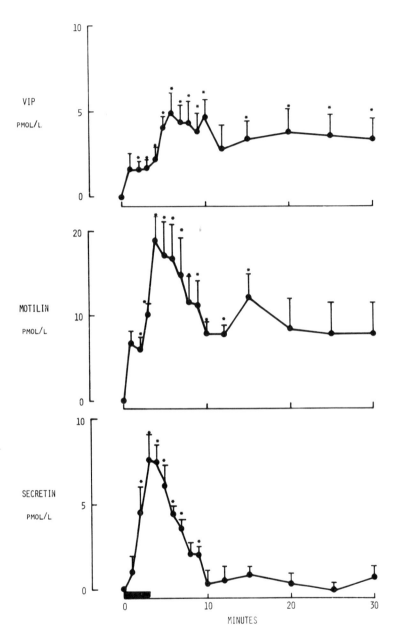

Fig. 11. Incremental concentrations of plasma VIP, motilin and secretin after 50 ml of 0·1 mol/l HCl (black bar) was given intraduodenally to nine volunteers. Stars indicate $p < 0.05$.

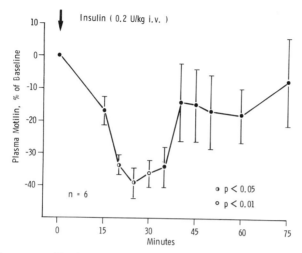

Fig. 12. Plasma motilin following insulin-induced hypoglycaemia in six healthy subjects expressed as a percent of the basal motilin concentration.

more classical hormones secretin and glucagon as well as with a newer hormonal peptide VIP (see Fig. 13). All the members of this family of hormones show similar pharmacological properties. For example they all inhibit gastric acid and they all stimulate insulin secretion. They are all sensitive to degradation by proteolytic enzymes and are thus relatively unstable in plasma. Within the mammals there is no evidence for any interspecies differences in amino acid sequence, though isolation of pure GIP has only been achieved in the pig. Unlike the cholecystokinin–gastrin family, there is no minimal active fragment for any member of the GIP group which may imply that tertiary structure is important in receptor binding. Considerable difficulties have been encountered in the attempt to synthesise porcine GIP and even apparently pure preparations seem to have a biological activity considerably below that of natural GIP. In addition to inhibiting gastric acid (Pederson and Brown, 1972) and stimulating insulin release (Dupre, Ross, Watson and Brown, 1973), GIP also stimulates secretion of digestive juice from the small intestine (Barbezat and Grossman, 1971), though there is some evidence that the mechanism is different from the juice stimulation produced by VIP (Gaginella, Phillips, Dozois and Go, 1978).

2. Distribution

GIP is predominantly found in the upper small intestine (Fig. 14) and has recently been shown by electronimmunocytochemistry to be produced by

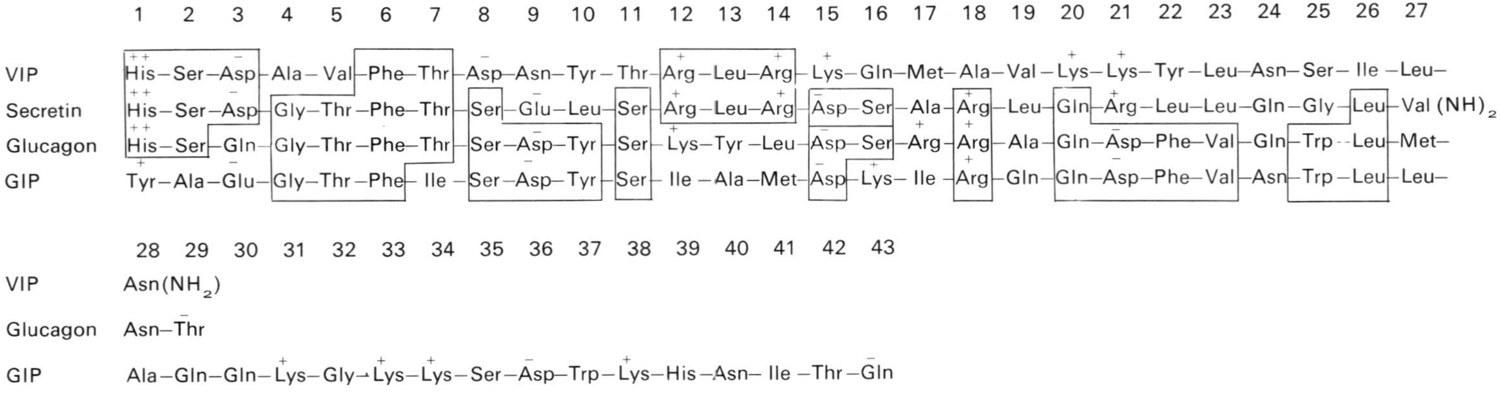

	1	2	3	4	5	6	7	8	9	10	11	12	13	14	15	16	17	18	19	20	21	22	23	24	25	26	27
VIP	His	Ser	Asp	Ala	Val	Phe	Thr	Asp	Asn	Tyr	Thr	Arg	Leu	Arg	Lys	Gln	Met	Ala	Val	Lys	Lys	Tyr	Leu	Asn	Ser	Ile	Leu—
Secretin	His	Ser	Asp	Gly	Thr	Phe	Thr	Ser	Glu	Leu	Ser	Arg	Leu	Arg	Asp	Ser	Ala	Arg	Leu	Gln	Arg	Leu	Leu	Gln	Gly	Leu	Val (NH)$_2$
Glucagon	His	Ser	Gln	Gly	Thr	Phe	Thr	Ser	Asp	Tyr	Ser	Lys	Tyr	Leu	Asp	Ser	Arg	Arg	Ala	Gln	Asp	Phe	Val	Gln	Trp	Leu	Met—
GIP	Tyr	Ala	Glu	Gly	Thr	Phe	Ile	Ser	Asp	Tyr	Ser	Ile	Ala	Met	Asp	Lys	Ile	Arg	Gln	Gln	Asp	Phe	Val	Asn	Trp	Leu	Leu—

	28	29	30	31	32	33	34	35	36	37	38	39	40	41	42	43
VIP	Asn(NH$_2$)															
Glucagon	Asn—Thr															
GIP	Ala	Gln	Gln	Lys	Gly	Lys	Ser	Asp	Trp	Lys	His	Asn	Ile	Thr	Gln	

Fig. 13. Sequences of porcine VIP, secretin, glucagon and GIP.

the mucosal K cell whose product was previously unknown (Buchan, Polak, Capella, Solcia and Pearse, 1978).

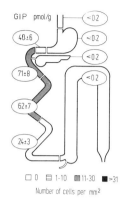

Fig. 14. GIP distribution in man (as Fig. 2).

3. Assay

Quantitative measurements of GIP have been made only by radioimmuno-assay (Kuzio, Dryburgh, Malloy and Brown, 1974), but it has proved to be a poor antigen. Thus GIP coupled by carbodiimide, gluteraldehyde or bis-diazotised benzidine to carrier proteins such as bovine serum albumin, thyroglobulin or haemocyanin results in antibody formation in less than 50% of the rabbits immunised. The responding animals frequently have low titre and low avidity antisera. Some antisera show cross-reaction with pancreatic glucagon though, as this hormone circulates in lower concentrations than GIP, it is rarely of practical significance. GIP has two tyrosine residues but the presence of tryptophan and methionine renders the molecules susceptible to oxidative damage. Accordingly iodination is difficult and the product often unstable. The technique of low level iodination, to reduce oxidative damage, and separation of mono-iodinated hormone by high resolution ion exchange chromatography has proved difficult with GIP as further hormone degradation often occurs during the separation procedure. Fortunately GIP is present in the circulation in reasonable concentrations and thus a high specific activity label is not required. The problem of the instability of endogenous GIP in plasma is overcome by addition of the proteolytic enzyme inhibitor, aprotinin, rapid separation of the blood sample and storage of the plasma at $-20°$. Under these conditions plasma levels do not appear to alter even after storage for one year. Gel chromatography of plasma demonstrates at least two molecular forms of GIP, the majority

in the position of the pure 43 amino acid porcine standard and a significant
minority eluting in a high molecular weight position (Brown, Dryburgh,
Frost, Otte and Pederson, 1978). The nature of this larger material is unknown
and it is possible that it is a different hormone which cross-reacts in the assay.
Radioimmunoassays for GIP appear relatively easily affected by non-
specific plasma effects and this may account for the wide variation of resting
plasma levels which have been reported from different laboratories.

4. Plasma Concentrations

Reported fasted human plasma levels of GIP range from 15–100 pmol/l
(Kuzio *et al.*, 1974; Bloom, 1975; Creutzfeldt, Ebert, Arnold, Frerichs and
Brown, 1976; Falko, Crockett, Cataland and Mazzaferri, 1975). All workers
agree that there is a rise after a meal and that this is relatively prolonged.
High levels on prolonged fasting, in diabetic patients and in subjects with
duodenal ulcer have been reported (Ebert and Creutzfeldt, 1978) but these
results have not been fully confirmed. The author, for example, has so far

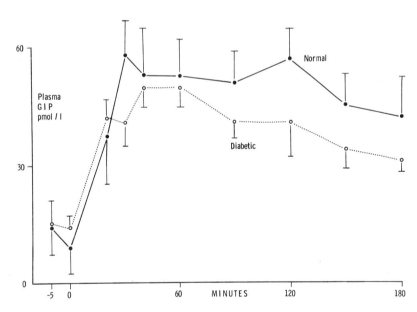

Fig. 15. Plasma GIP concentrations following a standard meal at times zero in seve:
well controlled diabetics and seven healthy normal subjects matched for age an
weight.

been unable to find any significant elevation of GIP in well controlled diabetic subjects (Fig. 15). GIP infusions in human volunteers have shown that at blood levels near the physiological range there is a considerable enhancement of glucose-induced insulin release (Dupre *et al.*, 1973; Brown *et al.*, 1974). Little effect on insulin is seen, however, when subjects are studied in the fasting state. In the isolated perfused pancreas preparation a similar glucose-dependence of the insulinotrophic action of GIP is seen (Pederson and Brown, 1976). Thus GIP has been renamed Glucose-dependent Insulin-releasing Peptide and has been proposed as the main hormone enhancing insulin release when nutriments are taken by mouth and may thus be the major component of the entero-insular axis.

D. NEUROTENSIN

1. Properties

Neurotensin is a 13 amino acid straight chain peptide (mw 1673) and was originally isolated from bovine brain because of its vascular effects (see Fig. 16) (Carraway and Leeman, 1975). Synthetic bovine neurotensin (Folkers,

```
  1    2    3    4    5    6    7    8    9   10   11   12   13
  +              −         +         +    +                        −
Glu−Leu−Tyr−Glu−Asn−Lys−Pro−Arg−Arg−Pro−Tyr−Ile−Leu
```

Fig. 16. Sequence of bovine neurotensin.

Chang, Humphries, Carraway, Leeman and Bowers 1976) is freely available. It has not yet been isolated from man. Pharmacological studies have shown that it is a potent vasodilatory agent and also increases vascular permeability leading, in the whole animal, to cyanosis (Carraway and Leeman, 1973). Neurotensin also causes hyperglycaemia and release of glucagon, insulin (Ukai, Inoue and Itatsu, 1977; Folkers *et al.*, 1976; Brown and Vale, 1976; Ishida, 1977) ACTH, FSH and LH. It is an inhibitor of gastric acid production (Andersson, Chang, Folkers and Rosell, 1976) and motor activity (Andersson, Rosell, Hjelmquist, Chang and Folkers, 1977) and causes a rise in plasma gastrin (Ishida, 1977). Its effects are short-lived and it is unstable in plasma.

2. Distribution

In the gastro-intestinal tract neurotensin is localised particularly to the ileum (Fig. 17) (Carraway and Leeman, 1976). There it is found in specific mucosal endocrine cells containing large granules (the NT cell) (Polak, Sullivan, Bloom, Buchan, Facer, Brown and Pearse, 1977).

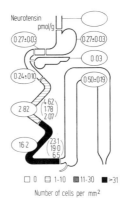

Fig. 17. Human distribution of neurotensin (as in Fig. 1, but where n < 4 individual values given).

3. Assay

Antibodies may be raised to synthetic bovine neurotensin in rabbits (Carraway and Leeman 1976) with neurotensin acting as a hapten coupled by conventional bifunctional coupling reagents to protein carriers such as bovine serum albumin. Less than 5% of rabbits immunised by such techniques, however, produce an antisera of sufficient titre and avidity to be useful for radioimmunoassay. Antibodies raised to bovine neurotensin do not appear to cross-react well with canine neurotensin though they readily detect neurotensin-like immunoreactivity in man. Iodination presents few difficulties and the product is stable for several months. Assay sensitivity of 5–10 pmol/l plasma has been achieved but is barely adequate for plasma hormone measurement. In addition, and perhaps because of the low sensitivity, plasma interference effects appear to be troublesome.

4. Plasma Concentrations

The fasting human neurotensin concentration is probably well below 50 pmol/l (Carraway and Leeman, 1976; Blackburn, Bloom, Ebeid and Ralphs, 1978), but current assays are insufficiently sensitive to produce accurate figures. The release after a meal in normal subjects is about 5 pmol/l though this rise is several times greater in patients with the dumping syndrome. There is little other information so far on neurotensin concentrations in disease. In addition there are as yet no studies which might indicate whether neurotensin was sufficiently potent to have any physiological effect at the low concentrations found in plasma.

E. ENTEROGLUCAGON

1. Properties

An intestinal material which cross-reacted with pancreatic glucagon assays was first detected by Unger et al., 1961. The material was found to have different physico-chemical properties from glucagon (Valverde, Rigopoulou, Exton, Ohneda, Eisentraut and Unger, 1968) in particular having a larger molecular weight component, and so the term glucagon-like immuno-reactivity (GLI) has been introduced. Further, antibodies which react with the C-terminal portion of pancreatic glucagon do not detect this enteric material, while N-terminal reacting antibodies react with it to a variable extent (Assan and Slusher, 1972). It is not yet even certain whether GLI in the intestine is a single hormone with several molecular forms of a family of hormones each having separate physiological roles. The presence of only one cell type containing glucagon-like immunoreactivity in the intestine (Grimelius, Polak, Solcia and Pearse, 1978), however, would favour the former hypothesis. Nomenclature is thus still confused, some workers favouring the term GLI or even N-GLI and others gut glucagon. The author feels that in the present state of knowledge the simple direct name enteroglucagon has as much to commend it as any other term being used. Moody and colleagues working in the Novo Institute in Denmark have recently been able to obtain a small amount of the pure porcine material (Moody, Jacobsen and Sunby, 1978) and have suggested it contains the entire amino acid sequence of pancreatic glucagon with an additional N-terminal sequence. As it appears to be approximately 100 amino acids in size they have invented a further name "glicentin". The full amino acid sequence has not yet been elucidated. Presumably, like glucagon, it belongs to the secretin, GIP, VIP family of peptides and may be expected to have pharmacological similarities. Confirmation of this, however, will have to await elucidation of the complete sequence and synthesis of adequate quantities of material.

2. Distribution

While the nature of enteroglucagon is the subject of considerable controversy, its distribution is not in doubt (Fig. 18). It is found in increasing concentrations as the small intestine is descended and significant amounts are found throughout the colon. No significant assayable enteroglucagon is found in the human stomach or the pancreas.

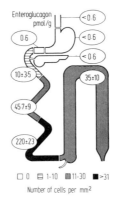

Fig. 18. Human distribution of enteroglucagon (as in Fig. 2).

3. Assay

Enteroglucagon is detected only as an immunological cross-reactant with antibodies raised to pancreatic glucagon. Measurement validity thus depends on the degree of cross-reaction of the particular pancreatic glucagon antisera used. When many pancreatic glucagon antibodies are screened it is possible to find a continuous distribution from almost no cross-reactivity (pancreatic glucagon specific antibodies) to maximum cross-reactivity, the latter being demonstrated by about 10% of antibodies. It is of interest that, however many antisera are looked at, no greater degree of cross-reactivity than this apparent maximum is ever found. This would imply that at this point full molar cross-reactivity is indeed being observed (Bloom, 1972). Partial confirmation of this point has recently been achieved using weighed amounts of standards of apparently pure "glicentin" (Moody et al., 1978) which gave the expected, i.e. "correct" reading of molar glucagon equivalence. As both pancreatic glucagon and enteroglucagon are present in the circulation and the cross-reacting assay measures both, it is necessary to also specifically measure the pancreatic glucagon component using a C-terminal reactive antisera and to subtract this value. Thus enteroglucagon is determined as total glucagon minus pancreatic glucagon. Such a subtractive assay necessarily involves an increased possibility of assay errors, though, as circulating enteroglucagon levels are considerably higher than pancreatic glucagon levels, in practice reasonably accurate estimations of enteroglucagon are achieved. The assay uses I^{125} pancreatic glucagon as label. Stable monoiodinated undamaged I^{125} glucagon for this purpose is best prepared by iodinating only a small proportion of the molecules (trace labelling) followed by high resolution ion exchange chromatography at pH 8 to separate out specifically the mono-iodinated glucagon (Jorgensen and Larsen, 1972). Two major forms of enteroglucagon can be distinguished in the circulation using gel chromatographic separation (Valverde et al., 1968). A larger one with a molecular weight between 7 and 12,000 and a smaller peak, often of lesser amount, with a molecular weight of between 3 and 5000. To date most reported assays have not investigated the differential release of these two forms into the circulation and their individual significance is unknown.

4. Plasma Concentrations

Fasting human plasma enteroglucagon levels have been reported to be about 20 pmol/l rising after a normal meal to about 40 pmol/l (Besterman, Bloom, Sarson, Blackburn, Johnston, Patel, Stewart, Modigliani, Guerin and Mallinson, 1978). As pure enteroglucagon is not available, there is no direct information on its possible physiological role. A single patient has been reported with an apparent enteroglucagon-producing tumour in which gross mucosal hypertrophy was noted (Bloom 1972). On this evidence it is possible to consider enteroglucagon as a trophic hormone, or a "growth hormone of the gut". In favour of this rather speculative hypothesis is the finding of low enteroglucagon levels following starvation and high enteroglucagon levels associated with hyperphagia. Thus after partial gut resection enteroglucagon rises rather than falls (Jacobs, Polak, Bloom and Dowling, 1976) and very high enteroglucagon levels are found in patients after a jejuno-ileal bypass (Frame, 1977). Similarly in states of mucosal damage, often associated with malabsorption e.g., coeliac disease, enteroglucagon levels are found to be elevated, (Fig. 19) (Besterman et al., 1978). Enteroglucagon is probably an important hormone in the physiology of the alimentary tract but wider recognition of this is prevented by the controversy over nomenclature and the failure to obtain sufficient quantities of pure material to develop direct assays or be able to study its pharmacology.

F. VASOACTIVE INTESTINAL PEPTIDES

1. Properties

VIP is a straight chain peptide of 28 amino acid residues (mw 3326) with two arginine and three lysine residues producing a strong positive charge and a very high pI. It was first isolated as a vasoactive substance from the intestine but subsequently shown to have considerable sequence (Bodanszky, Klausner and Said, 1973) and pharmacological similarities to secretin, glucagon and GIP. Only porcine VIP has so far been sequenced and a small amount has been prepared synthetically. The considerable quantities found in various tissues of the body and the ease of separation, because of its high charge, have led to a relatively free availability of the natural peptide. The presence of a double lysine bond, however, renders it highly susceptible to proteolytic degradation. Its main recognised pharmacological properties include vasodilation (Said and Mutt, 1970), inhibition of gastric acid, stimulation of pancreatic bicarbonate juice secretion (Said

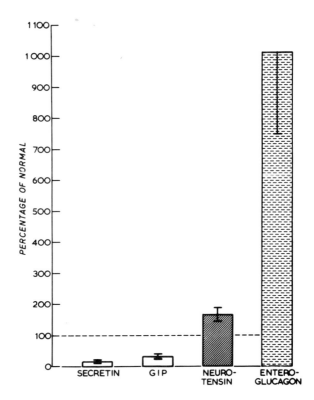

Fig. 19. The integrated release of secretin, GIP, neurotensin and enteroglucagon in patients with active coeliac disease following IV acid (secretin) or a test meal (GIP, neurotensin and enteroglucagon) expressed as the percentage of the hormone release in a matched group of healthy control subjects (horizontal dotted line). It can be seen that whereas the release of hormones from the area affected by the disease process is much reduced (secretin and GIP) the release of neurotensin and enteroglucagon from the ileum, beyond the diseased area of bowel, is greatly enhanced.

and Mutt, 1972), dilation of the gall bladder (Vagne and Troitskaja, 1976), stimulation of release of insulin, PP and glucagon (Adrian et al., 1978), stimulation of small intestinal juice production (Barbezat and Grossman, 1971) and mucosal adenyl cyclase (Schwartz, Kimberg, Sheerin, Field and Said, 1974) and inhibition of gastro-intestinal motor activity (Kachelhoffer, Mendel, Dauchel, Hohmatter and Grenier, 1976).

2. Distribution

VIP is a brain–gut peptide (see Table 3). It is found in high concentrations in various parts of the CNS (Bryant, Bloom, Polak, Albuquerque, Modlin and Pearse, 1976) where it has been localised to the synaptosomal fraction (Giachetti, Rosenberg and Said, 1976). It is also widely found throughout the peripheral tissues of the body in fine nerve fibres (Larsson, 1977; Larsson, Fahrenkrug and Schaffalitzky de Muckadell, 1977). It is one of the major components of the peptidergic nervous system (Polak and Bloom, 1978) whose existence has only recently been recognised. The components of this system, which is larger than the classical adrenergic or cholinergic autonomic nervous systems, include nerves containing bombesin, enkephalin, somato-statin, substance P and other less well recognised components. The VIPergic nerves are, however, the most numerous. VIP is also found in a few endocrine cells in the gut mucosa, particularly in the ileum and colon (Solcia et al., 1978).

3. Assay

As in the case of the other newer gut hormones the only accepted method of measurement is by radioimmunoassay (Fahrenkrug and Schaffalitzky de Muckadell, 1977; Bloom, 1978a), though receptor assays have been reported (Laburtle, Bataille and Rosselin, 1977). Antibodies to VIP have been raised in numerous laboratories and show different specificities for the C and N-terminal portion of the molecule. Cross-reaction with other hormones has not been seen. There is no evidence so far for any species differences in the molecular configuration of the VIP found in various experimental mammals or in man. Iodination of VIP presents some difficulties because of the presence of an oxidisable methionine and also VIP's suscep-tibility to proteolysis. VIP shows strong adherence to certain types of surface, perhaps because of its high charge. As circulating VIP concentrations are low, it is necessary to prepare a high specific activity ^{125}I VIP using high resolution ion exchange chromatography to purify the monoiodinated hormone (Mitchell and Bloom, 1978). The product may then be stored at $-20°$ in pure solutions containing protein for several months without obvious deterioration. VIP is unstable in plasma and even addition of the proteolytic enzyme inhibitor aprotinin and rapid freezing of the plasma samples after venepuncture is not sufficient to prevent some losses. Subsequent freezing and thawing and prolonged storage are also deleterious. Several assays have been reported with a sensitivity below 10 pmol/l plasma (Fahrenkrug and Schaffalitzky de Muckadell, 1977; Bloom, 1978) but this may still be inadequate to detect fasting levels in all individuals. The majority of VIP present in human gut and brain extracts elutes on gel chromatography in a similar position to pure porcine VIP (Bryant *et al.*, 1976). However, ion exchange analysis reveals several lesser components with differing properties (Dimaline and Dockray, 1977). VIP secreted into the plasma by tumours is far more heterogeneous and, includes several large molecular weight forms (Bloom, Bryant, Adrian and Mallinson, 1978).

4. Plasma Concentrations

Using a sensitive radioimmunoassay the mode fasting plasma VIP is 1·5 pmol/l but there is a skew distribution so that the upper end of the normal range is 21 pmol/l and mean normal is 2·1 pmol/l (Mitchell and Bloom, 1978). VIP has been reported to be released into the blood stream after vagal stimulation (Schaffalitzky de Muckadell, Fahrenkrug and Holst, 1977) and also after intraduodenal osmotic loads (Ebeid, Soeters, Murray and Fischer, 1977) or acid (Bloom, Mitchell, Greenberg, Christofides, Domschke, Domschke, Mitznegg and Demling, 1978). Significant elevations in portal plasma have been shown to follow intestinal ischaemia in pigs. (Fig. 20) (Modlin, Bloom and Mitchell, 1978). Perhaps the most dramatic elevations are seen with VIP-producing tumours. Verner and Morrison (1974) described a syndrome of severe watery diarrhoea associated with reduction in gastric acid output and a tumour of the pancreas. Tumour removal produced cure and they postulated that a tumour produced hormone was responsible. These tumours were subsequently found to contain VIP and plasma VIP was always grossly elevated (e.g. above 60 pmol/l) (Bloom, 1978b). Another tumour associated with diarrhoea, which is common in children, is the ganglioneuroma or ganglioneuroblastoma. These tumours have also been shown to contain VIP and to release it into the circulation. In both conditions the severity of the diarrhoea roughly correlated with the plasma VIP level and treatment which reduced VIP production, such as administration of the cytotoxic drug, streptozotocin, produces remission of the clinical symptoms. Measurement of plasma VIP has been produced as a diagnostic aid for detecting this rather rare cause of diarrhoea and some values obtained from new patients are depicted in Fig. 21. In each case a tumour was found. Other causes of watery diarrhoea, including cholera, addiction to purgatives, acute bowel infections, medullary carcinoma of the thyroid and ulcerative colitis for example are not associated with any significant elevation of plasma VIP. Thus VIP measurement is a very useful screening test for the detection of VIPomas. Too many of these tumours are found at post-mortem and a greater awareness of the value of the VIP assay in this context is important.

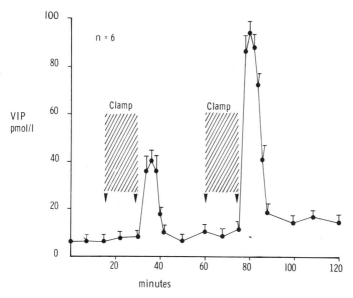

Fig. 20. Portal plasma VIP concentrations in six anaesthetised pigs following two 15 min periods of intestinal ischaemia produced by clamping of the superior mesenteric vascular pedicle. A highly significant rise in VIP levels follows release of the clamp.

G. SOMATOSTATIN

1. Properties

Somatostatin was isolated from the ovine hypothalamus as an inhibitor of growth hormone secretion by the pituitary. It is a **peptide** of 14 amino acids (mw 1640) bridged across between cystines at the 3rd and 14th positions by an S–S link (see Fig. 22). The original molecule and several active analogues are freely available in synthetic form. Pharmacological studies have demonstrated that it is one of the most potent and universal inhibitors of endocrine secretion that is known (Raptis and Gerich, 1978). Thus it has been shown to not only completely inhibit the release of growth hormone but also that of TSH, insulin, glucagon, pancreatic polypeptide, gastrin, secretin, motilin,

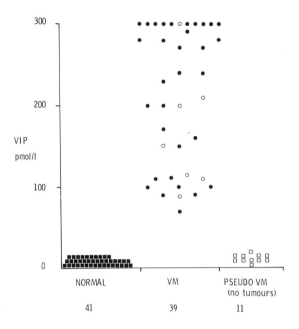

Fig. 21. Plasma VIP concentrations in the first received sample from 39 patients with the Verner–Morrison syndrome (severe watery diarrhoea) all of whom subsequently were shown to have either a pancreatic tumour (solid dots) or a ganglioneuroma (open circles). Also shown are the concentrations in 41 healthy subjects and 11 patients with severe watery diarrhoea, clinically suggesting the Verner–Morrison syndrome, but in whom at laparotomy no tumour could be found (pseudo-Verner–Morrison syndrome).

enteroglucagon and neurotensin. In addition it can inhibit the effect of these hormones on their target tissues and thus will prevent acid secretion during pentagastrin infusion and pancreatic bicarbonate secretion during secretin infusion. The finding that certain analogues are relatively selective in their actions when tested in the rat (Brown, Rivier and Vale, 1977), e.g. D Ser[13], Des Asn[5] somatostatin inhibits insulin and growth hormone more than

1   2   3   4   5   6   7   8   9   10   11   12   13   14

Ala–Gly–Cys–Lys–Asn–Phe–Phe–Trp–Lys–Thr–Phe–Thr–Ser–Cys

Fig. 22. Sequence of ovine somatostatin.

glucagon, while D Cys[14] somatostatin inhibits glucagon to a greater degree, has not been fully substantiated in other species. The analogue of somatostatin Des[1,2,4,5,12,13], D Tryp[8] is almost as potent as the parent molecule in spite of missing six of the 14 amino acids.

2. Distribution

Somatostatin is found throughout the brain but high concentrations are present in the hypothalamus, particularly the median eminence (Fig. 23)

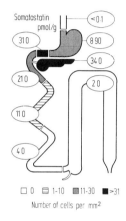

Fig. 23. Distribution of somatostatin in man (as Fig. 2).

(Kobayashi, Brown and Vale, 1978). In the gut the greatest amounts are found in the antrum and upper small intestine and also in the pancreas (Arimura, Sato, Dupont, Nishi and Schally, 1975). It is mainly localised in the mucosa of the alimentary tract and the islets of Langerhans to the endocrine D-cell (Polak, Pearse, Grimelius, Bloom and Arimura, 1975) which has long been recognised but whose product was hitherto unknown. Somatostatin is also seen in small numbers of fine nerve fibres in various tissues (Hokfeldt, Johansson, Efendic, Luft and Arimura, 1975).

3. Assay

Measurement of plasma somatostatin has not proved easy for several reasons. Among these is the fact that the circulating concentrations are near the limits of sensitivity of reported assays, the material appears highly unstable and it seems to exist in several forms, the majority of which may be of larger molecular weight than somatostatin itself. When synthetic somatostatin is added to human blood in known amounts, it is difficult to achieve full recovery even in the presence of EDTA, aprotinin and with rapid storage of plasma at $-20°$. It is not certain if the larger forms of somatostatin are actually big molecules, or merely non-covalent associations (Dupont and Alberado-Urvia, 1976), are biologically active, or indeed whether they react fully with current antisera. Most success has so far been achieved using isolated organ preparations where it is possible to find changes in the somatostatin content of the effluent perfusate in response to physiological stimuli. For example with the isolated perfused pancreas somatostatin release occurs for the most part in response to the same stimuli that release insulin, and the patterns of these two hormones are frequently parallel (Patton, Ipp, Dobbs, Orci, Vale and Unger, 1977; Schauder, McIntosh, Paten, Arends, Arnold, Frerichs and Creutzfeldt, 1977). Addition to the perfusate of somatostatin antisera in sufficient quantities to prevent biological activity of added somatostatin results in an increased output of insulin (Taniguchi, Utsumi, Hasegawa, Kobayashi, Watanabe, Murakami, Seki, Tsutou, Makimura, Sakoda and Baba, 1977) suggesting that the locally released somatostatin is having a significant inhibitory effect. Present indications suggest that the plasma level of somatostatin produced by exogenous somatostatin infusion, which is just sufficient to produce measurable pharmacological effects, is an order of magnitude higher than those found naturally. If this is confirmed it may indicate that the most important role of somatostatin is not as a circulating hormone but as a local, or paracrine, regulatory substance. The discovery of endocrine pancreatic tumours containing large quantities of somatostatin (Ganda and Soeldner, 1977; Larsson, Hirsch, Holst, Ingemansson, Kuhl, Jensen, Lundquist, Rehfeld and Schwartz, 1977) and producing high circulating levels, low gastric acid output and diabetes may yield further information on somatostatin's physiological role. In addition a number of other endocrine and neural tumours also produce somatostatin-like immunoreactivity in small amounts (Fig. 24).

H. OTHER HORMONALLY ACTIVE GUT PEPTIDES

The field of gut endocrinology is still advancing rapidly and further hormones are bound to be discovered. A considerable body of evidence is now available that a substance, chymodenin (Adelson and Rothman, 1975) is elaborated in the upper small intestine and acts to stimulate the release from the pancreas of chymotrypsin. So far shortage of material has not allowed full confirmation of this work. There are several reports of an inhibitor of pancreatic exocrine secretion (pancreotone) (Debas and Yamagishi, 1977) being released from

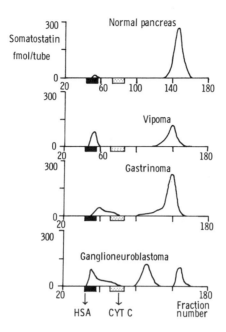

Fig. 24. G50 Sephadex gel chromatogram of somatostatin-like immunoreactivity in extracts of a normal human pancreas, a VIP-producing pancreatic tumour, a gastrin-producing pancreatic tumour and an abdominal ganglioneuroblastoma. The solid bar is the elution position of human serum albumin and the speckled bar of cytochrome C. The major peak of somatostatin immunoreactivity elutes in the same position as synthetic ovine somatostatin.

the lower small intestine or colon. This substance, however, has not yet been isolated. Many other putative hormones have been proposed but the reports await confirmation. In addition it is uncertain how often brain–gut peptides, such as substances P, bombesin, enkephalin etc. (see Fig. 25), are released into the circulation in sufficient quantity to influence distant tissues and thereby act as "occasional hormones".

	1	2	3	4	5	6	7	8	9	10	11	12	13	14

Substance P   Arg–Pro–Lys–Pro–Gln–Gln–Phe–Phe–Gly–Leu–Met(NH$_2$)

Bombesin   Glp–Gln–Arg–Leu–Gly–Asn–Gln–Trp–Ala–Val–Gly–His–Leu—Met(NH$_2$)

Fig. 25. Sequence of substance P and bombesin.

CONCLUSIONS

It is clear that the circulating hormones from the gastro-intestional tract are only one specialised branch of the tripartite control system, viz. hormonal, paracrine and neural. Initially it seemed enough to investigate the physiology of single hormones. It soon became apparent that such organs as the pancreas were controlled by several different hormones and that the measurement of any one gave an incomplete picture. Now it seems that the story is even more complicated and that even the measurement of the complete circulating gut hormone profile is inadequate to describe the physiological control of digestive function. It is frustrating that in spite of knowing what ought to be investigated, the technology lags behind. It is still extremely difficult to envisage methods for accurate quantitation of the influence of the neural and paracrine system. However, as described in this chapter, even the role played by the circulating hormones of the gut is, in almost every case, the subject of active controversy. We are passing through an era of rapid advance where, in the midst of general confusion the fundamental corner stones are being laid for the future. The comprehensive understanding of neuro-endocrine control of the gut is an important subject not only because there are numerous troublesome disorders of the alimentary tract whose patho-physiology is quite unknown, but also because the gut forms a model system whose mechanisms may be directly applicable to the understanding of the control of other vital organs.

REFERENCES

Adelson, J. W. and Rothman, S. S. (1975). *Am. J. Physiol.* **229**, 1680.
Adrian, T. E., Bloom, S. R., Besterman, H. S., Barnes, A. J., Cooke, T. J. C., Russell, R. C. G. and Faber, R. G. (1977). *Lancet*, **i**, 161.
Adrian, T. E., Bloom, S. R., Besterman, H. S. and Bryant, M. G. (1978). "Gut Hormones", p. 254. Churchill Livingstone, Edinburgh.
Adrian, T. E., Bloom, S. R., Hermansen, K. and Iversen, J. (1978). *Diabetologia*, **14**, 413.
Adrian, T. E., Greenberg, G. R., Besterman, H. S., McCloy, R. F., Chadwick, V. S., Barnes. A. J., Mallinson, C. N., Baron, J. H., Alberti, K. G. G. M. and Bloom, S. R. (1978). "Gut Hormones", p. 265. Churchill Livingstone, Edinburgh.
Andersson, S., Chang, D., Folkers, K. and Rosell, S. (1976). *Life Sci.* **19**, 367.
Andersson, S., Rosell, S., Hjelmquist, U., Chang, D. and Folkers, K. (1977). *Acta physiol. scand.* **100**, 231.
Arimura, A., Sato, H., Dupont, A., Nishi, N. and Schally, A. V. (1975). *Science*, **189**, 1007.
Assan, R. and Slusher, N. (1972). *Diabetes*, **21**, 843.
Babkin, B. P. (1949). "Pavlov: A Biography." University of Chicago Press, Chicago.

Barbezat, G. O. and Grossman, M. I. (1971). *Science*, **174**, 422.
Bayliss, W. M. and Starling, E. H. (1902). *J. physiol. (Lond.)* **28**, 325.
Besterman, H. S., Bloom, S. R., Sarson, D. L., Blackburn, A. M., Johnston, D. I., Patel, H. R., Stewart, J. S., Modigliani, R., Guerin, S. and Mallinson, C. N. (1978). *Lancet*, **i**, 785.
Blackburn, A. M., Bloom, S. R., Ebeid, F. H. and Ralphs, D. N. L. (1978). *Gut*, **19**, A447.
Bloom, S. R. (1972). *Gut*, **13**, 520.
Bloom, S. R. (1975). *Diabetologia*, **11**, 334.
Bloom, S. R. (1978a). "Methods of Hormone Radioimmunoassay", p. 553. Academic Press, London and New York.
Bloom, S. R. (1978b). *Am. J. dig. Dis.* **23**. 373.
Bloom, S. R., Adrian, T. E., Bryant, M. G. and Polak, J. M. (1978). *Lancet*, **i**, 1155.
Bloom, S. R., Bryant, M. G., Adrian, T. E. and Mallinson, C. N. (1978). *Gastroenterology*, **74**, 1011.
Bloom, S. R., Christofides, N. D., Modlin, I. and Fitzpatrick, M. L. (1978). *Gastroenterology*, **74**, 1010.
Bloom, S. R., Mitchell, S. J., Greenberg, G. R., Christofides. N. D.. Domschke, W., Domschke, S., Mitznegg, P. and Demling, L. (1978). *Acta hepatogastroent.* **25**. 365.
Bloom, S. R., Mitznegg, P. and Bryant, M. G. (1976). *Scand. J. Gastroent.* **11** (Suppl. 39), 47.
Bodanszky, M., Klausner, Y. S. and Said, S. I. (1973). *Proc. natn. Acad. Sci., USA*, **70**, 382.
Brown, J. C., Cook, M. A. and Dryburgh, J. R. (1973). *Can. J. Biochem.* **51**. 533.
Brown, J. C. and Dryburgh, J. R. (1971). *Can. J. Biochem.* **49**, 867.
Brown, J. C., Dryburgh, J. R.. Frost. J. L.. Otte. S. C. and Pederson. R. A. (1978). "Gut Hormones", p. 277. Churchill Livingstone. Edinburgh.
Brown, M. and Vale, W. (1976). *Endocrinology*, **98**, 819.
Brown, M., Rivier, J. and Vale, W. (1977). *Science*, **196**, 1467.
Bryant, M. G., Bloom, S. R., Polak, J. M., Albuquerque, R. H., Modlin, I. and Pearse, A. G. E. (1976). *Lancet*, **i**, 991.
Buchan, A. M. J., Polak, J. M., Capella, C., Solcia, E. and Pearse, A. G. E. (1978). *Histochemistry*, **56**, 37.
Carraway, R. and Leeman, S. E. (1973). *J. biol. Chem.* **248**, 6854.
Carraway, R. and Leeman, S. E. (1975). *J. biol. Chem.* **250**, 1907.
Carraway, R. and Leeman, S. E. (1976). *J. biol. Chem.* **251**, 7045.
Christofides, N. D. and Bloom, S. R. (1978a). *Experientia*, **34**, 809.
Christofides, N. D. and Bloom, S. R. (1978b). *Gut*, **20**, 102.
Creutzfeldt, W., Ebert, R., Arnold, R., Frerichs, H. and Brown, J. C. (1976). *Diabetologia*, **12**, 279.
Debas, H. T. and Yamagishi, T. (1977). *Gastroenterology*, **72**, 1045.
Debas, H. T., Yamagishi, T. and Dryburgh, J. R. (1977). *Gastroenterology*, **73**, 777.
Dimaline, R. and Dockray, G. J. (1977). *J. Physiol. (Lond.)* **276**, 551.
Dockray, G. J. (1976). *Nature, Lond.* **264**, 568.
Domschke, S., Domschke, W., Schmack, B., Tympner, F., Junge, O., Wünsch, E., Jaeger, E. and Demling, L. (1976). *Am. J. dig. Dis.* **21**, 789.
Dryburgh, J. R. and Brown, J. C. (1975). *Gastroenterology*, **68**, 1169.
Dupont, A. and Alvarado-Urbina, G. (1976). *Life Sci.* **19**, 1431.
Dupre, J., Ross, S. A., Watson, D. and Brown, J. C. (1973). *J. clin. Endocr.* **37**, 826.
Ebeid, A. M., Soeters, P. B., Murray, P. and Fischer, J. E. (1977). *J. surg. Res.* **23**, 25.

354   S. R. BLOOM

Ebert, R. and Creutzfeldt, W. (1978). "Gut Hormones", p. 294. Churchill Livingstone, Edinburgh.
Edkins, J. S. (1905). *Proc. R. Soc. B.* **761**, 376.
Fahrenkrug, J. and Schaffalitzky de Muckadell, O. B. (1977). *J. Lab. clin. Med.* **89**, 1379.
Falko, J. M., Crockett, S. E., Cataland, S. and Mazzaferri, E. L. (1975). *Clin. Endocr.* **41**, 260.
Floyd, J. C., Jr., Fajans, S. S., Pek, S. and Chance, R. E. (1977). *Rec. Prog. Horm. Res.* **33**, 519.
Folkers, K., Chang, D., Humphries, J., Carraway, R., Leeman, S. E. and Bowers, C. Y. (1976). *Proc. natn. Acad. Sci., USA*, **73**, 3833.
Frame, C. M. (1977). *Am. J. clin. Nutr.* **30**, 1004.
Gaginella, T. S., Phillips, S. F., Dozois, R. R. and Go, V. L. W. (1978). *Gastroenterology*, **74**, 11.
Ganda, O. P. and Soeldner, J. S. (1977). *New. Engl. J. Med.* **297**, 1352.
Giachetti, A., Rosenberg, R. N. and Said, S. I. (1976). *Lancet*, **ii**, 741.
Greenberg, G. R., McCloy, R. F., Adrian, T. E., Chadwick, V. S., Baron, J. H. and Bloom, S. R. (1978). *Lancet*, **ii**, 1280.
Grimelius, L., Polak, J. M., Solcia, E. and Pearse, A. G. E. (1978). "Gut Hormones", p. 365. Churchill Livingstone, Edinburgh.
Heitz, Ph., Polak, J. M., Bloom, S. R. and Pearse, A. G. E. (1976). *Gut*, **17**, 755.
Hökfelt, T., Johansson, O., Efendic, S., Luft, R. and Arimura, A. (1975). *Experientia*, **31**, 852.
Ishida, T. (1977). *Endocr. jap.* **24**, 335.
Jacobs, L. R., Polak, J. M., Bloom, S. R. and Dowling, R. H. (1976). *Clin. Sci. mol. Med.* **50**, 14.
Jennewein, H. M., Hummelt, H., Siewert, R. and Waldeck, F. (1975). *Digestion*, **13**, 246.
Jorgensen, K. H. and Larsen, U. D. (1972). *Horm. Metab. Res.* **4**, 223.
Kachelhoffer, J., Mendel, C., Dauchel, J., Hohmatter, D. and Grenier, J. F. (1976). *Am. J. dig. Dis.* **21**, 957.
Kimmel, J. R., Pollock, H. G. and Hazelwood, R. L. (1968). *Endocrinology*, **83**, 1323.
Kimmel, J. R., Pollock, H. G. and Hazelwood, R. L. (1971). *Fed. Proc.* **30**, 1318.
Kobayashi, R. M., Brown, M. and Vale, W. (1978). *Brain Res.* (In Press).
Kuzio, M., Dryburgh, J. R., Malloy, K. M. and Brown, J. C. (1974). *Gastroenterology*, **66**, 357.
Laburthe, M., Bataille, D. and Rosselin, G. (1977). *Acta endocr., Copenh.* **84**, 588.
Larsson, L.-I., Fahrenkrug, J. and Schaffalitzky de Muckadell, O. B. (1977a). *Life. Sci.* **21**, 503.
Larsson, L. I., Fahrenkrug, J. and Schaffalitzky de Muckadell, O. B. (1977b). *Science*, **197**, 1374.
Larsson, L.-I., Hirsch, M. A., Holst, J. J., Ingemansson, S., Kühl, C., Jensen, S. L., Lundqvist, G., Rehfeld, J. H. and Schwartz, T. W. (1977). *Lancet*, **i**, 666.
Lin, T. M. and Chance, R. E. (1972). *Gastroenterology*, **62**, 852.
Lin, T. M. and Chance, R. E. (1978). "Gut Hormones", p. 242. Churchill Livingstone, Edinburgh.
Lin, T. M., Evans, D. C. and Bromer, W. W. (1974). *Gastroenterology*, **66**, 852.
Mitchell, S. J. and Bloom, S. R. (1978). *Gut*, **19**, 1043.
Modlin, I. M., Bloom, S. R. and Mitchell, S. J. (1978). *Experientia*, **34**, 535.
Modlin, I. M., Mitznegg, P. and Bloom, S. R. (1978). *Gut*, **19**, 399.

Moody, A. J., Jacobsen, H. and Sunby, F. (1978). "Gut Hormones", p. 369. Churchill Livingstone, Edinburgh.

Patton, G. S., Ipp, E., Dobbs, R. E., Orci, L., Vale, W. and Unger, R. H. (1977). *Proc. natn. Acad. Sci., USA*, **74**, 2140.

Pearse, A. G. E. (1969). *istochem. Cytochem.* **17**, 303.

Pearse, A. G. E. (1976a). *Lancet*, **i**, 915.

Pearse, A. G. E. (1976b). *Nature, Lond.* **262**, 92.

Pearse, A. G. E., Polak, J. M., Bloom, S. R., Adams, C., Dryburgh, J. R. and Brown, J. C. (1974). *Virchows Arch. Abt. B.* **16**, 111.

Pederson, R. A. and Brown, J. C. (1972). *Gastroenterology*, **62**, 393.

Pederson, R. A. and Brown, J. C. (1976). *Endocrinology*, **99**, 780.

Polak, J. M. and Bloom, S. R. (1978). *Invest. cell. Path.* **1**, 301.

Polak, J. M., Pearse, A. G. E., Grimelius, L., Bloom, S. R. and Arimura, A. (1975). *Lancet*, **i**, 1220.

Polak, J. M., Sullivan, S. N., Bloom, S. R., Buchan, A. M. J., Facer, P., Brown, M. R. and Pearse, A. G. E. (1977). *Nature, Lond.* **270**, 183.

Raptis, S. and Gerich, J. E. (1978). *Metabolism*, **27** (Suppl. 1).

Rehfeld, J. (1978). *J. biol. Chem.* **253**, 4016.

Said, S. I. and Mutt, V. (1970). *Nature, Lond.* **225**, 863.

Said, S. I. and Mutt, V. (1972). *Eur. J. Biochem.* **28**, 199.

Schaffalitzky de Muckadell, D. B., Fahrenkrug, J. and Holst, J. J. (1977). *Gastroenterology*, **72**, 373.

Schauder, P., McIntosh, C., Panten, U., Arends, J., Arnold, R., Frerichs, H. and Creutzfeldt, W. (1977). *FEBS Lett.* **81**, 355.

Schwartz, C. J., Kimberg, D. V., Sheerin, H. E., Field, M. and Said, S. I. (1974). *J. clin. Invest.* **54**, 536.

Schwartz, T. W., Holst, J. J., Fahrenkrug, J., Jensen, S. L., Nielsen, O. V., Rehfeld, J. F., Schaffalitzky de Muckadell, D. B. and Stadil, F. (1978). *J. clin. Invest.* **61**, 781.

Schwartz, T. W., Stadil, F., Chance, R. E., Rehfeld, J. F., Larsson, L.-I. and Moon, N. (1976). *Lancet*, **i**, 1102.

Solcia, E., Polak, J. M., Pearse, A. G. E., Forssman, W. G., Larsson, L.-T., Sundler, F., Lechago, J., Grimelius, L., Fujita, T., Creutzfeldt, W., Gepts, W., Faulmer, S., Lefranc, G., Heitz, Ph., Hage, E., Buchan, A. M. J., Bloom, S. R. and Grossman, M. I. (1977). "Gut Hormones", p. 40. Churchill Livingstone, Edinburgh.

Strunz, U., Domschke, W., Domschke, S., Mitznegg, P., Wünsch, E., Jaeger, E. and Demling, L. (1976). *Scand. J. Gastroent.* **11**, 199.

Strunz, U., Domschke, W., Mitznigg, P., Domschke, S., Schubert, E., Wünsch, E., Jaeger, E. and Demling, L. (1975). *Gastroenterology*, **68**, 1485.

Taniguchi, H., Utsumi, M., Hasegawa, M., Kobayashi, T., Watanabe, Y., Murakami, K., Seki, M., Tsutou, A., Makimura, H., Sakoda, M. and Baba, S. (1977). *Diabetes*, **26**, 700.

Taylor, I. L., Walsh, J. H., Rotter, J. and Passaro, E., Jr. (1978). *Lancet*, **i**, 845.

Ukai, M., Inoue, I. and Itatsu, T. (1977). *Endocrinology*, **100**, 1284.

Unger, R. H., Eisentraut, A., Sims, K., McCall, M. S. and Madison, L. L. (1961). *Clin. Res.* **9**, 53.

Vagne, M. and Troitskaja, V. (1976). *Digestion*, **14**, 62.

Valverde, I., Rigopoulou, D., Exton, J., Ohneda, A., Eisentraut, A. and Unger, R. H. (1968). *Am. J. med. Sci.* **255**, 415.

Vantrappen, G., Janssens, J., Peeters, T. L., Bloom, S. R., van Tongeren, J. and Hellemans, J. (1978). *Gastroenterology*, **74**, 1149.

Verner, J. V. and Morrison, A. B. (1974). *Arch. int. Med.* **133**, 492.
Wingate, D. L., Ruppin, H., Thompson, H. H., Green, W. E. R., Domschke, W., Wünsch, E., Demling, L. and Ritchie, H. D. (1977). *Acta hepatogastroent.* **24**, 278.

VIII. Gastro-intestinal Hormones II. Gastrin, Cholecystokinin and Secretin

G. J. DOCKRAY

A. GASTRIN

1. Chemistry

(a) Heptadecapeptide gastrin

Three years after Bayliss and Starling discovered secretin, Edkins (1905) identified in extracts of pyloric antral mucosa a gastric secretagogue which he named gastrin. However, the specificity of the antral secretagogue later fell in doubt when it became clear that extracts of gastric mucosa contained histamine, which was a strong stimulant of acid secretion and widely distributed throughout the body. Komarov (1938) produced the first evidence of a gastric secretagogue in antral mucosa which was distinct from histamine, and physiological evidence of an antral hormone was later provided by Grossman, Robertson and Ivy (1948). Final proof of the existence of gastrin was obtained when Gregory and Tracy (1964) isolated from hog antral mucosa two heptadecapeptides which strongly stimulated acid secretion.

Gregory and Tracy (1964) used the techniques of gel permeation chromatography, and ion exchange chromatography on diethylaminoethyl (DEAE) and aminoethyl (AE) celluloses, to isolate from boiling-water extracts of hog antral mucosa two highly acidic heptadecapeptides, designated gastrins I and II. The two gastrins were shown by Kenner and coworkers to have identical sequences but for a sulphate group on the tyrosine residue of gastrin II, and the structures were confirmed by synthesis (Kenner and Sheppard, 1968). The heptadecapeptides contain no basic amino acid residues, and a sequence of five glutamic acid residues in the mid-portion of the chain, together with a penultimate aspartic acid, impart the strong acidic charge (Fig. 1). At acid pH, poly-L-glutamic acid is known to form an α-helical

```
 1   2    3    4    5    6    7    8    9   10  11  12  13  14  15  16  17
Glp–Leu–Gly–Pro–Gln–Gly–His–Pro–Ser–Leu–Val–Ala–Asp–Pro–Ser–Lys–Lys–
```

```
 18  19  20  21  22  23  24  25  26  27  28  29  30  31  32        34
Gln–Gly–Pro–Trp–Leu–Glu–Glu–Glu–Glu–Glu–Ala–Tyr–Gly–Trp–Met–Asp–Phe–NH₂
                                              |
                                              R
```

Fig. 1. The amino acid sequence of human big gastrin. Note that there are differences in the immunochemical properties of the NH_2-terminal regions of natural and synthetic big gastrins, so that this sequence (at least in the NH_2-terminal regions) cannot be regarded as proven by synthesis (see text). Heptadecapeptide gastrin (G17) corresponds to sequence 18–34 (enclosed in box), except for the NH_2-terminal residue which is pyrrolidone carboxylic acid. Minigastrin (G14) corresponds to sequence 21–34. The biologically inactive NH_2-terminal tridecapeptide of G17 corresponds to sequence 18–30. R = H or SO_3H

conformation and gastrin may well have a partial α-helical conformation in acid solution, but at physiological pH it is likely to exist as a random coil (Piszkiewica, 1974). The NH_2-terminal residue of the heptadecapeptides is blocked as pyrollidone carboxylic acid, and the COOH-terminus is blocked as phenylalanine amide.

Biological testing of fragments produced during the synthesis of gastrin led to the discovery that the COOH-terminal tetrapeptide (–Trp–Met–Asp–Phe–NH_2) possessed significant biological activity, being about one-tenth as potent as the whole molecule in stimulating acid secretion, whereas NH_2-terminal fragments were inactive (Tracy and Gregory, 1964). The COOH-terminal tetrapeptide is sometimes referred to as the minimal active fragment of gastrin, but smaller fragments such as the tri- and dipeptides also have a trace of biological activity (Lin, 1972). An analogue of the COOH-terminal tetrapeptide—Pentagastrin (βAla–Trp–Met–Asp–Phe–NH_2) is now widely used in assessing gastric secretion. Removal of the COOH-terminal amide group completely abolishes the activity of gastrin, and oxidation of the methionine also causes inactivation (Morley, 1968). However, the methionine residue in the COOH-terminal tetrapeptide may be substituted with leucine or norleucine to produce a stable, active analogue.

Pairs of heptadecapeptides similar to those in hog have been isolated from several mammalian species (dog, cat, cow and sheep) including man (Kenner and Sheppard, 1968). Heptadecapeptides have also been isolated from human gastrinoma tissue (Zollinger–Ellison tumours) and shown by finger-printing techniques to be identical with human antral gastrin (Gregory, Tracy, Agarwal and Grossman, 1969). The gastrins of species studied so far differ only in one or two amino acid substitutions in the mid- and NH_2-terminal parts of the molecule and these have little or no influence on biological activity. Immunochemical studies indicate that rodent (rat and mouse) gastrins may differ substantially from other mammalian gastrins in the NH_2-terminal region (Dockray, Best and Taylor, 1977), but the sequences of rodent gastrins have not yet been reported.

The COOH-terminal pentapeptide of gastrin is identical with that in cholecystokinin (CCK), and like gastrin II, CCK has a sulphated tyrosine residue (Mutt and Jorpes, 1968). However in CCK the sulphated tyrosine is at the seventh position from the COOH-terminus whereas in gastrin it is at the sixth position from the COOH-terminus. Because the COOH-terminal parts of these hormones determine biological activity the recognition of structural similarities between gastrin and CCK has had important implications for the study and interpretation of structure–activity relationships and in the search for specificity in bioassays and radioimmunoassays. The structural similarities suggest a common evolutionary history for the two hormones (Barrington and Dockray, 1976; Dockray, 1977a).

(b) Big gastrin

The observation of molecular variants of other hormones, notably insulin and parathyroid hormone, led Berson and Yalow to analyse gastrin in the plasma of hypergastrinaemic patients (pernicious anaemia and gastrinomas) and to the discovery that the major circulating form of gastrin was larger and less acidic than the heptadecapeptides (Yalow and Berson, 1970b); the new component was called big or basic gastrin. Soon after the discovery of big gastrin, Gregory and Tracy (1972) reported the isolation from hog antral mucosa and human gastrinoma tissue of pairs of peptides with properties similar to the component described by Berson and Yalow. The two big gastrins in both species contained 34 amino acid residues. The COOH-terminal 17 residues in both species were identical with the corresponding heptadecapeptides, and as in the heptadecapeptides the two forms of big gastrin in each species differed only in the presence or absence of a sulphated tyrosine residue. The NH_2-terminal region of big gastrin is a linear peptide chain, which is blocked at the NH_2-terminus as pyrollidone carboxylic acid, and linked through two lysine residues to the COOH-terminal heptadecapeptide (Fig. 1). According to conditions, trypsin cleaves big gastrin either between, or to the carboxyl side of the two lysine residues (Gregory and Tracy, 1975). Human and porcine big gastrins have been synthesised and shown to have similar biological activity to natural big gastrins (Kenner and Gregory, personal communication). However, we have recently obtained an antiserum against natural porcine big gastrin, that is specific for the NH_2-terminal region of this peptide and cross-reacts only weakly (< 0.0005) with synthetic porcine or human big gastrin (Dockray, Gregory and Kenner, 1978). There are therefore immunochemical differences in the NH_2-terminal regions of natural and synthetic big gastrins, although the basis of these differences is, as yet, uncertain. On this evidence the structure of big gastrin cannot yet be regarded as having been proven by synthesis.

A widely used notation for identifying the different biologically active forms of gastrin is based on the prefix "G" followed by the number of amino acid residues in the molecule, so that heptadecapeptide gastrin becomes G17, and the big gastrins are G34; the designations -I and -II are used to denote unsulphated and sulphated forms respectively.

(c) Fragments of G17

Two other biologically active gastrin-like peptides (sulphated and un-sulphated minigastrins) have been isolated in small amounts from gastrinomas (Gregory and Tracy, 1974) and identified by radioimmunoassay (RIA) in the serum of gastrinoma patients in low concentrations (Rehfeld and Stadil, 1973). At first these components were thought to correspond to the COOH-terminal tridecapeptide of G17, but they are now known to have the composition of the COOH-terminal tetradecapeptide, or G14 (Fig. 1). Both peptides have biological properties closely resembling those of G17 (Carter, Taylor, Elashof and Grossman, 1978).

A component with the amino acid composition of the NH_2-terminal 13 residues of G17 has been isolated from hog antral mucosa (Gregory, 1974), and a component with similar properties can also be identified in the blood and tumours of gastrinoma patients (Dockray and Walsh, 1975). NH_2-

terminal fragments are biologically inactive, but the NH_2-terminal tridecapeptide is of interest in that if it was produced by endopeptidase cleavage of G17 the co-product would be the COOH-terminal tetra-peptide. The tetrapeptide cross-reacts poorly in most gastrin radioimmunoassays and has not so far been identified in gastrin-containing tissues. It is of interest, however, that a factor with the properties of the tetrapeptide occurs in brain and intestine in association with CCK-like peptides (Dockray, 1976).

(d) Big big gastrin and component I

Yalow and Berson (1972) have described a factor with gastrin-like immunoreactivity which emerges in the void volume on Sephadex G50, and is therefore likely to be larger than G34. This component, big big gastrin (BBG), was shown to account for about 2 % of immunoreactive gastrin in the serum of gastrinoma patients, and was also found in semi-purified gastrinoma extracts and in extracts of small intestine. Treatment of BBG with trypsin produced a complex mixture of immunoreactive components which could have included G17. Later, Yalow and Wu (1973) reported that BBG was a major component in the blood of normal fasting subjects, and that concentrations did not change with feeding. More recently it has been shown that G17 and G34 in normal serum can be selectively removed by immunoadsorption to gastrin antisera immobilised on Sepharose beads, whereas serum BBG cannot be adsorbed in this way (Rehfeld, Schwartz and Stadil, 1977). This observation suggests that although BBG inhibits binding of labelled gastrin to antibodies in RIA, it does not bind directly to the antibodies. High concentrations of protein are known to have a non-specific effect in inhibiting binding of label to antibody in many RIA systems including gastrin (Dockray, Debas, Walsh and Grossman. 1975), and since serum proteins emerge in the void volume on Sephadex G50, it would seem probable that some, and possible that all, BBG in normal fasting plasma is an artifact of RIA.

In addition to the components already described, Rehfeld and Stadil (1973) have identified by high resolution gel filtration a factor, designated component I, in the serum of gastrinoma patients which emerges from Sephadex G50 immediately before G34, and so is probably a slightly larger peptide. Trypsin converts component I to a G17-like factor, suggesting that component I consists of an NH_2-terminal extension to G17. Component I has been identified in low concentration in the circulation of normal and duodenal ulcer patients after feeding (Stadil, Rehfeld, Christiansen and Malmstrom, 1975). It seems unlikely that this component makes a significant contribution to circulating biological activity, but it may be of importance in the biosynthesis of gastrin as a large precursor of G34.

2. Distribution and Biosynthesis

(a) The G-cell

Study of the cellular origins of gastrin and the other gut hormones has been revolutionised by the development of immunocytochemical techniques. Endocrine-like cells in the antral mucosa had been provisionally designated gastrin, or G-cells, on the basis of ultrastructural studies (Solcia, Vassallo and Sampietro, 1967). The first direct demonstration of the cellular origins of gastrin was made by McGuigan (1968b) who showed a population of cells scattered throughout the mid portion of the antral pyloric glands which reacted with fluorescein-labelled antibodies raised against 2–17 G17; these observations have since been amply confirmed. Ultrastructural studies reveal G-cells to extend to the gut lumen where they terminate in a tuft of microvilli. Since luminal stimuli regulate gastrin release it is possible that these microvilli bear receptors for the active luminal factors. The secretory granules which contain gastrin are located in the basal parts of the cell as is appropriate for secretion of hormone into the blood stream. It should be noted, however, that significant amounts of gastrin are also apparently secreted in the gastric lumen, although the physiological significance of this is far from clear (Uvnas-Wallensten, 1977).

The distribution of G-cells revealed by immunocytochemistry broadly agrees with the distribution of gastrin indicated by bioassay or radio-immunoassay of tissue extracts. Highest concentrations of gastrin occur in the antral mucosa; in mammals such as man, dog and pig antral gastrin concentrations are 1–12 nmol/g, over 90% of which is accounted for by G17 and most of the rest is G34 (Nilsson, Yalow and Berson, 1973; Malmstrom, Stadil and Rehfeld, 1976; Dockray, Debas, Walsh and Grossman, 1975). The concentration of immunoreactive gastrin in human proximal duodenum is 10–50% that in antral mucosa, and about half of this is attributable to G34 (Berson and Yalow, 1971; Malstrom et al., 1976). In man, duodenal, gastrin probably contributes significantly to circulating hormone after a meal (Stern and Walsh, 1973). In contrast, in other species such as dog and hog, there are much smaller amounts of gastrin in the duodenum and it is unlikely that intestinal gastrin makes a significant contribution to the increase in circulating gastrin after feeding. There are reports of trace amounts of gastrin in extracts of mouse pancreatic islets, and of vagus and pituitary (Dockray et al., 1977; Uvnas-Wallensten, Rehfeld, Larsson and Uvnas, 1977; Rehfeld, 1978a). However, concentrations are generally less than 1% those in antral mucosa, and these tissues therefore probably do little to influence circulating concentrations of gastrin.

(b) *Biosynthesis*

The biosynthesis of many secretory proteins and peptides including hormones and enzymes, proceeds by way of the translation from mRNA of large precursor polypeptides which are packaged into granules and cleaved by intracellular proteases to yield the final secretory product. By analogy, the biosynthesis of gastrin probably proceeds via a large precursor which is converted first to G34 and then G17. The relatively high concentrations of G34 in human duodenal mucosa might suggest that in duodenal G-cells the conversion of G34 to G17 proceeds less readily than in antral G-cells. There is evidence to support the idea that G34 is a precursor for G17. Thus cleavage of G34 *in vitro* with trypsin liberates G17 and the site of cleavage is two consecutive lysine residues (Gregory and Tracy, 1975). Studies on the biosynthetic processing of other hormones, for example insulin and parathyroid hormone, indicate that the site at which the precursor is cleaved to produce the active peptide consists of two consecutive basic residues, and cleavage is by a trypsin-like enzyme possibly working together with other enzymes such as carboxypeptidase B (Steiner, 1976). If G17 was produced by tryptic-like cleavage of G34 in G-cells then one would expect to find in the same cells the NH_2-terminal tryptic peptide of G34. In keeping with this we have recently identified in extracts of hog antral mucosa a component with the chromatographic and immunochemical properties of the NH_2-terminal tryptic peptide of G34, and we have shown by immunocytochemistry that this component is located in the same antral G-cells as G17 (Dockray, Vaillant and Hopkins, 1978).

(c) *Ontogeny*

In late foetal and neonatal rats concentrations of gastrin are relatively low in antrum, and high in pancreas and duodenum (Zelenkova and Gregor, 1971; Larsson, Rehfeld, Sundler and Hakanson, 1976). The concentrations in pancreas and duodenum decrease rapidly in the first few days after birth, while concentrations in antrum progressively rise and may show a particularly sharp increase at the time of weaning (Zelenkova and Gregor, 1971; Larsson *et al.*, 1976). In the human foetus gastrin and G-cells are present in the duodenum at 11 weeks, but do not appear in the antrum until later (19 weeks); unlike rat, there appears to be little or no gastrin in the human foetal pancreas (Larsson, Rehfeld and Goltermann, 1977). It is of interest that serum gastrin concentrations in human cord blood are higher than in the maternal circulation suggesting that there are elevated serum gastrins in the newborn infant (Euler, Byrne, Cousins, Ament, Leake and Walsh, 1977), although it is not known whether this gastrin is of antral origin.

(d) *Gastrinomas*

Gastrin-secreting tumours (gastrinomas, Zollinger-Ellison tumours) arise most commonly in the pancreas, occasionally in the duodenum and quite rarely in the antrum (Isenberg, Walsh and Grossman, 1973). Tumour gastrin concentrations are often in the same range as antral gastrin concentrations, but may be as high as 1300 nmol/g or as low as 50 pmol/g (Dockray, Walsh and Passaro, 1975). In extracts of gastrinomas the ratio of G17 : G34 is about 4:1, in other words there is rather more G34 than in antral mucosa (Dockray *et al.*, 1975); a small number of gastrinomas may contain predominantly G34. Gastrinomas frequently contain substantial amounts of the inactive NH_2-terminal tridecapeptide-like fragment of G17 (Dockray and Walsh, 1975), but other components such as Rehfeld's component I and big big gastrin together usually account for less than 5% total immunoreactive gastrin (Yalow and Berson, 1972; Rehfeld and Stadil, 1973).

3. Control

(a) *Regulation of secretion*

The secretion of gastrin is known to be mediated by luminal, nervous and blood-borne stimuli. The principal luminal stimuli for gastrin release are the products of protein digestion. By itself, undigested protein e.g. bovine serum albumin (BSA), is almost completely ineffective in releasing gastrin, but after partial digestion with pepsin, and dialysis to remove free amino acids, the resulting mixture of polypeptides is a strong stimulant (Debas, Csendes, Walsh and Grossman, 1974). Most amino acids will release gastrin when infused through a gastric fistula in dogs, but particularly effective are cysteine, tryptophan, tyrosine and phenylalanine (Struntz, Walsh and Grossman, 1978b). However, there is no simple relationship between the gastrin released and the rate of acid secretion evoked by intragastric amino acids, since some amino acids strongly stimulate acid secretion but weakly stimulate gastrin, e.g. β alanine, indicating that other mechanisms are also involved. Such mechanisms could include direct stimulation of oxyntic cells (Debas and Grossman, 1975), activation of inhibitory mechanisms, or of stimulatory mechanisms other than gastrin. Other luminal stimuli for gastrin release include calcium in man and cat, but not dog, and alcohol in dog but not man. Carbohydrate and fat have little effect on gastrin release. The pH of the luminal contents plays an important part in regulating gastrin release. In normal subjects the gastrin released by intragastric amino acids at pH 2·5 is diminished by about 70% compared with pH 5·5 (Walsh, Richardson and Fordtran, 1975). The inhibitory effect of acid therefore provides a feedback mechanism for autoregulation of gastrin release. Neutralisation of the antral mucosa does not by itself stimulate gastrin release.

It has long been recognised that distension of an antral pouch in dogs releases gastrin (Grossman et al., 1948). In addition, Debas, Walsh and Grossman (1975) have shown that distension of an innervated fundic pouch increases gastrin secretion from an innervated antral pouch. The so-called oxynto-pyloric reflex is nervous not hormonal, since distension of a denervated fundic pouch has no effect on serum gastrin. Several lines of evidence support the idea of cholinergic mechanisms stimulating gastrin release, at least in dogs. For example, atropine abolishes the response to distension of an antral pouch, and irrigation of an antral pouch with acetylcholine stimulates an increase in serum gastrin which is also abolished by topical atropine. Cholinergic stimulatory mechanisms may involve both local and vagal pathways. Thus in dogs, atropine abolishes the vagal stimulation of gastrin release evoked by sham feeding and insulin hypoglycaemia (Nilsson, Simon, Yalow and Berson, 1972; Csendes, Walsh and Grossman, 1972), and also inhibits the basal and meal-stimulated hypergastrinaemia in vagotomised animals, presumably by blocking local cholinergic pathways (Debas, Walsh and Grossman, 1976). However, the physiological significance of these mechanisms is uncertain since in both man and intact dog, low doses of atropine enhance rather than diminish the serum gastrin response to a normal meal (Walsh, Yalow and Berson, 1971; Impicciatore, Walsh and Grossman, 1977). It seems possible, then that there might also exist cholinergic mechanisms inhibiting gastrin release, or that non-cholinergic stimuli (or atropine-resistant cholinergic mechanisms) play an important physiological role in the stimulation of gastrin release (Walsh and Grossman, 1975).

The existence of inhibitory fibres in the vagus is suggested by the observation that in both man and dog, serum gastrin increases after vagotomy. There is also direct experimental evidence. Cairns, Deveney and Way (1974) have shown that cooling of the vagus increases the gastrin response to insulin hypoglycaemia in dogs, probably due to selective blockade of inhibitory fibres. In addition, atropine enhances the gastrin response to insulin hypoglycaemia in man; the effect persists when gastric pH is maintained constant so it cannot be attributed to atropine inhibition of acid secretion and consequent removal of acid inhibition of gastrin release (Farooq and Walsh, 1975). However, in man although not in dog, vagotomy does not abolish the increase in gastrin produced by insulin, so that extra-vagal mechanisms are also involved in mediating the action of insulin (Tepperman, Walsh and Preshaw, 1972; Stadil, 1972). The non-vagal effects of insulin may be due to release of adrenaline, since there is evidence that catecholamines release gastrin, and the increase in plasma adrenaline after insulin hypoglycaemia would be sufficient to stimulate some gastrin release (Brandsborg, Brandsborg and Christensen, 1975).

Several hormonal and related peptides are known to inhibit the release of gastrin, e.g. secretin, gastric inhibitory polypeptide, vasoactive intestinal peptide, glucagon, calcitonin and somatostatin (Walsh and Grossman, 1975). In general, high exogenous doses of these peptides are needed to suppress serum gastrin, and it is unlikely that the physiological concentrations of the peptides in blood would be sufficient to depress serum gastrin. However, it is possible that some of these peptides modulate gastrin release by a paracrine (or local) action, that is to say by diffusing from one endocrine cell in antral mucosa to another (Pearse, Polak and Bloom, 1977). For example, somatostatin-like immunoreactivity has been identified in D-cells in antral mucosa, as well as elsewhere in the gut and pancreas (see Pearse *et al.*, 1977), and it is conceivable that locally high concentrations of somatostatin in antral mucosa might be sufficient to inhibit the release of gastrin. Similarly there are also VIP- and glucagon-like immunoreactive endocrine cells in the antral mucosa and a paracrine effect of these peptides cannot yet be excluded.

In this context it is of interest that bombesin-like activity has been localised by immunocytochemistry to gut endocrine cells (Polak, Bloom, Hobbs, Solcia and Pearse, 1976) and found by RIA in tissue extracts including those of antral mucosa (Erspamer and Melchiorri, 1975; Walsh and Dockray, 1978). Bombesin and related peptides were originally isolated from the skin of certain frogs e.g. *Bombina bombina* (Erspamer and Melchiorri, 1973), and have a wide spectrum of biological activity including potent stimulation of gastrin release (Melchiorri, 1978). In mammalian gut there are at least two major components which cross-react in radioimmunoassays for the amphibian peptide, one of these has chromatographic properties similar to the amphibian tetradecapeptide, the other is probably a larger peptide. The mammalian peptides stimulate gastrin release in the rat with potencies similar to those of immunochemically comparable amounts of synthetic bombesin tetradecapeptide (Walsh and Dockray, unpublished). It is tempting to speculate, therefore, that mammalian bombesin-like factors act as releasing agents for gastrin. Unlike other stimuli of gastrin release, the action of bombesin is relatively resistant to acidification of the antrum. Moreover, it is significant that in antral pouch dogs perfusion of the stomach and small intestine by liver extract produces a rise in serum gastrin which is not abolished by acidification of the antral pouch (Thompson, Debas, Walsh and Grossman, 1976); this phenomenon could be explained by release of a bombesin-like factor.

(b) Metabolism

Several lines of evidence point to the kidney and small intestine as being important sites of gastrin degradation. For example, after bilateral nephrectomy the half life of exogenous G17 in dog increases from 2·5 to 5·1 min, and in rat, serum concentrations of endogenous gastrin increase (Clendinnen, Reeder, Brandt and Thompson, 1973; Davidson, Moore, Shippey and Conovaloff, 1974). In addition, there are elevated serum gastrin concentrations in patients with renal failure, which return to normal after renal transplantation (Hanksy, King and Holdsworth, 1975). Serum gastrin concentrations are also raised in patients, and in dogs, after massive small bowel resection (Straus, Gerson and Yalow, 1974; Becker, Reeder and Thompson, 1973b), but it is not clear whether this is due to depressed clearance of gastrin or to removal of an intestinal factor that normally suppresses gastrin release. The arterio-venous difference in gastrin concentration across the kidney is about 30%. However, Strunz, Walsh and Grossman (1978a) have shown that during intravenous infusion of G17 the a–v difference across the kidney is no more than across several other vascular beds including head and hind limb, suggesting that all vascular beds metabolise gastrin to some extent. The difference in G17 concentration across the liver was about 40%; taking into account the relative contributions of hepatic portal vein and hepatic artery to total hepatic blood flow Strunz et al. (1978a) concluded that the metabolism of G17 by the liver was no greater than that by other tissues. However, there is good evidence that small COOH-terminal fragments of gastrin such as the pentapeptide may be almost completely cleared by the liver on a single pass, and that there is also appreciable inactivation of COOH-terminal fragments up to nine residues long (Strunz, Thompson, Elashoff and Grossman, 1978). When ^{14}C-labelled COOH-terminal pentapeptide of G17 is injected intravenously, two radioactive components can be identified in bile (Varro, Varga, Csernay, Nafradi, Penke and Balaspiri, 1973). One of these corresponds to the unchanged peptide, the other has the properties of the free acid i.e. desamido-pentapeptide. Walsh and Laster (1973) have identified in homogenates of liver an enzyme which selectively cleaves the COOH-terminal amide group from the COOH-terminal tetrapeptide of gastrin, leaving the biologically inactive tetrapeptide free acid. A similar enzyme also occurs in homogenates of kidney and small intestine, and might play a part in the inactivation of gastrin.

The main circulating forms of gastrin (G17 and G34) differ in their metabolic clearance rates. Infusion of equimolar amounts of G17 and G34 in man and dog, gives approximately 5 fold higher serum gastrin concentrations of G34 compared with G17 (Walsh, Debas and Grossman, 1974; Walsh, Isenberg, Ansfield and Maxwell, 1976). The spaces of distribution of G17 and G34 are similar, so that the metabolic clearance rate of G34 is about one-fifth that of G17. The differences in metabolic clearance rates are in good agreement with observations that after intravenous infusion in man, the half time of G17 to disappear from blood is about 7 min, compared with

35 min for G34. The possibility that different tissues differ in their capacity to metabolise G17 and G34 has not yet been systematically examined, but it is of interest that in patients with renal failure G34 accounts for almost all the circulating gastrin (Hansky et al., 1975; Taylor and Dockray, unpublished), suggesting that the kidney is particularly important in the metabolism of this molecular form.

In man and in dog there is little or no conversion of G34 to G17, or smaller forms of gastrin, in the peripheral circulation (Walsh et al., 1976). In contrast, in the cat G34 is virtually absent from the peripheral circulation, and the main circulating forms of gastrin have the gel filtration properties of G17 and G14 (Blair, Grund, Lund, Piercy, Reed, Sanders, Shale, Shaw and Wilkinson, 1977; Uvnas-Wallensten and Rehfeld, 1976). Antral gastrin in the cat is mainly G17, but there are also small amounts of G34. It seems, then, that in the cat there occurs conversion of G17 (and possibly G34) to smaller fragments in the circulation. In keeping with this idea Blair, Grund, Lund and Sanders (1977), have shown that incubation of G17 with cat plasma in vitro results in the formation of a G14-like component presumably through the action of plasma enzymes. The mechanism of cleavage of G17 has yet to be elucidated, but since the COOH-terminal part of the molecule appears to be unaffected it is not likely that biological potency is seriously impaired.

4. Methods of Determination in the Circulation

(a) Bioassay

Until the introduction of RIA the only way of estimating gastrin was by its effect on gastric acid secretion from pouches, or the whole stomach, in conscious or anaesthetised animals, usually dogs, cats or rats. Anaesthetised rats (Lai, 1964) and cats (Blair, Keenlyside, Newell, Reed and Richardson, 1968) have been used to assay gastrin in plasma. In one study serum from 10 of 25 patients with gastrinomas stimulated acid secretion in the rat (Wilson, Mathison, Schulte and Ellison, 1968), and in another study 79 of 88 serum samples from patients with a gastrinoma were biologically active (Bonfils, Dubrasquet, Accary, Girodet and Mignon, 1978). Serum contains both G17 and G34, and these differ in their potency for acid secretion, so not surprisingly there is no direct correlation between total serum gastrin measured by radioimmunoassay and by bioassay (Temperley and Stagg, 1971). Plasma from normal subjects, either fasting or post-prandial, has no effect on acid secretion in the rat (Colin-Jones and Lennard-Jones, 1972; Hansky, Royle and Korman, 1974). In contrast, there are several reports that serum from patients with peptic ulcer stimulates acid secretion in rats.

Hansky *et al.* (1974), found that fasting serum from 12 of 17 duodenal ulcer subjects stimulated rat gastric acid secretion, and Colin-Jones and Lennard-Jones (1972) reported post-prandial plasma from 18 of 20 duodenal ulcer patients was active in the rat bioassay. Recently, extracts of fasting plasma from five of seven patients with duodenal ulcer and basal acid secretion greater than 15 mmol/hr, were shown to be active in the rat bioassay, but extracts of normal plasma were inactive; the active factor was heat stable (Bugat, Walsh, Ippoliti, Elashoff and Grossman, 1976). About 5 pmol. (10 ng) of human G17 are needed to stimulate acid secretion in rats, and fasting or post-prandial serum gastrin concentrations in normal or duodenal ulcer subjects measured by RIA are generally less than 100 pmol/l. In the reports cited 0·1–5·0 ml of plasma were tested in the bioassays so that it is clear that there exists a considerable discrepancy between the bioassay and immuno-assay data. Conceivably there is a biologically active form of gastrin in the circulation, the concentration of which is elevated in peptic ulcer disease and is not measured by radioimmunoassay. An alternative possibility is that there is in blood a gastric secretagogue other than gastrin, and that this is elevated in some duodenal ulcer patients.

Loveridge, Bloom, Welbourn and Chayen (1974) have described a cyto-chemical assay for gastrin based on the histochemical estimation of carbonic anhydrase in slices of guinea-pig gastric mucosa exposed to gastrin. The sensitivity of this assay for G17 in plasma was claimed to be 0·05 pg/ml which is at least 10 times lower than that of RIA. The relative potencies of different forms of gastrin were not reported, but there was said to be good agreement between cytochemical and RIA estimates of total serum gastrin in normal plasma, implying equal potencies of the main forms of gastrin in the two systems.

(b) Radioimmunoassay

Within a few years of the purification of gastrin, several groups had developed RIA systems sufficiently sensitive to measure concentrations of hormone in blood (McGuigan, 1968a; Hansky and Cain, 1969; Yalow and Berson 1970a). Gastrin RIA is now used routinely in physiological studies and in estimating serum gastrin in the diagnosis of gastrinomas. The principles on which gastrin RIA are based are the same as those originally formulated by Berson and Yalow for RIA of insulin, that is to say standard and unknown samples are compared for the ability to inhibit binding of radiolabelled peptide to antiserum. The methods for gastrin RIA have been reviewed several times recently and will be given only in outline (Jaffe and Walsh, 1978; Rehfeld, 1978b).

The first application of gastrin antisera in RIA was made by McGuigan (1967) using an antiserum raised against the COOH-terminal tetrapeptide conjugated to bovine serum albumin and ^{3}H tetrapeptide label. The antiserum cross-reacted about equally with tetrapeptide, G17 and CCK, but was insufficiently sensitive to measure hormone in blood. It is now clear that antisera with appropriate titre, affinity and specificity for the assay of gastrin in blood can be readily obtained by immunising rabbits or guinea-pigs with natural or synthetic human or porcine G17. Most workers prefer to conjugate peptide to a larger protein e.g. BSA, using a method such as carbodiimide condensation (Goodfriend, Levine and Fasman, 1964), but useful antisera may also be obtained by immunising with pure G17, emulsified in Freund's adjuvant, or with a crude tissue extract containing G17.

Radiolabelled gastrin for use in RIA is usually obtained by iodinating porcine or human G17, or the COOH-terminal hexadecapeptide (2–17 G17), with ^{125}I by the chloramine T method (Hunter and Greenwood, 1962). Unsulphated gastrins are generally employed since the sulphated tyrosine is less readily iodinated. If a relatively high ratio of chloramine T to peptide is used the iodinated gastrin loses its biological activity due to oxidation of the methionine residue. However, low ratios of peptide to chloramine T, e.g. 1:3, give biologically active iodinated gastrin. The yields obtained in this way are usually low, but the iodinated gastrin can be separated from unlabelled gastrin and other reaction products by ion exchange chromatography on AE or DE cellulose (Dockray, Walsh and Grossman, 1976).

The majority of gastrin antisera raised against G17 are specific for the COOH-terminus of the molecule. These antisera usually cross-react poorly with small COOH-terminal fragments like the pentapeptide; they may vary somewhat in their cross-reactivity with G17, G14 and G34, so that each antisera must be individually checked for cross-reactivity with the main forms of gastrin. The peptides needed for this sort of characterisation are now available (Grossman 1976a). The cross-reactivity with CCK varies between antisera from about 0·2–0·0001 relative to G17; in routine gastrin RIA cross-reactivity with CCK should seldom present any problems. Most gastrin antisera cross-react about equally with sulphated and unsulphated forms of gastrin, but Hansky, Soveny and Korman (1974) have described an antiserum raised against unsulphated G17 which cross-reacts poorly with sulphated G17. A few gastrin antisera have specificity for the NH_2-terminus of the molecule. These may be obtained by immunising with the 1–13 fragment of G17 (Agarwal, Grudzinski, Kenner, Rodgers, Sheppard and McGuigan, 1971), but they may also be obtained in rabbits immunised with G17 conjugated to BSA (Dockray and Walsh, 1975). Such antisera cross-react with G17 and NH_2-terminal fragments such as 1–13 G17, but not with G34 or G14. The hope that they might be used to specifically measure G17 has been frustrated by the finding of cross-reacting biologically inactive NH_2-terminal fragments in tissues and blood (Dockray and Walsh, 1975). A third and unusual type of gastrin antiserum shows virtually absolute specificity for G17. We obtained one such antiserum in a rabbit immunised with a mixture of sulphated and unsulphated porcine G17 conjugated to BSA (Dockray and Taylor, 1976). Of the naturally occurring forms of gastrin, only G17 cross-reacted with this antiserum, and there was negligible cross-reactivity with G34, and with COOH- and NH_2-terminal fragments of G17. Antisera specific for the NH_2-terminus of G34 which do not cross-react with G17 or its fragments, have been obtained in rabbits immunised with porcine G34 conjugated to BSA (Dockray, Vaillant et al., 1978). We obtained one such antiserum which originally contained two populations of antibodies—one specific for the COOH-terminus of G34 and therefore cross-reacting with G17, the other specific for the NH_2-terminus did not cross-react with G17. The former population could be selectively bound to G17 immobilised on Sepharose beads and therefore separated from the NH_2-terminal specific population.

Because gastrin circulates in various forms of differing biological activity it is essential that the relative concentrations of these forms are estimated in attempting to relate hormone concentration to biological response. Gel filtration on columns of Sephadex G50 has been widely used to separate G34 and G17 which are then measured in the column eluates by RIA. An alternative approach is to measure G17 and G34 in unfractionated samples by RIA employing antisera specific for different regions of these peptides. For example, antisera such as the one described above, that have high specificity for G17 can be used to estimate this form, while COOH-terminal specific antisera are used to measure both G17 and G34. By subtraction, an estimate may be obtained of G34 concentration, although it should be noted that the minor components such as G14, Rehfeld's component I, etc., may account for up to 10% of this fraction (Dockray and Taylor, 1976).

A number of different standards are currently in use for gastrin RIA. Synthetic or natural human G17 is obviously appropriate for laboratories doing routine clinical assays. Many workers quote total serum gastrin concentrations in terms of pg/ml, equivalent to G17. However, where concentrations of different forms have been measured and related to standards of G17 and G34, it would be more appropriate to express concentrations of the different forms in pmol/l referred to the relevant standard.

5. Concentrations in the Circulation

(a) Normal concentration

Estimates of normal fasting serum gastrin concentrations vary between laboratories, but most workers with experience in gastrin RIA would expect normal serum gastrin to be less than about 25 pmol/l or 50 pg/ml (human G17 equivalent). Variation in antibody specificity and in the potency of different standard preparations may account for some of the interlaboratory variation. In addition serum proteins cause a non-specific inhibition in gastrin RIA that varies between antisera. It is likely that at least some of the so-called BBG activity in normal serum is accounted for by non-specific effects of serum proteins (Rehfeld et al., 1977; Dockray et al., 1975). The errors arising from this sort of artifact can be eliminated by reading serum gastrin concentrations against standard curves prepared in gastrin-free serum. Previously attempts have been made to prepare gastrin-free serum by adsorption of G17 and G34 to charcoal. However a more satisfactory and specific method is to use an immunoadsorbant to strip serum gastrin. This can be prepared by conjugating the gamma-globulin fraction of a gastrin antisera to a solid support system such as Sepharose beads (Dockray and Taylor, 1976). In our laboratory the concentrations of G17 and G34 in normal fasting serum estimated by region specific antisera were both approximately 5–7 pmol/l when account was taken of the non-specific effects of serum (Dockray and Taylor, 1976).

In normal subjects, a meal such as eggs and toast stimulates an increase in total serum gastrin measured by COOH-terminal specific antisera, which reaches a peak at about 30–60 min and then declines to basal over the next one or two hours. Gel filtration of post-prandial serum indicates that the increases are almost entirely due to G17 and G34 (Stadil et al., 1975). Using RIA employing antisera with high specificity for G17 we found the peak increase in G17 after a standard meal was 15–20 pmol/l, and from the difference between estimates with G17-specific antisera and COOH-terminal specific antisera (which cross-reacts with both G17 and G34) the increase in G34 was estimated to be 25–30 pmol/l (Dockray and Taylor, 1976). In a second study slightly lower increases were found (Dockray and Taylor, 1977) and the reasons for these differences are not yet clear. Peak concentrations of G17 were achieved 20 min after the meal, but peak concentrations of G34 were reached later at 45–60 min (Fig. 2).

G17 and G34 are almost equipotent on a molar basis in stimulating acid secretion if potencies are compared on the basis of exogenous dose. However, if potency is described in terms of concentration in blood required for a given rate of acid secretion, i.e. endogenous potency, then in both man and dog G17 is about five times more potent than G34 (Walsh et al., 1974, 1976). It follows that total serum gastrin concentration is not a reliable indicator of circulating biological activity, and that interpretation of the physiological significance of serum gastrin concentrations depends on a knowledge of the relative concentrations of the two forms. It seems likely that G17 accounts for nearly all the circulating gastrin biological activity after a normal meal (Dockray and Taylor, 1976). Support for this idea has recently been provided by Feldman, Walsh, Wong and Richardson (1978) who showed that intragastric instillation of a mixture of amino acids increased serum G17 by 13 pmol/l and acid secretion by 12·8 mmol/hr; during intra-venous infusion of exogenous G17 in the same subjects a rise of 13 pmol/l

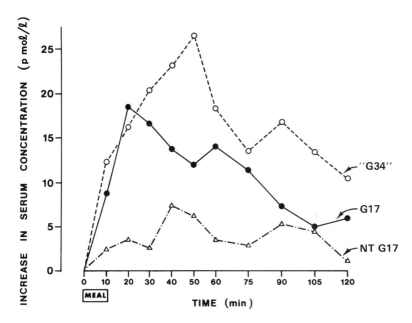

Fig. 2. Increase in concentration of different forms of gastrin after a standard meal (two hard boiled eggs, one piece of dry toast and a cup of Oxo). G17: heptadecapeptide gastrin concentrations measured by radioimmunoassay using antiserum specific for this molecular form. "G34": concentrations of G34 estimated from difference between total serum gastrin measured by COOH-terminal specific antiserum and G17 measured by specific radioimmunoassay. NT G17: NH_2-terminal fragments of G17 estimated by difference between immunoreactivity measured with antiserum specific for NH_2-terminus of G17 and antiserum with nearly absolute specificity for G17. Reproduced from Dockray and Taylor (1976), with permission.

in serum was found to correspond to a rate of acid secretion of about 14·8 mmol/hr. The rise in G17 after the test meal therefore fully accounted for the increase in acid secretion.

In dogs, instillation of liver extract in an antral pouch produces serum gastrin concentrations similar to, or higher than, those seen after feeding in intact animals. After three hours stimulation of the antral pouch the ratio of G17 to G34 in serum was 1:4 whereas the ratio in antral mucosal biopsies was about 9:1. The relatively higher amounts of G34 in blood can be explained in part by the lower metabolic clearance rate of G34 compared with G17, but even so there is still relatively more G34 in serum than predicted from the tissue proportions and the relative metabolic clearance rates (Dockray, Debas, Walsh and Grossman, 1975). One explanation for this discrepancy could be that there is preferential release of G34 by gastrin-secreting cells. In gastrinoma patients there is also proportionately more G34 relative to G17 in serum than predicted from relative metabolic clearance rates and tumour concentrations (Dockray, Walsh and Passaro, 1975).

(b) *Gastrinomas*

The Zollinger–Ellison syndrome is characterised by recurrent peptic ulceration, gastric acid hypersecretion and non-β islet cell tumour of the pancreas (Zollinger and Ellison, 1955). Gregory et al. (1969) established that these tumours produce large quantities of gastrin, hence the descriptive name, gastrinoma. It is now well recognised that elevated serum gastrin concentrations in patients with this disease lead to gastric acid secretion and in turn to peptic ulceration. Radioimmunoassay is today widely used in the diagnosis of gastrinoma. The tumours are usually slow-growing and frequently form metastases. Complete resection of the tumour is often not possible and the preferred surgical treatment is total gastrectomy (Isenberg *et al.*, 1973).

Serum gastrin concentrations above 500 pmol/l (1 ng/ml) and accompanied by gastric acid hypersecretion are virtually diagnostic of gastrinoma. Patients with achlorhydria may have serum gastrins in the gastrinoma range (McGuigan and Trudeau, 1970; Yalow and Berson, 1970a), but can be readily distinguished on the basis of acid secretory tests. A very small number of patients may have hypergastrinaemia and hyperchlorhydria due to an isolated antrum from previous surgery, in other words gastrojejunostomy and an antral remnant attached to the duodenal stump (Korman, Scott, Hansky and Wilson, 1972). The antral remnant is removed from the acid stream and is therefore free to secrete gastrin without restraint.

In recent years it has become clear that many gastrinoma patients have serum gastrin levels which overlap with the upper end of the range for normal subjects and patients with ordinary peptic ulcer. For example, in a recent survey of 15 patients no fewer than six had serum gastrin concentrations less than 500 pg/ml (Creutzfeldt, Arnold, Creutzfeldt and Track, 1975). One or more provocative tests are needed to establish the presence of a gastrinoma in such patients. The most widely used tests are the standard test meal, the secretin test and calcium challenge. The secretion of gastrin in patients with gastrinoma is generally considered to be unaltered by feeding. This is true for most patients with high serum gastrin levels, but some patients with gastrinoma and low serum gastrin levels (less than 250 pmol/l) may show a slight increase after a normal meal (Walsh and Grossman, 1975). In contrast, rapid intravenous injection of secretin stimulates a marked increase of gastrin in about 80 % of all gastrinoma patients which peaks at 2·5–10 min (Isenberg, Walsh, Passaro, Moore and Grossman, 1972). At peak concentrations there is relatively more G17 in serum than in the basal state suggesting that secretin acts by releasing tumour stores of gastrin which are mainly G17 (Dockray, Walsh and Passaro, 1975). In normal subjects, and in patients with ordinary peptic ulcer, achlorhydria or isolated retained antrum, secretin tends to depress serum gastrin (Korman et al., 1972; Hansky, Soveny and Korman, 1971). The reason for the paradoxical effect of secretin on the release of gastrin from gastrinomas is not known; it is claimed that the structurally related hormone glucagon has a similar effect to secretin (Becker, Reeder and Thompson, 1973a), but it is not yet known whether other related peptides (VIP and GIP) also have this action. The action of secretin in patients with gastrinoma is of further significance in that acid entering the duodenum tends to release endogenous secretin (Straus and Yalow, 1977), and this in turn evokes secretion of tumour gastrin and more acid. On this evidence the release of gastrin from gastrinomas would seen to be under tonic secretin stimulation.

Patients with gastrinoma also respond with a marked increase of serum gastrin levels after calcium infusion (Passaro, Basso and Walsh, 1972). In one study six out of six patients responded with 1·4–47 fold increases (Creutz-feldt et al., 1975). Calcium may provoke a modest rise in serum gastrin levels in normal subjects and in patients with duodenal ulcer, but these responses usually fall short of those seen in patients with gastrinoma (at least 250 pmol/l (500 pg/ml)). There is an association between gastrinoma and hyperpara-thyroidism, and hypercalcaemia may exacerbate the release of gastrin from tumours.

(c) Peptic ulcer

The role of gastrin in peptic ulcer uncomplicated by gastrinoma has been the subject of intensive study. There is now evidence to indicate that patients with duodenal ulcer secrete more gastrin than normal in response to feeding and are also more sensitive than normal to gastrin. However, the role of gastrin in the pathogenesis of peptic ulcer remains uncertain. Basal serum gastrin concentrations in duodenal ulcer patients are similar to those in normal subjects, but several groups have shown that the gastrin responses to feeding are higher than normal (Walsh and Grossman, 1975). As in normal subjects G17 and G34 account for most of the increase in gastrin after a meal (Stadil et al., 1975). Using region specific antisera to measure G17 and G34, we found that after a standard meal the mean peak increases in serum G17 was about 18 pmol/l in duodenal ulcer patients compared with 13 pmol/l in a group of age and sex matched normals, but the difference was not significant. In contrast, serum G34 in duodenal ulcer increased by about 27 pmol/l and this was significantly higher than in normal subjects (15 pmol/l) (Dockray and Taylor, 1977). Most of the increased post-prandial gastrin in duodenal ulcer is therefore G34. Because G34 is a weak stimulant of acid secretion, relative to G17, it is not yet certain whether there is significant elevation of circulating gastrin biological activity in duodenal ulcer. However, it is established that patients with duodenal ulcer tend to have a higher than normal basal and maximal rates of acid secretions and are also more sensitive than normal to exogenous gastrin (Isenberg, Grossman, Maxwell and Walsh, 1975). Berson and Yalow (1971) have commented that the higher gastrin responses to feeding in duodenal ulcer are inappropriate in the presence of higher than normal rates of acid secretion. It seems likely that there exists a defect in the mechanism of acid inhibition of gastrin release in duodenal ulcer. Consistent with this Walsh *et al* (1975) found that at pH 2·5 the secretion of gastrin in response to intragastric amino acids in patients with duodenal ulcer was suppressed by 50% compared with pH 5·5, whereas in normal subjects serum gastrin was suppressed by 70%.

Patients with gastric ulcer have elevated basal and post-prandial serum gastrin concentrations (Trudeau and McGuigan, 1971). However, these patients also show a tendency towards lower basal and maximal acid outputs than normal, and it seems likely that their higher serum gastrin is a consequence of decreased acid inhibition. We recently found that the mean peak increase in G17 after feeding in gastric ulcer subjects was similar to normal (17 pmol/l), but the increase is G34 was about four times higher than normal (62 pmol/l), so that as in duodenal ulcer subjects most of the elevated postprandial serum gastrin in G34 (Dockray and Taylor, 1977).

Surgical treatment of duodenal ulcer by vagotomy leads to a reduction in acid output and an increase in basal and meal-stimulated gastrin release (Stadil and Rehfeld, 1974; Jaffe, Clendinnen, Clarke and Alexander Williams, 1974). The absence of vagal tone on parietal cells in part accounts for the failure of the elevated serum gastrin to stimulate acid secretion. In turn, the decreased acid output probably contributes to higher serum gastrin concentrations by removal of acid inhibition; it is also possible that the absence of vagal inhibitory fibres contributes to the higher serum gastrin. When vagotomy is accompanied by antrectomy and gastroduodenostomy, basal and meal-stimulated gastrin release is decreased, but not abolished, probably because in man the duodenum has relatively large stores of gastrin (Stern and Walsh, 1973). However, gastrin responses to feeding are negligible in patients with vagotomy accompanied by antrectomy and gastrojejunostomy in which the duodenum is by-passed. Tissue gastrin concentrations in antral mucosa may increase considerably after vagotomy due to hyperplasia of the G-cells, suggesting that either the vagal inhibitory fibres or acid inhibition exerts a restraining influence on G-cell proliferation (Hughes and Hernandez, 1976).

Polak, Stagg and Pearse (1972) have described a group of patients with serum gastrin in the gastrinoma range, and acid hypersecretion but apparently without gastrinomas; these patients were shown to have hyperplasia of the antral G-cells. The designation Zollinger–Ellison syndrome type I was proposed for this condition to distinguish it from Zollinger–Ellison type II or gastrinoma. However, antral G-cell hyperplasia would seem a more appropriate and generally acceptable term. Straus and Yalow (1975) have also identified patients with hyperchlorhydria and hypergastrinaemia who were distinguished from gastrinoma patients, in this case on the basis of exaggerated gastrin responses to feeding and lack of response to calcium and secretin; no evidence was presented on G-cell hyperplasia in this group of patients. As a group, duodenal ulcer patients have a tendency towards higher basal and meal-stimulated acid responses, and have higher post-prandial increases in serum gastrin than normal. It is not clear therefore, whether so-called G-cell hyperplasia is a separate entity or merely the upper end of a normal distribution of duodenal ulcer subjects. Hyperplasia of G-cells frequently occurs after vagotomy so that it is particularly difficult to assess the functional significance of G-cell hyperplasia in patients with recurrent ulceration after vagotomy (Ganguli, Polak, Pearse, Elder and Hegarty, 1974).

(d) Hypergastrinaemia and hypochlorhydria

Because acid normally inhibits gastrin release the reduction or absence of acid secretion leads to increased serum gastrin. Patients with pernicious anaemia in which atrophic gastritis has spared the antrum often have very high gastrin concentrations (McGuigan and Trudeau, 1970; Yalow and Berson, 1970a). Intragastric instillation of HCl into these subjects lowers serum gastrin, although even with prolonged acidification the serum gastrin does not fall into the normal range (Yalow and Berson, 1970a), perhaps because there is an increase in G-cell mass. Immunocytochemical evidence suggests G-cell hyperplasia in pernicious anaemia subjects which probably reflects the long term effects of acid in limiting numbers of G-cells (Creutzfeldt, Arnold, Creutzfeldt, Feurle and Ketterer, 1971).

B. CHOLECYSTOKININ

1. Identification, Isolation and Characterisation

It is now well recognised that cholecystokinin (CCK) and pancreozymin are a single substance, but until the work of Jorpes and Mutt (1966, 1973) there seemed no reason to doubt that these were separate hormonal entities. Cholecystokinin had been discovered and named by Ivy and Oldberg (1928). It was already established in the 1920's that the presence of fat in the duodenum stimulated contraction of the gall bladder. Ivy and Oldberg showed that the intravenous injection of duodenal extracts had the same effect, and by means of cross-circulation experiments in pairs of dogs they provided evidence that a gall bladder-contracting substance was released into the blood from the duodenum. The discovery of pancreozymin by Harper was made quite independently and about 15 years after that of CCK. At that time the role of secretin in the control of the flow of pancreatic juice was generally accepted, but there was uncertainty about the regulation of enzyme secretion. Mellanby (1925) had maintained that the vagus was responsible for the stimulation of enzyme secretion, but some—although not all—preparations of secretin could also be clearly shown to evoke enzyme release. Harper and Vass (1941) established that instillation of food (casein) into the duodenum increased pancreatic enzyme release after all extrinsic nerves were severed, and they suggested that a hormone mediated this effect. In a later study Harper and Raper (1943) demonstrated the presence in intestinal extracts of a factor, pancreozymin, which was distinct from secretin and which evoked the release of pancreatic enzymes.

The work of Jorpes and Mutt (1966) on the purification of the intestinal hormones has brought together the observations on pancreozymin and CCK. During the purification of these activities from hog intestine it was observed that they always moved in parallel, up to and including the final purified preparations, and on this evidence it was proposed that CCK and pancreozymin were one and the same hormone. Jorpes and Mutt (1973) cite two other pieces of evidence to support this view. Thus treatment of the purified peptide with hydrogen peroxide to oxidise methionine abolished the activity on both gall bladder and pancreas, and reduction with cysteine restored both activities (Mutt, 1964). Secondly the synthetic COOH-terminal tryptic peptide of CCK (octapeptide) possesses the activity of both hormones. For some years the name cholecystokinin-pancreozymin was used to describe this hormone, but more recently it has become customary to shorten this to cholecystokinin irrespective of the hormonal action under consideration.

The molecule isolated from hog duodenum by Jorpes and Mutt is a basic peptide of 33 amino acid residues (Fig. 3). The final stages of purification included a step to remove what was at first considered to be contaminating material but is now known to include a peptide of 39 residues, corresponding to the form of 33 residues extended at the NH_2-terminus by six residues (Fig. 3); the larger form is known as CCK-variant or CCK-v (Mutt and Jorpes, 1968; Mutt, 1976). By analogy with the abbreviated designations for different

1	2	3	4	5	6	7	8	9	10	11	12	13	14	15	16	17	18	19	20

Tyr–Ile–Gln–Gln–Ala–Arg–Lys–Ala–Pro–Ser–Gly–Arg–Val–Ser–Met–Ile–Lys–Asn– Leu–Gln–

21	22	23	24	25	26	27	28	29	30	31	32	33	34	35	36	37	38	39

Ser–Leu–Asp–Pro–Ser–His–Arg–Ile–Ser–Asp–Arg– Asp–Tyr–Met–Gly–Trp–Met–Asp–Phe–NH$_2$

SO$_3$H

Fig. 3. The amino acid sequence of porcine triacontanonapeptide cholecystokinin (CCK39). The sequence of CCK33 corresponds to the COOH-terminal 7-39 fragment, and the sequence of CCK8 corresponds to the COOH-terminal octapeptide 32-39 (enclosed in box).

forms of gastrin it is convenient to refer to the cholecystokinins as CCK33 and CCK39. During the elucidation of sequence of CCK33, Jorpes and Mutt (1967a) noted that the COOH-terminal octapeptide terminated in the same dipeptide amide as gastrin (–Asp–Phe–NH_2) and subsequently gastrin and CCK were found to share a common COOH-terminal pentapeptide. Like gastrin, CCK also has a sulphated tyrosine residue. although unlike gastrin this occurs at position 7 from the COOH-terminus as opposed to position 6; so far as is known only the sulphated forms of CCK occur naturally.

2. Origins and Activity

(a) Distribution

The distribution of CCK has been studied by bioassay, immunoassay and immunocytochemistry; CCK-like activity occurs in the brain and intestine of a wide range of vertebrate species from cyclostomes to mammals, and in the skin of a few amphibian species (Barrington and Dockray, 1976; Dockray, 1977a). In mammals, intestinal CCK cells were first demonstrated by immunocytochemistry using gastrin antisera with COOH-terminal specificity which cross-react with CCK. Gastrin is virtually absent from the jejunum so that immunoreactive cells in that part of the small intestine were presumably CCK-cells. Evidence to support this interpretation has now been obtained by using antisera specific for the mid- or NH_2-terminal regions of CCK which do not cross-react with gastrin (Buffa, Solcia and Go, 1976; Polak, Pearse, Bloom, Buchan, Rayford and Thompson, 1975). The CCK cell corresponds to the I-cell previously identified by electron microscopy. I-cells are relatively abundant in the mucosa of duodenum and jejunum, are less common in ileal mucosa, and are scarce elsewhere in the gut.

In 1975, Vanderhaeghen, Signeau and Gepts reported gastrin-like immunoreactivity in boiling water extracts of brain of a variety of species. However, in our laboratory the quantitative pattern of cross-reactivity of the brain activity with several different antisera was found to resemble a COOH-terminal fragment of CCK more closely than gastrin (Dockray, 1976); others have since obtained similar results (Muller, Straus and Yalow, 1977; Rehfeld, 1978a; Robberecht, Deschodt-Lankman and Vanderhaeghen, 1978). Consistent with these observations we have recently isolated from sheep brain two peptides with the amino acid sequence, immunochemical and biological properties of the COOH-terminal octapeptide of CCK (CCK8) (Fig. 3). One peptide has chromatographic properties indistinguishable from synthetic CCK8, but the other is less acidic; the basis for the difference between the two octapeptides is not yet known (Dockray, Gregory, Harris, Hutchison and Runswick, 1978). These findings establish CCK-like peptides as members of a growing group of molecules known to occur in both gut endocrine cells and central or peripheral neurones (e.g. substance P, somatostatin, neurotensin) (Pearse, 1976). Many of these peptides occur in high concentrations in hypothalamus, but preliminary studies on the distribution of CCK8 indicate that this peptide occurs in highest amounts in cerebral cortex (Rehfeld, 1978a).

Peptides closely related to CCK have also been isolated from the skin of some amphibian species. During the course of a systematic examination of biologically active substances in amphibian skin, Erspamer and his coworkers have isolated numerous peptides and amines, amongst which are the CCK-like peptides or caeruleins (Erspamer and Melchiorri, 1973). Caerulein was first isolated from the skin of the Australian tree frog, *Hyla caerulea*, but the same or closely related peptides have since been found in high concentration in the skin of several other species including *Xenopus laevis* (Anastasi, Erspamer and Endean, 1968; Anastasi, Bertaccini, Cei, de Caro, Erspamer, Impicciatore and Roseghini, 1970). The decapeptide caerulein has an identical COOH-terminal octapeptide with porcine CCK but for the substitution of threonine for methionine at position 6 counting from the COOH-terminus. In *X. laevis*, and probably in other species, caerulein is associated with granules contained in specialised dermal glands on the dorsal surface which are distinct from mucous glands (Dockray and Hopkins, 1975). The caerulein-rich granules are extruded through a pore onto the surface of the skin and may be collected intact in isotonic media. Discharge is brought about by adrenergic stimuli which initiate contraction of myoepithelial cells enveloping the glands. The biological significance of caerulein is unknown but amphibian skin glands might well prove to be a useful system for studying cellular aspects of synthesis and storage of CCK-like peptides.

(b) Heterogeneity and biosynthesis

The first indication of heterogeneity of CCK was the isolation from hog intestine of the peptides CCK33 and 39; these remain the only forms of CCK to be isolated from intestine and fully characterised (Mutt, 1976). However CCK8 has now been isolated from sheep brain (Dockray, Gregory, Harris *et al.*, 1978). In addition, there is accumulating evidence to suggest several other immunoreactive forms of CCK occur in gut and brain. The molecular forms of CCK identified in immunochemical studies of tissue extracts depend on both antibody specificity and the method of extraction used (Dockray, 1977b; Muller, Straus and Yalow, 1977). When hog duodenum is extracted by acid, which is the method used by Jorpes and Mutt, the major form of CCK obtained has chromatographic properties corresponding to CCK33 and 39. In contrast, only trace amounts of this activity are obtained after extraction in boiling water. However, boiling water extracts of hog intestine contain relatively large amounts of two other components, one resembling CCK8, the other emerging between CCK33 and CCK8 on Sephadex G50 and so probably of intermediate size (Dockray, 1977b). Re-extraction in acid of the residue of the boiling water extracts recovers CCK33-like activity in good yield suggesting that the differences between the extraction methods are not due to degradation or interconversion of molecular forms. Boiling water extracts of intestine also contain two minor components which are probably larger than CCK39; one of these emerges between the void volume and CCK39 on Sephadex G50, the other, which is also present in brain, runs in the void volume. In both intestine and in brain there is an additional minor component which emerges after CCK8 on Sephadex G50 and is likely to be a small peptide such as the COOH-terminal tetrapeptide of CCK (Dockray, 1977b).

There are at present differences of opinion as to the relative distribution of immunoreactive forms of CCK in brain and gut. In our hands the principal immunoreactive forms of CCK in boiling water extracts of hog cerebral cortex corresponds to CCK8 (about 100 pmol/g); acid extracts of cortex contain much smaller amounts of CCK33, less than 5% relative to CCK8. In duodenum we have found about 40 pmol/g CCK8 and 20 pmol/g CCK33-like activity, while in jejunum the concentrations were 15 and 27 pmol/g, respectively (Dockray, 1976, 1977b). In contrast, Straus and Yalow (1978) using an antiserum specific for the mid- or NH_2-terminal region of CCK33 reported 200 pmol/g of CCK33-like activity in acid extracts of cortex and about 2 fold higher amounts in intestine; the concentrations of CCK8-like activity in several species measured by a COOH-terminal specific antiserum were said to be 50–200 pmol/g in brain and about 5 fold higher in gut. The reasons for the differences between these studies are not yet known, but the possibility that the antisera used vary in their pattern of cross-reactivity with the different molecular forms of CCK needs careful consideration.

It seems probable that CCK33 and CCK39 are biosynthetic precursors of the smaller CCK-like peptides such as CCK8; CCK33 and 39 may themselves be the product of cleavage of large precursors. By analogy with the biosynthetic processing of peptides in other endocrine cells, e.g. insulin (Steiner, 1976) it is reasonable to expect that if CCK8 is produced by cleavage of CCK33 then there would also be produced an inactive NH_2-terminal fragment. Such fragments have not yet been reported, but they might well cross-react with antisera specific for the mid- or NH_2-terminal regions of CCK33, as for example that described by Straus and Yalow (1978).

(c) *Biological relationships*

The distribution of CCK-like peptides in central neurones and in gut endocrine cells suggests that these peptides might function as both neuro-transmitters and hormones. Almost nothing is known of the physiological role of CCK in brain. In the gut the evidence suggests a physiological role in the regulation of motility in gall bladder and intestine, and secretion of the pancreas. The physiological actions of CCK on the pancreas are likely to include not only stimulation of enzyme release but also potentiation of the action of secretin and a trophic effect in stimulating the growth of the organ (Debas and Grossman, 1973; Meyer, Spingola and Grossman, 1971; Johnson, 1976). CCK also affects smooth muscle other than gall bladder, for example there is evidence of a physiological role in the inhibition of gastric emptying (Debas, Farooq and Grossman, 1975), relaxation of the sphincter of Oddi (Lin, 1975), and stimulation of small intestinal contraction (Gutierrez, Chey and Dinoso, 1974).

Because the COOH-terminal pentapeptide amides of gastrin and CCK are identical and contain the minimal active fragment with biological activity it is not surprising to find considerable overlap in the biological properties of the two hormones. The results of several studies on structure–activity relationships point to the fact that in mammals there are two patterns in the spectrum of actions of these peptides. The so-called gastrin pattern is defined by relatively high potency for acid secretion and low potency for gall bladder contraction and pancreatic enzyme secretion, while the CCK pattern is characterised by high potency for the stimulation of gall bladder and pancreas. The critical factor governing the pattern of activity is the position and sulphation of the tyrosine residue. When the tyrosine is at position 7 from the COOH-terminus and is sulphated, then the pattern is CCK-like, whereas when the tyrosine is shifted either to position 6 (gastrin) or 8 from the COOH-terminus, or when it is desulphated, then the pattern is gastrin-like (Grossman, 1976b). Other structural features may modify the potency for a particular action. For example, in the dog CCK8 is about three times more potent than CCK33 in stimulating gall bladder contraction and enzyme secretion, but about 12 times more potent in stimulating acid secretion. The NH_2-terminal part of CCK therefore decreases the activity on parietal cells more strongly than on gall bladder or pancreas, with the result that CCK33 is a more specific stimulant of gall bladder and pancreas relative to acid secretion than is CCK8.

3. Control

The release of CCK has so far been studied for the most part by biological methods which involve monitoring gall bladder contraction or pancreatic enzyme secretion in response to the instillation of foodstuffs into the small intestine. This approach has several limitations. For example the same stimulus may release more than one active factor; thus, HCl strongly releases secretin and also weakly releases CCK, and these interact in stimulating pancreatic secretion. Moreover, using this approach there is little opportunity to study the concentrations of CCK in blood, nor is it possible to estimate the relative amounts of different circulating molecular forms.

The balance of evidence from physiological studies indicates that CCK is released by the products of protein and fat digestion. Like gastrin, pure undigested protein does not stimulate hormone release, but after partial proteolysis and dialysis the mixture of polypeptides is a strong stimulus (Meyer and Kelly, 1976). Amino acids also stimulate CCK release. In man and in dog, phenylalanine and tryptophan are strong stimulants, and in man, but not dog, methionine and valine are also effective releasers of CCK (Go, Hofman and Sumerskill, 1970; Meyer, Kelly, Spingola and Jones, 1976). The pancreatic response to intraluminal amino acids is related to the load of amino acid delivered to the intestine, rather than to the concentration. That is to say, responses are dependent on the total amounts delivered and on the length of intestine exposed. Fatty acids with chain length longer than nine carbons also stimulate CCK release; activity is improved by formation of micelles. Undigested fat and glycerol do not stimulate CCK release. Little is known of the influence of peptide hormones on CCK release, although it has been reported that somatostatin inhibits the increase in circulating CCK in response to olive oil (Schlegel, Raptis, Harvey, Oliver and Pfeiffer, 1977). Earlier suggestions that bombesin might release CCK in the same way as it releases gastrin, were based in the assumption that pancreatic and gall bladder responses could be used as an index of CCK release (Erspamer, Improta, Melchiorri and Sopranzi, 1974). However, there is now good evidence to indicate that bombesin has a direct CCK-like action on pancreatic acinar cells, so that the possible release of CCK by bombesin remains an open question (Deschodt-Lankman, Robberecht, De Neef, Lammans and Christoffe, 1976).

After vagotomy in dogs the pancreatic response to exogenous CCK is unchanged but the response to stimulation by tryptophan or oleate in the intestine is decreased (Debas, Konturek and Grossman, 1975). One interpretation of this observation is that intact vagal innervation is required for release of CCK. However, Soloman and Grossman (1977) have now shown that the response of an autotransplanted pancreas in dogs to luminal stimuli is unaffected by vagotomy. The responses of autotransplanted pouches are solely dependent on hormonal stimuli, so that taken together these observations suggest that in intact dogs a vago-vagal nervous reflex mediates some of the action of luminal stimuli on pancreatic secretion, in addition to the hormonal (CCK) reflex.

4. Measurement in Blood

(a) *Bioassay*

The purification of CCK from tissue extracts has been monitored by bioassay on the guinea pig gall bladder *in vivo* (Ljungberg, 1964), and by pancreatic enzyme secretion in dog, cat and rat, *in vivo*, but these assays are not sensitive enough to measure hormone concentrations in blood. However, rabbit gall bladder strips *in vitro* provide a sensitive and specific assay for CCK, and in superfusion systems it is claimed that this preparation can detect 40 pg/ml, which should be adequate to measure the increase in circulating CCK after a meal (Johnson and McDermott, 1973). Using the rabbit gall bladder strip *in vitro* Berry and Flower (1971) were able to detect release of CCK into the hepatic portal vein by intraduodenal HCl in cats; short and long chain fatty acids and peptone also stimulated CCK release, although not as effectively as HCl. Hexamethonium blocked the release of CCK by HCl, but atropine had no effect, suggesting a non-cholinergic nervous mechanism was involved in modulating release. Other bioassays that have been used for the estimation of CCK include phospholipid turnover in exocrine pancreatic cell membranes (Dhariwal, Schally, Meyer, Sun, Jorpes and Mutt, 1963), inhibition of ^{3}H-caerulein binding to rat pancreas plasma membranes and adenylate cyclase activation in rat pancreatic plasma membranes (Robberecht, Deschodt-Lanckman and Vanderhaeghen, 1978). On the whole biological assays have not been extensively used to measure circulating CCK.

(a) Radioimmunoassay

There have been a number of reports of RIA estimation of CCK, but the measurement of this hormone in the circulation still presents several problems (Go, Ryan and Summerskill, 1971; Reeder, Becker, Smith, Rayford and Thompson, 1973; Harvey, Dowsett, Hartog and Read, 1973; Rehfeld, 1978c). The principal difficulties include raising antisera with appropriate specificity and affinitiy, preparing labelled peptide, and safeguarding the stability of standards, label and biological samples during storage. None of these problems should be unsurmountable.

Antisera to CCK have been raised in rabbits, guinea-pigs, sheep and chickens immunised with crude, partially purified or pure CCK either alone or after conjugation to BSA. When pure CCK33 is used as label many of the antisera raised in this way cross-react poorly, or not at all, with CCK8, indicating specificity for the mid- or NH_2-terminal regions of CCK. Such antisera may be expected to cross-react with naturally occurring NH_2-terminal fragments of CCK, and since these are biologically inactive the physiological significance of results obtained with such antisera need careful examination. Some antisera raised to porcine CCK cross-react poorly with CCK of other species suggesting species differences in the NH_2-terminal regions of the CCK (Go et al., 1971; Straus and Yalow, 1978), obviously such antisera have a limited application.

Antisera which cross-react at the COOH-terminus of CCK may be readily obtained by immunisation of rabbits with CCK8 conjugated to BSA. However, these antisera often cross-react almost equally with CCK8, CCK33 and COOH-terminal fragments of gastrin, so that they too lack the appropriate degree of specificity needed for assay of CCK in blood. It might be possible, however, to estimate CCK in blood from the differences of values obtained with such antisera and those obtained with COOH-terminal specific antisera which cross-react poorly with CCK.

The preparation of ^{125}I labelled CCK by means of the conventional chloramine T method (Hunter and Greenwood, 1962) presents problems because the single tyrosine residue in CCK33 is sulphated, and sulphated tyrosine residues are not readily substituted with iodine. This problem might be circumvented by using synthetic CCK in which the tyrosine is unsulphated. An alternative solution is to iodinate pure natural porcine CCK39, since the NH_2-terminal amino acid in this molecular form is unsulphated tyrosine. Rehfeld (1978c) has reported that with several antisera the immunoreactivities of CCK8 and CCK33 were markedly reduced after oxidation by exposure to chloramine T. However, this is not true for all antisera since we routinely iodinate unsulphated CCK8 by the chloramine T method with little or no reduction in immunoreactivity with an antiserum raised against CCK8. To overcome the potential problems of oxidation damage, CCK may be iodinated by the method of Bolton and Hunter (1973) in which free amino groups of lysine and arginine residues are labelled with ^{125}I hydroxyphenylpropionic acid hydroxy-succinimide ester (Rehfeld, 1978c).

Some authors still prefer to describe concentrations of CCK-like immunoreactivity in blood or tissue extracts in terms of Ivy dog units; 3 Ivy dog units are equivalent to 1 μg or 255 pmol of CCK33; since there are differences in the biological potencies of CCK33 and CCK8, it can be misleading and unnecessary to use Ivy dog units to describe the activity of CCK8. When pure natural or synthetic peptides are used as standards, and some of these are now available (Grossman, 1976a), concentrations should be expressed in molar terms equivalent to the appropriate standard. Human CCK may well differ in immunoreactivity from porcine CCK, so that until the human peptides are isolated estimates of their concentration will necessarily be relative.

5. Plasma Concentrations

(a) Normal

The application of radioimmunoassay to the measurement of circulating CCK can be expected to clarify and extend our understanding of the mechanisms of CCK release and mode of action. However, the RIA data presently available do little to resolve these problems. Estimates of fasting CCK concentrations in normal man vary from 26 pg/ml (equivalent to porcine CCK33) to 17,800 pg/ml (Harvey et al., 1973; Reeder et al., 1973). Failure to solve satisfactorily the problems of CCK radioimmunoassay almost certainly for these differences.

Estimates of CCK release following stimulation by feeding are also highly variable. In one study a pint of milk was reported to increase circulating CCK in man by 8–16 ng/ml (Harvey et al., 1973), and in another study serum CCK increased from 200 to 300 pg/ml after a standard meal (Rayford, Schafmayer, Teichmann and Thompson, 1978). Some idea of likely increase in post-prandial CCK can be obtained by an analysis of dose-response and pharmacokinetic data. Thus the dose of exogenous CCK needed to give half maximal stimulation of pancreatic enzyme output in dogs is 250 pmol/kg/hr (Debas and Grossman, 1973). The half life of exogenous CCK is reported to be about 2·5 min in man and in dog (Rayford, Fender,

Ramus and Thompson, 1975). Assuming a space of distribution comparable to that of other gut hormones (G17, etc) the increase in plasma CCK during an infusion of 250 pmol/kg/hr would be about 100 pmol/l or about 400 pg/ml.

(b) *Disease*

According to Low-Beer, Harvey, Davies and Read (1975) there are elevated basal concentrations of CCK in patients with coeliac disease, but the peak post-prandial concentrations are not significantly different from normal. The gall bladder response to a fatty meal in patients with coeliac disease was delayed compared with normal, and Low-Beer *et al.* (1975) suggest this may be associated with resistance to CCK due to prolonged exposure. Since it is now clear that CCK exists in several forms differing in biological activity, the possiblity of alterations in ratios of different forms must also be considered in relating total concentrations in blood to biological response.

Physiological studies suggest that pancreatic proteolytic enzymes (trypsin and chymotrypsin) inhibit CCK release and so provide a reflex regulation of pancreatic secretion (Green and Lyman, 1972). Patients with pancreatic insufficiency have been reported by Harvey *et al.* (1973) to have elevated circulating CCK concentrations and this could be a consequence of failure of pancreatic enzymes to inhibit CCK release.

C. SECRETIN

1. Chemistry

The discovery by Bayliss and Starling (1902) of secretin and its role in the regulation of the pancreas is rightly regarded as being the first demonstration of an endocrine reflex. In spite of this auspicious beginning it was not until 65 years later that secretin was finally obtained in a homogeneous state and its structure elucidated. Jorpes and Mutt (1973) have reviewed the many early attempts to isolate secretin, and have attributed their own final success to the introduction of modern methods of preparative protein chemistry notably ion-exchange chromatography, electrophoresis and counter current distribution. A crucial innovation introduced by Jorpes and Mutt (1973) was the initial extraction of porcine secretin into acetic acid followed by adsorption on alginic acid, elution with HCl and precipitation with sodium chloride (Mutt, 1959). The product of this procedure provides the starting material for further purification and is about 30 times more active than preparations obtained by other initial extraction methods. The same starting material has also been used for the purification of other peptides such as CCK, vasoactive intestinal peptide (VIP) and gastric inhibitory peptide (GIP). Extraction of the acid-sodium chloride precipitate with methanol separates secretin and VIP which are methanol-soluble from CCK and GIP which are insoluble. Subsequent purification by gel filtration, ion exchange and counter current distribution was used to give a homogenous preparation of secretin (Jorpes and Mutt, 1973). The secretin isolated by Jorpes and Mutt from hog duodenum was characterised as a basic peptide of 27 amino acid residues (Fig. 4) with marked similarities

```
1   2   3   4   5   6   7   8   9   10  11  12  13  14
His–Ser–Asp–Gly–Tyr–Phe–Thr–Ser–Glu–Leu–Ser–Arg–Leu–Arg–

15  16  17  18  19  20  21  22  23  24  25  26  27
Asp–Ser–Ala–Arg–Leu–Gln–Arg–Leu–Leu–Gln–Gly–Leu–Val–NH₂
```

Fig. 4. Amino acid sequence of porcine secretin.

in sequence to glucagon (Mutt and Jorpes, 1967b). Similarities in sequence with VIP and GIP are now recognised also, and together these suggest that this group of peptides evolved from a common ancestral molecule (Dockray, 1977a). Recently secretin has been isolated from chicken intestine but the sequence of this molecule has not yet been reported (Nilsson, 1975). Secretin has been found by radioimmunoassay in extracts of human intestine, but the human peptide has not yet been isolated.

The synthesis of porcine secretin was first described by Bodanszky, Ondetti, Levine, Narayanan, von Saltza, Sheehan, Williams and Sabo (1966), and has since been achieved by several other groups. Synthetic preparations of secretin have been obtained which have the full potency and range of biological actions of the natural molecule. Optical rotatory dispersion and circular dicroism spectra of synthetic secretin and related peptides and fragments indicate a possible helical conformation in the COOH-terminal part of the molecule (Bodanszky, Fink, Funk and Said, 1976).

Early studies of structure–activity relationships indicated that fragments and analogues of secretin, such as des-His[1], and Asp[6] secretin, had little or no activity on pancreatic bicarbonate output. These observations suggested that the intact peptide is needed for full activity and that there is no minimal active fragment comparable to that in gastrin or CCK (Jorpes and Mutt, 1973). In more recent studies it has been shown that COOH-terminal synthetic fragments such as 5–27 secretin displace ^{125}I secretin from its high affinity receptors on pancreatic acinar cell membranes, but unlike secretin itself do not stimulate adenylate cyclase. In contrast NH_2-terminal fragments such as 1–14 secretin, bind the high affinity secretin receptor and also stimulate adenylate cyclase, although weakly. These results suggest that the NH_2-terminal sequence of secretin is required for biological activity, and that affinity for the receptor is increased by the COOH-terminal portion of the molecule (Robberecht, Conlon and Gardner, 1976).

2. Distribution

Bayliss and Starling (1902, 1903) recorded secretin activity in jejunum and duodenum of a wide range of vertebrate species, and noted that the activity was absent from stomach and ileum. They also showed that secretin was predominantly located in mucosal cells, as opposed to the muscle layers of the intestine. Numerous later studies using bioassay, RIA and immunocytochemistry have confirmed this distribution. Acid perfusion of different segments of the intestine in pancreatic fistula dogs reveals that secretin is released in greatest amounts from the duodenum and proximal jejunum and in decreasing amounts down the gut (Konturek, Tasler and Obtulowicz, 1971). Secretin activity has been localised by bioassay to the transitional zone between crypts and villi in jejunum and duodenum (Krawitt, Zimmerman and Clifton, 1966), and immunocytochemical studies have confirmed the presence of scattered cells with secretin-like immunoreactivity in this region (Polak, Bloom, Coulling and Pearse, 1971; Bussolati, Capella, Solcia, Vassallo and Vezzadini, 1971). The secretin cell corresponds to the S-cell (S for small granules) identified by electron microscopy. The frequency of S-cells in the jejunum is about one-third to a half that in duodenum, but the greater length of the jejunum relative to duodenum means that the bulk of intestinal secretin is jejunal in origin (Larsson, Sundler, Alumets, Hakanson, Schaffalitzky de Muckadell and Fahrenkrug, 1977). In the duodenum of foetal rats (18–21 days) S-cells are apparently more frequent than in the adult. The principal stimulus for secretin release is acid, but in the foetal duodenum, and in the adult jejunum, there is seldom, if ever, likely to be sufficient acid to liberate secretin, suggesting that other factors might also control the release of the hormone.

3. Control

There has been considerable discussion in recent years of the mechanisms governing secretin release and the control of pancreatic bicarbonate output in response to a normal meal. The results of physiological studies in pancreatic fistula dogs, and more recently of RIA of plasma secretin, indicate that the presence of acid in the duodenum is a strong stimulant of secretin release. In addition fatty acids with 10 or more carbons in the chain weakly stimulate secretin release, but undigested fat has no activity (Meyer and Jones, 1974). The threshold for release is about pH 4·5, and below this the amount of secretin released is proportionate to the load of acid entering the small intestine (Meyer, Way and Grossman, 1970a). The intestinal mucosa neutralises acid by a saturable mechanism, so that with increasing loads of acid progressively greater lengths of intestine are exposed to pH 4·5 or less with a corresponding increase in secretin release (Meyer, Way and Grossman, 1970b). During normal digestion in dogs the mean pH in the duodenal bulb is about 3·5, and the mean pH in the mid duodenum about 5·5 (Brooks and Grossman, 1970). The optimal conditions for secretin release are therefore normally attained only in the first few centimetres of duodenum. On this evidence one might expect very modest increases in plasma secretin after a normal meal, and recent estimates of plasma secretin by RIA confirm this. Nevertheless, as Grossman and Konturek (1974) have shown, the secretion of bicarbonate from the pancreas closely matches the entry of acid into the duodenum, and there can be no doubt that gastric acid drives pancreatic bicarbonate output. It seems likely that the increase in plasma secretin after a normal meal is by itself insufficient to stimulate the pancreas. However, there is abundant evidence to indicate that the action of secretin on the pancreas is strongly potentiated by CCK (Meyer et al., 1971). The small amounts of secretin that are normally released by feeding are therefore likely to be effective in stimulating the pancreas because they are accompanied by CCK.

4. Measurement in Blood

(a) Bioassay

Although bioassays for secretin have been widely used to monitor purification of the peptide, these methods are too insensitive to permit estimation of the concentrations in blood. The most widely used test systems are the flow and bicarbonate output of the pancreas in conscious or anaesthetised dogs, cats and rats. The sensitivity of these preparations can be improved by simultaneous infusion of a low dose of CCK, due to the potentiation between the two hormones. In dog and rat, CCK stimulates not only enzyme secretion but also the flow and bicarbonate output so that pancreatic flow and bicar- bicarbonate responses in these two species are not absolutely specific for secretin. Moreover VIP stimulates pancreatic secretion in all three species. Clearly then, crude tissue extracts containing mixtures of secretin, CCK and VIP cannot be reliably assayed in dog, cat or rat (Barrington and Dockray, 1976; Dockray, 1977a). A number of groups have studied binding of [125]I- labelled secretin to plasma membranes of pancreas and fat cells (Robberecht,

Conlon and Gardner, 1976), and it might be possible to use a membrane preparation in a radioreceptor assay for secretin.

(b) *Radioimmunoassay*

At present RIA offers the best chances for providing sensitive and specific assays of secretin in blood. Secretin radioimmunoassays have now been devised in many laboratories and the application of these assays to the measurement of circulating hormone has recently been reviewed (Straus, 1978). Because secretin circulates in low concentrations it is clear that RIA systems for this hormone must be of the highest possible sensitivity which means employing antisera of high affinity and labelled secretin of high specific activity and quality.

Antisera have been obtained in rabbits immunised with unconjugated secretin, and with secretin conjugated to albumin. Although VIP, GIP and glucagon are related in sequence to secretin, cross-reactivity of these peptides in secretin radioimmunoassays does not seem to be a problem. Neither does heterogeneity of secretin in blood and tissues present any problems, since the presently available evidence suggests that secretin exists as a single immunoreactive form with properties compatible with the standard heptacosapeptide isolated by Jorpes and Mutt. Secretin does not possess a tyrosine residue, but early fears that it might therefore prove difficult to label with ^{125}I have proved unfounded. Secretin can be iodinated to high specific activity by labelling the histidine residue with ^{125}I either using the chloramine T method (Tai, Korsch and Chey, 1975; Straus, Urbach and Yalow, 1975b) or lactoperoxidase (Holohan, Murphy, Flanagan, Buchanan and Elmore, 1973). Secretin analogues with tyrosine substituted at position 6 or 12 have been synthesised and these are readily labelled with ^{125}I. However some secretin antisera show diminished immunoreactivity with the tyrosine-substituted analogues, and these have not therefore found general application as labelled preparations in secretin RIA.

Several different units have been employed to describe the activity of secretin preparations. The Crick Harper Raper unit was said to correspond to 12 Hammersten cat units, and 20 Hammersten cat units were equivalent to one clinical unit. From 1966 onwards there has been a 4 fold increase in the strength of clinical units used to describe the activity of the preparations produced by Jorpes and Mutt; pure natural secretin is now said to have an activity of 4 clinical units per µg (Jorpes and Mutt, 1973). In view of the widespread availability of pure natural and synthetic preparations, and the confusion surrounding the older biological units, it is clear that secretin concentrations should be expressed in pg/ml (porcine equivalent) or pmol/l. Estimates of the real, or absolute, concentration of secretin in species other than pig, will have to await purification of secretin from those species.

5. Concentrations in Blood

(a) *Normal*

Estimates of the concentration of secretin in human fasting plasma vary from 0·6 to over 50 pg/ml (0·2–20 pmol/l). As in other radioimmunoassays plasma proteins can cause non-specific inhibition of binding of labelled secretin to antiserum and so give misleadingly high estimates of secretin concentrations. To minimise this effect it is essential to use a plasma blank and this is most readily obtained by stripping secretin from normal plasma by affinity immunoadsorption to antisera conjugated to a solid support. When label and antiserum of appropriate quality are used, and when care is taken to minimise non-specific effects of plasma proteins, the concentration of secretin in human fasting plasma is estimated to be 1–3 pmol/l (Fahrenkrug and Schaffalitzky de Muckadell, 1977; Hacki, Greenberg and Bloom, 1978).

In dog, pig and man, intraduodenal HCl is a good stimulant of plasma immunoreactive secretin. Plasma concentrations rise rapidly after instillation of acid and reach a peak at about 3 min before declining to basal levels in about 20 min. The relatively rapid decline in plasma secretin is consistent with a half life of about 3 min in man (Kolts and McGuigan, 1977). Graded amounts of secretin produce a graded increase in plasma concentrations (Isenberg, Cano and Bloom, 1977). During infusion of exogenous secretin in man an increase of about 15 pmol/l is associated with half maximal rates of pancreatic bicarbonate secretion (Hacki, Bloom, Mitznegg, Domschke, Domschke, Belohlavek, Demling and Wunsch, 1977). Comparable increases of endogenous secretin are seen with acid loads corresponding to maximal or near maximal rates of gastric acid secretin (Schaffalitzky de Muckadell, Fahrenkrieg and Holst, 1977; Hacki *et al.*, 1978; Isenberg *et al.*, 1977).

Undigested fat and amino acids have no effect on plasma secretin. There are reports that glucose (Chisholm, Young and Lazarus, 1969) and alcohol (Straus, Urbach and Yalow, 1975a) increase immunoreactive secretin in blood, but these reports have not been confirmed by other groups. Henry, Flanagan and Buchanan (1975) reported that plasma secretin in man increased during 72 hr starvation, but this observation could not be confirmed in another study (Hacki *et al.*, 1978). It is of interest, however, that in dogs plasma secretin rose during six weeks of parenteral feeding (Johnson, Schanbacher, Dudrick and Copeland, 1978). The significance of these observations is not yet clear, but the possibility that the long term absence of food from the gut increases release of secretin deserves consideration. Early estimates of plasma secretin by RIA suggested that there was no increase after a normal meal. However, with technical improvements in secretin radioimmunoassays, it has become clear that small, but nevertheless measurable, increases do occur in normal subjects during a digestion of a meal. In two recent studies secretin increased from fasting levels of about 2 pmol/l to a peak of 5–6 pmol/l after a standard meal (Hacki *et al.*, 1978; Schaffalitzky de Muckadell and Fahrenkrug, 1978). These small increases are likely to be effective in stimulating the pancreas because of the accompanying presence of CCK and the strong potentiation between the two hormones.

(*b*) *Plasma secretin in disease*

In keeping with the idea that acid is the main stimulus for secretin release it is not surprising that secretin concentrations are elevated in patients with gastric acid hypersecretion e.g. gastrinomas (Straus and Yalow, 1977). Other conditions characterised by elevated plasma secretin have not yet been described. However, there are reports that secretin may be produced by pancreatic tumours of the watery diarrhoea syndrome. These reports are based on the observation of secretin-like biological activity in crude tumour extracts tested on the pancreas in dog, cat or rat (Zollinger, 1975); there have not so far been any reports of elevated plasma secretin measured by RIA in these patients. VIP has weak secretin-like biological activity, and is known to occur in pancreatic tumours of the watery diarrhoea syndrome (Bloom, Polak and Pearse, 1973). Plasma VIP is elevated in patients with watery diarrhoea syndrome, and it seems likely that this peptide rather than secretin accounts for the symptoms of these patients.

It is tempting to suppose that patients with duodenal ulcer might have a deficiency of secretin, and therefore a failure of the mechanisms which neutralise acid in the duodenum. In one study patients with duodenal ulcer were found to have lower than normal plasma secretin concentrations in the fasting state and in response to intraduodenal acid (Bloom and Ward, 1975). However, in a second study using the same RIA the fasting concentration of secretin in blood was slightly higher than in normals, and increases in response to graded amounts of HCl were similar in the two groups (Isenberg *et al.*, 1977). Pancreatic bicarbonate secretion in response to intraduodenal acid in duodenal ulcer patients has been described as lower (Wormsley, 1970) or slightly higher than normal (Isenberg *et al.*, 1977). The reasons for these discrepancies are at present unexplained and emphasise the need for further study.

In patients with coeliac disease an increased number of S-cells was found by immunocytochemistry, and granule content appeared higher than normal possibly due to failure of hormone release (Polak, Pearse, Van Noorden, Bloom and Rossiter, 1973). Evidence of decreased secretion of secretin in patients with coeliac disease has also been briefly described (Hacki *et al.*, 1978).

REFERENCES

Agarwal, K. L., Grudzinsky, S., Kenner, G. W., Rodgers, N. H., Sheppard, R. C. and McGuigan, J. E. (1971). *Experientia*, 27, 514.

Anastasi, A., Bertaccini, G., Cei, J. M., de Caro, G., Erspamer, V., Impicciatore, M. and Roseghini, M. (1970). *Br. J. Pharmacol.* 38, 221.

Anastasi, A., Erspamer, V. and Endean, R. (1968). *Arch. Biochem. Biophys.* 125, 57.

Barrington, E. J. W. and Dockray, G. J. (1976). *J. Endocr.* 69, 299

Bayliss, W. M. and Starling, E. H. (1902). *J. Physiol.* 28, 325.

Bayliss, W. M. and Starling, E. H. (1903). *J. Physiol.* 29, 174.

Becker, H. D., Reeder, D. D. and Thompson, J. C. (1973a). *Gastroenterology*, 65, 28.

Becker, H. D., Reeder, D. D. and Thompson, J. C. (1973b). *Gastroenterology*, 65, 903.

Berson, S. A. and Yalow, R. S. (1971). *Gastroenterology*, 60, 215.

Berry, H. and Flower, J. (1971). *Gastroenterology*, 60, 409.

Blair, E. L., Keenlyside, R. M., Newell, R. J., Reed, J. D. and Richardson, D. D. (1968). *J. Physiol.* 198, 614.

Blair, E. L., Grund, E. R., Lund, P. K., Piercy, A., Reed, J. D., Saunders, D. J., Shale, D., Shaw, B. and Wilkinson, J. (1977). *J. Physiol.* 266, 157.

Blair, E. L., Grund, E. R., Lund, P. K. and Saunders, D. J. (1977). *J. Physiol.* 273, 561.

Bloom, S. R., Polak, J. M. and Pearse, A. G. E. (1973). *Lancet*, ii, 14.

Bloom, S. R. and Ward, A. S. (1975). *Br. med. J.* 1, 126.

Bodanszky, M., Fink, M. L., Funk, K. W. and Said, S. I. (1976). *Clin. Endocr.* 5 (Suppl.), 195s.

Bodanszky, M., Ondetti, M. A., Levine, S. D., Narayanan, V. L., Von Saltza, M., Sheehan, J. T., Williams, N. J. and Sabo, E. F. (1966). *Chem. Indust.* 42, 1757.

Bolton, A. E. and Hunter, W. M. (1973). *Biochem. J.* 133, 529.

Bonfils, S., Dubrasquet, M., Accary, J. P., Girodet, J. and Mignon, M. (1978). *In* "Gut Hormones" (S. R. Bloom, ed.), p. 158. Churchill Livingston, Edinburgh).

Brandsborg, O., Brandsborg, M. and Christensen, N. J. (1975). *Gastroenterology*, 68, 455.

Brooks, A. M. and Grossman, M. I. (1970). *Gastroenterology*, 59, 85.

Buffa, R., Solcia, E. and Go, V. L. W. (1976). *Gastroenterology*, 70, 528.

Bugat, R., Walsh, J. H., Ippoliti, A., Elashoff, J. and Grossman, M. I. (1976). *Gastroenterology*, 71, 1114.

Bussolati, G., Capella, C., Solcia, E., Vassallo, G. and Vezzadini, P. (1971). *Histochemie*, 26, 218.

Cairns, D., Deveney, C. W. and Way, L. W. (1974). *Surg. Forum*, 25, 325.

Carter, D. C., Taylor, I. L., Elashoff, J. and Grossman, M. I. (1979). *Gut*, (In press).

Chisholm, E. J., Young, J. D. and Lazarus, L. (1969). *J. clin. Invest.* 38, 1453.

Clendinnen, B. G., Reeder, D. D., Brandt, E. N., Jr. and Thompson, J. C. (1973). *Gut*, 14, 462.

Colin-Jones, D. G. and Lennard-Jones, J. E. (1972). *Gut*, 13, 88.

Creutzfeldt, W., Arnold, R., Creutzfeldt, C., Feurle, G. and Ketterer, H. (1971). *Eur. J. clin. Invest.* 1, 461.

Creutzfeldt, W., Arnold, R. Creutzfeldt, C. and Track, N. S., (1975). *Hum. Path.* 6, 47.

Csendes, A., Walsh, J. H. and Grossman, M. I. (1972). *Gastroenterology*, 63, 257.

Davidson, W. D., Moore, T. C., Shippey, W. and Conovaloff, A. J. (1974). *Gastroenterology*, 66, 522.

Debas, H. T., Csendes, A., Walsh, J. H. and Grossman, M. I. (1974). *In* "Endocrinology of the Gut" (W. Y. Chey and F. P. Brooks, eds), p. 222. Charles B. Slack· Inc, Thorofare, New Jersey.
Debas, H. T., Farooq, O. and Grossman, M. I. (1975). *Gastroenterology*, **68**, 1211.
Debas, H. T. and Grossman, M. I. (1973). *Digestion*, **9**, 469.
Debas, H. T. and Grossman, M. I. (1975). *Gastroenterology*, **69**, 651.
Debas, H. T., Konturek, S. J. and Grossman, M. I. (1975). *Am. J. Physiol.* **228**, 1172.
Debas, H. T., Walsh, J. H. and Grossman, M. I. (1975). *Gastroenterology*, **68**, 687.
Debas, H. T., Walsh, J. H. and Grossman, M. I. (1976). *Gastroenterology*, **70**, 1082.
Deschodt-Lankman, M., Robberecht, P., De Neef, P., Lammans, M. and Christoffe, J. (1976). *J. clin. Invest.* **58**, 891.
Dharival, A. P. S., Schally, A. V., Meyer, J., Sun, D. C. H., Jorpes, J. E. and Mutt, V. (1963). *Gastroenterology*, **44**, 316.
Dockray, G. J. (1976). *Nature, Lond.* **264**, 568.
Dockray, G. J. (1977a). *Gastroenterology*, **72**, 344.
Dockray, G. J. (1977b). *Nature, Lond.* **270**, 359.
Dockray, G. J., Best, L. and Taylor, I. L. (1977). *J. Endocr.* **72**, 143.
Dockray, G. J., Debas, H. T., Walsh, J. H. and Grossman, M. I. (1975). *Proc. Soc. exp. Biol. Med.* **149**, 550.
Dockray, G. J., Gregory, R. A., Harris, J. I., Hutchinson, J. and Runswick, M. J. (1978). *J. Physiol.* **280**, 16P.
Dockray, G. J., Gregory, R. A. and Kenner, G. W. (1978). *Gastroenterology*, **75**, 556.
Dockray, G. J. and Hopkins, C. R. (1975). *J. cell Biol.* **64**, 724.
Dockray, G. J. and Taylor, I. L. (1976). *Gastroenterology*, **71**, 971.
Dockray, G. J. and Taylor, I. L. (1977). *Gastroenterology*, **72**, 814.
Dockray, G. J. and Walsh, J. H. (1975). *Gastroenterology*, **68**, 222.
Dockray, G. J., Walsh, J. H. and Grossman, M. I. (1976). *Biochem. biophys. Res. Commun.* **69**, 339.
Dockray, G. J., Walsh, J. H. and Passaro, E. (1975). *Gut*, **16**, 353.
Dockray, G. J., Vaillant, C. and Hopkins, C. R. (1978). *Nature, Lond.* **273**, 770.
Edkins, J. S. (1905). *Proc. R. Soc. B.* **76**, 376.
Erspamer, V., Improta, G., Melchiorri, P. and Sopranzi, N. (1974). *Br. J. Pharm.* **52**, 227.
Erspamer, V. and Melchiorri, P. (1973). *Appl. Chem.* **35**, 463.
Erspamer, V. and Melchiorri, P. (1975). *In* "Gastrointestinal Hormones" (J. C. Thompson, ed.), p. 575. University of Texas Press, Austin, Texas.
Euler, A. R., Byrne, W. J., Cousins, L. M., Ament, M. E., Leake, R. D. and Walsh, J. H. (1977). *Gastroenterology*, **72**, 1271.
Fahrenkrug, J. and Schaffalitzky de Muckadell, O. B. (1977). *Eur. J. clin. Invest.* **7**, 201.
Farooq, O. and Walsh, J. H. (1975). *Gastroenterology*, **68**, 662.
Feldman, M., Walsh, J. H., Wong, H. C. and Richardson, C. T. (1978). *J. clin. Invest.* **61**, 308.
Ganguli, P. C., Polak, J. M., Pearse, A. G. E., Elder, J. B. and Hegarty, M. (1974). *Lancet*, **i**, 583.
Go, V. L. W., Hofman, A. F. and Summerskill, W. H. J. (1970). *J. clin. Invest.* **49**, 1558.
Go, V. L. W., Ryan, R. J. and Summerskill, W. H. J. (1971). *J. Lab. clin. Med.* **77**, 684.
Goodfriend, T. L., Levine, L. and Fasman, G. D. (1964). *Science*, **144**, 1344.
Green, G. M. and Lyman, R. L. (1972). *Proc. Soc. exp. Biol. Med.* **140**, 6.
Gregory, R. A. (1974). *J. Physiol.* **241**, 1.

Gregory, R. A. and Tracy, H. J. (1964). *Gut,* 5, 103.
Gregory, R. A. and Tracy, H. J. (1972). *Lancet,* ii, 797.
Gregory, R. A. and Tracy, H. J. (1974). *Gut,* 15, 683.
Gregory, R. A. and Tracy, H. J. (1975). *In* "Gastrointestinal Hormones" (J. C. Thompson, ed.), p. 13. University of Texas Press, Austin, Texas.
Gregory, R. A., Tracy, H. J., Agarwal, K. L. and Grossman, M. I. (1969). *Gut,* 10, 603.
Grossman, M. I. (1976a). *Gastroenterology,* 71, 166.
Grossman, M. I. (1976b). *In* "Peptide Hormones" (J. A. Parsons, ed.), p. 105. Macmillan Press, London.
Grossman, M. I. and Konturek, S. J. (1974). *Scand. J. Gastro.* 9. 299.
Grossman, M. I., Robertson, C. R. and Ivy, A. C. (1948). *Am. J. Physiol.* 153, 1.
Gutierrez, J. G., Chey, W. Y. and Dinoso, V. P. (1974). *Gastroenterology,* 67, 35.
Hacki, W. H., Bloom, S. R., Mitznegg, P., Domschke, W., Domschke, S., Belohlavek, D., Demling, L. and Wunsch, E. (1977). *Gut,* 18, 191.
Hacki, W. H., Greenberg, G. R. and Bloom, S. R. (1978). *In* "Gut Hormones" (S. R. Bloom, ed.), p. 182. Churchill Livingston, Edinburgh.
Hansky, J. and Cain, M. D. (1969). *Lancet,* ii, 1388.
Hansky, J., King, R. W. and Holdsworth, S. (1975). *In* "Gastrointestinal Hormones", (J. C. Thompson, ed.), p. 115. University of Texas Press, Austin. Texas.
Hansky, J., Royle, J. P. and Korman, M. G. (1974). *AJEBAK,* 52, 841.
Hansky, J., Soveny, C. and Korman, M. G. (1971). *Gastroenterology,* 61, 62.
Hansky, J., Soveny, C. and Korman, M. G. (1974). *Digestion,* 10, 97.
Harper, A. A. and Raper, H. S. (1943). *J. Physiol.* 102, 115.
Harper, A. A. and Vass, C. C. N. (1941). *J. Physiol.* 99, 415.
Harvey, R. F., Dowsett, L., Hartog, M. and Read, A. E. (1973). *Lancet,* ii, 826.
Henry, R. W., Flanagan, R. W. J. and Buchanan, K. D. (1975). *Lancet,* ii, 202.
Holohan, K. N., Murphy, R. F., Flanagan, R. J. W., Buchanan, K. D. and Elmore, D. (1973). *Biochim. biophys. Acta,* 322, 178.
Hughes, W. S. and Hernandez, A. J. (1976). *Gastroenterology,* 71, 720.
Hunter, W. M. and Greenwood, F. C. (1962). *Nature, Lond.* 194, 495.
Impicciatore, M., Walsh, J. H. and Grossman, M. I. (1977) *Gastroenterology,* 72, 995.
Isenberg, J. I., Cano, R. and Bloom, S. R. (1977). *Gastroenterology,* 72, 6.
Isenberg, J. I., Grossman, M. I., Maxwell, V. and Walsh, J. H. (1975). *J. clin. Invest.* 55, 330.
Isenberg, J. I., Walsh, J. H. and Grossman, M. I. (1973). *Gastroenterology,* 65, 140.
Isenberg, J. I., Walsh, J. H., Passaro, E., Jr., Moore, E. H. and Grossman, M. I. (1972). *Gastroenterology,* 62, 626.
Ivy, A. C. and Oldberg, E. (1928). *Am. J. Physiol.* 86, 599.
Jaffe, B. M., Clendinnen, B. G., Clarke, R. J. and Alexander Williams, J. (1974). *Gastroenterology,* 66, 994.
Jaffe, B. M. and Walsh, J. H. (1978). *In* "Methods of Hormone Radioimmunoassay" (B. M. Jaffe and H. R. Behrman, eds). Academic Press, New York and London.
Johnson, A. G. and McDermott, S. J. (1973). *Lancet,* ii, 589.
Johnson, L. R. (1976). *Gastroenterology,* 70, 278.
Johnson, L. R., Schanbacher, L. M., Dudrick, S. J. and Copeland, E. M. (1978). *Am. J. Physiol.* 233, E524.
Jorpes, J. E. and Mutt, V. (1966). *Acta physiol. scand.* 66, 196.
Jorpes, J. E. and Mutt, V. (1973). *Hand. exp. Pharm.* 34, 1.
Kenner, G. W. and Sheppard, R. C. (1968). *Proc. R. Soc. B.* 170, 89.
Kolts, B. E. and McGuigan, J. E. (1977). *Gastroenterology,* 72, 55.

Komarov, S. A. (1938). *Proc. Soc. exp. Biol. Med.* **58**, 514.
Konturek, S. J., Tasler, J. and Obtulowicz, W. (1971). *Am. J. Physiol.* **220**, 124.
Korman, M. G., Scott, D. H., Hansky, J. and Wilson, H. (1972). *Aus. N.Z. J. Med.* **3**, 266.
Krawitt, E. L., Zimmerman, G. R. and Clifton, J. A. (1966). *Am. J. Physiol.* **211**, 935.
Lai, K. S. (1964). *Gut*, **5**, 327.
Larsson, L.-I., Rehfeld, J. F., Sundler, F. and Hakanson, R. (1976). *Nature, Lond.* **262**, 609.
Larsson, L.-I., Rehfeld, J. F. and Goltermann, N. (1977). *Scand. J. Gastro.* **12**, 869.
Larsson, L.-I., Sundler, F., Alumets, J. Hakanson, R., Schaffalitzky de Muckadell, O. B. and Fahrenkrug, J. (1977). *Cell Tiss. Res.* **181**, 361.
Lin, T-M. (1972). *Gastroenterology*, **63**, 922.
Lin, T-M., (1975). *Gastroenterology*, **69**, 1006.
Ljunberg, S. (1964). *Svensk, farmaceut. Tidskr.* **68**, 351.
Loveridge, N. Bloom, S. E., Welbourn, R. B. and Chayen, J. (1974). *Clin. Endocr.* **3**, 389.
Low-Beer, T. S., Harvey, R. F., Davies, E. R. and Read, A. E. (1975). *New Engl. J. Med.* **292**, 961.
McGuigan, J. E. (1967). *Gastroenterology*, **53**, 697.
McGuigan, J. E. (1968a). *Gastroenterology*, **54**, 1005.
McGuigan, J. E. (1968b). *Gastroenterology*, **55**, 315.
McGuigan, J. E. and Trudeau, W. L. (1970). *New Engl. J. Med.* **282**, 358.
Malmstrom, J. Stadil, F. and Rehfeld, J. F. (1976). *Gastroenterology*, **70**, 697.
Melchiorri, P. (1978). *In* "Gut Hormones" (S. R. Bloom, ed.), p. 534. Churchill Livingston, Edinburgh.
Mellanby, J. M. (1925). *J. Physiol.* **60**, 85.
Meyer, J. H. and Jones, R. S. (1974). *Am. J. Physiol.* **226**, 1178.
Meyer, J. H. and Kelly, G. A. (1976). *Am. J. Physiol.* **231**, 682.
Meyer, J. H., Kelly, G. A., Spingola, L. J. and Jones, R. S. (1976). *Am. J. Physiol.* **231**, 669.
Meyer, J. H., Spingola, L. J. and Grossman, M. I. (1971). *Am. J. Physiol.* **221**, 742.
Meyer, J. H., Way, L. W. and Grossman, (1970a). *Am. J. Physiol.* **219**, 964.
Meyer, J. H., Way, L. W. and Grossman, M. I. (1970b) *Am. J. Physiol.* **219**, 971.
Morley, J. (1968) *Proc. Roy. Soc. B.,* **170**, 97.
Muller, J. E., Straus, E. and Yallow, R. S. (1977). *Proc. natn. Acad. Sci., USA,* **74**, 3035.
Mutt, V. (1959). *Arch. Chem.* **15**, 69.
Mutt, V. (1964). *Acta chem. scand.* **18**, 2185.
Mutt, V. (1976). *Clin. Endocr.* **5** (Suppl.), 175s.
Mutt, V. and Jorpes, J. E. (1967a). *Biochem. biophys. Res. Commun.* **26**, 392.
Mutt, V. and Jorpes, J. E. (1967b). *Recent Prog. Horm. Res.* **23**, 483.
Mutt, V. and Jorpes, J. E. (1968). *Eur. J. Biochem.* **6**, 156.
Nilsson, A. (1975). *FEBS Lett.* **47**, 284.
Nilsson, G., Simon, J., Yalow, R. S. and Berson, S. A. (1972). *Gastroenterology*, **63**, 51.
Nilsson, G., Yalow, R. S. and Berson, S. A. (1973). *In* "Frontiers of Gastrointestinal Hormone Research" (S. Andersson, ed.), p. 95. Almqvist Wicksell, Stockholm.
Passaro, E. Jr., Basso, N. and Walsh, J. H. (1972). *Surgery*, **72**, 60.
Pearse, A. G. E. (1976) *Nature, Lond.* **262**, 92.
Pearse, A. G. E., Polak, J. M. and Bloom, S. R. (1977). *Gastroenterology*, **72**, 746.
Piszkiewica, D. (1974). *Nature, Lond.* **248**, 341.
Polak, J. M., Bloom, S. R., Coulling, I. and Pearse, A. G. E. (1971). *Gut*, **12**, 605.

O

Polak, J. M., Bloom, S. R., Hobbs, S., Solcia, E. and Pearse, A. G. E. (1976). *Lancet*, i, 1109.

Polak, J. M., Pearse, A. G. E., Van Noorden, S., Bloom, S. R. and Rossiter, M. A. (1973). *Gut*, 14, 830.

Polak, J. M., Pearse, A. G. E., Bloom, S. R., Buchan, A. M. J., Rayford, P. L. and Thompson, J. C. (1975). *Lancet*, ii, 1016.

Polak, J. M., Stagg, B. and Pearse, A. G. E. (1972). *Gut*, 13, 72.

Rayford, P. L., Fender, H. R., Ramus, N. I. and Thompson, J. C. (1975). *Gastroenterology*, 68, 971.

Rayford, P. L., Shafmayer, A., Teichmann, R. K. and Thompson, J. C. (1978). *In* "Gut Hormones" (S. R. Bloom, ed), p. 208. Churchill Livingston, Edinburgh.

Reeder, D. D., Becker, H. D., Smith, N. J., Rayford, P. L. and Thompson, J. C. (1973). *Ann. Surg.* 177, 304.

Rehfeld, J. F. (1978a). *Nature, Lond.* 272, 771.

Rehfeld, J. F. (1978b). *In* "Gut Hormones" (S. R. Bloom, ed.), p. 145. Churchill Livingston, Edinburgh.

Rehfeld, J. F. (1978c). *J. biol. Chem.* 253, 4016.

Rehfeld, J. F., Schwartz, T. W. and Stadil, F. (1977). *Gastroenterology*, 73, 469.

Rehfeld, J. F. and Stadil, F. (1973). *Gut*, 14, 369.

Robberecht, P., Conlon, T. P. and Gardner, J. D. (1976). *J. biol Chem.* 251, 4635.

Robberecht, P. Deschodt-Lankman, M. and Vanderhaeghen, J. J. (1978). *Proc. natn. Acad. Sci., USA*, 75, 524.

Schaffalitzky de Muckadell, O. B. and Fahrenkrug, J. (1978). *In* "Gut Hormones" (S. R. Bloom, ed.), p. 197. Churchill Livingston, Edinburgh.

Schaffalitzky de Muckadell, O. B., Fahrenkrug, J. and Holst, J. J. (1977). *Scand. J. Gastro.* 12, 267.

Schlegel, A., Raptis, S., Harvey, R. F., Oliver, J. M. and Pfeiffer, E. F. (1977). *Lancet*, ii, 166.

Solcia, E., Vassallo, G. and Sampietro, R. (1967). *Z. Zellforsch.* 81, 474.

Soloman, T. E. and Grossman, M. I. (1977). *Gastroenterology*, 72, 1134.

Stadil, F. (1972) *Scand. J. Gastro.* 7, 225.

Stadil, F. and Rehfeld, J. F. (1974). *Gastroenterology*, 66, 7.

Stadil, F., Rehfeld, J. F., Christiansen, A. and Malmstrom, J. (1975). *Scand. J. Gastro.* 10, 863.

Steiner, D. F. (1976). *In* "Peptide Hormones" (J. A. Parsons ed.), p. 49. Macmillan, London.

Stern, D. H. and Walsh, J. H. (1973). *Gastroenterology*, 64, 363.

Straus, E. (1978). *Gastroenterology*, 74, 141.

Straus, E., Gerson, C. D. and Yalow, R. S. (1974). *Gastroenterology*, 66, 175.

Straus, E., Urbach, H-J. and Yalow, R. S., (1975a). *New Engl. J. Med.* 293, 1031.

Straus, E., Urbach, H-J. and Yalow, R. S. (1975b). *Biochem. biophys. Res. Commun.* 64, 1036.

Straus, E. and Yalow, R. S. (1975). *In* "Gastrointestinal Hormones" (J. C. Thompson, ed.), p. 99. University of Texas Press, Austin, Texas.

Straus, E. and Yalow, R. S. (1977). *Gastroenterology*, 72, 992.

Straus, E. and Yalow, R. S. (1978). *Proc. natn. Acad. Sci. USA*, 75, 486.

Stunz, U. T., Thompson, M. R., Elashoff, J. and Grossman, M. I. (1978). *Gastroenterology*, 74, 550.

Strunz, U. T., Walsh, J. H. and Grossman, M. I. (1978a). *Gastroenterology*, 74, 32.

Strunz, U. T., Walsh, J. H. and Grossman, M. I. (1978b). *Proc. Soc. exp. Biol. Med.* 157, 440.

Tai, H-H., Korach, B. and Chey, W. Y. (1975). *Anal. Biochem.* **69**, 34.
Temperley, J. M. and Stagg, B. H. (1971). *Scand. J. Gastro.* **6**, 735.
Tepperman, B. L., Walsh, J. H. and Preshaw, R. (1972). *Gastroenterology*, **63**, 973.
Thompson, M. R., Debas, H. T., Walsh, J. H. and Grossman, M. I. (1976). *Physiologist*, **19**, 390.
Tracy, H. J. and Gregory, R. A. (1964). *Nature, Lond.* **204**, 935.
Trudeau, W. L. and McGuigan, J. E. (1971). *New Engl. J. Med.* **284**, 408.
Uvnas-Wallensten, K. (1977). *Gastroenterology*, **73**, 487.
Uvnas-Wallensten, K. and Rehfeld, J. H. (1976). *Acta physiol. scand.* **98**, 217.
Uvnas-Wallensten, K., Rehfeld, J. F., Larsson, L-I. and Uvnas, B. (1977). *Proc. natn. Acad. Sci., USA*, **74**, 5707.
Vanderhaeghen, J. J., Signeau, J. C. and Gepts, V. (1975). *Nature, Lond.* **257**, 604.
Varro, V., Varga, L., Csernay, L., Nafradi, J., Penke, B. and Balaspiri, L. (1973). *Acta hepta-gastro.* **20**, 507.
Walsh, J. H., Debas, H. T. and Grossman, M. I. (1974). *J. clin. Invest.* **54**, 577.
Walsh, J. H. and Dockray, G. J. (1978). *Gastroenterology*, **74**, 1108.
Walsh, J. H. and Grossman, M. I. (1975). *New Engl. J. Med.* **292**, 1324.
Walsh, J. H., Isenberg, J. I., Ansfield, J. and Maxwell, J. (1976). *J. clin. Invest.* **57**, 1125.
Walsh, J. H. and Laster, L. (1973). *Biochem. Med.* **8**, 432.
Wilson, S. D., Mathison, J. A., Shulte, W. J. and Ellison, E. H. (1968). *Arch. Surg.* **97**, 437.
Walsh, J. H., Yalow, R. S. and Berson, S. A. (1971). *Gastroenterology*, **601**, 16.
Walsh, J. H., Richardson, C. T. and Fordtran, J. S. (1975). *J. clin. Invest.* **55**, 462.
Wormsley, K. G. (1970). *Scand. J. Gastro.* **5**, 353.
Yalow, R. S. and Berson, S. A. (1970a). *Gastroenterology*, **58**, 1.
Yalow, R. S. and Berson, S. A. (1970b). *Gastroenterology*, **58**, 609.
Yalow, R. S. and Berson, S. A. (1972). *Biochem. biophys. Res. Commun.* **48**, 391.
Yalow, R. S. and Wu, M. (1973). *Gastroenterology*, **65**, 19.
Zelenkova, J. and Gregor, O. (1971). *Scand. J. Gastro.* **6**, 653.
Zollinger, R. M. (1975). *Aust. N.Z. J. Surg.* **45**, 129.
Zollinger, R. M. and Ellison, E. H. (1955). *Ann. Surg.* **142**, 709.

IX. Oxytocin

C. R. W. EDWARDS

A. CHEMISTRY

Oxytocin is a peptide with nine amino acid residues of which two are hemi-cystines which form a bridge between positions 1–6 (Fig. 1). The molecular weight is 1007. The amino acid content of the molecule was determined by Pierce and du Vigneaud (1950) and the amino acid sequence by du Vigneaud, Ressler and Trippett (1953) leading to the synthesis of oxytocin (du Vigneaud, Ressler, Swan, Roberts, Katsoyannis and Gordon, 1953). Oxytocin differs from arginine vasopressin by two amino acids, having isoleucine instead of phenylalanine in position 3 and leucine instead of arginine in position 8. The chemistry of the neurohypophyseal hormones has been well reviewed by Acher (1974). The study of neurohypophyseal hormone evolution suggests that mesotocin, which differs from oxytocin by virtue of isoleucine rather leucine in position 8, may have been the ancestral molecule which was preserved in birds but underwent a single substitution in early mammals which resulted in enhanced oxytocic and milk-ejecting activity. Urry and Walter (1971) proposed a secondary structure for oxytocin. This contains one β-turn including the ring sequence L-tyrosyl-L-isoleucyl-L-glutaminyl-L-asparaginyl and a further β-turn involving the C-terminal sequence L-cysteinyl-L-prolyl-L-leucylglycine-amide. They suggested on the basis of the three-dimensional structure that positions 3, 4, 7 and 8 are the only loci at

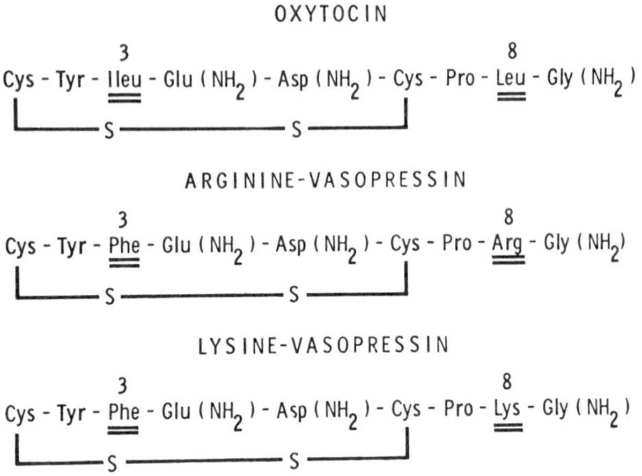

OXYTOCIN

$$
\begin{array}{c}
\overset{3}{\text{Cys - Tyr - \underline{Ileu} - Glu (NH}_2} \text{) - Asp (NH}_2 \text{) - Cys - Pro - \overset{8}{\underline{Leu}} - Gly (NH}_2 \text{)}
\end{array}
$$

ARGININE-VASOPRESSIN

$$
\overset{3}{\text{Cys - Tyr - \underline{Phe} - Glu (NH}_2} \text{) - Asp (NH}_2 \text{) - Cys - Pro - \overset{8}{\underline{Arg}} - Gly (NH}_2 \text{)}
$$

LYSINE-VASOPRESSIN

$$
\overset{3}{\text{Cys - Tyr - \underline{Phe} - Glu (NH}_2} \text{) - Asp (NH}_2 \text{) - Cys - Pro - \overset{8}{\underline{Lys}} - Gly (NH}_2 \text{)}
$$

Fig. 1. Amino acid sequence of oxytocin, arginine vasopressin and lysine vasopressin.

which naturally occurring neurohypophyseal peptides might be expected to differ (Walter, Schwartz, Darnell and Urry, 1971). The history of the evaluation of the structure–activity relationships of these peptides has been well reviewed by Pliska (1976) in his memorial lecture to Josef Rudinger.

B. BIOSYNTHESIS

The concept of neurosecretion and the transport of posterior pituitary peptides by axons from the hypothalamic nuclei to the neural lobe has been detailed elsewhere (see vasopressin biosynthesis). Olivecrona (1957) originally found that destruction of the paraventricular nuclei produced a marked lowering of the oxytocin content of the neural lobe but did not affect vasopressin. In contrast supraoptic nuclei destruction produced diabetes insipidus but not oxytocin depletion. One explanation of this was the synthesis of oxytocin in the paraventricular and vasopressin in the supraoptic nuclei. However, Olivecrona also suggested that the oxytocin and vasopressin producing cells were distinct and that the nuclear separation of secretion was not complete. Immunofluorescent studies have suggested that in the rat that the supraoptic and paraventricular nuclei contain both oxytocin and vasopressin secreting cells (Swaab, Nijeveldt and Pool, 1975).

Oxytocin is secreted together with a larger molecular weight protein (approximately 10,000) called neurophysin. This molecule is then transported down the axon together with oxytocin in neurosecretory granules. The neurophysins have been classified in various ways including their electro- phoretic mobility (neurophysin I and II) and the ability of certain stimuli to release them (oestrogen stimulated neurophysin-ESN and nicotine stimulated neurophysin-NSN) (for full review see Robinson, 1977). The neurophysins specifically bind to the neurohypophyseal hormones and hence have been proposed as carrier proteins within the neurohypophysis. The release of oxytocin is accompanied by the release of neurophysin but the low affinity of the binding, the pH and the calcium concentrations suggest that circulating oxytocin is probably not bound to neurophysin.

Immunocytochemical studies using antibodies against oxytocin, vaso- pressin and their specific neurophysins have confirmed that separate neurons in the supraoptic and paraventricular nuclei produce oxytocin and vaso- pressin (Vandesande and Dierickx, 1975; Vandesande, Dierickx and DeMey, 1975). The cells that contain oxytocin also have neurophysin I and those with vasopressin contain neurophysin II. Although the major proportion of axons from these cell bodies terminate in the posterior pituitary, oxytocin and its specific neurophysin have also been found in the median eminence (Vandesande et al., 1975; Dierickx, Vandesande and DeMey, 1976) and in the arcuate, anterior hypothalamic and medial preoptic nuclei (George, Staples and Marks, 1976). The role of oxytocin in these sites is unknown.

C. METABOLISM

The metabolism of oxytocin has been extensively reviewed by Lauson (1974). The major sites of inactivation are the liver and kidneys. There have been several studies on the binding of oxytocin to plasma proteins but these have nearly all used pharmacological doses of oxytocin and the results have been very variable in different species. In man, Fabian, Forsling, Jones and Pryor (1969) found that there was insignificant binding of concentrations of added oxytocin ranging from 50–400 µu/ml (100–796 pmol/l).

When oxytocin is added to serum from men or non-pregnant women it is not inactivated. However, pregnancy serum contains an aminopeptidase enzyme, oxytocinase, which increases 20–60 fold from the second to the ninth month of pregnancy, which is capable of inactivating oxytocin (Tuppy and Wintersberger, 1964). The significance of this enzyme is unclear as metabolic clearance studies of infused oxytocin post-partum have suggested that the enzyme plays little part in the clearance of the hormone (Chard, Boyd, Forsling, McNeilly and Landon, 1970a). Most authors are agreed that the half-life of oxytocin in the circulation is only a few minutes (approximately 3–5 min). These experiments have used infusions of synthetic oxytocin (Gonzalez-Panizza, Sica-Blanco and Mendez-Bauer, 1961; Fabian et al., 1969; Chard et al., 1970a) or ^{3}H-tyrosine oxytocin (Rydén and Sjöholm, 1969).

Walter and his colleagues have concentrated on the mechanism of tissue inactivation. Oxytocin labelled with ^{14}C in the C-terminal glycine residue was given to rats undergoing water diuresis (Walter and Shlank, 1971). The only radioactive compounds detected in the urine were ^{14}C-oxytocin and ^{14}C-glycinamide. This suggested that the cleavage of the leucylglycinamide bond was one of the mechanisms for the in vivo inactivation of the molecule. This was confirmed using in vitro studies with homogenates of various tissues (Koida, Glass, Schwartz and Walter, 1971). Only the kidney, spleen and liver inactivated the molecule and of these the kidney homogenates showed the highest activity. In some species Walter (1976) has found an additional enzyme which cleaves the molecule to liberate the dipeptide Leu–Gly–NH$_2$ (post-proline cleaving enzyme). A similar enzyme is thought to be present in the human uterus. The hypothalamus contains an enzyme system that releases the tripeptide (H-pro-Leu-Gly-NH$_2$). This molecule has been proposed as an inhibitor of MSH secretion but its role in man is unclear and its effect on β-lipotrophin release has not been studied.

Oxytocin is excreted in the urine. Boyd, Jackson, Hollingsworth, Forsling and Chard (1972) infused oxytocin into human subjects and found a direct relationship between the total amount of immunoreactive oxytocin excreted and the urine volume. Experiments with continuous infusions of vasopressin and oxytocin in rabbits showed that the vasopressin/oxytocin ratio increased 2–6 times when the hormones passed from the blood into the urine suggesting a different mechanism for the renal handling of the two peptides (Jensen, Frandsen and Nielsen, 1973).

D. ASSAY METHODS

1. Standards

A First International Standard (I.S.) for posterior pituitary established in 1925 consisted of a dry powder of acetone-extracted fresh dissected bovine posterior pituitaries and served as an I.S. for both oxytocin and vasopressin.

Similar Second and Third I.S. were subsequently established, the latter in 1957. This has been used to calculate some of the early results presented in this chapter. The International Units (u) for both oxytocin and vasopressin were defined as 0·5 mg of the dry powder. Weighed quantities of this powder were extracted with hot acetic acid giving extracts which contained a variety of peptides in addition to arginine vasopressin (AVP) and oxytocin. In 1957 it was not generally agreed whether oxytocin, vasopressin and anti-diuretic activities were due to different hormones and whether these were present in different relative proportions.

The Third I.S. for posterior pituitary was subsequently renamed the I.S. for oxytocin and vasopressin, but was replaced in 1978 by separate International Standards for each hormone and each consisting of highly purified (synthetic) peptide.

International collaborative assays of the Fourth I.S. for Oxytocin (code 76/575) have shown the unitage of this I.S. to be 12·5 u/ampoule, and that assays using the cockerel blood pressure method, the isolated rat or guinea-pig uterus method, or lactating rat mammary gland pressure method give similar results.

The results presented in this chapter have mostly been determined using this standard for radioimmunoassay.

A wide variety of bioassays and radioimmunoassays have been developed for oxytocin. The very low circulating levels of the hormone coupled with its spurt release have made these assays difficult research procedures. The bioassays have been reviewed by Fitzpatrick (1973) and the radioimmunoassays by Chard (1973). The relative merits of the different assays have been discussed by Chard and Forsling (1976).

2. Bioassays

Most of these assays have depended on the action of oxytocin on uterine smooth muscle or the myoepithelial cells of the mammary gland. The latter method is more sensitive. The vasodepressor action of oxytocin (Coon, 1939) has been widely used in the standardisation of oxytocin preparations but is too insensitive to be of use for plasma assays.

(a) Rat uterus assay

Both in vitro and in vivo assay methods have been described. The in vitro method (Holton, 1948) most commonly used is based on the response of the rat uterus. Young female rats weighing 120 to 150 g are used. The animal is killed by cervical dislocation and the uterus removed. The uterine horns are then separated and transferred to an organ bath containing the low calcium Van Dyke-Hastings solution which helps to minimise spontaneous contractions. The preparation is relatively insensitive and responds to about 0·5 mu (1·0 pmol). It is also affected by a variety of vasoactive materials including acetylcholine, angiotensin, bradykinin and 5-hydroxytryptamine.

The *in vivo* rat uterine assay method (Bisset, Haldar and Lewin, 1966) is based on changes in intra-uterine pressure. The ovarian end of one uterine horn is occluded by a ligature and the other end cannulated with a tube connected to the pressure recording system. The assay sample or standard is then given either intravenously or, if increased sensitivity is required, by intra-arterial administration. This assay is more specific than the *in vivo* preparation as it is much less responsive to potential interfering substances.

(b) Mammary gland assays

These assays have been used extensively to determine plasma levels of oxytocin. Both *in vivo* and *in vitro* preparations have been described but the *in vivo* preparation has enhanced specificity. The standard assay uses lactating rats two to ten days after parturition. The lower inguinal teat is catheterised and connected to a strain gauge manometer. The samples or standards are injected via an arterial cannula. The sensitivity of this preparation is about 5 μu (10 fmol). Vasopressin can interfere with the assay but this can be minimised by an extraction procedure (Forsling, 1971).

3. Radioimmunoassays

In an attempt to produce more specific and sensitive assays several groups have developed radioimmunoassays for oxytoxin (Table 1). Antisera have been produced either by immunisation with oxytocin alone or oxytocin conjugated to protein. The preparation of labelled hormone has been carried out by modifications of the chloramine-T method of Greenwood, Hunter and Glover (1963). Synthetic oxytoxin has been used both for iodination and for standards. Iodinated oxytocin has been purified by column chromatography such as Sephadex G-25 or by the batchwise addition of ion exchange resin to remove unreacted iodide. A variety of methods have been used to separate antibody bound from free hormone. Of these ammonium sulphate precipitation of the bound fraction is probably the simplest and cheapest (Chard, Forsling, James, Kitau and Landon, 1970b).

The majority of authors have used an extraction procedure before radioimmunoassay. This should remove substances that non-specifically interfere with antigen–antibody binding and can also be used to concentrate the hormone and thus improve the sensitivity of the assay. Chard, Boyd, Forsling, McNeilly and Landon (1970a) used Fuller's earth to extract oxytocin from plasma and then eluted with aqueous acetone. This was then partitioned against ether. The ether was aspirated and the aqueous layer blown to dryness, and reconstituted in buffer before assay. The same procedure was used by Seppala et al. (1972). Bashore (1972) used an acetone-ether ultrafiltration method. Kumaresan et al. (1974) did not use an extraction method and plasma samples were diluted 1:5 with assay bfffer. The blood samples were taken into tubes containing EDTA and phenanthroline to prevent destruction of

Table 1

Radioimmunoassays for oxytocin.

Sensitivity (pg/ml aqueous solution)[a]	Comment	References
—	Demonstrated production of specific oxytocin antisera	Gilliland and Prout (1965a, b)
24	—	Glick, Kumaresan, Kagan and Wheeler (1969)
10	By using extraction procedure sensitivity could be increased to 1 pg/ml plasma	Chard, Boyd, Forsling, McNeilly and Landon (1970a)
25	—	Seppälä, Aho, Tissari and Ruoslahti (1972)
50	—	Bashore (1972)
0·5	—	Kumaresan, Anandarangam and Vasicka (1972)
Not stated	Used unextracted plasma for assay	Kumaresan, Anandarangam, Dianzon and Vasicka (1974)
25	Used lactoperoxidase method for iodination	Dawood, Raghavan and Pociask (1978a)

[a] 1 pg/ml = 0·99 pmol/l.

oxytocin by oxytocinase in the samples taken during pregnancy or post-partum. If oxytocinase activity is not blocked then the enzyme will progressively destroy the labelled oxytocin so that it will no longer bind to antibody. This will then be interpreted as inhibition of antibody binding by cold hormone and hence give spuriously high values. It would seem likely that these methodological differences account for the very wide variations in plasma levels reported (see below).

4. Immunological–Biological Dissociation

As the antigenic determinant group may only be four to six amino acids it is not surprising that radioimmunoassays may detect fragments of the hormone that are not measured by the bioassays. Incubation of synthetic oxytocin with late pregnancy plasma much more rapidly inactivates biological activity than it affects radioimmunoassayable oxytocin (Chard and Forsling, 1976). However there is usually good agreement between the two assays (Chard et al., 1970b; Forsling, Boyd and Chard, 1971). Immunological–biological dissociation may occur when urinary oxytocin is measured (Forsling et al., 1971). Walter, Havran and Schwartz (1976) investigated the biological activity of the metabolites of oxytocin resulting from C-terminal enzymatic destruction. Their biological activity was very low but desglycinamide oxytocin had about the same effect as oxytocin on toad bladder permeability.

E. PLASMA LEVELS

1. Physiology

The true physiological role of oxytocin in the human female and especially the male remains obscure. In animals oxytocin clearly has a role in both parturition and milk ejection. A variety of other actions have been ascribed to the hormone but the majority can only be demonstrated when pharmacological doses of oxytocin are given.

(a) Role of oxytocin in the initiation of labour

Following the description of the effect of posterior pituitary extract on the uterus (Dale, 1906) only three years elapsed before the use of such preparations in human obstetrics (Blair-Bell, 1909). It was therefore not surprising that oxytocin was thought to play a major role in human labour. Bioassays suggested that high levels of oxytocin were secreted during labour and especially during the second stage (Table 2). However, indirect estimates of the levels required to stimulate uterine contraction suggested that the levels might be 10 μu/ml (20 pmol/l) or less (Theobold, 1968). Using a specific radioimmunoassay and an extraction procedure designed to remove substances non-specifically inhibiting antigen–antibody binding Chard, Hudson, Edwards and Boyd (1971) found that oxytocin was undetectable (i.e. < 0·75 μu/ml (1·5 pmol/l)) in 81 % of samples of maternal blood taken during labour. In the 19 % in which oxytocin was detectable the levels ranged from 2–18 μu/ml (4–36 pmol/l). These results were in marked contrast to the clearly elevated levels found in the goat during labour using the same assay

(Chard et al., 1970a). Similarly, in the guinea-pig this assay, with a Spherosil XOA 400 extraction rather than Fullers earth, showed that oxytocin was undetectable before or during the first stage of labour but that levels up to 1500 μu/ml (2985 pmol/l) were present during the expulsive phase.

Gibbens, Boyd and Chard (1972) used frequent sampling to see whether there was spurt release of oxytocin during human labour. Eight blood samples

Table 2

Plasma oxytocin levels in human labour.

Assay method	Level (μu/ml)[a]	Comment	References
Rat uterus	140	Highest levels during second stage	Fitzpatrick (1961)
Rabbit milk ejection	25–250	Also measured jugular vein oxytocin levels in second stage (300–900 μu/ml)	Coch et al. (1965)
In vivo bioassay using intraductal mammary pressure	—	0/12 positive in first stage; 2/12 positive in second stage	Cobo et al. (1968)
Radioimmunoassay after extraction	<0·75 μu/ml in 81% samples 2–18 μu/ml in 19% samples		Chard et al. (1971)
Radioimmunoassay after extraction	Serial sampling from 32 women; 83/264 samples contained oxytocin (1–12·5 μu/ml); results suggested spurt release		Gibbens et al. (1972)
Radioimmunoassay without extraction	181 ± 10 (35–435)	Gradually increasing levels from 25 weeks	Kumaresan et al. (1974)
Radioimmunoassay with extraction	20·2 ± 4·9 61·9 ± 11·8	First stage increase during Second stage	Dawood et al.
Radioimmunoassay	64–199·7	No significant increase during labour as compared to pregnancy	Vasicka et al. (1978)

[a]1 μu/ml = 1·99 pmol/l.

were collected over a period of 4–8 min. Of the 264 samples obtained, 83 had measurable oxytocin (1–12·5 μu/ml (2–24·9 pmol/l)). There was a progressive increase in the frequency of positive results. Early in the first stage, 10% of samples had detectable levels compared with 50% at the end of the first stage. During the second stage of labour 58 % of samples contained oxytocin (2·5–10 μu/ml; 5·0–20 pmol/l). These results were a marked contrast to those found by Kumaresan and his colleagues (Kumaresan et al., 1974; Vasicka, Kumaresan, Han and Kumaresan, 1978). Using a direct radioimmunoassay without an extraction procedure they found much higher levels (Table 2). Oxytocin levels gradually increased during pregnancy and the hormone was present in maternal plasma before labour. There was no surge at the onset of labour but increased levels were found with cervical dilatation and vaginal distension. This suggested that Ferguson's reflex was present in the human.

Dawood et al. (1978a) used a similar extraction procedure and assay to that of Chard. Of the 116 pregnant women tested 88 (77 %) had detectable oxytocin. Serial samples showed a significant increase in oxytocin from the first to the second stage of labour (Table 2). Their levels were higher than those found by Chard but lower than the Kumaresan results.

(b) Levels of oxytocin in umbilical arterial and venous plasma

Chard, Hudson, Edwards and Boyd (1971) measured levels of oxytocin and vasopressin present in paired umbilical arterial and venous samples. Oxy-tocin was found in 76 % of arterial samples taken at delivery, the mean level being 27 μu/ml (54 pmol/l). This was significantly higher than that of the venous blood sample (15 μu/ml (30 pmol/l)) (Fig. 2). Lower levels were found in samples taken at Caesarean section in labour. Patients undergoing elective Caesarean section had even lower levels and an anencephalic foetus had undetectable oxytocin in cord blood. These levels were higher than those found in the maternal circulation and raised the question as to whether or not the foetal release of oxytocin might play a significant role in human labour. The roles of foetal and maternal oxytocin in the onset of labour have been reviewed by Chard (1974).

Dawood et al. (1978b) confirmed the presence of oxytocin in human umbilical arterial plasma (spontaneous labour and vaginal delivery 55·6 ± 8·3 (s.e.m.) μu/ml (111 ± 16 pmol/l); Caesarean section in labour 57·2 ± 8·6 μu/ml (114 ± 17 pmol/l); elective Caesarean section 16·1 ± 3·6 μu/ml (32 ± 7·2 pmol/l)) and found that the levels were always significantly higher than in the umbilical venous plasma. Dawood, Ylikorkala, Wilson, Trivedi and Fuchs (1978c) extended these studies by looking at maternal and foetal oxytocin in the baboon. Foetal jugular and cardiac blood had higher oxy-tocin levels than maternal peripheral blood. Oxytocin injected into the umbilical artery near term produced an increase in maternal plasma oxytocin in 3–9 min indicating that oxytocin can cross the placenta from the foetal to the maternal side.

Theobald (1968) postulated that it was not an increase in oxytocin levels that initiated labour but increasing sensitivity of the uterus in the presence of low levels of circulating oxytocin. Soloff (1978) updated this hypothesis by showing that in the rat there was a marked increase in the binding of [^{3}H]-oxytocin to particulate fractions of myometrium at term. He suggested that the low amount of binding of oxytocin to the myometrium before labour explained the relative insensitivity of the rat uterus to oxytocin except near term. The factors that lead to this increased binding were unclear and did not depend on changes in the levels of oestradiol and progesterone.

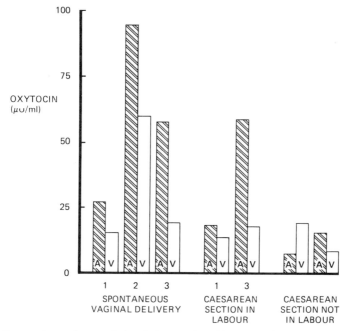

Fig. 2. Comparison of oxytocin levels in samples of foetal umbilical plasma collected at time of delivery (umbilical arterial samples, shaded A; umbilical venous samples, unshaded V). Data from: 1 = Chard, Hudson, Edwards and Boyd (1971), 2 = Kumaresan, Han, Anandarangam and Vasicka (1975), 3 = Dawood, Wang, Gupta and Fuchs (1978b).

(c) *Role of oxytocin in milk ejection*

The history of the milk-ejection reflex has been excellently summarised by Folley (1969) in his Dale lecture entitled "the milk-ejection reflex; a neuro-endocrine theme in biology, myth and art". The discovery by Ott and Scott (1911) of the galactogogue effect of the posterior pituitary extract in lactating animals was initially thought to be due to stimulation of milk production. Subsequent experiments showed that the effect of oxytocin was to stimulate the myoepithelial cells in the mammary gland and hence eject milk—the so-called "let down" reflex. The elegant studies of Cross and Harris (1951, 1952) and Andersson (1951) established the neurohormonal concept of the milk-ejection reflex in which an initial stimulation of the sensory nerves in the nipple leads to the release of oxytocin which then initiates milk-ejection. Using his very sensitive bioassay system Fitzpatrick (1961) demonstrated an increase in circulating oxytocin in ewes during suckling. Folley and Knaggs (1966) emphasized the nature of oxytocin release in spurts during milk ejection.

McNeilly (1972) measured oxytocin by guinea-pig mammary gland bioassay in 36 series of blood samples collected from 12 goats during suckling. The transient appearance of oxytocin (5–86 μu/ml (10–171 pmol/l) plasma) was found in 24 of the series. A further series of 40 samples was collected during hand-milking and oxytocin found transiently in 25 (5–160 μu/ml (10–318 pmol/l) plasma). Even though oxytocin was detectable in over 60% of cases, milk yields appeared normal whether oxytocin was detected or not. McNeilly (1972) suggested that milk ejection could be produced by direct mechanical stimulation of the myoepithelium and that oxytocin was not essential for milk ejection.

Two approaches have been taken to the problem of assessing oxytocin release during lactation in human subjects. One has been the measurement of intramammary pressure using catheters inserted into lactiferous ducts connected to sensitive pressure transducers (Sica-Blanco, Mendez-Bayer, Sala, Cabot and Caldeyro-Barcia, 1959), or by placing a perspex cylinder over the mamilla which is then connected to the transducer and held in place by a suction cup (Friedman, 1960). The alternative approach has been the direct measurement of oxytocin by bioassay or radioimmunoassay during lactation.

The *in vivo* bioassay approach has usually been calibrated by determining the dose of exogenous oxytocin required to produce the same rise in intramammary pressure as that produced by suckling on the non-cannulated breast. A pressure curve of the type observed during lactation can be produced by intravenous infusion of oxytocin in a dose of 4–8 mu/min (8–16 pmol/min). An obvious problem with this type of approach is the observation that maternal stress can inhibit milk ejection (Newton and Newton, 1948); this may be related to catecholamine release inhibiting the effect of oxytocin (Cross, 1955).

Using bioassays for oxytocin Hawker and Roberts (1957) and Hawker, Walmsley, Roberts, Blackshaw and Downes (1961) could not detect oxytocin in peripheral blood samples during suckling in human subjects. Coch, Fielitz, Brovetto, Cabot, Coda and Fraga (1968), however, were able to find oxytocin in internal jugular venous blood during human lactation; the oxytocin levels ranged from 12–25 μu/ml (24–50 pmol/l) plasma. Fox and

Knaggs (1969) measured peripheral venous oxytocin levels during human suckling. Out of 17 samples taken over three periods of suckling oxytocin was only detectable in two. Amounts of 112 (223) and 11 μu/ml (22 pmol/l) were found. These data suggests that in the human as in other species studied there is episodic or spurt release of oxytocin.

In addition to its role in milk ejection oxytocin may also affect the production of milk protein. Ollivier-Bousquet (1976) suggested that physiological amounts of oxytocin such as 1 μu/ml (2 pmol/l) of medium can increase intracellular protein transport and the release of casein from rabbit mammary gland tissue *in vitro*.

(d) Other possible roles for oxytocin

In the male oxytocin has no known function. However, many studies have suggested that oxytocin could play a role in sperm transport (Fjelstrom, Kihlstrom and Melin, 1968; Knight and Lindsay, 1970; Voglmayr, 1975). One possible mechanism of action is an effect on smooth muscle in the seminiferous tubules. As large amounts of oxytocin were used in these studies the physiological relevance was not clear. Sharma and Hays (1976) reported the results of an interesting study using a drug methallibure, a dithiocarbamoyl-hydrazine derivative, that blocks the release of oxytocin (Benson and Zagni, 1965). When the drug was given to male rabbits it produced a 45% reduction in sperm number. However, when oxytocin was given with methallibure no significant change in the sperm count was found. The authors suggested that oxytocin may act on smooth muscle in the seminiferous tubules or vas deferens thus enhancing the transport of sperm and refilling of the duct system. This suggested for the first time that physiological as opposed to pharmacological amounts of oxytocin could affect the male reproductive tract.

Fox and Knaggs (1969) measured oxytocin in blood by bioassay in association with coitus. Two experiments were carried out. In the first, a blood sample was taken 1 min after male and female orgasm, and in the second, samples were taken 5 min before and 1 min after male and female orgasm. A control sample was obtained several hours before each experiment. Oxytocin was found in both cases in the blood sample taken after female orgasm but was not detected in any of the samples from the male or the controls. If, therefore, endogenous oxytocin plays a role in sperm transport it is not clear when it is released.

McNeilly and Ducker (1972) confirmed the release of oxytocin by the female in association with coitus. They measured bioactive oxytocin in jugular vein samples collected from 33 oestrous female goats during mating. Oxytocin was intermittently released and was present in 28 of 36 series of blood samples (2–190 μu/ml (4–378 pmol/l)). However, they also observed that oxytocin release often occurred before coitus and could continue for several minutes after the male had left.

Under certain experimental conditions it has been possible to demonstrate a natriuretic action of some neurohypophyseal peptides. Several investigators have, therefore, looked at oxytocin levels in relation to the natriuresis associated with extracellular fluid volume expansion. Massry, Vorherr and Kleeman (1969) measured jugular vein oxytocin levels in dogs during extracellular fluid volume expansion. They found no consistent change in oxytocin levels in association with the natriuresis. They also infused amounts of oxytocin sufficient to give blood levels ranging from 41 (82) to 105 μu/ml (209 pmol/l) and observed no enhancement of the natriuresis. Schrier *et al.* (1968) also measured plasma oxytocin levels in dogs during saline infusion and did not find any change in either oxytocin or vasopressin. Acute haemorrhage elevated plasma AVP levels but did not alter oxytocin levels.

Chan (1976) investigated the molecular requirements for the natriuretic, antidiuretic and oxytocic actions of the neurohypophyseal peptides and analogues. Substitution of leucine in the 4-position apparently considerably enhanced the natriuretic effect and conferred an anti-ADH effect. Chan looked at 12 analogues of oxytocin and lysine vasopressin with leucine substitutions. He suggested that the effect of the substitution was probably not to enhance the natriuretic effect but rather to abolish the antidiuretic action. It was this lack of antidiuretic effect that unmasked the intrinsic natriuretic effects of the peptides. Chan found that oxytocin was the most potent natriuretic peptide when given to rats during an osmotic diuresis which blocked the antidiuretic effect. One analogue (4-phenylalanine) oxytocin had the same anti-ADH potential as (4-leucine) oxytocin but had no natriuretic activity. This suggests that there may be a receptor associated with sodium transport separate and distinct from the receptor related to water permeability.

A large number of other actions of oxytocin have been described such as insulin-like activity, involution of the corpus luteum and inhibition of the release of prolactin. These experiments have involved the use of pharmacological rather than physiological amounts of oxytocin and their relevance is unclear. Bonne and Cohen (1975) however, have identified two types of oxytocin receptor on isolated rat epididymal fat cells and suggest that there may be a specific insulin-like action of oxytocin.

2. Pathophysiology

(a) Oxytocin deficiency

It is not surprising given the unclear nature of the physiological role of oxytocin that little should be known about its pathophysiology. A large

number of patients with diabetes insipidus have been studied during pregnancy. The general view is that the neurohypophyseal disease does not affect
the onset of spontaneous labour or delivery (Hendricks, 1954) suggesting
that the maternal posterior pituitary is not necessary for normal delivery.
However, little critical evaluation has been applied to determining whether
these patients are actually deficient in oxytocin. Sende, Pantelakis, Susuki
and Bashore (1976), for example, measured oxytocin levels in maternal
plasma in a patient with diabetes insipidus and found that the levels were
similar to those found in normal labour.

In contrast to vasopressin no syndrome of oxytocin deficiency has been
found. If the foetal posterior pituitary was important in human parturition
it might be imagined that foetal oxytocin deficiency might affect parturition.
Malpas (1933) first pointed out that anencephaly could be associated with
prolonged pregnancy. Subsequently Bell and Robson (1937) suggested that
the foetal posterior pituitary could act as a stimulus to labour. In animals
it is well known that foetal hypophysectomy leads to a prolongation of
pregnancy (Liggins et al., 1967; Liggins 1973). This has been thought to be
due to the effect of the operation on the hypothalamic–pituitary–adrenal
axis but obviously it will also affect posterior pituitary function. Even if
foetal oxytocin plays a role in human parturition it seems unlikely that it is
a vital one as labour can proceed normally in pregnancy with an ancephalic
foetus in whom neither oxytocin nor vasopressin was detectable in the
umbilical circulation (Chard et al., 1971).

If oxytocin was the only factor responsible for milk ejection it might be
expected that oxytocin deficiency might affect lactation. However, even this
does not seem to be the case as the denervated, transplanted udder of the goat
(in which the normal milk let-down reflex is lost) can maintain a normal
milk yield (Linzell, 1963). Other experiments, however, with the production
of lesions in the neurohypophysis in animals, have produced abnormal
parturition and milk ejection (Fitzpatrick, 1966). Chau, Fitzpatrick and
Jamieson (1969) studied milk ejection in a patient with diabetes insipidus
compared with ten normal women. Intramammary pressure was recorded
by inserting catheters into lactiferous ducts. The increase in pressure in one
breast when the other was suckled was taken as an index of the reflex release
of oxytocin. The magnitude of the oxytocin effect was assessed by matching
the reflex response with that following the administration of single doses of
oxytocin. In the normal women a clear response to suckling was seen with
an increase in intra-mammary pressure which began about 30 sec after
stimulation of the nipple by the infant. The pressure increase was equivalent
to that induced by giving 10–20 mu (20–40 pmol) oxytocin intravenously.
The patients with diabetes insipidus showed identical pressure responses
to suckling and exogenous oxytocin as did the normal subjects. This sug-

gested that oxytocin secretion was unimpaired. Of interest was the finding that suckling in the normal subjects was associated with an antidiuresis but this was not found in the patient with diabetes insipidus. This indicated that oxytocin and vasopressin secretion were probably dissociated. However, the fact that this patient's diabetes insipidus could be controlled with a lysine vasopressin nasal spray suggests that her condition was relatively mild. Thus this dissociation might reflect a quantitative rather than a qualitative difference in oxytocin and vasopressin secretion.

Similar studies to those of Fitzpatrick (1966) were carried out by Cobo, de Bernal and Gaitan (1972). They measured uterine and milk-ejecting activities in a 35-yr-old woman with diabetes insipidus during two spontaneous labours and three lactational periods. The uterine activity during labour was in the low normal range and the response of the uterus to exogenous oxytocin was similar to that found in normal subjects. Similarly the milk-ejecting activity was equivalent to that found in normal women but the response to exogenous oxytocin was markedly enhanced. They thought that the high sensitivity of the mammary myoepithelium was an adaptation phenomenon which maintained normal milk ejection despite low endogenous oxytocin levels. Obviously, a large number of factors can affect these *in vivo* bioassay systems and the results must therefore be interpreted with caution.

(b) Oxytocin excess

The commonest cause of oxytocin excess is where pharmacological amounts are infused for the induction of labour. Only rarely is endogenous oxytocin secretion elevated. Apart from the physiological causes which have been discussed oxytocin can be secreted ectopically by some tumours (Table 3). As these tumours can also synthesise neurophysin and vasopressin (Hamilton, Upton and Amatruda, 1972; Rees, 1975) it is not clear what role oxytocin is playing in the clinical syndromes described.

Rees (1975) reported the results of gel filtration studies on an extract of an oat cell carcinoma of the lung associated with inappropriate secretion of vasopressin. The tumour was extracted with HCl/acetone and then passed through a Sephadex G-25 column (2 cm^2 × 60 cm) eluted with 0·05 M tris-HCl buffer containing human serum albumin. The tumour contained immunoreactive vasopressin, oxytocin and neurophysin. However, not only was there immunoreactive vasopressin and oxytocin eluting in the expected position but also in the void volume with neurophysin. This could be peptide adsorbed on to or binding to neurophysin or a large molecular weight precursor molecule containing oxytocin and vasopressin.

A clearer concept of the effects of oxytocin excess has emerged from studies in patients given large doses of oxytocin for termination of pregnancy or the induction of labour. Two problems, in particular, have been identified—water intoxication and neonatal jaundice. Ahmed, Clark and Jacobs (1975) have reviewed the literature and found 23 cases of water intoxication reported since 1962. In these patients high doses of oxytocin given with large volumes of electrolyte-free fluid have produced a picture similar to that of the syndrome of inappropriate secretion of antidiuretic hormone.

Table 3
Ectopic production of oxytocin.

Tumour	Oxytocin[a]	References
Pancreatic adenocarcinoma	1,000,000 pg/ml	Marks et al. (1968)
Oat cell carcinoma of lung	114,238 pg/mg[b]	Vorherr et al. (1968)
Oat cell carcinoma of lung	16–40 pg/mg	Whitelaw (1969)
Oat cell carcinoma of lung	Oxytocin, neurophysin and arginine vasopressin in tumour	Rees et al. (1974, 1975)

[a] 1 pg = 0·99 fmol.
[b] Milk-ejecting activity, however, activity could probably be accounted for by vasopressin content of tumour extract.

Adbul-Karim and Assali (1961) showed that the antidiuretic effect of an infusion of oxytocin began at an infusion rate of about 15 mu (30 pmol)/min and was maximal at 45 mu (90 pmol)/min. As with vasopressin it would be expected that a variety of factors would affect the renal threshold including the endogenous level of vasopressin, which may be elevated by the stress and pain of the procedure, circulating corticosteroid levels and the renal solute load. It is of interest that in many of the reported cases of water intoxication with oxytocin therapy the patients have had grand mal seizures at levels of serum sodium that would not normally be associated with symptoms in patients with inappropriate ADH secretion (i.e. above 125 mmol/l). The extracellular fluid volume is already increased during pregnancy and it has been suggested that pregnant patients are more prone to develop convulsions than non-pregnant women.

Ghosh and Hudson (1972) suggested that the observed increase in the incidence of neonatal jaundice could be due to an increase in the use of oxytocic drugs in the management of labour. They postulated that oxytocin produced a reduction in placental blood flow and thus foetal hypoxia;

this was not sufficient to produce foetal distress but could affect the hepatic enzyme system for conjugation of bilirubin. Davies, Gomersall, Robertson, Gray and Turnbull (1973) carried out a prospective study of 78 neonates delivered either by amniotomy and oxytocin or spontaneous vaginal delivery. The groups whose mothers had been given oxytocin had significantly higher mean total serum bilirubin levels than the control group. Even though this suggested that oxytocin was responsible they pointed out that there were several other possibilities such as differences in neonatal corticosteroid levels and other drugs given to the mothers. Calder, Moar, Ounsted and Turnbull (1974) suggested that artificial interruption of pregnancy by any cause such as amniotomy, prostaglandin administration or oxytocin could lead to neonatal hyperbilirubinaemia.

CONCLUSIONS

The introduction of more specific sensitive assays for oxytocin has clarified some of the problems raised by the less specific bioassays. However, there is still considerable disagreement between the results produced by the different radioimmunoassays. These appear to be related to technical differences between the different assays and until these problems have been resolved many of the controversies associated with the physiology and pathophysiology of oxytocin will remain.

REFERENCES

Abdul-Karim, R. and Assali, N. S. (1961). J. Lab. clin. Med. 57, 522.
Acher, R. (1974). In "Handbook of Physiology Sect. 7: Endocrinology" (R. O. Greep and E. A. Astwoods, eds), Vol. 4, p. 119. Am. Physiol. Soc., Washington.
Ahmed, A. J., Clark, G. H. and Jacobs, H. S. (1975). Postgrad. med. J. 51, 249.
Andersson, B. (1951). Acta physiol. scand. 23, 1.
Bashore, R. A. (1972). Am. J. Obstet. Gynec. 113, 488.
Bell, G. H. and Robson, J. M. (1937). Q. J. exp. Physiol. 27, 205.
Benson, G. K. and Zagni, P. A. (1965). J. Endocr. 32, 275.
Bisset, G. W., Halder, J. and Lewin, J. E. (1966). In "Endogenous Substances Affecting the Myometrium" (V. Pickles and R. J. Fitzpatrick, eds), p. 185. Memoir 14, Soc. Endocr., London. Cambridge University Press, Cambridge.
Blair-Bell, W. (1909), Br. med. J. 2, 1609.
Bonne, D. and Cohen, P. (1975). Eur. J. Biochem. 56, 295.
Boyd, N. R. H., Jackson, D. B., Hollingsworth, S., Forsling, M. L. and Chard, T. (1972). J. Endocr. 52, 59.
Calder, A. A., Moar, V. A., Ounsted, M. K. and Turnbull, A. C. (1974). Lancet, ii, 1339.
Chan, W. Y. (1976). J. Pharmacol. exp. Ther. 196, 746.

Chard, T. (1973). *J. Endocr.* **58**, 143.

Chard, T. (1974). *In* "Avortement et Parturition Provoqués", p. 169. Masson, Paris.

Chard, T., Boyd, N. R. H., Forsling, M. L., McNeilly, A. S. and Landon, J. (1970a). *J. Endocr.* **48**, 223.

Chard, T., Forsling, M. L., James, M. A. R., Kitau, M. J. and Landon, J. (1970b). *J. Endocr.* **46**, 532.

Chard, T. and Forsling, M. L. (1976). *In* "Hormones in Human Blood" (H. N. Antoniades, ed.), p. 488. Harvard University Press, Massachusetts.

Chard, T., Hudson, C. N., Edwards, C. R. W. and Boyd, N. R. H. (1971). *Nature, Lond.* **234**, 352.

Chau, S. S., Fitzpatrick, R. J. and Jamieson, B. (1969). *J. Obstet. Gynec.* **76**, 444.

Cobo, E., de Bernal, M. and Gaitan, E. (1972). *Am. J. Obstet. Gynec.* **114**, 861.

Cobo, E., de Bernal, M. M., Quintero, C. A. and Cuadrado, E. (1968). *Am. J. Obstet. Gynec.* **101**, 479.

Coch, J. A., Brovetto, J., Cabot, H. M., Fielitz, C. A. and Caldeyro-Barcia, R. (1965). *Am. J. Obstet. Gynec.* **91**, 10.

Coch, J. A., Fielitz, C., Brovetto, J., Cabot, H., Coda, H. and Fraga, A. (1968). *J. Endocr.* **40**, 137.

Coon, J. M. (1939). *Arch. Int. Pharmacodyn. Ther.* **62**, 79.

Cross, B. A. (1955). *J. Endocr.* **12**, 29.

Cross, B. A. and Harris, G. W. (1951). *J. Physiol., Lond.* **113**, 35.

Cross, B. A. and Harris, G. W. (1952). *J. Endocr.* **8**, 148.

Dale, H. H. (1906). *J. Physiol.* **34**, 163.

Davies, D. P., Gomersall, R., Robertson, R., Gray, O. P. and Turnbull, A. C. (1973). *Br. Med. J.* **3**, 476.

Dawood, M. Y., Raghavan, K. S. and Pociask, C. (1978a). *J. Endocr.* **76**, 261.

Dawood, M. Y., Wang, C. F., Gupta, R. and Fuchs, F. (1978b). *Obstet. Gynec.* **52**, 205.

Dawood, M. Y., Ylikorkala, O., Wilson, K., Trivedi, D. and Fuchs, F. (1978c). *Endocrinology*, **102**, 327.

Dierickx, K., Vandersande, F. and De Mey (1976). *Cell Tissue Res.* **168**, 141.

Du Vigneaud, V., Ressler, C., Swan, J. M., Roberts, C. W., Katsoyannis, P. G. and Gordon, S. (1953). *J. Am. Chem. Soc.* **75**, 4879.

Du Vigneaud, V., Ressler, C. and Trippett, S. (1953). *J. biol. Chem.* **205**, 949.

Fabian, M., Forsling, M. L., Jones, J. J. and Pryor, J. S. (1969). *J. Physiol., Lond.* **204**, 653.

Fitzpatrick, R. J. (1961). *In* "Oxytocin" (R. Caldeyro-Barcia and H. Heller, eds), p. 360. Pergamon Press, Oxford.

Fitzpatrick, R. J., (1966). *In* "The Pituitary Gland" (G. W. Harris and B. T. Donovan, eds), p. 453. Butterworths, London.

Fitzpatrick, R. J. (1973). *In* "Peptide Hormones" (S. A. Berson and R. S. Yalow, eds), p. 694. North Holland Publishing Co., Amsterdam.

Fjellostrom, D., Kihlstrom, J. E. and Melin, P. (1968). *J. reprod. Fert.* **17**, 207.

Forsling, M. L. (1971). *In* "Radioimmunoassay Methods" (K. E. Kirkham and W. M. Hunter, eds), p. 560. Churchill Livingstone, Edinburgh and London.

Forsling, M. L., Boyd, N. R. H. and Chard, T. (1971). *In* "Radioimmunoassay Methods" (K. E. Kirkham and W. M. Hunter, eds), p. 349. Churchill Livingstone, Edinburgh and London.

Folley, S. J. (1969). *J. Endocr.* **44**, ix.

Folley, S. J. and Knaggs, G. S. (1966). *J. Endocr.* **34**, 197.

Fox, C. A. and Knaggs, G. S. (1969). *J. Endocr.* **45**, 145.
Friedman, E. A. (1960). *Am. J. Obstet. Gynec.* **30**, 119.
George, J. M., Staples, S. and Marks, B. M. (1976). *Endocrinology*, **98**, 1430.
Ghosh, A. and Hudson, F. P. (1972). *Lancet*, **ii**, 823
Gibbens, D., Boyd, N. R. H. and Chard, T. (1972). *J. Endocr.* **53**, liv.
Gilliland, P. F. and Prout, T. E. (1965a). *Metabolism*, **14**, 912.
Gilliland, P. E. and Prout, T. E. (1965b). *Metabolism*, **14**, 918.
Glick, S. M., Kumaresan, P., Kagan, A. and Wheeler, M. (1968). *In* "Protein and Polypeptide Hormones" (M. Margoulies, ed.), Excerpta Medica Foundation, Amsterdam.
Gonzalez-Panizza, V. H., Sica-Blanco, Y. and **Mendez-Bauer**, C. (1961). *In* "Oxytocin" (R. Caldeyro-Barcia and H. Heller, eds), Pergamon Press, Oxford.
Greenwood, F. C., Hunter, W. M. and Glover, J. S. (1963). *Biochem. J.* **89**, 114.
Hamilton, B. P. M., Upton, G. V. and Amatruda, T. T. (1972). *J. clin. Endocr. Metab.* **35**, 764.
Hawker, R. W. and Roberts, V. W. (1957). *Br. vet. J.* **113**, 459.
Hawker, R. W., Walmsley, C. F., Roberts, V. S., Blackshaw, J. K. and Downes, J. C. (1961). *J. clin. Endocr. Metab.* **21**, 985.
Hendricks, C. H. (1954). *Obstet. Gynec. Surv.* **9**, 323.
Holton, P. (1948). *Br. J. Pharmacol. Chemother.* **3**, 328.
Jensen, S. E., Frandsen, P. and Nielsen, A. T. (1973). *Acta endocr., Copenh.* **73**, 643.
Knight, T. W. and Lindsay, D. R. (1970). *J. Reprod. Fert.* **21**, 523.
Koida, M., Glass, J. D., Schwartz, I. L. and Walter, R. (1971). *Endocrinology*, **88**, 633.
Kumaresan, P., Anandarangan, B. and Vasicka, A. (1972). Abst. 4th Int. Cong. Endocr., p. 206. Int. Cong. Series No. 256. Excerpta Medica Foundation, Amsterdam.
Kumaresan, P., Anandarangam, P. B., Dianzon, W. and Vasicka, A. (1974). *Am. J. Obstet. Gynec.* **119**, 215.
Kumaresan, P., Han, G. S., Anandarangam, P. B. and Vasicka, A. (1975). *Obstet. Gynec.* **46**, 272.
Lauson, H. D. (1974). *In* "Handbook of Physiology Sect. 7 "Endocrinology" (R. O. Greep and E. B. Astwood, eds), Vol. 4, p. 287. Am. Physiol. Soc., Washington.
Liggins, G. C., Kennedy, P. C. and Holm, L. W. (1967). *Am. J. Obstet. Gynec.* **98**, 1080.
Liggins, G. C. (1973). *In* "Endocrine Factors in Labour" (A. Klopper and J. Gardner, eds), p. 119. Cambridge University Press, Cambridge.
Linzell, J. L. (1963). *Q. J. Exp. Physiol.* **48**, 34.
Malpas, P. (1933). *J. Obstet. Gynec. Br. Emp.* **40**, 1046.
Marks, L. J., Berde, B., Klein, L. A., Roth, J., Goonan, S. R., Blumen, D. and Nabseth, D. C. (1968). *Am. J. Med.* **45**, 967.
Massry, S. G., Vorherr, H. and Kleeman, C. R. (1969). *Proc. Soc. exp. Biol. Med.* **130**, 1276.
McNeilly, A. S. (1972). *J. Endocr.* **52**, 177.
McNeilly, A. S. and Ducker, H. A. (1972). *J. Endocr.* **54**, 399.
Newton, M. and Newton, N. R. (1948). *J. Paediat.* **35**, 698.
Olivecrona, H. (1957). *Acta physiol. scand.* **136** (Suppl.) 1.
Ollivier-Bousquet, M. (1976). *C.r. Acad. Sci., Paris*, **282**, 1433.
Ott, I. and Scott, J. C. (1911). *Proc. exp. Biol. Med.* **8**, 48.
Pierce, J. G. and Du Vigneaud, V. (1950). *J. biol. Chem.* **182**, 359.
Pliska, V. (1976). Proc. 14th Eur. Peptide Symp. (A. Loffet, ed.), p. 33. Editions de L'Universite de Bruxelles.

Rees, L. H. (1975). *J. Endocr.* **67**, 143.

Rees, L. H., Bloomfield, G. A., Rees, G. M., Corrin, B., Franks, C. M. and Ratcliffe, J. G. (1974). *J. clin. Endocr. Metab.* **38**, 109.

Robinson, A. G. (1977). *Clin. Endocr. Metab.* **6**, 261.

Ryder, G. and Sjöholm, I. (1969). *Acta endocr., Copenh.* **61**, 425.

Schrier, R. W., Verroust, P. J., Jones, J. J., Fabian, M., Lee, J. and de Wardener, H. E. (1968). *Clin. Sci.* **35**, 433.

Sende, P., Pantelakis, N., Susuki, K. and Bashore, R. (1976). *Obstet. Gynecol.* **48** (Suppl.), 38.

Seppala, M., Aho, I., Tissari, A. and Ruoslahti, E. (1972). *Am. J. Obstet. Gynecol.* **114**, 788.

Sharma, O. P. and Hays, R. L. A. (1976). *J. Endocr.* **68**, 43.

Sica-Blanco, Y., Mendez-Bauer, C., Sala, N., Cabot, H. M. and Caldeyro-Barcia, R. (1959). *Arch. Gynec. Obstet.* **17**, 63.

Soloff, M. S. (1978). *Endocrinology*, **102**, 323.

Swaab, D. F., Nijveldt, F. and Pool, C. W. (1975). *J. Neural Transm.* **36**, 195.

Theobald, G. W. (1968). *Obstet. Gynec. Surv.* **23**, 109.

Tuppy, H. and Wintersberger, G. (1964). *In* "Oxytocin, Vasopressin and their Structural Analogues" (J. Rudinger, ed). Pergamon Press, London.

Urry, D. W. and Walter, R. (1971). *Proc. natn. Acad. Sci., USA*, **68**, 956.

Vandesande, F. and Dierickx, K. (1975). *Cell Tiss. Res.* **164**, 153.

Vandesande, F., Dierickx, K. and De Mey (1975). *Ann. Endocr., Paris*, **36**, 379.

Vasicka, A., Kumaresan, P., Han, G. S. and Kumaresan, M. (1978). *Am. J. Obstet. Gynecol.* **130**, 263.

Voglmayr, J. K. (1975). *J. Reprod. Fert.* **43**, 119.

Vorherr, H., Massry, S. G., Utiger, R. D. and Kleeman, C. R. (1968). *J. clin. Endocr. Metab.* **28**, 162.

Walter, R. (1976). *Biochim. biophys. Acta*, **422**, 138.

Walter, R., Havran, R. T. and Schwartz, I. L. (1976). *J. med. Chem.* **19**, 328.

Walter, R., Schwartz, I. L., Darnell, J. H. and Urry, D. W. (1971). *Proc. natn. Acad. Sci., USA*, **68**, 1355.

Walter, R. and Shlank, H. (1971). *Endocrinology*, **89**, 990.

Whitelaw, A. G. L. (1969). *Br. J. Cancer*, **23**, 69.

X. Vasopressin

C. R. W. EDWARDS

A. CHEMISTRY

Arginine vasopressin (AVP) is the major mammalian antidiuretic hormone and is secreted by the human neurohyophysis (Fig. 1). AVP is a peptide with a molecular weight of 1084 and contains nine amino acid residues with a disulphide bridge between amino acids 1 and 6. Lysine vasopressin (LVP) is the hormone secreted by Suiformes including the pig, hippopotamus and peccary. The amino acid sequence of AVP was demonstrated by Turner, Pierce and du Vigneaud (1951) using bovine posterior pituitary extracts, and that of LVP by Popenoe, Lawler and du Vigneaud (1952) with porcine posterior pituitary extracts (Fig. 1). The structure of AVP was simultaneously discovered by du Vigneaud, Lawler and Popenoe (1953) and Acher and Chauvet (1953). Lysine vasopressin was synthesised in 1957 by du Vigneaud, Bartlett and Johl, and AVP in 1958 by du Vigneaud, Gish, Katsoyannis and Hess.

Studies on non-mammalian species such as birds, reptiles and amphibians showed that the neurohypophyseal peptides differed from those present in mammals. Arginine vasotocin was the antidiuretic principle secreted rather than vasopressin (Fig. 1) and mesotocin was the non-mammalian equivalent of oxytocin. It would seem likely that the structures of the two main types of hormone are coded for by two separate genes. Mutation of one gene has

	1	2	3	4	5	6	7	8	9
Arginine vasopressin					Cys-Tyr-Phe-Glu(NH$_2$)-Asp(NH$_2$)-Cys-Pro-Arg-Gly(NH$_2$)				

Arginine vasopressin   Cys-Tyr-Phe-Glu(NH$_2$)-Asp(NH$_2$)-Cys-Pro-Arg-Gly(NH$_2$)

Lysine vasopressin   Cys-Tyr-Phe-Glu(NH$_2$)-Asp(NH$_2$)-Cys-Pro-Lys-Gly(NH$_2$)

Phenylalanine lysine vasopressin   Cys-Phe-Phe-Glu(NH$_2$)-Asp(NH$_2$)-Cys-Pro-Lys-Gly(NH$_2$)

Ornithine vasopressin   Cys-Tyr-Phe-Glu(NH$_2$)-Asp(NH$_2$)-Cys-Pro-Orn-Gly(NH$_2$)

Oxytocin   Cys-Tyr-Ile -Glu(NH$_2$)-Asp(NH$_2$)-Cys-Pro-Leu-Gly(NH$_2$)

Arginine vasotocin   Cys-Tyr-Ile -Glu(NH$_2$)-Asp(NH$_2$)-Cys-Pro-Arg-Gly(NH$_2$)

Fig. 1. Amino acid sequences of posterior pituitary peptides.

resulted in the substitution of phenylalanine in position 3 instead of isoleucine. This has biological advantage for the mammals in that it has enhanced antidiuretic but reduced oxytocic activity. For further discussion of the postulated ancestral molecule for vasopressin and oxytocin the reader is referred to the excellent review by Acher (1974).

Recent studies have concentrated on determination of the tertiary structure of the neurohypophyseal peptides (Walter, Ballardin, Schwartz, Gibbons and Wysstrod, 1974; Fric, Kodicek, Flegel and Zaoral, 1975; Roy, Havran, Schwartz and Walter, 1975).

B. BIOSYNTHESIS

Vasopressin is synthesised within hypothalamic nuclei and is then transported along the axons of the neurohypophyseal tract to be stored in the posterior pituitary. This secretory function of the nerve cells was first realised by Scharrer and Scharrer (1940) and subsequent assays of the paraventricular and supraoptic nuclei showed that they contained bioactive oxytocin and vasopressin (Hild and Zetler, 1951). Other nuclei may also be involved, as Burlet and Marchetti (1975), and Swaab, Pool and Nijveldt (1975) have found vasopressin in the suprachiasmatic nucleus.

The classical studies of Sachs and his colleagues confirmed the neurosecretion hypothesis (Sachs, 1963; Takabatake and Sachs, 1964). They infused [^{35}S]-cysteine into the third ventricle of dogs and showed the incorporation of the label into oxytocin and vasopressin isolated from the posterior pituitary. These studies suggested that a large molecular weight precursor hormone was formed on the ribosomes of the hypothalamic nuclei and the active hormone released during axonal transport. The precursor molecule is packed into neurosecretory granules in the Golgi apparatus. These granules have a diameter of about 200 nm (Palay, 1957; Barer, Heller and Lederis, 1963) and vasopressin is stored together with a specific protein called neurophysin. This protein was discovered by Acher and Fromageot (1957). Subsequent work has demonstrated that a variety of different neurophysins are produced. These proteins have a molecular weight of about 10,000 and are released into the circulation at the same time as oxytocin and vasopressin. The functions of the neurophysins are obscure but they may act as binding proteins for the posterior pituitary peptides within the neurohypophysis (see review by Breslow, 1975). The nomenclature of the neurophysins has been somewhat confused. The idea that one neurophysin is related to one hormone is well established in some animals such as the pig where lysine vasopressin is associated with neurophysin I and oxytocin with neurophysin II. In other species, however, more than two neurophysins have been found and in the guinea-pig only one. In man, Robinson (1975) has identified two neurophysins which he has called nicotine-stimulated neurophysin (NSN) and oestrogen-stimulated neurophysin (ESN). The NSN levels rose after stimuli which would release vasopressin but ESN levels did not appear to reflect oxytocin secretion.

As neurophysin assays are much easier to establish than those for vasopressin it was hoped that measurement of plasma neurophysin would reflect plasma AVP levels. After acute stimuli such as haemorrhage, plasma AVP and neurophysin levels rise (Fig. 2). The levels of neurophysin then fall more slowly than AVP. This is presumably a reflection of the different rates of metabolic clearance of the two molecules (Forsling, Martin, Sturdy and Burton, 1973).

Experiments using labelled amino acid incorporation into posterior pituitary peptides suggest that the neurosecretory granules move down the axons in the neurohypophyseal tract at about 1–3 mm/hr (Jones and Pickering, 1970; Norström and Sjöstrand, 1971; Burford and Pickering, 1973). This appears to be considerably faster than the normal axoplasmic flow.

The release of vasopressin appears to be calcium-dependent and is thought to be by exocytosis (Douglas, Nagasawa and Schulz, 1971; Douglas, 1973; Douglas, 1974). The events leading up to release are termed stimulus–secretion coupling and have been well reviewed by Douglas (1974). In the process of exocytosis the neurosecretory granules fuse with the plasmalemma of the axon. There is then rupture of the granule at the site of fusion with ejection of the granule contents and retention of the granule membrane as part of the plasmalemma. This process of recapture of the granule membrane is referred to as micropinocytosis. Swann and Pickering (1976) injected rats with intracisternal [^{35}S]-cysteine or [^{3}H]-choline and showed incorporation

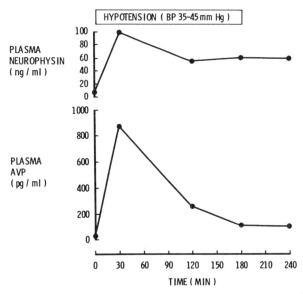

Fig. 2. Release of arginine vasopressin and neurophysin in response to haemorrhage producing hypotension in a sheep (1 pg/ml vasopressin = 0·92 pmol/l).

of the [^{35}S]-cysteine into the granular contents and [^{3}H]-choline into the granular membrane. When hormone release was stimulated by giving the injected animals 2% saline to drink the [^{35}S]-cysteine disappeared from the gland as expected but the [^{3}H]-choline was retained indicating granular membrane conservation. Further proof for the concept of exocytosis has come from electron microscopy and other ultrastructural studies (Dreifuss, Nordman, Akert, Sandrix and Moor, 1974; Dempsey, Bullivant and Watkins, 1974).

C. METABOLISM

The metabolism of vasopressin has been excellently reviewed by Lauson (1974). The kidneys are the major sites for the clearance of vasopressin from the circulation. When Pitressin (mixture of LVP and AVP) was injected into rats with ligated renal pedicles Ginsburg and Heller (1953) found that renal clearance accounted for 56% of the total clearance; further studies showed that the liver was also an important site for clearance but probably accounts for only about 10–15% (Beuzeville and Lauson, 1964; Little, Klevay, Radford and McGandy, 1966).

These studies have prompted both *in vitro* and *in vivo* experiments to discover the mechanism of inactivation of AVP by the kidney. Thorn and Willumsen (1963) used kidney slices to demonstrate that the papillary zone was a principal site for vasopressin inactivation. Borth, Hutter, Pliska and Sorm (1969) showed that both lysine and arginine vasopressin could be destroyed by enzymes in both the soluble and particulate fractions of the porcine kidney. More detailed studies were performed by Walter and Shlank (1975) who used rat kidneys; the kidneys were homogenised and centrifuged at 150,000 g for 1 hr. The supernatant was capable of degrading $[9^{-14}C]$-glycinamide vasopressin. The major method of inactivation was by cleavage of the Pro–Arg bond to release Arg–$[^{14}C]$Gly–NH$_2$. Some $[^{14}C]$Gly–NH$_2$ was also found but this was thought to be due to further metabolism of Arg–Gly–NH$_2$ This result was therefore at slight variance with their previous studies where $[^{14}C]$-glycinamide vasopressin was infused into isolated perfused rat kidneys (Walter and Bowman, 1973). The only radioactive substances detected in the urine were the intact hormone and one metabolite, glycinamide. Presumably if Arg–$[^{14}C]$Gly–NH$_2$ had been formed it had been further metabolised to glycinamide. Nardacci, Mukhopadhyay and Campbell (1975) have isolated the peptidase responsible for this C-terminal inactivation and have shown that it is a chymotrypsin-like enzyme. This

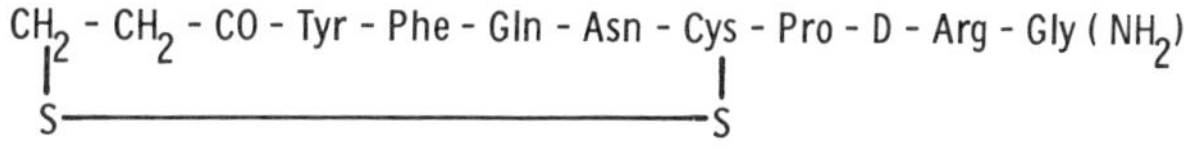

$$\text{CH}_2 - \text{CH}_2 - \text{CO} - \text{Tyr} - \text{Phe} - \text{Gln} - \text{Asn} - \text{Cys} - \text{Pro} - \text{D} - \text{Arg} - \text{Gly} \,(\text{NH}_2)$$
$$\text{S} \rule{6cm}{0.4pt} \text{S}$$

Fig. 3. Amino acid sequence of 1-desamino-8-D-arginine vasopressin (DDAVP).

method of metabolism appears to be much more important than enzymic cleavage of the N-terminal end of the molecule with destruction of the penta-peptide ring. A typical example of this method of inactivation is the vaso-pressinase present in late pregnancy plasma. Analogues of vasopressin such as DDAVP (1-desamino-8-D-arginine vasopressin) (Fig. 3) are pro-tected from both N-terminal and C-terminal destruction (Edwards, Kitau, Chard and Besser, 1973; Robinson, 1976) and this presumably is responsible for the prolonged half-life of this molecule as compared to LVP and AVP (Fig. 4).

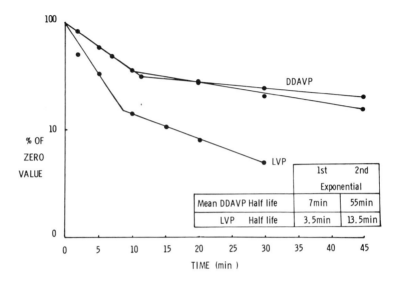

	1st	2nd
	Exponential	
Mean DDAVP Half life	7min	55min
LVP Half life	3.5min	13.5min

Fig. 4. Studies on the metabolic clearance of DDAVP as compared to LVP in normal subjects after single intravenous injections of the peptides.

D. ASSAY METHODS

1. Standards

Hitherto, the First, Second and Third International Standards (I.S.) for vasopressin have been the same as those used for oxytocin (see Ch. IX). The Third I.S. for vasopressin and oxytocin has now been replaced by three separate standards prepared from highly purified synthetic materials: (i) the First I.S. for arginine vasopressin, (ii) the First I.S. for lysine vasopressin, (iii) the Fourth I.S. for oxytocin. International collaborative assays have shown that the First I.S. for arginine vasopressin should be assigned as containing 8·1 u/ampoule (code 77/501).

In addition to bovine pituitary extracts, lysine vasopressin (which is much easier to synthesise than AVP) has been widely used in clinical medicine. A First I.S. for lysine vasopressin (code 77/512) has been established consisting of a highly purified synthetic peptide and the unitage obtained from international collaborative assays has been assigned as 7·7 u/ampoule. With both arginine vasopressin and lysine vasopressin the collaborative assays showed clearly that assay of vasopressor and antidiuretic activities gave similar results.

2. Bioassays

Most bioassays for vasopressin make use of either the pressor or the anti-diuretic actions of the hormone. The pressor assays lack the sensitivity of the antidiuretic assays but because of their precision and ease of performance have been used for the standardisation of vasopressin preparations and for the measurement of vasopressin in samples containing large amounts of the hormone. In general the bioassays can be divided into those that are based on changes in water balance and those that use the effect of vasopressin on smooth muscle as their end point.

(a) Bioassays based on changes in water balance

(1) The antidiuretic assay. The first assay was introduced by Bijlsma, Burn and Gaddum (1928). They used hydrated, non-anaesthetised dogs and human volunteers but the assays were very insensitive. Gibbs (1930) and Burn (1931) produced more satisfactory assays but the major advance was the introduction of the ethanol-anaesthetised rat preparation by Jeffers, Livezey and Austin (1942). This preparation had the advantage that ethanol acted both as an anaesthetic and as an inhibitor of the release of vasopressin. This assay was very much more sensitive (20 μu = 50 pg) (46 fmol) than previous methods (2000 μu) (4·6 pmol) and has been the bioassay of choice for the measurement of plasma levels of vasopressin. Since the original method was described various modifications have been introduced to improve the sensitivity and with these about 1 μu (2·3 fmol) can be detected (Ames and Van Dyke, 1951; Heller and Stulc, 1959, 1960; Czaczkes, Kleeman and Koenig, 1964; Tata and Gauer, 1966).

(2) Other methods involving changes in water balance. Various methods have been described using the vasopressin-induced changes in permeability of amphibian skin or bladder mucosa (Brunn, 1921; Buchborn, 1957; Bentley, 1958). However, these methods are relatively insensitive and non-specific when applied to biological fluids.

(b) Bioassays based on vasopressin effects on smooth muscle

(1) Pressor assay. After the initial discovery of the pressor action of vaso-pressin by Oliver and Schafer in 1895, various authors have described assays based on the blood pressure response (Dale and Laidlaw, 1912; Landgrebe, Macaulay and Waring, 1946). The standard assay was introduced by Dekanski (1951, 1952) who pretreated rats with the adrenergic blocking drug dibenamine. This drug blocked the pressor effect of other substances

P

such as adrenaline, noradrenaline and tyramine, avoided the need for vagotomy, increased sensitivity and abolished the pressor response to large
sample volumes. The sensitivity was about 0·5 mu (1.25 ng) (1·12 pmol)
vasopressin and this assay is recommended by both the United States and
British Pharmacopeias for standardisation of vasopressin preparations.

(2) *Other methods*. Several types of smooth muscle will respond to vasopressin including the hen oviduct (Munsick, Sawyer and Van Dyke, 1960),
the mud puppy oviduct (Heller, Ferreri and Leathers, 1967) and the guinea-
pig colon (Botting, 1965). The major use of these tissues has been distinguishing between different hormone analogues such as AVP, arginine vasotocin
(AVT) and lysine vasopressin. The sensitivity of mud puppy oviduct to AVT
is remarkable in that it responds to concentrations as low as 0·003 pg/ml
(3 fmol/l).

3. Radioimmunoassays

Despite the fact that the first radioimmunoassay for vasopressin was published
in 1966 (Klein, Roth and Peterson, 1966) there was considerable delay before
the measurement of circulating levels was satisfactory (Beardwell and Wright,
1968; Robertson, Klein, Roth and Gorden, 1970). The major reasons for the
initial failure to measure plasma levels were the relative insensitivity of the
assays and the presence in plasma of interfering substances that inhibited
antigen–antibody binding (Robertson et al., 1970). One of the major problems
was the production of satisfactory high affinity antisera. The low molecular
weight of AVP (1084) is associated with poor antigenicity. However, antibodies have been produced against both unconjugated and conjugated
immunogens (Table 1). In general the antibodies against unconjugated
antigen (Klein *et al.*, 1966; Edwards, Chard, Kitau and Forsling, 1970;
Edwards, Chard, Kitau, Forsling and Landon, 1972) have been of lower
titre and affinity than those produced against conjugated vasopressin
(Beardwell and Wright, 1968; Oyama, Kagan and Glick, 1971; Skowsky
and Fisher, 1972; Van Wimersma-Greidanus, Bohus, Hollemans and de
Yong, 1974; Burguburu and Geelen, 1974; Morton, Padfield and Forsling,
1975: Fukuchi. Nakajima. Takeuchi, Nishizato and Michimata, 1975).
The low circulating levels of vasopressin and the presence in plasma of
substances non-specifically inhibiting antigen–antibody binding stimulated
the development of extraction procedures for both plasma (Edwards *et al.*,
1970; Robertson *et al.*, 1970, 1973; Ratcliffe and Edwards, 1971) and urine
(Beardwell and Wright, 1968; Edwards, 1971). The early radioimmunoassays
had advantages of specificity over existing bioassays but lacked the sensitivity
to measure basal levels of the hormone. The production of more satisfactory
antisera resulted in assays with adequate sensitivity but the vasopressin

radioimmunoassay remains one of the most difficult. For a full review of vasopressin radioimmunoassays the reader is referred to Chard (1973), Robinson and Frantz (1973) and Chard and Forsling (1976). The radio-immunoassays that have been developed are included in Table 1.

Recently two direct assays for the measurement of vasopressin in plasma have been published (Wagner et al., 1975; Fyhrquist et al., 1976). In the abstract published by Wagner and his colleagues no details of the antiserum used are given and it is impossible to assess adequately their assay. Fyhrquist and his colleagues used a very high titre antiserum prepared by immunising with LVP coupled to bovine thyroglobulin. Labelled AVP was purified using chromatography on Sephadex G25. The assay buffer contained ε-aminocaproic acid (EACA) at a concentration of 10 mmol/l to minimise enzymic breakdown of ^{125}I-AVP on exposure to plasma during the 72-hr incubation period. Investigation of a variety of compounds showed that EACA was the most satisfactory and the authors suggested that the majority of the non-specificity reported in previous direct assays could be accounted for by damage to the labelled hormone. This damaged material had decreased immunoreactivity and the resultant loss of binding led to falsely high mea-surements. This observation with EACA is an extremely important one and, if confirmed by others, may solve many of the problems of vasopressin radioimmunoassay.

4. Immunological–Biological Dissociation

Despite the large number of vasopressin radioimmunoassays that have been developed relatively few attempts have been made to compare the results of bioassays and radioimmunoassays. In plasma samples, the results show a good correlation (Edwards, 1971, 1977; Morton et al., 1975). In urine, however, there may be a marked immunological-biological dissociation as radioimmunoassays may measure biologically inactive metabolites of vaso-pressin (Edwards, 1974; Forsling, 1977). The extent of this dissociation will depend on the specificity of the antiserum used. Surprisingly, despite the small size of the vasopressin antigenic determinant group the antibodies raised by immunisation with AVP may show profound differences in cross-reactivity (Fig. 5). This problem has been very fully investigated by Thomas and Lee (1976). They carried out specificity studies on antisera produced by immunisation with AVP conjugated to bovine serum albumin using the carbodiimide method. One antiserum bound predominantly the ring struc-ture and was insensitive to the tripeptide tail. One of the other antisera bound the tail but not the ring. Plasma samples were extracted using Florisil and then assayed using these two antisera. The antiserum that bound the ring gave much lower plasma levels than that binding the tail. When mea-

P*

Table 1

Vasopressin radioimmunoassays.

Immunogen	Extraction procedure	Comment	References
Unconjugated AVP	—	Very high plasma levels due to non-specificity	Klein et al. (1966)
LVP conjugated to BSA[a] (TDI[b] or CDI[c])	—	Suggested plasma had non-specific effect	Permutt et al. (1966)
AVP conjugated to BSA (CDI)	Ethanol or trichloracetic precipitation	First results that agreed with levels predicted by bioassay	Beardwell and Wright (1968)
LVP conjugated to BSA (CDI)	—	Measured pituitary levels; immunoassay–bioassay correlation $r = 0.94$, $p < 0.001$	Miller and Moses (1969)
AVP unconjugated AVP or LVP conjugated to egg albumin (TDI or CDI)	Spherosil XOA 400	Measured plasma levels in response to haemorrhage, nicotine; immunoassay–bioassay correlation $r = 0.98$, $p < 0.001$	Edwards et al. (1970, 1971, 1972)
Unconjugated AVP/LVP	Ammonium acetate precipitation Sephadex G25	First clear demonstration that majority of immunoreactivity was not AVP	Robertson et al. (1970)
AVP conjugated to BSA (CDI)	Florisil	—	Beardwell (1971)
AVP conjugated to BSA (glutaraldehyde)	Unextracted urine	—	Oyama et al. (1971)
LVP conjugated to BSA (glutaraldehyde)	Fuller's earth	Used macrophage harvesting technique for antibody production	Johnston (1972)
AVP conjugated to BSA (glutaraldehyde)	Acetone	Excellent high titre and affinity antiserum	Husain et al. (1973)
Used Glick antiserum (Husain et al., 1973)	Acetone/petroleum ether	Simple extraction procedure removed non-specificity.	Robertson et al. (1973)
LVP conjugated to bovine thyroglobulin	Bentonite	—	Skowsky et al. (1974)

AVP conjugated to rabbit γ-globulin (CDI)	Ammonium sulphate/Florisil	—	Morton et al. (1975)
No details given	Unextracted serum	First unextracted assay but reference only in abstract form	Wagner et al. (1975)
AVP conjugated to porcine γ-globulin (CDI)	Acetone	—	Mohring and Mohring (1975)
AVP conjugated to BSA (CDI)	Florisil	Minor modifications of Beardwell (1971)	Beardwell et al. (1975)
No details	Acetone/petroleum ether	—	Conte-Devolx et al. (1976)
LVP conjugated to bovine thyroglobulin	Unextracted plasma	First published validated direct assay	Fyhrquist et al. (1976)
LVP conjugated to BSA (CDI)	Acetone	—	Shamamoto et al. (1976)
AVP conjugated to BSA (CDI)	Florisil	Major difference in plasma levels measured by two antisera	Thomas and Lee (1976)
AVP conjugated to thyroglobulin (CDI)	Acetone	Lactoperoxidase iodination	Hayward et al. (1976)
AVP conjugated to bovine thyroglobulin (CDI)	Florisil	—	Baylis and Heath (1977a)

[a] Bovine serum albumin.
[b] Toluene disocyanate used for conjugation.
[c] Carbodiimide used for conjugation.

sured by the ring antiserum the plasma AVP levels correlated with the urinary AVP excretion rate but this was not found for the tail antiserum. Both antisera produced similar results for urinary AVP when subjects were dehydrated suggesting excretion of native AVP. However, there was a very marked discrepancy between the values obtained for samples of urine from hydrated subjects. Very few investigators have carried out such detailed specificity studies and it is presumably such differences that account for some of the major discrepancies between the plasma and urine levels reported.

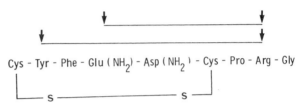

Cys - Tyr - Phe - Glu (NH$_2$) - Asp (NH$_2$) - Cys - Pro - Arg - Gly

Fig. 5. Differences of the antibody combining sites of two antisera produced by immunisation with unconjugated arginine vasopressin.

E. PLASMA LEVELS

1. Physiology

A wide variety of physiological stimuli such as changes in plasma osmolality or plasma volume or various central nervous system influences may affect vasopressin secretion. The most important factor appears to be the osmolality of the plasma. Dunn, Brennan, Nelson and Robertson (1973) measured vasopressin levels in rats by radioimmunoassay during experiments with hypertonic saline. A 1 % rise in plasma osmolality stimulated AVP release. In contrast, an 8 % decrease in blood volume was needed to produce the same effect. In man the osmolar control mechanism was as sensitive as that in the rat but the volume control was less sensitive as a 10–20 % decrease in blood volume was required to stimulate vasopressin (Robertson 1977). The relative importance of these two control mechanisms is best seen in patients with essential hypernatraemia where there is ineffective osmotic but intact volume-mediated control of vasopressin secretion (De Rubertis, Michelis, Beck, Field and Davis, 1971a). Robertson (1977) showed that infusion of hypertonic saline in such a patient did not release vasopressin but a 15 % decrease in blood volume was an effective AVP stimulus.

The most commonly used test for neurohypophyseal function is the water deprivation test (Dashe, Cramm, Crist, Habener and Solomon, 1963; Price and Lauener, 1966; Edwards and Besser, 1974). The plasma levels of vasopressin measured by radioimmunoassay after water deprivation of normal subjects are given in Table 2. These results are in reasonable agreement with those obtained by bioassay (see Edwards, 1977 for review).

Table 2

Plasma levels of vasopressin in normal subjects measured by radioimmunoassay
($1 \mu u = 2 \cdot 5$ pg $= 2 \cdot 3 \times 10^{-3}$ pmol).

State of Hydration	Plasma level (pg/ml)[a]	References
Overnight dehydration	M.3·2	Beardwell and Wright
Rehydration	M.1·3	(1968)
Partial hydration	2·7 ± 1·4 (S.D.)	Robertson et al. (1973)
16–20 hr fluid deprivation	5·4 ± 3·4	
Water load (20 ml/kg) 60 min	1·4 ± 0·8	
Overnight dehydration	1·3–7·0 (M.3·5)	Husain et al. (1974)
25 hr fluid deprivation	2·5–8·5 (M.3·9)	
Water load (20 ml/kg) 1·5 hr	< 1·2	
Partial hydration	M. 3·5	Skowsky et al. (1974)
Overnight dehydration	M. 18	
Partial hydration	5·4 ± 0·69	Morton et al. (1975)
12 hr fluid deprivation	7·36 ± 1·47	
24 hr fluid deprivation	8·74 ± 0·55	
Water load (20 ml/kg)	3·40 ± 1·74	
Overnight dehydration	5·7 ± 4·2	Beardwell et al. (1975)
Water load (20 ml/kg)	3·5 ± 1·6	
12 hr fluid deprivation	52 ± 21·8	Wagner et al. (1975)
Water load (20 ml/kg)	2·25 ± 1·75	
Partial hydration (lying)	3·4 ± 2·2	Uhlich et al. (1975)
4 hr post-hydration	1·4 ± 0·8	
Overnight dehydration	13·0 ± 2	Conte-Devolx et al.
Water load (15 ml/kg)	5·4	(1976)
Nicotine	53·25	
Partial hydration (lying)	2·0 ± 1·22	Fyhrquist et al. (1976)
Partial hydration (standing)	6·2 ± 4·3	
Water load (10–20 ml/kg) (lying)	1·6 ± 1·5	
Water load (10–20 ml/kg (standing)	3·9 ± 4·3	
Overnight dehydration	4·9 ± 1·2	Shimamoto et al. (1976)
Water load (20 ml/kg)	1·2 ± 0·4	
Partial hydration	0·57 ± 0·20	Thomas and Lee (1976)
Water load (25 ml/kg)	0·16 ± 0·10	
22–24 hr fluid deprivation	3·2 ± 2·52	
Partial hydration (lying)	1·75 ± 0·96	Baylis and Heath (1977a)
Partial hydration (standing)	1·58 ± 1·47	
12–16 hr fluid deprivation	3·18 ± 1·74	
Water load (20 ml/kg)	1·42 ± 0·54	
Exercise (5 min)	4·39 ± 3·16	

[a] 1 pg/ml vasopressin = 0·92 pmol/l.

Partially hydrated normal subjects had mean bioactive plasma AVP levels between 1–5 pg/ml (0·9–4·6 pmol). With water loading these fell to about 0·5 pg/ml (0·46 pmol/l) and after water deprivation rose to 12–30 pg/ml (11–28 pmol/l). The bioassay results for water deprivation seem to be much higher than the majority of levels measured by radioimmunoassay.

The effect of posture on plasma AVP levels is controversial. Using bioassay Segar and Moore (1968) found that there was a rise in plasma AVP on standing. The basal levels in six partially hydrated normal subjects when recumbent were 1·0 ± 1·5 pg/ml (0·9 ± 1·4 pmol/l) and rose significantly to 7·75 ± 3·75 pg/ml (7·13 ± 3·45 pmol/l) on quiet standing. When levels have been measured by radioimmunoassay the effect of standing has been small and variable (Padfield and Morton, 1974; Beardwell et al., 1975). Using a direct radioimmunoassay Fyhrquist et al. (1976) reported that standing produced a rise in plasma AVP in both partially hydrated subjects (from 2·0 ± 1·27 (S.D.) pg/ml to 6·2 ± 4·3 pg/ml) (1·8 ± 1·15 pmol/l–5·7 ± 3·9 pmol/l) and those that had been water loaded (from 1·6 ± 1·5 pg/ml to 3·9 ± 4·3 pg/ml) (1·5 ± 1·4 pmol/l–3·6 ± 4·0 pmol/l).

This problem was further investigated by Baylis and Heath (1977b). They studied the effect of posture on plasma AVP levels in two groups of normal subjects. One consisted of five subjects with no known tendency to syncope and the other five subjects with a known tendency to syncope. In the non-syncopal group there was no significant increase in plasma AVP levels after standing for either 10 min or 40 min when they were partially hydrated. However, when the same subjects were dehydrated and restudied they showed a significant rise in plasma AVP after standing for 40 min but not after 10 min. In contrast the five normal subjects with a known syncopal tendency had a very large rise in plasma AVP within 1 min of the onset of symptoms. In these subjects standing was associated with a bradycardia, pallor and sweating.

The time of day when plasma AVP is measured needs to be taken into consideration. There is reasonable evidence to suggest that there is a circadian rhythm in vasopressin secretion which results in the normal nocturnal antidiuresis. George et al. (1975) studied the circadian changes in plasma AVP using the radioimmunoassay described by Robertson et al. (1973). Eight male subjects were allowed free access to fluids and were recumbent throughout the 24 hr except when voiding. Blood samples were taken at 08.00, 10.00, 16.00, 20.00, 24.00, 04.00 and 08.00 hr by direct venepuncture. A nocturnal rise in plasma AVP was found in 80% of the cycles studied. In five subjects there was a progressive rise during the night but in three there was a peak at 24.00 or 04.00 hr followed by a fall. The 10.00 hr plasma AVP levels were significantly lower than those found at 08.00 hr; this may account for some of the difference between published basal levels. The mean nocturnal peak was 140 % higher than the level at 10.00 hr. In addition to these studies two subjects were given dexamethasone (1 mg the evening before the experiment and then 1 mg six hourly starting at 08.00 hr on the experimental day) and then restudied. Dexamethasone did not affect the pattern of secretion but induced a highly significant decrease in plasma AVP.

Many authors have attempted to find a simple, easy, reproducible stimulus to release vasopressin. With water deprivation the rise in plasma AVP has been extremely variable. Beardwell et al. (1975) found that overnight dehydration produced levels which ranged from undetectable to 16·4 pg/ml (15·1 pmol/l). A wide range was also reported by Robertson et al. (1973). Beardwell suggested that it was unlikely that such a stimulus would be adequate to differentiate normal subjects from those with a partial deficiency of AVP production and that it was doubtful whether measurement of AVP under such circumstances had any advantage over measurement of urinary osmolality. Most authors, however, would agree that even if there is overlap between normal subjects and partial diabetes insipidus when AVP alone is considered that the two groups can be readily separated when the plasma AVP level after water deprivation is related to the plasma osmolality.

Nicotine has been used by several authors as a test of neurohypophyseal function. It was thought that nicotine acted as a specific cholinergic stimulus to the posterior pituitary. However, it would seem more likely that nicotine acts by altering the systemic arterial pressure which in turn produces an alteration in baroreceptor-mediated parasympathetic-induced vasopressin release (Cadnapaphornchai, Boykin, Berl, McDonald and Schrier, 1974). Edwards (1971) measured plasma immunoreactive AVP in samples from the internal jugular vein in a normal subject before and after the intravenous administration of 0·25 mg and 1·0 mg nicotine base. After the lower dose of nicotine the AVP level rose from 46 to 158 pg/ml (42–145 pmol/l) but there was no antidiuresis. After the higher dose the jugular level of AVP rose to 238 pg/ml (219 pmol/l) and there was a prolonged antidiuresis. Beardwell (1971) and Husain et al. (1973, 1975) showed that smoking produced a marked increase in plasma AVP but was commonly accompanied by nausea and faintness in non-smokers. Very high levels after nicotine have also been reported by Conte-Devolx et al. (1976).

The infusion of hypertonic saline as an osmotic stimulus to vasopressin release seems to offer no advantage compared with water deprivation (Husain et al., 1973). Frusemide dehydration (Koutsaimanis and Tasker, 1973) produces more severe dehydration than prolonged water deprivation but does seem to result in higher AVP levels than overnight dehydration (Beardwell et al., 1975).

Haemorrhage can act as a potent stimulus to release vasopressin. Morton et al. (1975) measured the vasopressin response to venesection of 500 ml blood over 10 min in six normal subjects. No significant vasopressin release was observed. In a patient with a major gastro-intestinal bleed and a blood pressure of 80/60 mm Hg the plasma AVP was extremely high (162 pg/ml) (149 pmol/l) and fell to 3·9 pg/ml (3·6 pmol/l) after a 2l blood transfusion. Robertson et al. (1973) showed that hypotension produced by intravenous trimetaphan was an effective stimulus to AVP release.

Prolonged weightlessness stimulates a diuresis probably by changing fluid distribution by shift from the lower extremities to the thorax. Conversely lower body negative pressure produces an antidiuresis. Rogge and Moore (1968) demonstrated that − 40 and − 30 mm Hg (− 5·3 and − 4 kP) produced a significant rise in plasma bioactive AVP levels. Baylis, Stockley and Heath (1978) also showed increases in plasma immunoreactive AVP but these occurred only in subjects that had syncopal symptoms and hypotension. Further validation of their results was provided by gel filtration of the presyncopal plasma on Sephadex G-25. The immunoreactive AVP from the plasma eluted in the position of synthetic AVP.

Exercise has long been known to be associated with an antidiuresis. Kozlowski, Szczepanska and Zielinski (1967) measured plasma levels of AVP by bioassay in normal subjects exercising with a bicycle ergometer. There was a significant rise in AVP after 20 min exercise at a high work rate. Beardwell et al. (1975) measured plasma AVP levels by radioimmunoassay before and after 15 min exercise (150 W for men, 100 W for women) on a bicycle ergometer. Three out of the five subjects showed an increase in plasma AVP after exercise. In a further study they measured plasma AVP before and after vigorously running up and down a flight of stairs five times. This produced a significant rise in plasma AVP to 13·2 ± 16·2 pg/ml (12·1 ± 14·9 pmol/l) and only one out of the 12 subjects failed to show a rise in vasopressin concentration.

Baylis and Heath (1977c) investigated the use of insulin-induced hypoglycaemia as a stimulus to AVP release. Ten patients with normal posterior pituitary function and three patients with cranial diabetes insipidus were studied. Blood samples for AVP were taken at 0, 30 and 60 min. In the subjects with normal posterior pituitary function plasma AVP increased from 1·34 ± 0·15 (1·23 ± 0·14 pmol/l) pg/ml to 4·01 ± 0·71 pg/ml (3·69 ± 0·65 pmol/l) ($p < 0.0005$). The maximum fall in blood glucose coincided with the peak in plasma AVP at 30 min. The plasma osmolality was unchanged. Patients who were given TRH and LHRH alone had no change in plasma AVP. In the three patients with cranial DI there was no rise in plasma AVP. As the intravenous TRH and LHRH had no effect on plasma AVP the insulin tolerance test can be used as part of the combined pituitary-stimulation test to investigate anterior and posterior pituitary function simultaneously. The mechanism for the release of AVP is unclear.

In the foetus very high levels of plasma AVP may be found at the time of delivery. Hoppenstein, Miltenberger and Moran (1968) found elevated levels in foetal cord blood samples by bioassay. These results were confirmed using radioimmunoassay (Chard *et al.*, 1971). Very high levels are present in umbilical arterial plasma compared with those of venous samples taken after spontaneous vaginal delivery (Fig. 6). Much lower levels were present

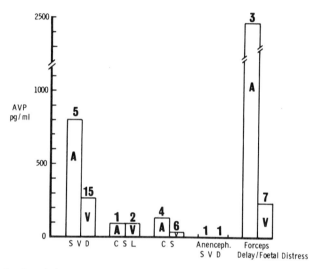

Fig. 6. Levels of arginine vasopressin measured by radioimmunoassay in cord blood samples (umbilical artery—A; umbilical vein—V) after spontaneous vaginal delivery (SVD) at Caesarean section in labour (CSL) at elective Caesarean section (CS). Numbers above columns refer to number of blood samples taken (1 pg/ml = 0·92 pmol/l).

in samples taken during Caesarean section either when the patient was in labour or as an elective procedure. The highest levels were found in umbilical arterial samples during foetal distress. These levels would be expected to have a marked pressor effect and would alter placental blood flow (Somlyo and Somlyo, 1970).

One possible mechanism stimulating vasopressin release in the foetus is hypoxia. This has been demonstrated in the foetal sheep (Alexander, Forsling, Martin, Nixon, Ratcliffe, Redstone and Turnbridge, 1972). Claybaugh, Hansen and Wozniak (1978) further investigated the role of hypoxia in releasing vasopressin in adult man using the standard anti-diuretic bioassay. Eight men breathed 20·9% (normal oxygen), 13·9% (mild hypoxia) or 11·1% (severe hypoxia) oxygen in nitrogen gas mixtures during three 20 min periods. Mild hypoxia suppressed the concentration of ADH by about 60% in contrast to severe hypoxia where the suppression was not significant.

2. Pathophysiology

(a) Diabetes insipidus

Relatively few studies have been performed measuring plasma AVP levels in patients with either cranial or nephrogenic diabetes insipidus (DI). In cranial DI the sensitivity of the assays used has been the limiting factor. Some of the plasma levels measured by radioimmunoassay that have been reported are shown in Table 3. Robertson *et al.* (1973) found that on *ad libitum*

Table 3

Plasma levels of vasopressin in patients with diabetes insipidus measured by radioimmunoassay.

No. of patients	Plasma levels (pg/ml)[a]		References
	Basal	After water deprivation	
8[c]	0·8 ± 0·3	Levels usually increased	Robertson *et al.* (1973)
6[c]	<1·2	—	Husain *et al.* (1973)
2[c]	<0·75–1·25	—	Skowsky *et al.* (1974)
8[c]	1·2–4·2 (2·9)	No increase	Morton *et al.* (1975)
4[c]	<0·8–1·2	—	Shimamoto *et al.* (1976)
7[c]	1·01 ± 0·31	—	Baylis and Heath (1977a)
1[d]	—	3·5[b]	Beardwell and Wright (1968)
2[d]	12, 11·5	—	Robertson *et al.* (1973)
4[d]	11	—	Skowsky *et al.* (1974)

[a] 1 pg/ml = 0·92 pmol/l.
[b] After 2 hr water deprivation: plasma osmolality 310 mosmol/kg.
[c] Cranial diabetes insipidus.
[d] Nephrogenic diabetes insipidus.

fluid intake that the plasma levels of AVP were detectable in patients with DI and overlapped with the normal range. However, the basal plasma osmolality in these patients was clearly much higher than in normal subjects (295 ± 5·8 m-osmol/kg). After fluid restriction plasma AVP levels usually increased but the increase was very subnormal relative to the degree of plasma hypertonicity. Robertson also measured plasma AVP levels in patients with psychogenic polydipsia and nephrogenic DI. In contrast to the results with cranial DI these patients had plasma AVP levels which showed the same relationship to plasma osmolality as found in normal subjects.

Despite the improvement of assay sensitivity with the introduction of radioimmunoassay the best documented paper on plasma AVP levels in nephrogenic DI remains that of Holliday, Burstin and Harrah (1963) who used a rat antidiuretic bioassay with a sensitivity of 3·75 pg/ml (3·45 pmol/l). They studied four boys with congenital nephrogenic DI. Blood samples were taken from the internal jugular vein after overnight water deprivation and in some cases were repeated after water loading. In most instances the assay was validated by thioglycollate inactivation. Higher levels were found in jugular vein plasma than in femoral or antecubital vein plasma, and the levels rose with water deprivation and fell with water loading.

(b) *Syndrome of inappropriate secretion of antidiuretic hormone (SIADH)*

Inappropriate antidiuretic hormone secretion has been thought to be the cause of the dilutional hyponatraemia in a very large number of conditions but in only very few has the plasma level of vasopressin been measured (Edwards, 1977b) (Table 4). There has recently been controversy over the use of the term "inappropriate" in that some authors have suggested that the release of AVP from the posterior pituitary in response to non-osmotic stimuli may be an appropriate response to stress (Schrier, 1974; Thomas et al., 1978). The term, however, was originally defined on the basis that the AVP level was inappropriately high for the plasma osmolality, and if this definition is used then the term is worth retaining.

Robertson and Mahr (1973) were the first to suggest that inappropriate antidiuresis could occur without inappropriate vasopressin secretion. They studied 11 patients who fulfilled the usual clinical criteria for inappropriate ADH secretion. In eight of these with elevated urine osmolality (300–710 m-osmol/kg) and low plasma osmolality (242–278 m-osm/kg) the plasma AVP levels were inappropriately high (3·2–22 pg/ml) (2·9–20 pmol/l) compared with 12 water-loaded normal subjects (urine osmolality 48–96 m-osmol/kg; plasma osmolality 264–275 m-osmol/kg; plasma AVP 0·3–2·0 pg/ml) (0·3–1·8 pmol/l). In three patients, however, the plasma AVP was thought to be appropriately suppressed (0·5–1·7 pg/ml) (0·5–1·6 pmol/l) to levels which should permit maximum diuresis. They suggested that antidiuresis in these patients resulted from factors other than AVP.

Beardwell et al. (1975) measured plasma AVP in 19 patients with hyponatraemia and a clinical syndrome suggesting inappropriate ADH secretion. In seven patients with proved bronchial carcinoma high levels of plasma AVP were found. In none was the level below 11 pg/ml (10 pmol/l). In contrast in the other 12 patients in only one was a level above 11 pg/ml (10 pmol/l) found and in many the level was undetectable (< 2 pg/ml) (< 1·8 pmol/l) in the presence of a urine osmolality greater than that of the plasma. This suggested that the finding of high levels of vasopressin in a patient with

Table 4

Plasma levels of vasopressin in patients with syndrome of inappropriate secretion of antidiuretic hormone (SIADH) measured by radioimmunoassay.

No. of patients	Cause of SIADH	Plasma levels (pg/ml)[a]	References
2	Not stated	33·3 and 41·7	Beardwell and Wright (1968)
4	Bronchial carcinoma	24·0–102·1	Beardwell (1971);
4	Bronchial carcinoma	12·8–77·5	Baumann et al. (1972)
11	Not stated	8 cases 3·2–22	Robertson and Mahr (1973)
		3 cases 0·5–1·7	
6	Bronchial carcinoma	27·5–605	Skowsky et al. (1974)
19[b]	Bronchial carcinoma (7)	11·9–527	Beardwell et al. (1975)
	Other causes (12)	<2–18	
5	Bronchial carcinoma	11–234	Morton et al. (1975)
1	Ewing's sarcoma	4·6	Zimbler et al. (1975)
		81 ± 37	Padfield et al. (1976)
6	Bronchial carcinoma	5·5–22·2	Shimamoto et al. (1976)
2	Bronchial carcinoma	9·6 and 16·4	Baylis and Heath (1977a)
1	Hypoplastic corpus Callosum	1·2–11·9	Fyhrquist et al. (1977)
17*	Bronchial carcinoma (4)	0·7–315	Thomas, Morgan and Swaminathan (1978)
	Chest infection (4)	0·8–46	
	Myxoedema (1)	2·8	

[a] 1 pg/ml = 0·92 pmol/l.
[b] Number of patients with dilutional hyponatraemia.

SIADH strongly suggests the diagnosis of ectopic secretion by a bronchial carcinoma. Similar results have been found when vasopressin is measured in urine (Edwards, 1974).

A further study of severe hyponatraemia was reported by Thomas et al. (1978). They measured plasma AVP in 17 patients with severe hyponatraemia and found that all had excessively high levels. Only 13 patients had the typical features of SIADH. Four were thought to have carcinoma of the lung; it was not clear why the diagnosis could not be confirmed in these. In this last group a very wide scatter of plasma AVP was found (0·7, 2·3, 2·5, 315 pg/ml) (0·6, 2·1, 2·3, 290 pmol/l). A similar wide scatter was found in patients with SIADH and chest infection. In this group plasma AVP fell as the plasma sodium increased towards normal. They suggested that the increase in plasma sodium was too rapid to be produced by water deprivation treatment and was due to a return of plasma AVP to normal.

Thomas et al. (1978) concluded that the term SIADH implies an understanding of pathophysiology that does not exist and that as a diagnosis it did not help in management or prognosis. They suggested that descriptive terminology such as "hyponatraemia with carcinoma of the lung" would be more useful and less confusing. If acted upon, these conclusions would represent a retrograde step. In a subject with suspected carcinoma of the bronchus the finding of very high levels of plasma AVP with SIADH would seem to be useful in confirming the diagnosis and clearly therefore helps in determining the prognosis and obviously also affects management. The serial measurement of plasma AVP would also seem to be useful as a rapid fall to normal suggests a benign aetiology for SIADH. Relatively little is known about the use of plasma AVP as a tumour marker in the treatment of oat cell carcinoma despite the fact that water load studies suggest that 35 % of such tumours may produce vasopressin (Rees, 1976). For this reason it would seem prudent to look for evidence of inappropriate vasopressin secretion in all patients with oat cell carcinoma. In other causes of dilutional hyponatraemia where plasma AVP is inappropriately elevated for the hypotonicity of the plasma it would seen reasonable to retain the use of the term SIADH as originally defined. The fact that we do not understand the pathophysiology underlying the vasopressin secretion does not seem to be a valid reason for not using the term. All, however, would agree that to use the term for all cases of dilutional hyponatraemia is clearly wrong as in many of these ADH does not play a role.

Padfield and his colleagues (1976) measured plasma AVP levels in 17 patients with SIADH associated with a bronchogenic carcinoma and in 14 patients with bronchogenic carcinoma without clinical evidence of SIADH. In the group with the syndrome markedly elevated plasma AVP levels were found (Table 4). As expected the tumour histology was that of an oat cell carcinoma in all the known cases with the exception of one squamous cell and one anaplastic carcinoma. In the 14 patients without the clinical syndrome much lower AVP levels were found but the results were significantly higher than in normal subjects. This group also had a lower than normal plasma osmolality. These results confirm the suggestion made by Rees (1976) that inappropriate ADH excess may be much more common than is usually thought. Of interest was the finding that in one patient the immunoreactive vasopressin did not behave as the standard and dilutions were not parallel to the standard curve. This suggests that the material was not identical with the naturally occurring hormone. These authors also investigated the effect of fluid deprivation on the plasma AVP levels in patients with SIADH. Of 9 patients that were deprived of fluids plasma AVP levels rose in seven. The rise in plasma AVP was closely correlated with the rise in plasma osmolality. This rise could be due to a change in metabolic clearance rather than increased secretion of AVP. However, it is clearly possible that the tumours are not autonomous and respond to stimuli that normally control pituitary AVP release.

(c) Other conditions

Halter, Goldberg, Robertson and Porte (1977) measured plasma AVP levels in a patient with chronic hypernatraemia and selective osmoreceptor dysfunction. In these patients volume-mediated control of vasopressin secretion remains intact and is the dominant control mechanism for vasopressin release. Resting plasma AVP levels were inappropriately low for the degree of plasma hyperosmolality (plasma AVP 0·5–2·1 pg/ml (0·5–1·9 pmol/l) when plasma osmolality exceeded 300 m-osm/kg) but rose during hypertonic saline indicating some residual osmotic regulation. The osmolar threshold for AVP release was normal. In response to alteration in volume-mediated stimuli such as hypotension induced by trimetaphan plasma AVP rose normally to 50 pg/ml (46 pmol/l) indicating adequate neurohypophyseal stores of AVP. These studies confirm that the hypothalamic osmoreceptor/thirst area and the neurohypophysis are anatomically distinct in man.

Shimamoto, Watarai and Miyahara (1977) investigated plasma AVP levels in patients undergoing chronic haemodialysis. The levels were higher before dialysis (6·7 ± 0·4 pg/ml) (6·2 ± 0·4 pmol/l) than in normal subjects. After dialysis, plasma AVP levels increased in 10, did not change in two and decreased in 16 patients. Before dialysis the high AVP levels were probably due to the high plasma osmolality. However, despite the marked decrease in plasma osmolality with haemodialysis in many subjects plasma AVP did not fall and there was no correlation between plasma osmolality and plasma AVP. Clearly this is a complex problem as the removal of vasopressin and possibly calcium and angiotensin II by dialysis may alter vasopressin release and metabolism.

Primary hypothyroidism may be associated with a dilutional hyponatraemia which can be corrected by thyroxine or triidothyronine (Goldberg and Reivich, 1962). The aetiology of this is obscure. De Rubertis *et al.* (1971b) suggested that the impaired water excretion was due to decreased delivery of tubular fluid to the distal diluting segment of the nephron rather than to persistent vasopressin secretion. Skowsky and Fisher (1977) measured plasma AVP levels and the metabolic clearance of vasopressin in thyroidectomised sheep. The basal AVP levels in the euthyroid sheep (M. 3 pg/ml) (3 pmol/l) were significantly lower than in the hypothyroid animals (M. 12·75 pg/ml) (11·7 pmol/l). The serum osmolality in the euthyroid group was significantly higher than in the hypothyroid group. They calculated the mean blood production rates of vasopressin to be 0·6 ng/kg/hr (0·55 pmol/kg/hr) in the euthyroid and 7·1 ng/kg/hr (6·5 pmol/kg/hr) in the hypothyroid sheep. Thus vasopressin production and release by the neurohypophysis seems to be markedly increased in myxoedema.

Another controversial area is the role played by vasopressin in the abnormal water metabolism found in patients with adrenocortical insufficiency. Ahmed *et al.* (1967) using bioassay reported elevated plasma levels in untreated adrenocortical insufficiency. In the adrenalectomised dog Travis and Share (1971) showed that the increased plasma AVP concentration was largely due to pressure–volume stimuli rather than an absence of corticosteroid.

Many drugs have been reported to affect posterior pituitary function either by their role in vasopressin release or by altering its peripheral actions. These have been fully reviewed elsewhere (Edwards, 1977b). In the majority of cases plasma AVP levels have not been measured. Nicotine has been fairly extensively investigated and is discussed above (see Section E.1). Several groups have investigated the effect of anaesthetic agents on plasma AVP. Bonjour and Malvin (1970) found little change in plasma AVP after anaesthesia. Simpson and Forsling (1977) measured plasma AVP levels in two groups of patients during cardio-pulmonary bypass. One group was given 66% nitrous oxide in oxygen and the other was given halothane in addition. Significantly higher plasma AVP levels were found in the halothane-treated group.

Several drugs used in the treatment of diabetes insipidus are not primarily antidiuretic but act either by stimulating the release of vasopressin or altering the renal responsiveness to the hormone. Clofibrate appears to have a central mode of action (Moses, Howanitz, Gemert and Miller, 1973). Carbamazepine and chlorpropamide act by increasing the renal response. Meinders, Cejka and Robertson (1974) measured plasma AVP levels in patients on carbamazepine and noted that the antidiuretic effect was not associated with an increase in plasma AVP.

Opiates have been known for many years to produce an antidiuresis (DeBodo, 1944). Recently Weitzman *et al.* (1977) have shown that β-endorphin stimulates secretion of arginine vasopressin *in vivo* but not *in vitro.* The *in vivo* studies were performed in rabbits which were given 200 μg/kg synthetic β-endorphin. Plasma AVP rose significantly by 5 min and remained elevated for 25 min. Whether or not β-endorphin or any of the enkephalins play a role in the normal control of AVP synthesis or release remains to be elucidated.

CONCLUSIONS

The last few years has seen a dramatic improvement in the assays available for measurement of vasopressin in plasma. Before the introduction of radio-immunoassay, the ethanol-anaesthetised rat was the only method with adequate sensitivity for plasma assays. However, this is a difficult and variable preparation and does not have the sample capacity to enable multiple clinical samples to be measured. The majority of radioimmunoassays have used an extraction procedure to remove substances that produced non-specific inhibition of antigen–antibody binding. Recently however, direct assays for the measurement of plasma AVP have been described, and it is to be hoped that these will become more widely available. Only then will the role of AVP in many clinical conditions become clearer.

REFERENCES

Acher, R. (1974). *In* "Handbook of Physiology, Sect. 7: Endocrinology" (R. O. Greep and E. B. Astwood, eds), Vol. 4, p. 119. Am. Physiol. Soc., Washington.

Acher, R. and Chauvet, J. (1953). *Biochim. biophys. Acta*, **14**, 421.

Acher, R. and Fromageot, P. (1957). *In* "The Neurohypophysis" (H. Heller, ed.), p. 39. Butterworths, London.

Ahmed, A. B. J., George, B. C., Gonzalez-Auvert, C. and Dingman, J. F. (1967). *J. clin. Invest.* **46**, 111.

Alexander, D. P., Forsling, M. L., Martin, M. J., Nixon, D. A., Ratcliffe, J. G., Redstone, D. and Turnbridge, D. (1972). *Biol. Neonate*, **21**, 219.

Ames, R. G. and Van Dyke, H. B. (1951). *Proc. Soc. exp. Biol.* **76**, 576.

Barer, R., Heller, H. and Lederis, K. (1963). *Proc. R. Soc. Lond., Ser. B.* **158**, 388.

Baumann, G., Lopez-Amor, E. and Dingman, J. F. (1972). *Am. J. Med.* **52**, 19.

Baylis, P. H. and Heath, D. A. (1977a). *Clin. Endocr.* **7**, 91.

Baylis, P. H. and Heath, D. A. (1977b). *Clin. Endocr.*, **7**, 79.

Baylis, P. H. and Heath, D. A. (1977c). *Lancet*, **ii**, 428.

Baylis, P. H., Stockley, R. A. and Heath, D. A. (1978). *Clin. Endocr.* **9**, 89.

Beardwell, C. G. (1971). *J. clin. Endocr. Metab.* **33**, 254.

Beardwell, C. G., Geelan, G., Palmer, H. M., Roberts, D. and Salamonson, L. (1975). *J. Endocr.* **67**, 189.

Beardwell, C. G. and Wright, A. D. (1968). Abst. Brief Comm. 3rd Int. Cong. Endocr. Mexico, Int. Cong. Ser. 157, p. 48 (C. Gual, ed.). Excerpta Medica Foundation, Amsterdam.

Bentley, P. J. (1958). *J.Endocr.* **17**, 201.

Beuzeville, C. F. and Lauson, H. D. (1964). *Fed. Proc. Fed. Am. Soc. Exp. Biol.* **23**, 150.

Bijlsma, V. G., Burn, J. H. and Gaddum, J. H. (1928). *Q. J. Pharm. all. Sci.* **1**, 493.

Bonjour, J. P. and Malvin, R. L. (1970). *Am. J. Physiol.* **218**, 1555.

Borth, J., Hutter, H. J., Pliska, V. and Sorm, F. (1969). *Experientia*, **25**, 646.

Botting, J. H. (1965). *Br. J. Pharmacol.* **24**, 156.

Breslow, E. (1975). *Adv. Enzymol.* **40**, 271.

Brunn, F. (1921). *Z. ges. exp. Med.* **25**, 170.

Buchborn, E. (1957). *Endocrinology*, **61**, 375.

Burford, G. D. and Pickering, B. J. (1973). *Biochem. J.* **136**, 1047.

Burlet, A. and Marchetti, J. (1975). *C. r. Séanc. Soc. Biol.* **169**, 148.

Burguburu, A. M. and Geelen, G. (1974). *C. r. Séanc. Soc. Biol.* **168**, 965.

Burn, J. H. (1931). *Q. J. Pharm. Pharmacol.* **4**, 517.

Cadnapaphornchai, P., Boykin, J. L., Berl, J., McDonald, K. M. and Schrier, R. W. (1974). *Am. J. Physiol.* **227**, 1216.

Chard, T. (1973). *J. Endocr.* **58**, 143.

Chard, T., Boyd, N. R. H., Edwards, C. R. W. and Hudson, C. N. (1971). *Nature, Lond.* **234**, 352.

Chard, T. and Forsling, M. L. (1976). *In* "Hormones in Human Blood" (H. N. Antoniades, ed.), p. 488. Harvard University Press, Massachusetts.

Claybough, J. R., Hansen, J. E. and Wozniak, D. B. (1978). *J. Endocr.* **77**, 157.

Conte-Devolx, B., Rougon-Rapuzzi, G. and Millet, Y. (1976). *Ann. Endocr.* **37**, 291.

Czaczkes, J. W., Kleeman, C. R. and Koenig, M. (1964). *J. clin. Invest.* **43**, 1625.

Dale, H. H. and Laidlaw, P. (1912). *J. Pharmacol.* **4**, 75.

Dashe, A. M., Cramm, R. E., Crist, C. A., Habener, J. F. and Solomon, D. H. A. (1963). *J. Am. med. Assoc.* **185**, 699.

DeBodo, R. C. (1944). *J. Pharmacol. exp. Ther.* **82**, 74.

Dekanski, J. (1951). *Br. J. Pharmacol.* **6**, 351.

Dekanski, J. (1952). *Br. J. Pharmacol.* **7**, 567.

Dempsey, G. P., Bullivant, S. and Watkins, W. B. (1974). *In* "Neurosecretion, the Final Neuroendocrine Pathway" (F. Knowles and L. Vollrath, eds), p. 301. Springer Verlag, New York.

De Rubertis, F. R., Michelis, M. J., Beck, M., Field, J. B. and Davis, B. B. (1971a). *J. clin. Invest.* **50**, 97.

De Rubertis, F. R., Michelis, M. F., Bloom, M. E., Mintz, D. H., Field, J. B. and Davis, B. B. (1971b). *Am. J. Med.* **51**, 41.

Douglas, W. W. (1973). *Prog. Brain. Res.* **39**, 21.

Douglas, W. W. (1974). *In* "Handbook of Physiology, Sect. 7: Endocrinology" (R. O. Greep and E. B. Astwood, eds), Vol. 4, p. 191. Am. Physiol. Soc., Washington.

Douglas, W. W., Nagasawa, J. and Schulz, R. (1971). *Mem. Soc. Endocr.* **19**, 353.

Dreifuss, J. J., Nordman, J. J., Akert, K., Sandri, C. and Moor, H. (1974). *In* "Neurosecretion, the Final Neuroendocrine Pathway" (F. Knowles and L. Vollrath, eds), p. 31. Springer Verlag, New York.

Dunn, F. L., Brennan, T. J., Nelson, A. E. and Robertson, G. L. (1973). *J. clin. Invest.* **52**, 3212.

448   C. R. W. EDWARDS

du Vigneaud, V., Lawler, H. C. and Popenoe, E. A. (1953). *J. chem. Soc.* **75**, 4480.
du Vigneaud, V., Bartlett, M. F. and Johl, A. (1957). *J. Am. chem. Soc.* **79**, 5572.
du Vigneaud, V., Gish, D. T., Katsoyannis, P. G. and Hess, G. P. (1958). *J. Am. chem. Soc.* **80**, 3355.
Edwards, C. R. W. (1971). *Proc. R. Soc. Med.* **64**, 842.
Edwards, C. R. W. (1974). M. D. Thesis, University of Cambridge.
Edwards, C. R. W. (1977a). *Clin. Endocr. Metab.* **6**, 223.
Edwards, C. R. W. (1977b). *In* "Clinical Neuroendocrinology" (L. Martini and G. M. Besser, eds), p. 527. Academic Press, London and New York.
Edwards, C. R. W. and Besser, G. M. (1974). *Clin. Endocr. Metab.* **3**, 475.
Edwards, C. R. W., Chard, T., Kitau, M. J. and Forsling, M. L. (1970). *J. Endocr.* **48**, xi.
Edwards, C. R. W., Chard, T., Kitau, M. J., Forsling, M. L. and Landon, J. (1972). *J. Endocr.* **52**, 279.
Edwards, C. R. W., Kitau, M. J., Chard, T. and Besser, G. M. (1973). *Br. med. J.* **3**, 375.
Forsling, M. L. (1977). *In* "Antidiuretic Hormone". Churchill Livingstone, Edinburgh.
Forsling, M. L., Martin, M. J., Sturdy, J. C. and Burton, A. M. (1973). *J. Endocr.* **57**, 307.
Fric, I., Kodicek, M., Flegel, M. and Zaoral, M. (1975). *Eur. J. Biochem.* **56**, 493.
Fyhrquist, F., Holmberg, C., Perheentupa, J. and Wallenius, M. (1977). *J. clin. Endocr. Metab.* **45**, 691.
Fyhrquist, F., Wallenius, M. and Hollemans, H. J. G. (1976). *Scand. J. clin. Lab. Invest.* **36**, 841.
Fukuchi, S., Nakajima, H., Takeuchi, T., Nishizato, K. and Michimata, Y. (1975). *Horuman To Rinsho*, **23**, 85.
George, C. P. L., Messerli, F. H., Genest, J., Nowaczynski, W., Boucher, R., Kuchel, O. and Rojo-Ortega, M. (1975). *J. clin. Endocr. Metab.* **41**, 332.
Gibbs, O. S. (1930). *J. Pharmacol.* **40**, 129.
Ginsburg, M. and Heller, H. (1953). *J. Endocr.* **9**, 283.
Goldberg, M. and Reivich, M. (1962). *Ann. int. Med.* **56**, 120.
Halter, J. B., Goldberg, A. P., Robertson, G. L. and Porte, D. (1977). *J. clin. Endocr. Metab.* **44**, 609.
Hayward, J. N., Pavasuthipaisit, K., Perez-Lopez, F. R. and Sofroniew, M. V. (1976). *Endocrinology*, **98**, 975.
Heller, H., Ferreri, E. and Leathers, D. H. G. (1967). *J. Endocr.* **37**, xxxix.
Heller, J. and Stulc, J. (1959). *Physiol. bohem.* **8**, 558.
Heller, J. and Stulc, J. (1960). *Physiol. bohem.* **9**, 5.
Hild, W. and Zetler, G. (1951). *Naunyn-Schmiedebergs Arch. exp. Pathol. Parmakol.* **213**, 139.
Hoppenstein, J. M., Miltenberger, F. W. and Moran, W. H. (1968). *Surg. Gynec. Obst.* **127**, 966.
Holliday, M. A., Burstin, C. and Harrah, J. (1963). *Paediatrics*, **32**, 384.
Husain, M. K., Frantz, A. G., Ciarochi, F. and Robinson, A. G. (1975). *J. clin. Endocr. Metab.* **41**, 1113.
Husain, M. K., Fernando, N., Shapiro, M., Kagan, A. and Glick, S. M. (1973). *J. clin. Endocr. Metab.* **37**, 616.
Jeffers, W. A., Livezey, M. M. and Austin, J. H. (1942). *Proc. Soc. exp. Biol. Med.* **50**, 184.
Johnston, C. I. (1972), *J. Endocr.* **52**, 69.
Jones, C. W. and Pickering, B. T. (1970). *J. Physiol., Lond.* **208**, 73.

Klein, L. A., Roth, J. and Peterson, M. J. (1966). *Surg. Forum*, **17**, 240.
Koutsaimanis, K. G. and Tasker, P. R. W. (1973). *Clin. Sci. mol. Med.* **45**. 263.
Kozlowski, S., Szczepanska, E. and Zielinski, A. (1967). *Arch. int. Physiol. Biochem.* **75**, 218.
Landgrebe, F. W., Macaulay, M. H. and Waring, H. (1946). *Proc. R. Soc. Edinb.* **62**, 202.
Lauson, H. D. (1974). *In* "Handbook of Physiology Sect. 7: Endocrinology" (R. O. Greep and E. B. Astwood, eds), Vol. 4, p. 287. Am. Physiol. Soc., Washington.
Little, J. B., Klevay, L. M., Radford, E. P. and McGandy, R. B. (1966). *Am. J. Physiol.* **211**, 786.
Meinders, A. E., Cejka, V. and Robertson, G. L. (1974). *Clin. Sci.* **47**, 289.
Miller, M. and Moses, A. M. (1969). *Endocrinology*, **84**, 557.
Möhring, J. and Möhring, J. (1975). *Life Sci.* **17**, 1307.
Morton, J. J., Padfield, P. L. and Forsling, M. L. (1975). *J. Endocr.* **65**, 411.
Moses, A. M., Howanitz, J., Gemert, M. and Miller, M. (1973). *J. clin. Invest.* **52**, 535.
Munsick, R. A., Sawyer, W. H. and Van Dyke, H. B. (1960). *Endocrinology*, **66**, 860.
Nardacci, N. J., Mukhopadhyay, S. and Campbell, B. J. (1975). *Biochim. biophys. Acta*, **377**, 146.
Norström, A. and Sjöstrand, J. (1971). *J. Neurochem.* **18**, 2007.
Oliver, G. and Schafer, E. A. (1895). *J. Physiol.* **18**, 277.
Oyama, S. N., Kagan, A. and Glick, S. M. (1971). *J. clin. Endocr.* **33**, 739.
Padfield, P. L. and Morton, J. J. (1972). *Clin. Sci. mol. Med.* **47**, 16p.
Padfield, P. L., Morton, J. J., Brown, J. J., Lever, A. F., Robertson, J. I. S., Wood, M. and Fox, R. (1976). *Am. J. Med.* **61**, 825.
Palay, S. L. (1957). *In* "Ultrastructure and Cellular Chemistry of Neural Tissue" (H. Waelsch, ed.), p. 31. Harper (Hueber), New York.
Permutt, M. A., Parker, C. W. and Utiger, R. D. (1966). *Endocrinology*, **78**, 809.
Price, J. D. E. and Lauener, R. W. (1966). *J. clin. Endocr. Metab.* **26**, 143.
Ratcliffe, J. G. and Edwards, C. R. W. (1971). *In* "Radioimmunoassay Methods" (K. E. Kirkham and W. M. Hunter, eds), p. 502. Churchill, London.
Rees, L. H. (1976). *Clin. Endocr.* **5** (Suppl.), 363.
Robertson, G. L. (1977). *In* "Endocrinology" (V. H. T. James, ed.), Vol. 1, p. 126. Excerpta Medica, Amsterdam.
Robertson, G. L., Klein, L. A., Roth, J. and Gordon, P. (1970). *Proc. natn. Acad, Sci. USA*, **66**, 1298.
Robertson, G. L. and Mahr, E. A. (1973). Abst. Brief Comm. 4th Int. Cong. Endocr., p. 47. Int. Cong. Ser. 256. Excerpta Medica, Amsterdam.
Robertson, G. L., Mahr, E. A., Athar, S. and Sinha, T. (1973). *J. clin. Invest.* **52**, 2340.
Robinson, A. G. (1975). *J. clin. Invest.* **55**, 360.
Robinson, A. G. (1976). *New Engl. J. Med.* **294**, 507.
Robinson, A. G. and Frantz, A. G. (1973). *Metab. Clin. Exp.* **22**, 1047.
Rogge, J. D. and Moore, W. W. (1968). *J. Appl. Physiol.* **25**, 134.
Roy, J., Havran, R. J., Schwartz, I. L. and Walter, R. (1975). *Int. J. Peptide Protein Res.* **7**, 171.
Sachs, H. (1963). *J. Neurochem.* **10**, 299.
Scharrer, E. and Scharrer, B. (1940). *Res. Pub. Assoc. Res. Nerv. Ment. Dis.* **20**, 170.
Schrier, R. W. (1974). *West. med. J.* **121**, 62.
Segar, W. E. and Moore, W. W. (1968). *J. clin. Invest.* **47**, 2143.
Shimamoto, K., Murase, T. and Yamaji, T. (1976). *J. Lab. clin. Med.* **87**, 338.
Shimamoto, K., Watarai, I. and Miyahara, M. (1977). *J. clin. Endocr. Metab.* **45**, 714.

Simpson, P. and Forsling, M. (1977). *Clin. Endocr.* 7, 33.

Skowsky, W. R. and Fisher, D. A. (1972). *J. Lab. clin. Med.* **80**, 134.

Skowsky, W. R. and Fisher, D. A. (1977). *Endocrinology*, **100**, 1022.

Skowsky, W. R., Rosenbloom, A. A. and Fisher, D. A. (1974). *J. clin. Endocr. Metab.* **38**, 278.

Somlyo, A. P. and Somlyo, A. B. (1970). *Pharmacol. Rev.* **22**, 249.

Swaab, D. F., Pool, C. W. and Nijveldt, F. (1975). *J. Neural Transm.* **36**, 195.

Swann, R. W. and Pickering, B. J. (1976). *J. Endocr.* **68**, 95.

Tata, P. S. and Gauer, O. H. (1966). *Pflug. Arch. ges. Physiol.* **290**, 279.

Takabatake, Y. and Sachs, H. (1964). *Endocrinology*, **75**, 934.

Thomas, T. H. and Lee, M. R. (1976). *Clin. Sci. mol. Med.* **51**, 525.

Thomas, T. H., Morgan, D. B. and Swaminathan, R. (1978). *Lancet*, **i**, 621.

Thorn, N. A. and Willumsen, N. B. S. (1963). *Acta endocr., Copenh.* **44**, 563.

Travis, R. H. and Share, L. (1971). *Endocrinology*, **89**, 246.

Turner, R. A., Pierce, J. G. and du Vigneaud, V. (1951). *J. biol. Chem.* **191**, 21.

Uhlich, E., Weber, P., Groschel-Stewart and Roschlau, T. (1975). *Horm. Metab. Res.* **7**, 501.

Van Wimersma-Greidanus, J. B., Bohus, R. M., Hollemans, H. J. G. and de Yong, W. (1974). *Experientia*, **30**, 1217.

Wagner, H., Maier, V., Herrmann, H.-J. and Franz, H. E. (1975). *Acta endocr., Copenh.* **193** (Suppl.), 130.

Walter, R., Ballardin, A., Schwartz, I. L., Gibbons, W. A. and Wyssbrod, H. R. (1974). *Proc. natn. Acad. Sci. USA*, **71**, 4528.

Walter, R. and Bowman, R. H. (1973). *Endocrinology*, **92**, 189.

Walter, R. and Shlank, H. (1975). *Endocrinology*, **96**, 811.

Weitzman, R. G., Fisher, D. A., Minick, S., Ling, N. and Guillemin, R. (1977). *Endocrinology*, **101**, 1643.

Zimbler, H., Robertson, G. L., Bartter, F. C., Delea, C. S. and Pomeroy, T. (1975). *J. clin. Endocr. Metab.* **41**, 390.

Subject Index